BUDDHIST LOGIC

BUDDHIST LOGIC

Volume I

TH. STCHERBATSKY

MOTILAL BANARSIDASS
INTERNATIONAL
DELHI

Reprint Edition: Delhi, 2024
First Indian Edition: Delhi, 1993

ISBN : 978-81-19196-02-9 (Vol.-I)
ISBN : 978-81-19196-26-5 (Vol.-II)
ISBN : 978-81-19196-08-1 (Set)

Also available at
MOTILAL BANARSIDASS INTERNATIONAL
H. O. : 41 U.A. Bungalow Road, (Back Lane) Jawahar Nagar, Delhi - 110 007
4261/3 (basement), Ansari Road, Darya Ganj, New Delhi - 110 002
203 Royapettah High Road, Mylapore, Chennai - 600 004
12/1A, 2nd Floor, Bankim Chatterjee Street, Kolkata - 700 073
Stockist : Motilal Books, Ashok Rajpath, Near Kali Mandir, Patna - 800 004

Printed in India
MOTILAL BANARSIDASS INTERNATIONAL

TO THE DEAR MEMORY

OF

MY BELOVED MOTHER

TABLE OF CONTENTS

Page

ABBREVIATIONS

Anekāntaj.	Anekānta-jaya-patāka of Haribhadra (Jain).
AK.	Abhidharmakoša.
AKB.	Abhidharmakošabhāṣya.
BB.	Bibliotheca Buddhica.
BI.	Bibliotheca Indica.
CC.	The Central Conception of Buddhism and the Meaning of the term Dharma (London 1923, R. A. S.).
CPR.	Critique of Pure Reason by Kant, transl. by Max Müller.
ERE	Encyclopedia of Religion and Ethics.
GGN.	Göttinger Gelehrte Nachrichten.
IHQ.	Indian Historical Quarterly (Calcutta).
JBORS.	Journal of the Bihar and Orissa Research Society.
JRAS.	Journal of the Royal Asiatic Society.
Khand.	Khaṇḍana-khaṇḍa-khādya by Šrīharṣa.
Mallavādi.	Nyāya-bindu-ṭikā-ṭippaṇī by this author, different from the ṭippaṇī printed by me in the BB.
Madhy. v.	Mūla-mādhyamika-kārikā-vṛtti by Candrakīrti.
Nirvāṇa.	The Conception of Buddhist Nirvāṇa (Leningrad, 1927).
NB.	Nyāyabindu by Dharmakīrti.
NBT.	Nyāyabinduṭikā by Dharmottara.
NBTT (or Ṭipp. simply)	Nyāyabinduṭikā-ṭippaṇī ed. by me in the BB and erroneously ascribed to Mallavādī, g. c.
NBh.	Nyāya-bhāṣya.
NK.	Nyāya-kaṇikā (reprint from the Paṇdit).
NKandalī.	Nyaya-kandalī by Šrīdhara (Vizian).
NMukha.	Nyāya-mukha by Dignāga, transl. by Tucci.
NV.	Nyāya-vārtika (BI).
NVTT (also Tātp).	Nyāya-vārtika-tātparya-ṭikā (Vizian).
NS	Nyāya-sūtra.
Parišuddhi	Nyāya-vārtika-tātparya-ṭikā-parišuddhi (BI).
Pr. vārt.	Pramāṇa-vārtika by Dharmakīrti.
Pr. vinišc.	Pramāṇa-vinišcaya by the same.
Pr. samucc.	Pramāṇa-samuccaya by Dignāga.
SD.	Šāstra-dīpikā by Pārthasārathimišra.
SDS.	Sarvadaršanasangraha (Poona, 1924).
Tipp.	Nyāyabinduṭikā-ṭippaṇī by unknown author edited by me in the BB and erroneously ascribed to Mallavādī q. c.
Tātp.	cp. NVTT.
VS.	Vaišeṣika-sūtra.

PREFACE

This work claims the consideration of the historian of the culture of Asia, of the Sanscrit philologist and of the general philosopher.

It is the last of a series of three works destined to elucidate what is perhaps the most powerful movement of ideas in the history of Asia, a movement which, originating in the VI century BC. in the valley of Hindustan, gradually extended its sway over almost the whole of the continent of Asia, as well as over the islands of Japan and of the Indian archipelago. These works are thus concerned about the history of the ruling ideas of Asia, Central and Eastern.[1]

It also claims the consideration of the Sanscritist, because it is exclusively founded on original works belonging to the *šāstra* class; these are Indian scholarly compositions, written in that specific scientific Sanscrit style, where the argument is formulated in a quite special terminology and put in the form of laconic rules; its explanation and development are contained in numerous commentaries and subcommentaries. To elucidate this quite definite and very precise terminology is the aim of a series of analytical translations collected in the second volume.[2]

[1] A systematical review of the full extent of that literature which under the general name of the «Law of the Buddha» migrated from India into the northern countries, compiled by the celebrated Tibetan savant Bu-ston Rinpoche, is now made accessible to European scholars in a masterly translation by E. Obermiller, cp. his History of Buddhism by Buston (Heidelberg, 1931). The ruling ideas of all this enormous bulk of learning are 1) a monistic metaphysics and 2) a logic. The metaphysical part will be fully elucidated in a series of works of which the general plan has been indicated in the Introduction to our edition of the Abhisamayālankāra (*Bibl. Buddh. XXXIII*). In realization of this plan E. Obermiller has already issued two works, 1) The Sublime Science being a translation of Asanga's Uttara-tantra (*Acta Orient.*, 1931) and 2) The Doctrine of Prajñā-pāramitā according to the Abhisamayālankāra and its commentaries (A. O. 1932). The place which Logic (*tshad-ma*) occupies in the whole purview of Buddhist literature is indicated by Buston in his History, cp. p. 45—46, vol. I of the translation.

[2] In order to facilitate the verification of our analysis we quote the original term in a note. By utilizing the index of Sanscrit and Tibetan words appended to the second volume the contexts will be found, on which the interpretation of the term is based.

In addressing itself to the philosopher this work claims his consideration of a system of logic which is not familiar to him. It is a logic, but it is not Aristotelian. It is epistemological, but not Kantian.

There is a widely spread prejudice that positive philosophy is to be found only in Europe. It is also a prejudice that Aristotle's treatment of logic was final; that having had in this field no predecessor, he also has had no need of a continuator. This last prejudice seems to be on the wane. There is as yet no agreed opinion on what the future logic will be, but there is a general dissatisfaction with what it at present is. We are on the eve of a reform. The consideration at this juncture of the independent and altogether different way in which the problems of logic, formal as well as epistemological, have been tackled by Dignāga and Dharmakīrti will possibly be found of some importance.

The philosopher in thus considering and comparing two different logics will perceive that there are such problems which the human mind naturally encounters on his way as soon as he begins to deal with truth and error. Such are, e. g., the problems of the essence of a judgment, of inference and of syllogism; the problems of the categories and of relations; of the synthetical and analytical judjments; of infinity, infinite divisibility, of the antinomies and of the dialectical structure of the understanding. From under the cover of an exotic terminology he will discern features which he is accustomed to see differently treated, differently arranged, assigned different places in the system and put into quite different contexts. The philosopher, if he becomes conversant with the style of Sanscrit compositions, will be tempted not only to interpret Indian ideas in European terms, but also to try the converse operation and to interpret European ideas in Indian terms.

My main object has been to point out these analogies, but not to produce any estimate of the comparative value of both logics. On this point I would prefer first to hear the opinion of the professional philosopher who in this special department of knowledge has infinitely more experience than I may claim to possess. I would be amply satisfied if I only succeed to arouse his attention and through him to introduce Indian positive philosophers into the community of their European brotherhood.

Introduction.

§ 1. Buddhist Logic what.

Under Buddhist Logic we understand a system of logic and epistemology created in India in the VI—VIIth century A. D. by two great lustres of Buddhist science, the Masters Dignāga and Dharmakīrti. The very insufficiently known Buddhist logical literature which prepared their creation and the enormous literature of commentaries which followed it in all northern Buddhist countries must be referred to the same class of writings. It contains, first of all, a doctrine on the forms of syllogism[1] and for that reason alone deserves the name of logic. A theory on the essence of judgment,[2] on the import of names[3] and on inference[4] is in India, just as it is in Europe, a natural corollary from the theory of syllogism.

But the logic of the Buddhists contains more. It contains also a theory of sense perception or, more precisely, a theory on the part of pure sensation[5] in the whole content of our knowledge, a theory on the reliability of our knowledge[6] and on the reality of the external world as cognized by us in sensations and images.[7] These problems are usually treated under the heading of epistemology. Therefore we may be justified in calling the Buddhist system a system of epistemological logic. It starts with a theory of sensation as the most indubitable voucher for the existence of an external world. It then proceeds to a theory of a coordination[8] between that external world and the repre-

---

1 *parārtha-anumāna.*

2 *adhyavasāya = niścaya = vikalpa.*

3 *apoha-vāda.*

4 *svārtha-anumāna.*

5 *nirvikalpaka-pratyakṣa.*

6 *prāmāṇya-vāda.*

7 *bāhya-artha-anumeyatva-vāda.*

8 *sārūpya.*

sentation of it as constructed by our understanding in images and concepts. Next comes a theory of judgment, of inference and of syllogism. Finally a theory on the art of conducting philosophic disputations in public[1] is appended. It thus embraces the whole area of human knowledge, beginning with rudimentary sensation and ending with the complicated apparatus of a public debate.

The Buddhists themselves call this their science a doctrine of logical reasons[2] or a doctrine of the sources of right knowledge[3] or, simply, an investigation of right knowledge.[4] It is a doctrine of truth and error.

In the intention of its promotors the system had apparently no special connection with Buddhism as a religion, i. e., as the teaching of a path towards Salvation. It claims to be the natural and general logic of the human understanding.[5] However, it claims also to be critical. Entities whose existence is not sufficiently warranted by the laws of logic are mercilessly repudiated, and in this point Buddhist logic only keeps faithful to the ideas with which Buddhism started. It then denied a God, it denied the Soul, it denied Eternity. It admitted nothing but the transient flow of evanescent events and their final eternal quiescence in Nirvāṇa. Reality according to Buddhists is kinetic, not static, but logic, on the other hand, imagines a reality stabilized in concepts and names. The ultimate aim of Buddhist logic is to explain the relation between a moving reality and the static constructions of thought.[6] It is opposed to the logic of the Realists, the logic of the schools of Nyāya, Vaiśeṣika and Mīmāṃsā for whom reality is static and adequate to the concepts of our knowledge. By the champions of all other established religions in India the Buddhists were generally regarded as arrogant nihilists, and they, in their turn, called their opponents «outsiders»[7] and «pagans».[8] In that sense only is the logical doctrine created by the Buddhists a Buddhist logic.

---

1 *vāda-vidhi = codanā-prakaraṇa.*

2 *hetu-vidyā.*

3 *pramāṇa-vidyā.*

4 *samyag-jñāna-vyutpādana.*

5 *laukika-vidyā*, cp. Mādhy. vṛtti, p. 58. 14, and my Nirvāṇa, p. 140.

6 Cp. TSP, p. 259. 21 — *na kvacid arthe paramārthato vivakṣā asti, anvayino 'rthasya abhāvāt...* (*sarveṣu iti pakṣeṣu samānam dūṣaṇam*).

7 *bāhya = phyi-rol-pa.*

8 *tīrthika.*

§ 2. The place of Logic in the history of Buddhism.

Buddhist logic has its place in the history of Buddhism in India, and it has also its place in the general history of Indian logic and philosophy. In the broad field of Indian logic it constitutes an intermediate Buddhist period, while in the domain of Buddhist philosophy logic constitutes a remarkable feature of the third, concluding phase of Indian Buddhism.[1]

The history of Buddhism in India may be divided, and is divided by the Buddhists themselves, into three periods[2] which they call the three «Swingings of the Wheel of the Law».[3] During all of them Buddhism remains faithful to its central conception of a dynamic impersonal flow of existence. But twice in its history — in the Ist and in the Vth centuries A. D. — the interpretation of that principle was radically changed, so that every period has its own new central conception. Roughly speaking, if we reckon, beginning with 500 B. C., 1500 years of an actual existence of Buddhism in the land of its birth, this duration is equally distributed into three periods, each having a duration of about 500 years.

Let us briefly recall the results of two previous works devoted to the first and the second period.[4] The present work, devoted to its third and concluding period, must be regarded as their continuation.

§ 3. First Period of Buddhist philosophy.

At the time of Buddha India was seething with philosophic speculation and thirsty of the ideal of Final Deliverance. Buddhism started with a very minute analysis of the human Personality[5] into the elements[6] of which it is composed. The leading idea of this analysis was a moral one. The elements of a personality were, first of all,

---

1 *āntya-dharma-cakra-pravartana.*

2 The orthodox point of view is that Buddha himself made three different statements of his doctrine, one for simple men, another for men of middle capacities and a final one for acute minds. But this is evidently an afterthought.

3 *tricakra* = *ḥkhor-lo-gsum.*

4 The Central Conception of Buddhism and the Meaning of the word «Dharma», London, 1923 (R. A. S.) and The Conception of Buddhist Nirvāṇa, Leningrad, 1927 (Ac. of Sciences).

5 *pudgala.*

6 *dharma.*

divided into good and bad,[1] purifying and defiling,[2] propitious to salvation and averse[3] to it. The whole doctrine was called a doctrine of defilement and purification.[4] Salvation was imagined and cherished as a state of absolute quiescence.[5] Therefore life, ordinary life,[6] was considered as a condition of degradation and misery.[7] Thus the purifying elements were those moral features, or forces, that led to quiescence, the defiling ones those that led to, and encouraged,[8] the turmoil of life. Apart of these two classes of conflicting elements, some general, neutral, fundamental[9] elements were also found at the bottom of every mental life, but nothing in the shape of a common receptacle of them could be detected: hence no Ego, no Soul,[10] no Personality.[11] The so called personality consists of a congeries of ever changing elements, of a flow[12] of them, without any perdurable and stable element at all.

This is the first mainf eature of early Buddhism, its Soul-denial. The No-Soul theory[10] is another name for Buddhism.

The external world[13] was also analysed in its component elements. It was the dependent part of the personality, its sense-data. There were other systems of philosophy which preceded Buddhism and which envisaged the sense-data as changing manifestations of a compact, substantial and eternal principle, the Matter.[14] Buddhism brushed this principle away and the physical elements became just as changing, impermanent[15] and flowing, as the mental were found to be. This constitutes the second characteristic feature of early Buddhism: no Matter, no Substance,[16] only separate elements,[17] momentary flashes of

1 *sāsrava-anāsrava.*
2 *sāṃkleśa-vyāvadānika.*
3 *kuśala-akuśala.*
4 *sāṃkleśa-vyāvadāniko dharmaḥ.*
5 *nirodha = śānti = nirvāṇa.*
6 *saṃsāra.*
7 *duḥkha = saṃsāra.*
8 *anuśaya = duḥkha-poṣaka.*
9 *citta-mahā-bhūmikā dharmāḥ.*
10 *anātma-vāda.*
11 *pudgalo nāsti = anātmatva = nairātmya = pudgala-śūnyatā.*
12 *saṃskāra-pravāha.*
13 *bāhya-āyatana = viṣaya,* incl. everything external to the six *indriyas.*
14 *pradhāna = prakṛti.*
15 *anitya.*
16 *na kiṃcit sthāyi.*
17 *sarvam pṛthak.*

efficient energy without any substance in them, perpetual becoming, a flow of existential moments.

However, instead of the abandoned principles of a Soul and of a Matter, something must have come to replace them and to explain how the separate elements of the process of becoming are holding together, so as to produce the illusion of a stable material world and of perdurable personalities living in it. They were in fact substituted by causal laws,[1] laws of physical and moral causation. The flow of the evanescent elements was not a haphazard[2] process. Every element, although appearing for a moment, was a «dependently originating element».[3] According to the formula «this being, that arises»[4] it appeared in conformity with strict causal laws. The idea of moral causation, or retribution,[5] the main interest of the system, was thus receiving a broad philosophic foundation in a general theory of Causality. This is the third characteristic feature of early Buddhism. It is a theory of Causation.

A further feature consists in the fact that the elements of existence were regarded as something more similar to energies[6] than to substantial elements. The mental elements[7] were naturally moral, immoral or neutral forces. The elements of matter were imagined as something capable to appear as if it were matter, rather than matter in itself. Since the energies never worked in isolation, but always in mutual interdependence according to causal laws, they were called «synergies» or cooperators.[8]

Thus it is that the analysis of early Buddhism discovered a world consisting of a flow of innumerable particulars, consisting on the one side of what we see, what we hear, what we smell, what we taste and what we touch;[9] and on the other side — of simple awareness[10] accompanied by feelings, ideas, volitions,[11] whether good volitions or bad ones, but no Soul, no God and no Matter, nothing endurable and substantial in general.

---

1 *hetu-pratyaya-vyavasthā.*

2 *adhītya-samutpāda.*

3 *pratītya-samutpanna.*

4 *asmin sati idam bhavati.*

5 *vipāka-hetu = karma.*

6 *saṃskāra = saṃskṛta-dharma.*

7 *citta-caitta.*

8 *saṃskāra.*

9 *rūpa-śabda-gandha-rasa-spraṣṭavya-āyatanāni.*

10 *citta = manas = vijñāna.*

11 *vedanā-saṃjñā-saṃskāra.*

However, this flow of interconnected elements in which there were no real personalities was steering towards a definite aim. The steersmen were not personalities or souls, but causal laws. The port of destination was Salvation in the sense of eternal Quiescence of every vestige of life,[1] the absolutely inactive condition of the Universe, where all elements or all «synergies» will loose there force of energy and will become eternally quiescent. The analysis into elements[2] and energies had no other aim than to investigate the conditions of their activity, to devise a method[3] of reducing and stopping[4] that activity, and so to approach and enter into the state of absolute Quiescence, or Nirvāṇa. The ontological analysis was carried in order to clear the ground for a theory of the Path towards Moral Perfection and Final Deliverance, to the perfection of the Saint[5] and to the absolute condition of a Buddha. In this we have a further feature of Buddhism, a feature which it shares with all other Indian philosophic systems, with the only exception of the extreme Materialists. It is a doctrine of Salvation. In the teaching of a path towards this goal the Buddhists had predecessors in early Indian mysticism.[6] All India was divided at the time of Buddha in opponents and supporters of mysticism, in the followers of the Brahmans and those who followed the Shramans, in, so to speak, an open High Church and in popular sects strongly inclined to mysticism. The main idea of this mysticism consisted in the belief that through practice of concentrated meditation[7] a condition of trance could be attained which conferred upon the meditator extraordinary powers and converted him into a superman. Buddhism adapted this teaching to its ontology. Transic meditation became the ultimate member of the Path towards Quiescence, the special means through which, first of all, wrong views and evil inclinations could be eradicated, and then the highest mystic worlds could be reached. The superman, the Yogi, became the Saint,[8] the man or, more precisely, the assemblage of elements, where the element of Immaculate Wisdom[9]

---

1 *nirodha = nirvāṇa.*

2 *dharma-pravicaya.*

3 *mārga.*

4 *vihāna-prahāna.*

5 *ārya.*

6 *yoga.*

7 *dhyāna = samādhi = yoga.*

8 *ārya = arhat = yogin.*

9 *prajñā amalā.*

becomes the central and predominant principle of a holy life. This gives us the last feature of primitive Buddhism. It is a doctrine of the Saint.

Accordingly the whole doctrine is summarized in the formula of the so called four «truths» or four principles of the Saint,[1] viz. 1) life is a disquieting struggle, 2) its origin are evil passions, 3) eternal Quiescence is the final goal and 4) there is a Path where all the energies cooperating in the formation of life become gradually extinct.

These are the main ideas of Buddhism during the first period of its history, the first «Swinging of the Wheel of the Law». It can hardly be said to represent a religion. Its more religious side, the teaching of a path, is utterly human. Man reaches salvation by his own effort, through moral and intellectual perfection. Nor was there, for ought we know, very much of a worship in the Buddhism of that time. The community consisted of recluses possessing neither family, nor property, assembling twice a month for open confession of their sins and engaged in the practice of austerity, meditation and philosophic discussions.

The Buddhism of this period, i.e., after Ašoka, was divided into 18 schools on points of minor importance. The acceptance of a shadowy, semi-real personality by the school of the Vatsīputrīyas was the only important departure from the original scheme of that philosophy.

§ 4. Second period of Buddhist Philosophy.

At the verge of the fifth century of its history a radical change supervened in Buddhism, in its philosophy and in its character as a religion. It forsook the ideal of a human Buddha who disappears completely in a lifeless Nirvāṇa and replaced it by the ideal of a divine Buddha enthroned in a Nirvāṇa full of life. It forsook the egoistic ideal of a personal Salvation and replaced it by the Universal Salvation of every life. It changed at the same time its philosophy from a radical Pluralism into as radical a Monism. This change seems to have been contemporaneous with a development in the brahmanic religions of India where at the same epoch the great national Gods, Shiva and Vishnu, began to be worshipped and established on the background of a monistic philosophy.

The fundamental philosophic conception with which the new Buddhism started was the idea of a real, genuine, ultimate existence,

---

1 *catvāri ārya-satyāni = āryasya buddhasya tattvāni.*

or ultimate reality, a reality shorn of all relations, reality in itself, independent, unrelated reality.[1] Since all the physical and mental elements established by the pluralism of early Buddhism were admittedly interrelated elements,[2] or cooperating forces,[3] none of them could be viewed as ultimately real. They were interrelated, dependent and therefore unreal.[4] Nothing short of the whole of these elements, the whole of the wholes, the Universe itself viewed as a Unity, as the unique real Substance, could be admitted as ultimately real. This whole assemblage of elements,[5] this Elementness[6] as a Untity, was then identified with Buddha's Cosmical Body, with his aspect as the unique substance of the Universe.[7] The elements[8] established in the previous period, their classifications into five groups,[9] twelve bases of our cognition[10] and eighteen component parts[11] of individual lives were not totally repudiated, but allowed only a shadowy existence as elements not real in themselves, elements «devoid» of any ultimate reality.[12] In the former period all personalities, all enduring substances, Souls and Matter were denied ultimate reality. In the new Buddhism their elements, the sense data and the fundamental data of consciousness, nay even all moral forces,[13] followed the Souls in a process of dialectical destruction. The early doctrine receives the name of a No-Soul and No-Substance doctrine.[14] The new Buddhism receives the name of a No-Elements doctrine,[15] a doctrine of the relativity and consequent

---

[1] *anapekṣaḥ svabhāvaḥ = sarva-dharma-śūnyatā.*

[2] *saṃskṛta-dharma.*

[3] *saṃskāra.*

[4] *paraspara-apekṣa = śūnya. = svabhāva-śūnya.*

[5] *dharma-kāya = dharma-rāśi.*

[6] *dharmatā.*

[7] *Dharma-kāya = Buddha.*

[8] *dharma.*

[9] *skandha* (5).

[10] *āyatana* (12).

[11] *dhātu* (18).

[12] *svabhāva-śūnya.*

[13] *citta-samprayukta-saṃskāra.*

[14] *anātma-vāda=niḥ-svabhāva-vāda =pudgala-nairātmya=pudgala-śūnyatā.*

[15] *dharma-nairātmya = dharma-śūnyatā = svabhāva-śūnyatā = paraspara-apekṣatā,* or *śūnyatā* simply. By the references collected in my Nirvāṇa, p. 43 n. 1. it has been sufficiently established that *śūnyatā* does not mean *abhāva* simply, but *itaretara-abhāva =paraspara-apekṣatā*, which is want of *ultimate* reality (= *apariniṣpannatā*) or Relativity. The opponents called it *abhāva*, cp. Nyāya-sūtra, I. 1. 34, (cp. W. Ruben. Die Nyāyasūtras, An. 260). M-r. E. Obermiller

unreality of all elementary data into which existence has been analysed.

This is the first outstanding feature of the new Buddhism. It denies the ultimate reality of the elements accepted as real in early Buddhism.

The doctrine of Causality, causality as functional interdependence of every element upon all the others,[1] not as production of something out of other things,[2] this doctrine so characteristic of Buddhism from its beginning, is not only retained in the new Buddhism, but it is declared to be the foundation-stone of the whole edifice.[3] However, its meaning is slightly changed. In primitive Buddhism all elements are interdependent and real, in the new Buddhism, in accordance with the new definition of reality, they are unreal because interdependent.[4] Of the principle of «Interdependent Origination» the first part is emphasized, the second is dropped altogether. From the point of view of ultimate reality the universe is one motionless whole where nothing originates and nothing disappears. Neither does something originate out of the same stuff, as the Sānkhyas think, nor do the things originate from other things as the Vaišeṣikas maintain, nor do the elements flash into existence for a moment only as the early Buddhists think. There is no origination altogether.[5] This is the second feature of the new Buddhism, it repudiates real causality altogether by merging reality in one motionless Whole.

However, the new Buddhism did not repudiate the reality of the empirical world absolutely, it only maintained that the empirical reality was not the ultimate one. There were thus two realities, one on the surface[6] the other under the surface.[7] One is the illusive aspect of reality, the other is reality as it ultimately is. These two realities or «two truths» superseded in the new Buddhism the «four truths» of the early doctrine.

---

calls my attention to the following eloquent passage from Haribhadra's Abhisamayālankārāloka, (Minayeff MSS f. 71^{b}. 7—9) — *dharmasya dharmeṇa šūnyatvāt sarva-dharma-šūnyatā, sarva-dharmāṇām saṃskṛta-asaṃskṛta-rāšer itaretarāpekṣatvena svabhāva-aparinispannatvāt.*

1 *pratītya-samutpāda.*

2 *na svabhāvata utpādaḥ.*

3 Cp. the initial verses of Mādhyamika-kārikās and of TS.

4 Cp. my Nirvāṇa, p. 41.

5 Cp. ibid. p. 40 n. 2.

6 *saṃvṛti-satya.*

7 *sāṃvṛta-satya = paramārtha-satya.*

A further feature of the new Buddhism was the doctrine of complete equipollency between the empirical world and the Absolute, between Saṃsāra and Nirvāṇa.[1] All elements which were in early Buddhism dormant only in Nirvāṇa, but active energies in ordinary life, were declared to be eternally dormant, their activity only an illusion. Since the empirical world is thus only an illusory appearance under which the Absolute manifests itself to the limited comprehension of ordinary men, there is at the bottom no substantial difference between them. The Absolute, or Nirvāṇa, is nothing but the world viewed *sub specie aeternitatis*. Nor can this aspect of the absolutely Real be cognized through the ordinary means of empirical cognition. The methods and results of discursive thought are therefore condemned as quite useless for the cognition of the Absolute. Therefore all logic as well as all constructions of early Buddhism, its Buddhology, its Nirvāṇa, its four truths etc. are unflinchingly condemned as spurious and contradictory constructions.[2] The only source of true knowledge is the mystic intuition of the Saint and the revelation of the new Buddhist Scriptures, in which the monistic view of the universe is the unique subject. This is a further outstanding feature of the new Buddhism, its merciless condemnation of all logic, and the predominance given to mysticism and revelation.

Subsequently a school of more moderate tendencies broke off from the main stock of these Relativists, the so called Svātantrika school. It admitted some logic for the argumentative defense of its standpoint which nevertheless consisted in a dialectical destruction of all the fundamental principles on which cognition is based.

The Path towards Salvation was changed into the Grand Vehicle in that sense that the ideal of the former period, of the Small Vehicle, was declared to be egoistic, and another ideal, not personal Salvation, but the Salvation of mankind, nay of all the Universe of the living creatures, was declared to harmonise with the monistic tendency of speculation. The empirical world was allowed a shadow of reality only in that sense that as a field for the practise of transcendental altruistic virtues,[3] of the Universal Love,[4] it was a preparation for the realisation of the Absolute.[5] The Immaculate Wisdom which was

---

[1] Cp. ibid., p. 205.

[2] Ibid., p. 183.

[3] *pāramitā*.

[4] *mahā-karuṇā*.

[5] *nirvāṇa* = *dharma-kāya*.

one of the elements of the Saint, became now, under the name of the Climax of Wisdom,[1] identified with one aspect of Buddha's Cosmical Body,[2] his other aspect being the world *sub specie aeternitatis*.[3] Buddha ceased to be human. Under the name of his Body of Highest Bliss[4] he became a real God. He however was not the Creator of the World. This feature the new buddhology retained from the preceding period. He was still subject to the law of causation or, according to the new interpretation, to illusion.[5] Only the Cosmical Body, in its twofold aspect, was beyond illusion and causation. Buddhism in this period becomes a religion, a High Church. Just as Hinduism it gives expression to an esoteric Pantheism behind a kind of exoteric Polytheism. For its forms of worship it made borrowings in the current, thaumaturgic, so called «tantristic», rites. For the sculptural realisation of its ideals it made use, at the beginning, of the mastership of Greek artists.

Such were the deep changes which supervened in Buddhism in the second period of its history.

The new or High Church did not mean, however, an exclusion from the former or Low Church. The theory was developped that every man, according to his natural inclination, according to the «seed»[6] of Buddhahood which is in his heart, will either choose the Grand Vehicle or the Small one as a the proper means for his Salvation. Both churches continued to live under the roof of the same monasteries.

§ 5. The third period of Buddhist philosophy.

After another quinquentenary, at the verge of the first millennium of the history of Buddhism in India, a further important change supervened in the orientation of its philosophy. The following development became contemporaneous with the golden age of Indian civilization, when a great part of India was united under the prosperous rule of the national dynasty of the Guptas. Arts and sciences flourished and the Buddhists took a prominent part in this revival. The new direction was finally given to Buddhist philosophy

---

1 *prajñā-pāramitā*.
2 *jñāna-kāya*.
3 *svabhāva-kāya*.
4 *sambhoga-kāya*.
5 *saṃvṛti*; there is in the *sambhoga-kāya* «a little relic of *duḥkha-satya*»
6 *bīja* = *prakṛti-stham gotram*.

by two great men, natives of Peshaver, the brothers Saint Asanga and Master Vasubandhu. Evidently in accordance with the spirit of the new age, the condemnation of all logic which characterized the preceding period, was forsaken, and Buddhists began to take a very keen interest in logical problems. This is the first outstanding feature of that period, a keen interest in logic, which towards the end of the period becomes overwhelming and supersedes all the former theoretical part of Buddhism.

The starting point of the new departure seems to have been something in the kind of an Indian „*Cogito, ergo sum*". «We cannot deny the validity of Introspection, the Buddhists now declared, as against the school of total Illusionism, because, if we deny introspection, we must deny consciousness itself, the whole universe will then be reduced to the condition of absolute cecity». «If we do not really know that we cognize a patch of blue, we will never cognize the blue itself. Therefore introspection must be admitted as a valid source of knowledge». The problem of Introspection afterwards divided all India as well as the Buddhists into two camps, its advocates and its opponents,[2] but originally the theory, seems to have been directed against the extreme skepticism of the Mādhyamikas. It constitutes the second feature of Buddhist philosophy in its third period.

A further feature, a feature which gave its stamp to the whole period, consists in the fact that the skepticism of the preceding period was fully maintained, regarding the existence of an external world. Buddhism became idealistic. It maintained that all existence is necessarily mental[3] and that our ideas have no support in a corresponding external reality.[4] However, not all ideas were admitted as equally real; degrees of reality were established. Ideas were divided in absolutely fanciful,[5] relatively real[6] and absolutely real.[7] The second and the third cate-

---

1 SDS gives the formulation evidently from Pr. viniścaya, cp. NK., p. 261. Expressed more precisely the Indian formula would be — *cogitantem me sentio, ne sit caecus mundus omnis* — *svasaṃvedanam angīkāryam, anyathā jagad-āndhyam prasajyeta*. Prof. Sylvain Lévi has already compared the *sva-saṃvedana* to the *cogito ergo sum*, cp. Mahāyāna-sūtrālankāra, II, p. 20.

2 Cp. vol. II, p. 29 n. 4.

3 *vijñāna-mātra-vāda* = *sems-tsam-pa*.

4 *nirālambana-vāda*.

5 *parikalpita*.

6 *para-tantra*.

7 *pari-niṣpanna*

gory were considered as real. Two realities were admitted, the relatively and the absolutely real, whereas, in the preceding period, all ideas were declared to be unreal,[1] because they were relative.[2] This is the third feature of the last phase of Buddhist philosophy, it became a system of Idealism.

Finally, a prominent feature of the new Buddhism is also its theory of a «store-house consciousness»,[3] a theory which is predominant in the first half of the period and dropped towards its end. There being no external world and no cognition apprehending it, but only a cognition which is introspective, which apprehends, so to say, its own self, the Universe, the real world, was assumed to consist of an infinity of possible ideas which lay dormant in a «store-house» of consciousness. Reality becomes then cogitability, and the Universe is only the maximum of compossible reality. A Biotic Force[4] was assumed as a necessary complement to the stored consciousness, a force which pushes into efficient existence the series of facts constituting actual reality. Just as the rationalists in Europe assumed that an infinity of possible things are included in God's Intellect and that he chooses and gives reality to those of them which together constitute the maximum of compossible reality, just so was it in Buddhism, with that difference that God's Intellect was replaced by a «store-house consciousness»[5] and his will by a Biotic Force. This is the last outstanding feature of the concluding phase of Buddhist philosophy.

Just as the two preceding periods it is divided in an extreme, and a moderate[6] school. The latter, as will appear in the sequel of this work, dropped the extreme idealism of the beginning[7] and assumed a critical or transcendental idealism. Jt also dropped the theory of a «store house consciousness», as being nothing but a Soul in disguise.

As a religion Buddhism remained in this period much the same as it has been in the preceding one. Some changes were introduced in the theory of Nirvāṇa, of the Buddha and of the Absolute in order to bring it in line with the idealistic principles of the system. The

---

1 *śūnya.*

2 *paraspara-apekṣa.*

3 *ālaya-vijñāna.*

4 *anādi-vāsanā.*

5 *āgama-anusārin.*

6 *nyāya-vādin.*

7 Cp. below, vol. II, p. 329 n.

greatest men of this period seem to have been free thinkers. The elucidation of their system of philosophy is the object of the present work.

SCHEMA

of the three main phases of Buddhism

Periods	Central Conceptions		Schools	Chief exponents
First	Pluralism (*pudgala-śūnyatā*)	Extreme	Sarvāstivādins	—
		Moderate	Vātsiputriyas	
Middle	Monism (*sarva-dharma-śūnyatā*)	Extreme	Prāsangika Mādhyamikas	Nāgārjuna and Deva
		Moderate	Svātantrika Mādhyamikas	Bhavya
Concluding	Idealism (*bāhya-artha-śūnyatā*)	Extreme	Āgama-anusārins	Asanga and Vasubandhu
		Moderate	Nyāyavādins	Dignāga and Dharmakirti

§ 6. The place of Buddhist Logic in the history of Indian Philosophy.

Such was the state of affairs which the first Buddhist logicians have found in their own Buddhist home when they first took up the study of logic. They found there three different systems. But in the wider purview of All India the variety of philosophic opinion was still greater. It was really infinite. However, out of all this infinite variety seven philosophic systems seem to have exercised some traceable, either positive or negative, influence upon the formation of the different phases of Buddhist philosophy.[1] They were, 1) the Materialists, (Cārvāka-Bārhaspatya), 2) the Jains with their doctrine of universal animation, 3) the evolutionism of Sānkhya, 4) the mysticism of Yoga, 5) the Monism of Aupaniṣada-Vedānta, 6) the realism of the ortodox Mīmāṃsakas and 7) the realism of Nyāya-Vaišeṣika.

1) The Materialists.

The Indian Materialists[2] denied the existence of any spiritual substances, as all Materialists indeed are doing. Therefore no Soul, no God. The spirit only a product of certain material stuffs, just as wine-spirit is the product of fermentation.[3] They therefore, first of all, admitted of no other source of our knowledge than sense-perception.[4] Knowledge consists for them, so to speak, in physiological reflexes.

They, next to that, denied every established order in the Universe, other than a haphazard order. They admitted of no *a priori*, binding, eternal moral law. «The stick», they maintained, i. e. the penal code is the law. They therefore denied retribution, other than a haphazard retribution from the wordly power. To speak Indian, they denied the law of *karma*. It is a noticeable fact that materialism was fostered and studied in India especially in schools of political thought.[5] Political

---

1 Those systems are alone taken into account which have survived in literature. The influence of those contemporaries of Buddha whose work has not survived must have been still stronger. On the influence of the five heretical teachers on Jainism and Buddhism cp. the very interesting records collected by B. C. Law, Historical Gleanings, pp. 21 ff (Calcutta, 1922).

2 Mādhava's account in SDS remains till now our chief source for the knowledge of the arguments of Indian Materialism. Considerable addition to it has been recently done by prof. J. Tucci. Professor M. Tubiansky is at present engaged in a work of collecting information on this subject from Tibetan sources.

3 SDS, p. 7.

4 Ibid., p. 3.

5 Such as the Bārhaspatyas, the Aušanasas, etc.

men, having thus freed their conscience from every moral tie, preached a businesslike macchiavelism in politics. They supported the established order and the religion upon which it was founded, without caring to be religious themselves.[1] But not only did materialism flourish, so to speak, among the governing class of the Hindu society, it also had its votaries among the popular circles. From among the six successful popular preachers who were wandering through the villages of Hindustan during the life-time of Buddha, two at least were materialists.

A further feature of Indian materialism, which is but a consequence of the foregoing one, is that it denied every higher aim in life other than personal interest. The idea of a self-sacrifice, of a sacrifice of one's interests and even of one's life for a higher aim, this so prominent a feature of Buddhism, seemed ridiculous to them. To speak Indian, they denied Nirvāṇa. «Your death is your Nirvāṇa» they maintained,[2] there is no other!

In the denial of a Soul and of a God Buddhism fell in line with the Materialists. It diverged from them in maintaining Karma and Nirvāṇa.

2) Jainism.

In Jainism, on the other hand, the Buddhists met with a very developped theory of moral defilement and purification,[3] and a theory of spiritual existence extended even to plants and to inanimate, nonorganic things which were also supposed to possess Souls. But the Souls in Jainism were semi-material substances, coextensive with the body, and subject to growth in size together with the growth of the body. Moral impurity was imagined as an influx of a subtle filthy stuff through the pores of the skin into the interior of the Soul.[4] The Soul was then filled with this stuff as a bag with sand. Moral progress was explained as a shutting up of the openings for the filthy matter to stream in, and as the ultimate purification and elevation of the saintly Soul to a final Nirvāṇa in those highest spheres which are the limit of every movement.[5] Thus the moral law represents in Jainism a hypostasized super-realism. To speak Indian, the *karma* of the Jains is matter.[6]

---

[1] Cp. Kauṭalīya, I, 39—40.

[2] SDS., p. 7.

[3] Jainism can, like Buddhism, claim to be a *sāṃkleśa-vyavadāniko dharmaḥ*, i. e., a moral preaching.

[4] Cp. the excellent exposition of the Jaina doctrine of Karma in Prof. H. v. Glasenapp's work, devoted to this subject.

[5] Where the element *dharma* ceases and the element *adharma* begins.

[6] *karma paudgalikam.*

Between these two opposed outlooks Buddhism steered along what it itself called the Middle Path. It denied a substantial Soul and a God. It retained mental phenomena and it saved Karma and Nirvāṇa, but in clearing them of every tinge of super-realism.

The ontology of the Jains contains likewise many traits of similarity with Buddhism. The starting point of both systems is the same, it consists in a decisive opposition to the monism of the Āraṇyakas and Upanishads, where real Being is assumed as one eternal substance without beginning, change, or end. The Jains answered, just as the Buddhists, that Being is «joined to production, continuation and destruction».[1] The systems of that time were divided in India in «radical» and «non-radical» ones.[2] They maintained either that every thing was eternal in its essence, change only apparent, or they maintained that every thing was moving, stability only apparent. To this «radical» class belonged Vedānta and Sānkhya on the one side, Buddhism on the other. The second class admitted a permanent substance with real changing qualities. Jainism, the old Yoga school[3] and the Vaiśeṣikas or their forrunners adhered to this principle. Since Jainism is considerably older than the origin of Buddhism,[4] its leadership in the opposition against monistic ideas is plausible. For the defense of their intermediate position the Jains developped a curious dialectical method,[5] according to which existence and non-existence were inherent in every object, therefore any predicate could be partly true and partly false. Even the predicate of being «inexpressible»[6] could be asserted as well as denied of every thing at the same time. This method looks like an answer to the Mādhyamika method of prooving the «inexpressible» character[7] of absolute reality by reducing its every possible predicates ad absurdum and thus reducing empirical reality to a mirage.

3) The Sānkhya system.

The Sānkhya system of philosophy marks a considerable progress in the history of Indian speculation. It could not but influence all

---

1 Cp. H. Jacobi, ERE, art. Jainism.

2 *ekānta-anekānta,* cp. NS. IV. 1, 25, 29.

3 Svāyambhuva-yoga cp. NK., p. 32.

4 Cp. H. Jacobi, loc. cit.

5 *syād-vāda.*

6 *anirvacanīya-avaktavya.*

7 *anabhilāpya-anirvacanīya-śūnya.*

other Indian circles, whether in the pale of brahmanism or outside it. When the Buddhists, from their critical standpoint, attack brahmanical speculation, they, in the later period, especially direct their destructive critique against the idea of a God like Vishnu and of a substantive Matter like that of the atheistic Sānkhyas.[1] In its classical form[2] the Sānkhya system assumed the existence of a plurality of individual Souls on the one side, and of a unique, eternal, pervasive and substantial Matter[3] on the other. This Matter is supposed to begin by an undifferentiated condition[4] of equipoise and rest. Then an evolutionary process[5] is started. Matter is then never at rest, always changing, changing every minute,[6] but finally it again reverts to a condition of rest and equipoise. This Matter embraces not only the human body, but all our mental states as well, they are given a materialistic origin and essence.[7] The Souls represent only a pure, unchanging light which illumines the evolutionary process and the process of thought-reflexes as well. The connection between this always changing Matter and the perfectly motionless Spirit is a very feeble point of the system. The Buddhists destroyed and ridiculed this artificially constructed connection.[8] The beginning and the end of the evolutionary process remains also unexplicable, the explanation given is very week. But the idea of an eternal Matter which is never at rest, always evolving from one form into another, is a very strong point of the system, and it does credit to the philosophers of that school, that they at so early a date in the history of human thought so clearly formulated the idea of an eternal Matter which is never at rest.

The Buddhists in this point come very near to the Sānkhyas. They also were teaching that whatsoever exists is never at rest, and, therefore, they were constantly on guard[9] not to loose sight of the

---

1 *īsvara-pradhānādi,* cp. TSP, p. 11, 131, Tātp., p. 338, 14.

2 In its early form, as recorded by Caraka IV. 1, when pradhāna and brahman were the same entity, the parallelism with Buddhism is still greater, cp. especially IV. 1. 44 where the doctrine of *sārūpya* is mentioned.

3 *pradhāna.*

4 *avyakta.*

5 *pariṇāma.*

6 *pratikṣaṇa-pariṇāma.*

7 *jaḍa.*

8 Cp. NB and NBT transl. below, vol. II, pp. 203 ff.

9 Cp. AKB., V. 25 ff., and CC., p. 80.

fundamental difference between both systems, since this characteristic feature brought both systems very close together. There is between them an ascertainable reciprocal influence in the attempts to grapple with the idea of instantaneous being.[1] We shall revert to this point when analysing the Buddhist theory of a Universal Flux of Being. But we may mention already now that the Buddhists denied the existence of a substantial matter altogether. Movement consists for them of moments, it is a staccato movement, momentary flaches of a stream of energy. For the Sānkhyas movement is compact, it is a legato movement, the momentary changes are changes of a fluctuating substancial stuff with which they are identical. «Everything is evanescent»,[2] says the Buddhist, because there is no stuff. «Everything is persistent»,[3] says the Sānkhya, because although never at rest, it represents fundamentally one and the same stuff.[4]

Both systems share in common a tendency to push the analysis of Existence up to its minutest, last elements which are imagined as absolute qualities, or things possessing only one unique quality. They are called «qualities» (*guṇa-dharma*) in both systems in the sense of absolute qualities, a kind of atomic, or intra-atomic, energies of which the empirical things are composed. Both systems, therefore, agree in denying the objective reality of the categories of Substance and Quality,[5] and of the relation of Inherence uniting them. There is in Sānkhya philosophy no separate existence of qualities. What we call quality is but a particular manifestation of a subtle entity. To every new unit of quality corresponds a subtle quantum of matter which is called *guṇa* «quality», but represents a subtle substantive entity. The same applies to early Buddhism where all qualities are substantive[6] or, more precisely, dynamic entities, although they are also called *dharmas* «qualities».

---

1 Cp. CC. p. 42 ff.

2 «*sarvam anityam*», cp. NS, IV. 1. 25 ff.

3 «*sarvam nityam*», cp. ibid., IV. 1. 29 ff., notwithstanding this distinction both systems are advocates of *kṣaṇikatva*.

4 The result and the cause are the same stuff — *sat-kārya-vada*.

5 Cp. S. N. Dasgupta, History, I, pp. 243—4; he compares the *guṇas* of the Sānkhya system with the «Reals» of Herbart, which comparison is, in my opinion, very much to the point. The *guṇas*, as well as the *dharmas*, are in fact «*Dinge mit absolut einfacher Qualität*».

6 Cp. Yašomitra's remark: *vidyamānam dravyam* (CC., p. 26 n.), but *dravyam* is here *kṣaṇikam*, a «non-subsisting substance».

The Sānkhya system can thus be regarded as the first serious step that the Indian speculation took against naive realism. It became the ally of Buddhism in its fight with extreme realistic systems.

4) The Yoga system.

The yoga practices of concentrated meditation were a very popular feature of religious life in ancient India and all systems of philosophy, with the only exception of the Mīmāṃsakas, and of course of the Materialists, were obliged to adapt their theories so as to afford some opportunity for the entrance of mysticism. Some scholars have exagerated the importance of those features which Buddhism shares in common with the different schools of Yoga philosophy. The practical side of both these systems, the practice of austerities and of transic meditation, their moral teachings, the theory of *karma*, of the defiling and purifying moral forces are indeed in many points similar, but this similarity extends to the Jains and many other systems. The ontology of the Pātanjala-yoga school is borrowed almost entirely from the Sānkhya. But the old Yoga school, the Svāyambhuva yoga,[1] admitted the existence of a permanent matter alongside with its impermanent but real, qualities; it admitted the reality of a substance-to-quality relation and, evidently, all the consequences which this fundamental principle must have had for its ontology, psychology and theology. It enabled the Yogas to be, without contradiction, the champions of monotheism in ancient India. They believed in a personal, allmighty, omniscient and commiserative God. This feature alone separates them decidedly from not only the Buddhists, but equaly from the atheistic Sānkhyas.[2] As a «non-radical»[3] system the old genuine Yoga school could have but little in common with these two «radical»[4] schools. But its practical mysticism and its theory of *karma* constitutes the common stock of the great majority of Indian systems. Even the later Buddhist logicians, notwithstanding all their aversion to uncritical

---

[1] These Svāyambhuva Yogins were not at all *sat- kārya-vādins*, or they were it only moderately (*anekāntataḥ*), in a measure in which all realists can be so designated. Cp. NK, p. 32 and Tātp., 428. 20 ff. There is no necessity at all to surmise that the Yogas mentioned by Vātsyāyana ad NS, I, 1, 29 were Pātañjala Yogas as Mr. K. Chaṭṭopadhyāya, JRAS, 1927, p. 854 ff. evidently assumes.

[2] On all the contradictions which arise to the Pātañjalas by assuming a personal God cp. Tuxen, Yoga, p. 62 ff.

[3] *an-ekānta*

[4] *ekānta*.

methods of thought, were nevertheless obliged to leave a loop-hole for the entrance of full mysticism and thus to support the religious theory of a Saint and of a Buddha. This loop-hole was a kind of intelligible intuition[1] which was described as a gift to contemplate directly, as if present before the senses, that condition of the Universe which, abstractly and vaguely, appeared as a necessary consequence of logic to the philosopher. In later, idealistic Buddhism this mystic intuition of a rational construction[2] was the chief remainder of the old mysticism. In early Buddhism it was the last and most powerful stage in the path towards salvation and was destined to achieve supernatural results.

5) The Vedānta.

The interrelations between Buddhism and Vedānta, their mutual influences, their mutual attractions and repulsions at different times of their parallel development, is one of the most interesting chapters of the history of Indian philosophy; it deserves a special study. As has been just stated, Buddhism was sometimes obliged carefully to observe the line of demarcation separating it from the Sānkhya and Yoga systems, in order not to be confounded with them. But, as regards Vedānta, it really did sometimes fall in line with it, so as to leave no substantial difference, except the difference in phrasing and terminology. In the first period Buddhist philosophy represents the contradictorily opposed part to the philosophy of the Upanishads. Just as the latter declares that the Universe represents a real Unity, that it is One-without-a-Second, that subject and object, the Ego and the World, the individual Soul and the Soul of the Universe, coalesce in the same Unity, — just so does Buddhism emphatically declare that there is no real unity at all, every thing is discrete, it is splitt in an infinity of minutest elements, the Individual represents a congeries of physical and mental elements without a real Soul behind them, and the external world an assemblage of impermanent elements without any abiding stuff behind. But in the second period, as already mentioned, that Causality which is the only link between the separate elements becomes hypostasized, it becomes the Unique Substance of the Universe in which all the separate elements of the former period are merged and become «void» of any reality in themselves. The spirit of a revolt against Monism, after having produced a most interesting system of extreme Pluralism, did not

---

[1] *yogi-pratyakṣa*, cp. my Nirvāṇa, p. 16 ff.

[2] *bhūta-artha*, cp. NBT, p. 11. 17.

survive, it could not destroy Indian Monism which remained unshaken, so deeply was it rooted in its brahminical stongholds. On the contrary, Monism took the offensive and finally established itself triumphantly in the very heart of a new Buddhism. Transplanted upon a fresh soil the old Monism produced a powerful growth of various systems. In the schools of Nāgārjuna and Deva it received a dialectical foundation, in the way of a dialectical destruction of all other systems. In the schools of Asanga and Vasubandhu it became established dogmatically, as a system of Idealism, and finally, in the schools of Dignāga and Dharmakīrti it was established critically, upon a system of epistemology and logic. This exhuberant growth of argumentative defense could not but influence, in its turn, the old monistic circles and we see Gauḍapāda founding a new school of Vedānta and directly confessing his followship of Buddhism.[1] This feeling of just acknowledgment was superseded, in the person of Šankara-ācārya, by a spirit of sectarian animosity and even extreme hatred, but nevertheless we find, later on, in the same school a man like Šrīharṣa[2] liberally acknowledging that there is but an insignificant divergence between his views and those of the Mādhyamikas.

Thus it is that Buddhism and Vedānta appear in the history of Indian philosophy as mutually indebted parties.

6) The Mīmāṃsā.

The Mīmāṃsakas were the most orthodox theologists of the old brahmanical sacrificial religion. They were averse to any other kind of speculation than that attaining to sacrifice. The Scripture, Veda, was for them nothing but an assemblage of about 70 commands[3] enjoining sacrifice and establishing the kind of reward[4] that was produced by them. No religious emotion and no moral elevation in that religion, all is founded on the principle: pay the brahmin his fee and you will have the reward. However, they were driven by necessity to defend this businesslike religion, and for strengthening the authority of the Veda they imagined the theory of eternal sounds of speech. The ABC[5] of

---

1 Cp. Māṇḍūkyop. kārikā, IV; cp. S. N. Dasgupta, History, v. I, p. 422 ff.

2 Cp. Khaṇḍana-Khaṇḍa-Khādya, pp. 19 and 29 (Chowkh). — *Mādhyamikādi-vāg-vyavahārāṇām svarūpāpalāpo na śakyata iti.*

3 *utpatti-vidhi.*

4 *phala-vidhi.*

5 *gakārādi.*

which our speech consists were, according to this theory, not sounds as other sounds and noises are.[1] They were substances *sui generis,* eternal and ubiquitous, but imperceptible to ordinary men otherwise than in occasional manifestations. Just as light does not produce, but only makes manifest the objects upon which it falls, just so our articulation only makes manifest, but does not produce the sounds of Veda. This absurd idea, assailed by all other orthodox and unorthodox schools, the Mīmāṃsakas defended by arguments and sophisms of extraordinary dialectical subtlety. It apparently exhausted all their speculative wits, for in all other problems they maintained the most decidedly realistic, anti-metaphysical, negative position. No God Creator, no Omniscient Being, no Saints, no mysticism whatsoever, the world as it appears to our senses and nothing more. Therefore, no innate ideas, no constructive cognition, no images, no introspection, a bare consciousness,[2] a tabula rasa of sensitivity and memory, which registers and preserves all external experiences. The same spirit of super-realism which manifests itself in the theory of eternal articulate sounds, appears also in the theory of computed rewards. Every partial act of which a complicated sacrifice consists produces a partial result,[3] the results are then added together and produce as a combined reward,[4] that result which was aimed at by the sacrifice. In their realism and their logic the Mīmāṃsakas were hardly distinguishable from the realistic Nyāya-Vaišeṣika school, but the problem of eternal articulate sounds was the point at issue between them. Their most decided opponents were the Buddhists. There is hardly a single point in philosophy in which both these systems would not represent the one just the reverse of the other.

All these systems of philosophy, however different they be in their ontology, had this feature in common, that their theory of cognition remained, generally speaking, in the phase of naive realism. Even Vedānta, notwithstanding all its spiritualistic monism, admitted, on the empirical plane, a realistic theory of the origin of our knowledge. We find the same ray of light travelling towards the object, seizing its form and carrying it back to the Soul of the individual. The fact that this ray of light, this object and this individual Soul are but one

---

[1] For the Bhāṭṭa-Mīmāṃsakas *dhvani* is the *guṇa* of *ākāśa*, just as with the Vaišeṣikas, but *varṇa* is a substance, *dravya*, and it is *nitya*.

[2] *nirākāram vijñānam.*

[3] *bhāga-apūrva.*

[4] *samāhāra-apūrva*, cp. on *apūrva* Goldstückers's Dictionary.

and the same entity does not disturb the realistic habits of thought of these philosophers.

The theory of this realistic epistemology was elaborated and defended in the school of Nyāya-Vaišeṣika.

7) The Nyāya-Vaišeṣika system.

Buddhist logic was created in a spirit of a decisive opposition to the logic of these Realists, and, since in the course of our investigation we shall have often to refer to their system, it will not be amiss to dwell here on its leading principles.

The Indian Realists maintain that the external world is cognized by us in its genuine reality. There are no innate ideas[1] and no *a priori* principles.[2] Everything comes into the cognizing individual from without. All cognitions are experiences conducted by the apparatus of our senses[3] into the cognizing Soul, where they are sifted, ordered[4] and preserved as traces of former experiences. These dormant traces[5] are capable under favourable circumstances of being aroused and of producing recollections, which being mixed up with new experiences create qualified percepts.[6] Consciousness is pure consciousness,[7] it does not contain any images, but it contemplates, or illumines, external reality directly, by the light of cognition. It sheds a pure light of consciousness upon objects lying in the ken. The sense of vision is a ray of light which reaches the object,[8] seizes its form and communicates it to the cognizing Soul. There are no images lying between external reality and its cognition. Cognition is therefore not introspective,[9] it does not apprehend images, but it apprehends external reality, reality itself. Self-consciousness is explained as an inferential cognition[10] of the presence of knowledge in oneself or by a subsequent step in the act of perception.[11] The structure of the

---

1 *nirākāram vijñānam.*

2 *prāñcaḥ pratyayāḥ, na pratyañcaḥ*, NK, p. 267.

3 *trividha-sannikarṣa.*

4 *samākalita.*

5 *saṃskāra = smṛti-janaka-sāmagrī.*

6 *savikalpakam pratyakṣam.*

7 *nirākāram vijñānam.*

8 *prāpya-kārin.*

9 *svasaṃvedanam nāsti.*

10 *jñātatā-vašāt,* cp. NK, p. 267. 12.

11 *anu-vyavasāya.*

external world corresponds adequately to what is found in our cognition and in the categories of our language. It consists of substances and sensible qualities which can be picked up by our sense faculties. The qualities are inherent in real substances. All motions are likewise realities *per se*, inherent in corresponding substances. Universals are also external realities, realities connected with particular things in which they reside by a special relation called Inherence. This relation of Inherence is hypostasized and is also a special external reality. All other relations are entered in the catalogue of Being under the head of qualities, but Inherence is a «meaning»[1] which is nevertheless an external reality different from the things related. This makes together six categories of Being: Substances, Qualities, Motions, Universals, Particulars and Inherence, to which a seventh category has been added later on in the shape of «non-existence»,[2] also a real «meaning» accessible to perception by the senses through a special contact. Causality is creative, that is to say, material causes[3] and efficient causes[4] combine in the creation of a new reality which represents a new whole,[5] a thing which did not previously exist,[6] notwithstanding the enduring presence of its matter. The whole is another real entity different from the parts of which it is composed. This entire structure of the external world, its relations and causality—all is cognizable through the senses. The intellect,[7] or the reason, is a quality produced in the Soul by special agencies, it is not the Soul's essence. Through inferences it cognizes the same objects which have been cognized through the senses, but cognizes them with a higher degree of clearness and distinctness. The whole system represents nothing but the principle of realism consequently applied. If substances are real, the universals residing in them are also real and their relations are external realities as well. If all this is real, it must be equally amenable to sense-perception. The principle is laid down that the sense faculty which apprehends the presence of an object in the ken also apprehends its inherent

---

1 *padārtha.*

2 *abhāva = abhāva indriyeṇa gṛhyate*, cp. Tarka-bhāṣā, p. 30; the same admitted by old Sāṅkhya, cp. Cakrapāṇi ad Caraka, IV. 1. 28; it is a *viśeṣya-viśeṣaṇa-bhāva-sannikarṣa.*

3 *samavāyi-kāraṇa.*

4 *nimitta-kāraṇa.*

5 *avayavin.*

6 *asat-kāryam = pūrvam asat kāryam = pūrvam asad avayavi.*

7 *buddhi.*

universals and relations and the occasional non-existence, or absence, of the object as well.[1]

The theory of inference and the form of the syllogism were in the realistic systems in full agreement with their fundamental wholesale realism. No *a priori* notions, no necessary truths, no necessity in deductions. Every deduction founded on former experience, all knowledge casual. All invariable concomitance, being a result of former experience, reaches only so far as experience goes. There is no necessary *a priori* connection between the logical reason and its consequence.[2] Therefore all invariable concomitance is established on experience, on sense-knowledge. It is established as a summary[3] of that experience.

The syllogism is five-membered. It is a deductive step from a particular case to another particular case. Therefore the example plays the part of a separate member. The general rule,[4] of which the example ought to be an illustration, is included in the example as its subordinate part. The syllogism has five members because it is inductive-deductive. The members are: thesis, reason, example (including major premise), application (= minor premise), and conclusion (= thesis), e.g.:

1. Thesis. The mountain has fire.
2. Reason. Because it has smoke.
3. Example. As in the kitchen; wheresoever smoke, there also fire.
4. Application. The mountain has smoke.
5. Conclusion. The mountain has fire.

At a later date the Mīmāṃsakas, probably under the influence of the Buddhist critique, made the concession that either the first three members or the last three were sufficient to establish the conclusion. In the last three, if we drop the example, we will have a strictly Aristotelian syllogism, its first figure.

Beside a theory of sense-perception and a theory of the syllogism with its corollary, a theory of logical fallacies, the text books of early Nyāya contain a detailed code of rules for carrying on disputations, i. e., a teaching of dialectics.

The school of Nyāya had already a developed logic when the Buddhists began to manifest a keen interest in logical pro-

---

[1] *yena indriyeṇa vastu gṛhyate, tena tat-samaveta-guṇa-kriyā-sāmānyādi gṛhyate, tad-abhāvaś ca, ibid.*

[2] *yogyatā-sambandhaḥ = svabhāva-sambandhaḥ.*

[3] *upa-saṃhāreṇa.*

[4] *vyāpti.*

blems. The Buddhist doctrine then came to graft itself on the early pre-Buddistic stock. But then a clash supervened at once between two utterly incompatible outlooks. The brahmanical logic was formal and built up on a foundation of naive realism. The Buddhists at that time became critical idealists and their interest in logic was not formal, but philosophic, i. e., epistemological. A reform of logic became indispensable. It was achieved by Dignāga.

§ 7. Buddhist Logic before Dignāga.[1]

The fundamental treatise of the Nyāya school, the aphorisms composed by Gotama, contains, loosely mixed up together, rules of conducting disputations and a manual of logic. Its logical part, the part devoted to inference and syllogism, is comparatively insignificant. The system of realistic ontology was contained in the aphorisms of the sister school of the Vaišeṣikas. The major part of the first treatise is occupied by describing the different methods of carrying on a public debate. The *bona fide*[2] and *mala fide*[3] argument are described, the cavilling,[4] the futile answers,[5] logical fallacies[6] and finally all the cases are mentioned where the debater must be pronounced by the umpire to have lost the contest.[7] It is only in the reformed new brahmanical logic, the logic which emerged from the struggle with Buddhism, that this part is dropped altogether and the theory of syllogism begins to play the central part.

The date of origin of the Nyāya-aphorisms is not known with anything like precision.[8] In its systematic form the Nyāya system is

---

[1] Cp. on this subject the excellent article of Prof. J. Tucci, JBAS. July 1929, p. 451 ff. It is full of information regarding the logical parts of Asanga's and other works. His information on the contents of the Tarka-šāstra fragments however does not agree with the information collected by A. Vostrikov and B. Vassiliev.

[2] *vāda*.

[3] *chala*.

[4] *vitaṇḍā*.

[5] *jāti*.

[6] *hetv-ābhāsa*.

[7] *nigraha-sthāna*.

[8] On the pre-history of the Nyāya system cp. H. Jacobi, Zur Frühgeschichte der ind. Phil. (Preuss. Ak., 1911), S. C. Vidyābhūṣaṇa, History of Indian Logic, pp. 1—50, and Tucci, Pre-Dignāga Texts, Intro., p. XXVII. On the probable date of the Nyāya-sūtras of Gotama-Akṣapāda cp. H. Jacobi JAOS, 1911, p. 29, H. Ui, The Vaišeṣika Philosophy, p. 16 (RAS), L. Suali, Filosofia Indiana, p. 14, W. Ruben, Die Nyāya-sūtras, p. XII, S. N. Dasgupta, History, v. I, p. 277 ff. and my Erkenntnisstheorie u. Logik, Anhang II (München, 1924).

later than the other Indian classical systems. But in the form of some manual on the art of debate it is not improbable that it existed at a considerably earlier date. The Buddhist schools of the Hīnayāna have not preserved any manual of that sort, but it is highly probable that they must have existed. The opening debate of the Kathā-vatthu on the reality of a Soul is conducted with so high a degree of artificiality and every kind of dialectical devices that it suggests the probable existence of special manuals in which the art of debate was taught.[1] Syllogistic formulation of the thesis is quite unknown at that time, but dialectical tricks of every kind abound.

The oldest Buddhist compositions on the art of debate that have reached us in Tibetan translations are two tracts by Nāgarjuna, the «Repudiation of Contests»[2] and the «Dialectical splitting (of every thesis)».[3] Both contain the exposition and the vindication of that unique method of conducting a debate which consists in proving nothing positive, but in applying the test of relativity to every positive thesis of the opponent and thus destroying it dialectically. There is indeed absolutely nothing which would not be relative in some respect, and therefore everything can be denied ultimate reality when its dialectical nature is disclosed. The first of these tracts mentions the four methods of proof current in the Nyāya school and the second quotes the initial aphorism of Gotama in which the 16 topics to be examined in the treatise are enumerated. By applying his critical axe of relativity Nāgārjuna establishes that all the 16 topics are relational and therefore ultimately unreal. These facts allow us to assume that the fundamental treatise of the Nyāya school probably existed in some form or other at the time of Nāgārjuna. They also encourage the hypothesis that similar tracts might have been in existence already among the early schools of the Hīnayāna, and that Nāgārjuna was probably not the first Buddhist to have composed them. Be that as the case may be, Nāgārjuna at any rate either introduced

---

[1] This is also the opinion of Mrs C. A. F. Rhys Davids, art. Logic (Buddhist) in ERE., cp. Vidyābhūsana, History pp. 225—250 on the traces of logical works in the Pali canonical literature and, pp. 157—163, in Jaina canonical lit.

[2] Vigraha-vyāvartinī, cp. Tanjur, v. tsa, quoted several times by Candrakīrti. Summary by Vidyābhūsaṇa, op. cit., p. 250. The Vigraha-vyāvartinī is now available in a Sanscrit translation by Tucci in his Pre-Dignāga Texts.

[3] Vaidalya-sūtra and prakaraṇa, ibid. The 16 padārthas are examined in the prakaraṇa; the work is also called pramāna-viheṭhana and pramaṇa-vidhvaṃsana, cp. Vidyābhūsana, op. cit. p. 257. A third work of Nāgārjuna—cp. ibid.—is probably spurious.

or followed the habit of Buddhist writers to treat dialectics in special, separate manuals. From that time we see that every author of some renoun composes his own manual of dialectics containing instructions for carrying on public disputations.

During the centuries that followed, the Buddhists made no progress in logic. And this is quite natural. How could it have been otherwise as long as Nāgārjuna's ideas held the sway? For the cognition of the Absolute all logic was condemned. For practical aims in the empirical domain the realistic logic of the Naiyāyiks was admitted as quite sufficient.[1] The necessity of its critique and improvement did not yet dawn upon the Buddhists of that time. But with the advent of a new age, when Nāgārjuna's standpoint of extreme relativism was forsaken, the brothers Asanga and Vasubandhu took up the study of Nyāya logic and the work of its adaptation to the idealistic foundations of their philosophy.

Asanga was probably the first Buddhist writer who introduced the theory of the five-membered syllogism of the Naiyāyiks into the practice of Buddhist circles. He also established a body of rules on the art of debate, not materially different from the rules prescribed in the Nyāya school. He does not seem to have been very original in the domain of logic and dialectics.[2]

Vasubandhu was a renowned teacher of logic. He himself composed three logical treatises. They have not been translated into Tibetan, but an incomplete Chinese translation of one of them exists.[3] Its title

---

1 The relation between Gotama and Nāgārjuna seems to be of the sort that obtains between Jaimini and Bādarāyana, who mutually quote one another, cp. Vidyābhūsaṇa, op. cit., p. 46—47. The term *vitaṇḍā*, in NS. I. 1. 1, moreover, we probably must understand as meaning nothing else than the Mādhyamika-prāsangika method of discussion; Śrīharṣa, Khaṇḍ. loc. cit., uses the term *vaitaṇḍika* as a synonym of Mādhyamika. It follows that the Naiyāyika and Mādhyamika schools are evidently much older than Gotama and Nāgārjuna.

2 Cp. Vidyābhūsana, History, pp. 263—266. The Saptadaśa-bhūmi-śāstra is ascribed by him to Maitreya. Cp. J. Tucci, op. cit.

3 On this perplexing problem cp. Sugiura, op. cit. p. 32; Vidyābhūsana, op. cit., p. 267; Iyengar JBORS, XII, pp. 587—91, and IHQ., vol. V, pp. 81—86; 13 Keith, IHQ., vol. IV, pp. 221—227; J. Tucci, JRAS., 1928, p. 368, 1929, p. 451 and IHQ, vol. IV, p. 630. Tucci thinks that the Tarkaśāstra has nothing to do with Vādavidhi. But in a paper read at a meeting of the Buddhist Research Institution at Leningrad (shortly to appear in the press) M-r Boris Vassiliev has established that «Tarka-śāstra» was originally a work on the «science of logic» (*ju-shih-lun-tarka-śāstra*) in three volumes, in its present condition it represents one volume of collected fragments. M-r Andrew Vostrikov, in another

Vāda-vidhi means «the art of disputation». To judge by the extant part it very closely agrees with the fundamental textbook of the Naiyāyiks. The crucial points, the definitions of sense-perception, of inference, and of a sound thesis are not to be found in the preserved part of the Chinese translation, but they are quoted by Dignāga.[1] The definition of sense-perception states that by sense-perception that knowledge is understood which comes «from the object itself».[2] By this emphasis of «itself» the ultimately real object, the efficient reality of the thing, is understood. It is distinguished from the object as constructed in an image, such an object being only contingently real.[3] The definition, although in its phrasing very slightly different from that which is current in the Nyāya school,[4] is nevertheless quite Buddhistic. Dignāga however criticizes it as incorrectly expressed and adds a remark that this definition «does not belong to Master Vasubandhu». This remark has puzzled all subsequent interpretation. Jinendrabuddhi in his Višālāmalavatī[5] thinks it means that the definition is not what Vasubandhu would have said in his riper years when his critical faculties attained full development, i. e., that it was composed while he was yet a Vaibhāṣika. Rgyal-tshab[6] thinks that the definition might be interpreted as implying the reality of the atoms of which the thing is composed and this does not agree with the radical idealism of Vasubandhu. The remark of Dignāga would thus mean that the definition is not what Vasubandhu ought to have said from the standpoint of consequent idealism. In another work Vāda-vidhāna — a title meaning the same, but slightly different in form — Vasubandhu is supposed to have corrected his formulations. The definition of sense-perception, in any case, has passed over into many brahmanical works on logic[7] where it is ascribed to Vasubandhu

---

paper read at the same meeting, establishes 1) that the *ju-shih-lun* collection contains at present fragments of two or three different works, one of them is the Vādavidhi of Vasubandhu, and 2) that Vasubandhu wrote three different works on logic called the Vāda-vidhi, the Vāda-vidhāna, and the Vāda-hṛdaya, the second work being an emendation of the first.

1 Pr. Samucc., I. 15, etc.

2 Cp. the comment of Vācaspati, Tātp., p. 99 ff.

3 *saṃvṛtti-sat.*

4 *tato' rthād utpannam = arthendriya-sannikarṣa-utpannam*, ibid.

5 Tanjur, Mdo, v. 115.

6 In his comment on Pr. Samucc., Tshad-ma-btus-dar-ṭik, f. 20. a. 5 ff.

7 N. vārt. p. 42, Tātp., p. 99, Parišuddhi, p. 640—650., Prof. B. Keith thinks that this definition does not betray in Vasubandhu a sharp logician (?),

and criticized as such. The syllogism with which Vasubandhu operates is the five-membered syllogism of the Nyāya school, although, as appears from a passage in the supplement to the Abhidharma-koša, he sometimes makes use of the abridged, three-membered form.[1] The three aspects of the logical reason, this Buddhist method of formulating invariable concomitance, appears already in the treatise of Vasubandhu. The classification of reasons and fallacies is different from the one accepted in the Nyāya school and agrees in priciple with the one introduced by Dignāga and developed by Dharmakīrti. If we add that the definition of sense-perception as pure sensation which is so characteristic a feature of Dignāga's system is already found in a work of Asanga,[2] we cannot escape the conclusion that the great logical reform of Dignāga and Dharmakīrti was prepared by an adaptatory work of the realistic and formal Nyāya logic to the requirements of an idealistic system, this adaptatory work being begun in the schools of Asanga and Vasubandhu, perhaps even much earlier.

§ 8. The life of Dignāga.

The lives of Dignāga and Dharmakīrti, as recorded by the Tibetan historians Tāranātha, Bu-ston and others, are so full of quite incredible mythological details that it becomes a difficult task to extract some germs of truth out of them. There are however facts which with great probability must be assumed as correct. This refers, first of all, to the lineage of teachers, their caste and place of birth. Vasubandhu was the teacher of Dignāga, but he was probably an old and celebrated man when Dignāga came to attend to his lessons. Dharmakīrti was not the direct pupil of Dignāga. There is an intermediate teacher between them in the person of Išvarasena who was a pupil of Dignāga and the teacher of Dharmakīrti. Išvarasena has left no trace in the literary history of his school, although he is quoted by Dharmakīrti who accuses him of having misunderstood Dignāga. We have thus the following lineage of teachers — Vasubandhu-Dignāga-Išvarasena-Dharmakīrti.[3] Since Dharmakīrti flourished in the middle of the

---

cp. IHQ, vol. IV. All the implications of the laconic expression have evidently escaped his attention.

[1] Cp. my Soul Theory of the Buddhists, p. 952.

[2] Tucci, in the IHQ, vol. IV, p. 550. In Uttara-tantra, IV. 86 the «analytical» reason (*svabhāva-hetu*) is already used.

[3] Cp. Tāranātha's History.

VII century A. D., Vasubandhu could not have lived earlier than the close of the IV century.[1]

Both Dignāga and Dharmakīrti were natives of Southern India and born from brahmin parents. Dignāga was born in the neighbourhood of Kāñcī. He was at an early age converted to Buddhism by a teacher of the Vātsīputrīya sect and took the vows from him. This sect admitted the existence of a real personality as something different from the elements of which it is composed. Dignāga dissented on this point with his teacher and left the monastery.[2] He then travelled to the north in order to continue his studies in Magadha under Vasubandhu whose fame at that time must have been very great. Among the great names of later Buddhism the name of Vasubandhu occupies an exceptional position, he is the greatest among the great. He is the only master who is given the title of the Second Buddha. His teaching was encyclopaedic, embracing all the sciences cultivated in India at his time. He had a great many pupils, but four of them attained celebrity. They became «independent scholars»,[3] i. e., they freed themselves from the influence of their teacher and advanced further on, each in the special branch of his studies. These were the master Sthiramati—in the knowledge of the systems of the early 18 schools (*abhidharma*), the saint Vimuktasena—in monistic philosophy (*prajñā-pāramitā*), the master Guṇaprabha—in the system of discipline (*vinaya*) and master Dignāga in logic (*pramāṇa*). The works of all these savants are preserved in Tibetan translations. Dignāga seems to have dissented with his teacher on logical questions

---

1 M. Noel Péri, in his excellent paper on the date of Vasubandhu, arrives at an earlier date, but this apparently reposes on a confusion of the great Vasubandhu with another author of the same name, Vṛddhācārya-Vasubandhu, quoted in the AK. and also called bodhisattva Vasu, the author of Śataśāstra, who was a century earlier. The opinion of V. Smith, Early History, p. 328 (3d ed.) is founded on the same confusion.

2 The learned translator of Maṇi-mekhalai thinks that the Buddhists of the country of Kañcī may have studied logic before Dignāga. Since the sect of the Vātsīputrīyas has some affinities with the Vaiśeṣikas, cp. Kamalaśīla, p. 132. 6, this is not improbable. The theory of two *pramāṇas* and the definition of *pratyakṣa* as *nirvikalpaka* certainly have existed long before Dignāga in some Hīnayāna or Mahāyāna schools. Dignāga gave to these formulas a new signification, but he himself quotes in support of them a passage from the abhidharma of the Sarvāstivādins.

3 *rañ-las-mkhas-pa = svatantra-paṇḍita.*

just as he dissented with his first teacher on the problem of a real personality.[1]

To the time of his apprenticeship probably belong two early works, two manuals for the use of students. One of them is a condensed summary of the capital work of his teacher under the title of Abhidharmakoša-marma-pradīpa.[2] The other contains a breef summary (*piṇḍārtha*) in mnemonic verse of all the topics contained in the Aṣṭa-sāhasrika-prajñā-pāramitā-sūtra.[3] The first is a manual for the class of early Buddhist philosophy (*abhidharma*), the second a manual for the class of monistic philosophy (*pāramitā*). The remaining works of Dignāga are all devoted to logic.[4] He at first exposed his ideas in a series of short tracts some of which are preserved in Tibetan and Chinese translations[5] and then condensed them in a great *oeuvre d'ensemble*, the Pramāṇa-samuccaya, in 6 chapters of mnemonic verse with the author's own commentary. The commentary however is very laconic and evidently intended as a guide for the teacher. Without the very detailed, thorough-going and clear commentary of Jinendrabuddhi[6] it hardly could be understood. All the previous short tracts on logic were brought to unity in this great work.

The life of Dignāga after he had finished his studies was spent in the usual way, just as the life of every celebrated teacher at that time in India. He won his fame of a powerful logician in a famous debate with a brahmin surnamed Sudurjaya at the Nālandā monastery. After that he travelled from monastery to monastery, occasionally

---

1 His remark on Vasubandhu's definition of sense-perception, referred to above, is perhaps a polite way of expressing the fact that he disagreed with his teacher.

2 Tanjur, Mdo, v. LXX.

3 Tanjur, Mdo, v. XIV.

4 These are Ālambana-parīkṣā, Trikāla-parīkṣā, Hetu-cakra-samarthana (Hetu-cakra-hamaru?), Nyāyamukha (= Nyāya-dvāra), Pramāṇa-samuccaya with vṛtti, and Hetumukha (TSP., p. 339. 15).

5 It is remarkable that his chief work, Pramāṇa-samuccaya, has remained unknown in China and Japan. It has been replaced by Nyāya-praveša, a work by Šankara-svāmin, on whose authorship cp. M. Tubianski, On the authorship of Nyāya-praveša and Tucci, op. cit.; M-r Boris Vassiliev in his paper mentioned above establishes that the Chinese logicians knew about Pramāṇa-samuccaya only from hear-say.

6 Called Višālāmalavatī, cp. Tanjur, Mdo, v. 115. A specimen of it is translated in Appendix IV.

fixing his residence in one of them. There he was teaching, composing his works, partaking in public disputations. Such disputations were an outstanding feature of public life in ancient India. They often were arranged with great pomp, in the presence of the king, of his court and a great attendance of monks and laymen. The existence and prosperity of the monastery were at stake. The authorized winner received the support of the king and of his government for his community, converts were made and new monasteries were founded. Even now in Tibet and Mongolia every celebrated teacher is the founder of one or several monasteries, every monastery is a seat of intense learning and sometimes great scholarship.

Dignāga by the celebrity he won in disputations has been one of the most powerful propagators of Buddhism. He is credited with having achieved the «conquest of the world».[1] Just as an universal monarch brings under his sway all India, so is the successful winner of disputations the propagator of his creed over the whole of the continent of India. Cashmere seems to have been the only part of India where he has not been, but he was visited by representatives of that country who later on founded schools there. These schools carried on the study of his works and produced several celebrated logicians.

§ 9. The life of Dharmakīrti.

Dharmakīrti was born in the South, in Trimalaya (Tirumalla?) in a brahmin family and received a brahmanical education. He then became interested in Buddhism and adhered at first as a lay member to the church. Wishing to receive instruction from a direct pupil of Vasubandhu he arrived at Nālandā, the celebrated seat of learning where Dharmapāla, a pupil of Vasubandhu, was still living, although very old. From him he took the vows. His interest for logical problems being aroused and Dignāga no more living, he directed his steps towards Iśvarasena, a direct pupil of the great logician. He soon surpassed his master in the understanding of Dignāga's system. Iśvarasena is reported to have conceded that Dharmakīrti understood Dignāga better than he could do it himself. With the assent of his teacher Dharmakīrti then began the composition of a great work in mnemonic verse containing a thorough and enlarged commentary on the chief work of Dignāga.

The remaining of his life was spent, as usual, in the composition of works, teaching, public discussions and active propaganda.

[1] *dig-vijaya.*

He died in Kalinga in a monastery founded by him, surrounded by his pupils.

Notwithstanding the great scope and success of his propaganda he could only retard, but not stop the process of decay which befell Buddhism on its native soil. Buddhism in India was doomed. The most talented propagandist could not change the run of history. The time of Kumārila and Šankara-ācārya, the great champions of brahmanical revival and opponents of Buddhism, was approaching. Tradition represents Dharmakīrti as having combated them in public disputations and having been victorious. But this is only an afterthought and a pious desire on the part of his followers. At the same time it is an indirect confession that these great brahmin teachers had met with no Dharmakīrti to oppose them. What might have been the deeper causes of the decline of Buddhism in India proper and its survival in the border lands, we never perhaps will sufficiently know, but historians are unanimous in telling us that Buddhism at the time of Dharmakīrti was not on the ascendency, it was not flourishing in the same degree as at the time of the brothers Asanga and Vasubandhu. The popular masses began to deturn their face from that philosophic, critical and pessimistic religion, and reverted to the worship of the great brahmin gods. Buddhism was beginning its migration to the north where it found a new home in Tibet, Mongolia and other countries.

Dharmakīrti seems to have had a forboding of the ill fate of his religion in India. He was also grieved by the absence of pupils who could fully understand his system and to whom the continuation of his work could have been entrusted. Just as Dignāga had no famous pupil, but his continuator emerged a generation later, so was it that Dharmakīrti's real continuator emerged a generation later in the person of Dharmottara. His direct pupil Devendrabuddhi was a devoted and painstaiking follower, but his mental gifts were inadequate to the task of fully grasping all the implications of Dignāga's and his own system of transcendental epistemology. Some verses of him in which he gives vent to his deepest feelings betray this pessimistic mentality.

The second introductory stanza of his great work is supposed to have been added later, as an answer to his critics. He there says, «Mankind are mostly addicted to platitudes, they don't go in for finesse. Not enough that they do not care at all for deep sayings, they ar filled with hatred and with the filth of envy. Therefore neither do

I care to write for their benefit. However, my heart has found satisfaction in this (my work), because through it my love for profound and long meditation over (every) well spoken word has been gratified».

And in the last but one stanza of the same work he again says, «My work will find no one in this world who would be adequate easily to grasp its deep sayings. It will be absorbed by, and perish in, my own person, just as a river[1] (which is absorbed and lost) in the ocean. Those who are endowed with no inconsiderable force of reason, even they cannot fathom its depth! Those who are endowed with exceptional intrepidity of thought, even they cannot perceive its highest truth».[2]

Another stanza is found in anthologies and hypothetically ascribed to Dharmakīrti, because it is to the same effect. The poet compares his work with a beauty which can find no adequate bridegroom. «What was the creator thinking about when he created the bodily frame of this beauty! He has lavishly spent the beauty-stuff! He has not spared the labor! He has engendered a mental fire in the hearts of people who (theretofore) were living placidly! And she herself is also wretchedly unhappy, since she never will find a fiancé to match her!»

In his personal character Dharmakīrti is reported to have been very proud and self-reliant, full of contempt for ordinary mankind and sham scholarship.[3] Tāranātha tells us that when he finished his great work, he showed it to the paṇḍits, but he met with no appreciation and no good will. He bitterly complained of their slow wits and their envy. His enemies, it is reported, then tied up the leaves of his work to the tail of a dog and let him run through the streets where the leaves became scattered. But Dharmakīrti said, «just as this dog runs through all streets, so will my work be spread in all the world».

---

1 The Tib. translation points rather to the reading *sarid iva* instead of *paya iva.*

2 The *śleṣa* which Abhinavagupta finds in these words seems not to have been in the intention of the author. The commentators do not mention it. Cp. Dhvanyāloka comment, p. 217. According to Yamāri's interpretation the word *analpa-dhī-śaktibhiḥ* must be analysed in *a-dhī-* and *alpa-dhī-śaktibhiḥ*. The meaning would be: «How can its depth be fathomed by men who either have little or no understanding at all?» and this would refer to the incapacity of Devendrabuddhi.

3 Cp. Ānandavardhana's words in Dhvanyāloka, p. 217. A verse in which Dharmakīrti boasts to have surpassed Candragomin in the knowledge of grammar and Śūra in poetry is reported by Tāranātha and is found engraved in Barabudur, cp. Krom, p. 756.

§ 10. THE WORKS OF DHARMAKĪRTI.

Dharmakīrti has written 7 logical works, the celebrated «Seven treatises» which have become the fundamental works (*mūla*) for the study of logic by the Buddhists in Tibet and have superseded the work of Dignāga, although they originally were devised as a detailed commentary on the latter. Among the seven works one, the Pramāṇa-vārtika, is the chief one, containing the body of the system; the remaining six are subsidiary, its «six feet».[1] The number seven is suggestive, because the abhidharma of the Sarvāstivādins also consisted of seven works, a principal one and its «six feet». Evidently Dharmakīrti thought that the study of logic and epistemology has to replace the ancient philosophy of early Buddhism. The Pramāṇa-vārtika consists of four chapters dealing with inference, validity of knowledge, sense-perception and syllogism respectively. It is written in mnemonic verse and contains about 2000 stanzas. The next work Pramāṇa-viniścaya is an abridgment of the first. It is written in stanzas and prose. More than the half of the stanzas are borrowed from the principal work. The Nyāya-bindu is a further abridgment of the same subject. Both last works are in three chapters devoted to sense-perception, inference and syllogism respectively. The remaining four works are devoted to special problems. Hetubindu is a short classification of logical reasons, Sambandha-parīkṣā—an examination of the problem of relations—a short tract in stanzas with the author's own comment, Codanā-prakaraṇa—a treatise on the art of carrying on disputations and Santānāntara-siddhi—a treatise on the reality of other minds, directed against Solipsism. With the exception of the Nyāya-bindu all other works are not yet recovered in their sanscrit original, but they are available in Tibetan translations, embodied in the Tanjur. The Tibetan collection contains some other works ascribed to Dharmakīrti, viz. a collection of verse, comments on Śūra's Jātaka-mālā and on the Vinaya-sūtra, but whether they really belong to him is not sure.[2]

---

1 According to another interpretation the three first works are the body, the remaining four the feet, cp. Buston, History, pp. 44, 45.

2 He is also reported by Tāranātha to have written a work on tantrik ritual and the tantrists of Java reckoned him as a teacher of their school. But probably this was only their belief sprung up from the desire to have a celebrated name among their own school. The work is found in the Tanjur.

§ 11. The order of the chapters in Pramāṇa-vārtika.

Dharmakīrti had the time to write a commentary only upon the mnemonic stanzas of the first chapter of his great work, the chapter on inference. The task of writing comments upon the stanzas of the remaining three chapters he entrusted to his pupil Devendrabuddhi. However the latter could not acquit himself of the task to the full satisfaction of his teacher. Tāranātha reports that twice his attempts were condemned and only the third had met with a half-way approval. Dharmakīrti then said that all the implications of the text were not disclosed by Devendrabuddhi, but its *prima facie* meaning was rendered correctly.[1]

The order of the chapters in the Pramāṇa-vārtika makes a strange impression. Whereas the order in both the abridged treatises, in Pramāṇa-viniścaya and Nyāyabindu, is a natural one — perception comes first and is followed by inference and syllogism — an order moreover agreeing with Dignāga, who also begins by perception and inference,—the order in Pramāṇa-vārtika is an inverted one. It begins with inference, goes over to the validity of knowledge, then comes back to sense-perception which is followed by syllogism at the close. The natural order would have been to begin with the chapter upon the validity of knowledge and then to go over to perception, inference and syllogism. This is much more so because the whole chapter on the validity of knowledge is supposed to contain only a comment upon the initial stanza of Dignāga's work. This stanza contains a salutation to Buddha, who along with the usual titles is here given the title of «Embodied Logic» (*pramāṇa-bhūta*).[2] The whole of Mahāyānistic Buddhology, all the proofs of the existence of an absolute, Omniscient Being are discussed under that head.

We would naturally expect the work to begin with this chapter upon the validity of knowledge and the existence of an Omniscient Being, and then to turn to a discussion of perception, inference and syllogism, because this order is required by the subject-matter itself, and is observed in all other logical treatises throughout the whole of Buddhist and brahmanical logic. To begin with inference, to place the chapter on the validity of knowledge between inference and perception, to deal with sense-perception on the third place and to separate infe-

---

1 Cp. Tāranātha's History.

2 *pramāṇa-bhutāya jagad-dhitaiṣine,* etc. cp. Dutt, Nyāya-praveśa, Introd.

rence from syllogism by two other chapters, is against all habits of Indian philosophy and against the nature of the problems discussed.

This very strange circumstance did not fail to attract the attention of Indian and Tibetan logicians who commented upon the work of Dharmakīrti, and a great strife arose among them around this problem of the order of the chapters in Pramāṇa-vārtika. The arguments for changing the order into a natural one or for keeping to the traditional order have recently been examined by Mr A. Vostrikov. We take from his paper[1] the following details. The main argument for maintaining the traditional order is the fact that Devendrabuddhi, the immediate pupil of Dharmakīrti, supported it, and that Dharmakīrti had himself written a comment only on the chapter on inference. It is natural to assume that he began by writing the commentary on the first chapter, and was prevented by death to continue the work of commenting on the remaining chapters. A further notable fact is that the chapter on Buddhology, the religious part, is not only dropped in all the other treaties, but Dharmakīrti most emphatically and clearly expresses his opinion to the effect that the absolute omniscient Buddha is a metaphysical entity, something beyond time, space and experience, and that therefore, our logical knowledge being limited to experience, we can neither think nor speak out anything definite about him,[2] we can neither assert nor deny his existence. Since the chapter on Buddhology in the natural run must have been the earliest work of Dharmakīrti, begun at the time when he was studying under Iśvarasena, Mr A. Vostrikov admits a change in the later development of his ideas, a change, if not in his religious convictions, but in the methods adopted by him. Dharmakīrti then, at his riper age, abandoned the idea of commenting upon the first chapter, entrusted the chapter on perception to Devendrabuddhi and wrote the chapter on inference, as the most difficult one, himself.

§ 12. The philological school of commentators.

Be that as the case may be, Dharmakīrti's logical works became the starting point of an enormous amount of commenting literature. The works preserved in Tibetan translations may be divided in three groups, according to the leading principles by which the work

---

1 His paper has been read in a meeting of the Institution for Buddhist Research at Leningrad and will soon appear in the press.

2 Cp. the closing passage of Santānāntarasiddhi, and NB, III. 97.

of interpretation was guided. Devendrabuddhi initiated the school which can be termed the school of direct meaning. It is, so to speak, a school of «philological» interpretation. It aimed at exactly rendering the direct meaning of the commented text without loosing oneself in its deeper implications. To this school belonged, after Devendrabuddhi, his pupil and follower Šākyabuddhi whose work is extant in Tibetan,[1] and probably also Prabhābuddhi whose work is lost. They all commented on Pramāṇa-vārtika, leaving Pramāna-viniścaya and Nyāyabindu unnoticed. Commentaries on these latter works were written by Vinītadeva who followed in his works the same method of simplicity and literalism. Among the Tibetan authors Khaī-ḍub, the pupil of Tsoñ-khapa, must be referred to this school as its continuator in Tibet.[2]

§ 13. The Cashmere or philosophic school of commentators.

The next two schools of commentators are not content with establishing the direct meaning of Dharmakīrti's text, they strive to investigate its more profound philosophy. The second school can be termed the Cashmerian school, according to the country of its main activity, and the critical school, according to its main tendency in philosophy. According to that school the Buddha as a personification of Absolute Existence and Absolute knowledge, the Mahāyānistic Buddha, is a metaphysical entity, and therefore uncognizable for us, neither in the way of an affirmation nor in the way of a denial.[3] Pramāṇa-vārtika is nothing but a detailed comment on Dignāga's Pramāṇa-samuccaya which is a purely logical treatise. The initial salutatory verse of the latter mentions, it is true, the great qualities of the Mahāyānistic Buddha and identifies him with pure Logic, but this is only a conventional expression of reverential feelings, it has no theoretical importance. The aim of the school is to disclose the deep philosophic contents of the system of Dignāga and Dharmakīrti, regarding it as a critical system of logic and epistemology. The school aims at development, improvement and perfectness of the system.

The founder of the school was Dharmottara, its seat Cashmere, its active members were often brahmins. Dharmottara is held in high

---

[1] Tanjur, Mdo, vol. 97 and 98.

[2] Khaī-ḍub (Mkhas-grub) has written a detailed commentary on Pramāṇa-vārtika in two volumes (800 folios) and two minor independent works on logic.

[3] *deša-kāla-svabhāva-viprakṛṣṭa*, cp. NB, III. 97.

esteem by the Tibetans and reputed as being very acute. Although not a direct pupil of Dharmakīrti he was the sort of pupil the great master was wanting, for he not only accompanied his comments by weighty considerations of his own, but had also independent views and successful new formulations on important topics. Tāranātha does not contain his biography, probably because the field of his activity was Cashmere. He was not, however, a native of that country. He was invited to visit it by the king Jayāpīda when the latter saw in a dream that a «sun was rising in the West», as the Cashmerian chronicle reports. This must have happened round the year 800 A. D.[1] Dharmottara must have been by this time a celebrated man. Vācaspatimiśra living in the IX th century quotes him several times.[2]

He did not comment upon Pramāṇa-vārtika, the chief and first work of Dharmakīrti, but he wrote detailed commentaries on the Pramāṇa-viniścaya and Nyāya-bindu, the first being called his Great Comment, the second — his Small Comment.[3] Whether he at all had the intention of commenting upon the Pramāṇa-vārtīka is uncertain. The order of the chapters in this treatise is not discussed by him. He vehemently attacks Vinītadeva his predecessor in the work of commenting upon the Nyāya-bindu and a follower of the first school, the school of literal interpretation. Besides these two works Dharmottara composed four other minor works on special problems of logic and epistemology.[4]

The celebrated Cashmerian writer on the art of poetry, the brahmin Ānandavardhana composed a subcommentary (*vivṛtti*) on Dharmottara's Pramāṇa-viniścaya-ṭīkā. This work has not yet been recovered.[5]

---

1 Cp. Rājataranginī, IV. 498 — «He (the king) deemed it a favourable circumstance that the teacher Dharmottara had arrived in the land, because he then saw in a dream that a sun had arisen in the West (of India)». The translation of this stanza by sir A. Stein must be corrected, since the fact that *ācārya dharmottara* is a proper name has escaped his attention. Allowing a correction of about 20 years in the traditional chronology of the Cashmere chronicle we will be about the year 800 A. D. for the time when Dharmottara came to live and teach in that country.

2 Tātp., p. 109, 139.

3 Tanjur, Mdo, vol. 109 and 110.

4 Pramāṇa-parīkṣā, Apoha-prakaraṇa, Paraloka-siddhi, Kṣaṇa-bhanga-siddhi, all in the Tanjur, Mdo, vol. 112.

5 It seems from the passage of Abhinavagupta's Commentary on Dhvanyāloka, p. 233 (ed. Kāvyamālā) that Ānandavardhana had written a Pramāṇa-viniš-

Another subcommentary on the same work has been written by the Cashmerian brahmin Jñānaśrī.[1] Its Tibetan translation is preserved in the Tanjur collection. And finally the brahmin Śankarānanda, surnamed the Great Brahmin, undertook to comment on Pramāṇavārtika in a comprehensive work (*ṭīkā*) conceived on a very large scale. Unfortunately he did not finish it. The extant part contains only the comment on the first chapter (in the traditional order) and even that is not quite finished. It nevertheless fills up, in its Tibetan translation, an enormous volume of the Tanjur.[2] The whole work would have filled no less than four volumes, just as the comprehensive work of Yamāri belonging to the third school of commentators.

Among the Tibetan authors Tsoṅ-khapa's pupil Rgyal-tshab has some affinities with this school and can be reckoned as its Tibetan continuator. He has made logic his special study and has commented on almost all works of Dignāga and Dharmakīrti.[3]

§ 14. The third or religious school of commentators.

Just as the former one, this school strived to disclose the profound meaning of Dharmakīrti's works and to reveal their concealed ultimate tendency. It also treated the representatives of the first school, the school of direct meaning, with great contempt. However, both schools

---

caya-ṭīkā-vivṛtti, a subcommentary on Dharmottara's comment on Dharmakīrti's Pramāṇa-viniścaya, and that he sarcastically gave to his work the title of «Dharmottamā». That is the only way to understand the passage without much emendation, otherwise we must read dhārmottarāyām, cp. G. Bühler, Cashmer Report, p. 65 ff., H. Jacobi, p. 144 of the reprint of his translation of Dhvanyāloka, and my «Theory of Cognition of the later Buddhists» (Russian edition, St. Petersburg, p. XXXV. n. 2).

1 This author is usually quoted as Jñānaśrī, cp. SDS p. 26 (Poona, 1924), Pariśuddhi, p. 713, but there are two authors which can thus be quoted, Jñānaśrībhadra and Jñānaśrīmitra. Cp. S. Vidyābhūsana, History, p. 341 ff. Tārānātha, p. 108 mentions only Jñānaśrīmitra who lived during the reign of Nayapāla.

2 Tanjur, Mdo, vol. Pe.

3 Great commentaries (*ṭīk-chen*) by him exist on Pramāṇa-samuccaya, Pramāṇa-vārtika, Pramāṇa-viniścaya, Nyāya-bindu and Sambandha-parīkṣā, copies in the Mus. As. Petr. Upon the relation between the two pupils of Tsoṅ-khapa, Khai-ḍub and Rgyal-thsab in their way of commenting upon Pramāṇa-vārtika, cp. Loṅ-dol (Kloṅ-rdol) lama's Gtan-tshigs-rig-pai miṅ-gi rnams-graṅs, f. 2 a (A. Vostrikov).

differed radically in the definition of what for them was the central part and the ultimate aim of the system. The aim of Pramāṇa-vārtika, according to this school, was not at all to comment upon Dignāga's Pramāṇa-samuccaya, which work was a purely logical treatise, but to comment upon the whole of the Mahāyāna Scripture which establishes the existence, the omniscience and other properties of the Buddha, of his so called Cosmical Body,[1] in its twofold aspect of Absolute Existence[2] and Absolute Knowledge.[3] All the critical and logical part of the system has for this school no other aim than to clear up the ground for a new and purified metaphysical doctrine. The central, most important part of all the works of Dharmakīrti is contained, according to this school, in the second chapter (in the traditional order), of Pramāṇa-vārtika, the chapter dealing with the validity of our knowledge and, on that occasion, with religious problems, which for the Buddhist are the problems of Buddhology.

The founder of the school was Prajñākara Gupta, apparently a native of Bengal. His life is not recounted by Tārānātha, but he mentions that he was a lay member of the Buddhist community and lived under king Mahāpāla (? Nayapāla), successor to king Mahīpāla, of the Pal dynasty. This would bring his life into the XIth century A. D. However this can hardly be correct, because his work is quoted by Udayana-ācārya living in the Xth century.[4] He may possibly have been a contemporary of the latter. He commented upon the 2—4 chapters of Pramāṇa-vārtika leaving alone the first chapter (in the traditional order) as commented by the author himself. The work fills up, in its Tibetan translation, two large volumes of the Tanjur, the comment on the second chapter fills alone a whole volume. The work is not given the usual title of a comment (*ṭīkā*), but is called an «ornament» (*alankāra*), and the author is more known and quoted under the name of the «Master of the Ornament».[5] By this title he wished to intimate that a real comment would require much more space and would also require from the students such extraordinary power of comprehension as is very seldom to be found. He therefore composes a short «ornamentation» in order to elicit the salient points of the doctrine

---

1 *dharma-kāya.*

2 *svabhāva-kāya = ño-bo-ñid-sku.*

3 *jñāna-kāya = ye-śes-sku.*

4 Pariśuddhi, p. 730.

5 *rgyan-mkhan-po = alankāra-upādhāya.*

for the less gifted humanity. He vehemently assails Devendrabuddhi and his method of examining only the direct meaning. He calls him a fool.

The followers of Prajñākara Gupta can be divided in three sub-schools of which the exponents were Jina, Ravi Gupta and Yamāri respectively. Jina[1] is the most decided and spirited follower of Prajñākara Gupta and developer of his ideas. The genuine order of the chapters in Pramāṇā-vārtika is, according to him, the following one. The first chapter deals with the validity of knowledge, including Buddhology. It is followed by an investigation of sense perception, of inference and of syllogism occupying the 2d, 3d and 4th chapters. This clear and natural order has been misunderstood and inverted by the simpleton Devendrabuddhi, who has been misled by the circumstance that Dharmakīrti himself had had the time to write only the comment upon the stanzas of the third chapter which he, for some reason or other, probably because it is the most difficult one, had choosen to comment himself in his old age, not feeling himself capable of accomplishing the whole task. Jina accuses Ravi Gupta of having misunderstood his master.

Ravi Gupta was the direct personal pupil of Prajñākara Gupta. The field of his activity, however, seems to have been Cashmere where he lived probably contemporaneously with Jñānaśrī.[2] He is the exponent of a more moderate tendency than Jina. The genuine order of the chapters in Pramāṇa-vārtika is, according to him, the one accepted by Devendrabuddhi. Although the latter, in his opinion, was not a very bright man, but nevertheless he was not the fool to confound the order of chapters in the chief work of his teacher. The aim of Dharmakīrti was, in his opinion, the establishment of a philosophical basis for the Mahāyāna as a religion, and only partially also to comment upon the logical system of Dignāga.

The exponent of the third branch of Prajñākara Gupta's school was Yamāri.[3] He was the direct pupil of the Cashmerian

---

[1] Not mentioned by Tāranātha, his name in Tibetan *rgyal-ba-can* suggests a sanskrit original like *jetavān*. Being later than Ravi Gupta, the pupil of Prajñākara Gupta, he must have lived the XIth century A. D.

[2] S. Vidyābhūṣaṇa, History, p. 322, has confounded this Ravi Gupta with another author of that name who lived in the VIIth century, cp. Tāranātha, p. 113 and 130.

[3] According to Tāranātha, p. 177 (text) he seems to have been a lay-man and a mystic (tantrist).

Jñānašrī, but the field of his activity seems to have been Bengal. According to Tārānātha he lived contemporaneously with the great brahmin Šankarānanda, the final exponent of the Cashmere school, under king Nayapāla of the Pal dynasty.[1] This would bring both these authors into the XIth century A. D. The conciliatory tendency of Ravi Gupta is still more prominent with Yamāri. His work is full of acute polemics against Jina whom he accuses of having misunderstood the work of Prajñākara Gupta. Yamāri also thinks that Devendrabuddhi being the personal direct pupil of Dharmakīrti could not have confounded such a fundamental thing as the order of the chapters in the Pramāṇa-vārtika.

The work of Yamāri contains a commentary on all the three chapters of Prajñākara Gupta's work. It fills up four great volumes in the Tibetan Tanjur and was evidently conceived on the same comprehensive scale as the commentary of his contemporary, the last exponent of the Cashmerian school, the brahmin Šankarānanda.

It makes a strange impression that all the authors of this third school of commentators were laymen and apparently followers of tantric rites.

This school, for ought we know, has had no special continuation in Tibet. According to a tradition current among the paṇḍits of Tibet, Prajñākara Gupta interpreted Pramāṇa-vārtika from the standpoint of the extreme Relativists, of the Mādhyamika-Prāsangika school. Candrakīrti, the great champion of that school, rejected Dignāga's reform altogether and preferred the realistic logic of the brahmanical school of Nyāya, but Prajñākara Gupta deemed it possible to accept the reform of Dignāga with the same proviso as Candrakīrti, viz, that the absolute cannot be cognized by logical methods altogether.

Such is also the position of Šāntirakṣita and Kamalašīla. Although they studied the system of Dignāga and made a brilliant exposition of it, they were Mādhyamikas and religious men at heart. This clearly appears from their other writings. They belong to the mixed school of Mādhyamika-Yogācāras or Mādhyamika-Sautrāntikas.

---

1 The passage in Tārānātha's History, p. 188 text, which has been interpreted by Wassilieff, p. 239, as meaning that quotations from Šankarānanda have found their way into the text of Dharmottara, and just in the same way by Schiefner (!), means «as to the fact that passages from Šankarānanda are found in the text of the commentator Dharmottara, it is clear that this is a mistake, produced by the circumstance that these passages were inserted as marginal notes in the copy belonging to the translator Gsham-phan-bzañ-po».

A position quite apart is occupied by the Tibetan school founded by Sa-skya-paṇḍita.[1] This author maintained that logic is an utterly profane science, containing nothing Buddhistic at all, just as medicine or mathematics are. The celebrated historian Bu-ston Rin-poche shares in the same opinion. But the now predominant Gelugspa sect rejects these views and acknowledges in Dharmakīrti's logic a sure foundation of Buddhism as a religion.

The following table shows crearly the interconnection of the different schools of interpretation of the Pramāṇa-vārtika.

TABLE

SHOWING THE CONNECTION BETWEEN THE SEVEN COMMENTARIES AND SUB-COMMENTARIES OF PRAMĀṆA-VĀRTIKA. FIVE OF THEM DO NOT COMMENT UPON ITS FIRST CHAPTER.

1st school («philologicl» school)

Pramāṇa-vārtika.

Chapters. I. Svārthānumāna. II. Prāmāṇya-vāda. III. Pratyakṣa. IV. Parārthānumāna.

Comments. Auto-commentary. Commentary by Devendrabuddhi.

Commentary by Śākya-buddhi.

To this school we must refer also Vinītadeva who has not commented upon Pramāṇa-vārtika, but upon other works of Dharmakīrti.

Among the Tibetan authors Khai-ḍub (Mkhas-grub) belongs to this school.

2d school (critical school of Cashmere).

Pramāṇa-vārtika.

Chapters. I. Svārthānumāna. II. Prāmāṇya. III. Pratyakṣa. IV. Parārthānumāna.

Commentaries. Auto-commentary.

Sub-commentary by Paṇḍit Śankarānanda (unfinished).

Tibetan Commentary by Rgyal-tshab.

To this school belongs Dharmottara, who has commented upon Pramāṇa-viniścaya and Nyāya-bindu, and Jñānaśrī (bhadra) who has commented upon the first of these works. They have not commented upon Pramāṇa-vārtika.

---

[1] Kun-dgaḥ-rgyal-mthsan, the fifth of the grand lamas of Sa-skya (=*pāṇḍu-bhūmi*) monastery.

3d school (religious school of Bengal).

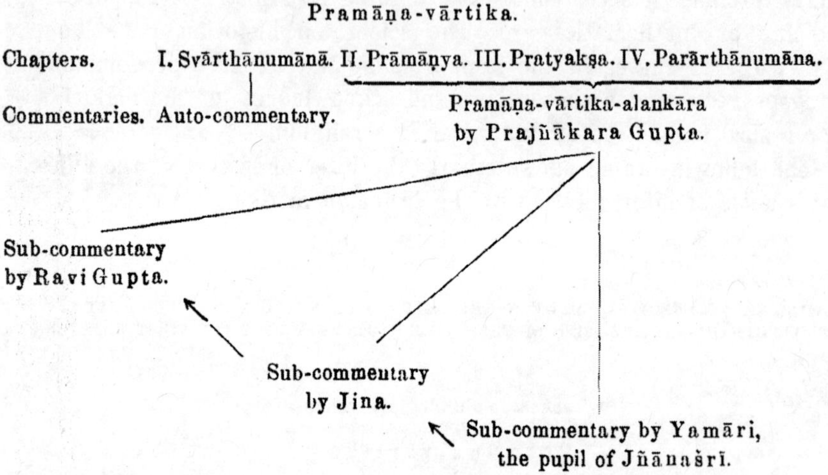

The school, as far as known, had no continuation in Tibet.
NB. The arrowed lines indicate against whom the attacks are directed.

§ 15. Post-Buddhist Logic and the struggle between Realism and Nominalism in India.

The high tide of the Buddhist sway in Indian philosophy lasted, as already mentioned, for about three centuries and constituted an intermezzo after which philosophy continued its historical life in India in the absence of any Buddhist opposition. Although the retired Buddhists were living close by, on the other side of the Himālaya, and Buddhist influence engendered in this new home a great literary activity, nevertheless the intercourse between the two countries was scarce and the atmosphere for mutual understanding unpropitious. India remains the Holy Land for the Tibetans, but only bygone India, the Buddhist India. The new, non-Buddhist India is quite a stranger to Tibetans and they seem to know nothing of what is going on there.

But although victors in the battle with Buddhism, the brahmanical schools of philosophy emerged from the struggle in a considerably changed condition and some of them suffered so much that their survival was very short lived. The Materialists seem to have disappeared as a separate school simultaneously with Buddhism. The Mimāṃsakas after having been reformed by Prabhākara disappeared together with the old sacrificial religion. The Sānkhyas, after a reform which brought them in the pale of Vedānta, ceased to exist as a separate school. Two schools only survived finally, although in a shape considerably modified by Buddhist influence, Vedānta as a monistic system and as the foundation of many popular religions, and the amalgamated Nyāya-Vaišeṣika as a school of ultra-realistic logic. This corresponds to the conditions prevailing in Tibet and Mongolia. We find there reigning the monistic system of the Mādhyamikas which is also the foundation of the popular religion and, on the other hand, Dharmakīrti's system of logic.

During its long life the school of Nyāya always defended the same principle of consequent realism. But its adversaries came from different quarters. Having begun as a naive realism and a formal logic it soon was obliged to cross arms with Sānkhya and Buddhism. From the VIth to the Xth century it fought with the school of Buddhist logicians who were nominalists and the most decided opponents of realism.

As indicated above, two independent schools were in India the champions of a most radical Realism. For them not only Universals, but all relations were real things, or real «meanings»,[1] having objective reality and validity. They were the Nyāya-Vaišeṣika school on the one hand and the Mīmāṃsaka school on the other. Their opponents were the Sānkhya system and the Hīnayāna Buddhists at the beginning, the Mahāyāna Buddhists and Vedānta in the sequel. These schools assailed Realism and vindicated a kind of Nominalism which denied the objective reality of the Universals and of the category of Inherence. The effect of the nominalistic critique was not the same in both these schools. The Realism of the Nyāya-Vaišeṣika school made no concessions at all to the assailing Buddhists. On the contrary it hardened its realistic position and did not yield a bit to Buddhist influence. Driven by the powerful logic of their opponents these realists retreated into the remotest recesses of consequent realism, into its quite absurd, but logically unavoidable, consequences. They thus with perfect *bona fides* reduced realism *ad absurdum*. They demonstrated practically that whosoever resolves to remain a realist to the end, must unavoidably people the universe with such a wealth of objective realities that life in such a realistic home must become quite uncomfortable. Time, Space, the Cosmical Ether, the Supreme Soul, all individual

---

[1] *padārtha*.

Souls, all Universals, the category of Inherence are ubiquitous external realities. The category of Non-existence, all motions, all relations and qualities, the primary ones, like magnitude etc., and the secondary ones, like the sensible qualities of objects, nay even the relations of relations — all are external realities *per se*, apart from the substances in which they inhere. The more these theories were assailed by the Buddhists, the more obstinately were they defended by the Naiyāyiks. If relations are objective realities *per se*, why should Inherence also not be a reality? If it is a reality, why should it not be a unique and ubiquitous force,[1] everywhere ready at hand to achieve the trick of uniting substances with qualities? This process of stiffening of the realistic point of view did set in as soon as the war with the first Buddhist logicians began.[2]

During this period the Nyāya school produced two remarkable men, the authors of a commentary and a sub-commentary on the fundamental aphorisms of Gotama Akṣapāda. The first of them, Vātsyāyana Pakṣilasvāmin, possibly a contemporary of Dignāga, does not materially deviate from the traditional interpretation of the aphorisms. He simply lays down in a concise comment the interpretations which were current and orally transmitted in the school from the time of its reputed founder.[3] This comment was it chiefly which furnished Dignāga the material for his attacks on realism. The second prominent writer of that period, a possible elder contemporary of Dharmakīrti, was the Bhāradvāja brahmin Uddyotakara. In his sub-commentary he defends Vātsyāyana and vehemently attacks Dignāga. This is a writer imbibed with a strong fighting temper and most voluble style. He does not mind at all to distort the opinion of his adversary and to answer him by some bluffing sophistry. His aim was not to introduce any changes in the system, but he is responsible for some traits

1 Cp. Prašastapāda on *samavāya*.

2 There is one point however, in which the Naiyāyiks went through a development offering some analogy with the Buddhist evolution. They forsook, just as the Buddhists, their former ideal of a lifeless, materialistic Nirvāṇa, and replaced it, not by a pantheistic one, like the Buddhists, but by a theistic eternity. This Nirvāṇa consists in an eternal and silent contemplative devotion to the Allmighty, *īśvara-praṇidhāna*, a condition analogous to the one so eloquently described by some European mystics, as, e. g., M. de Tillemont, one of the Mr. de Port Royal.

3 Dr. W. Ruben in his work «Die Nyāya-sūtras» has however made an attempt to find out material differences between the philosophies of Gotama and Vātsyāyana, cp. my review of this book in OLZ, 1929, № 11.

of super-realism[1] to which he resorted in polemical ardour and which after him remained in the system.

To the same period must be referred the Vaišeṣika philosopher Prašastapāda. He probably must have been an elder contemporary of Dignāga. In his ontology he remains thoroughly realistic, but his logic is strongly influenced by Buddhists.[2]

In the IXth century the school of Naiyāyiks produced in the person of Vācaspati-mišra a man who is perhaps the most distinguished among the scholarly philosophers of brahmanic India. His knowledge is overwhelming, his information always first-hand, his exposition, even of the most difficult and abstruse theories, very lucid, his impartiality exemplary. He is not a creator of new philosophic theories. But he is an historian of philosophy imbibed with a true scientific spirit. One of his first works the Nyāya-kaṇikā and his latest and ripest great work Nyāya-vārtika-tātparya-ṭīkā are almost entirely devoted to the exposition and refutation of Buddhist theories.[3]

His commentator and follower Udayana-ācārya is also mainly occupied in several works with the refutation of Buddhism.

These two authors close at the end of the Xth century A.D. the ancient period of the Nyāya school, the period of its struggle with Buddhism.

The creator of the new school of Nyāya logic, in that shape in which it emerged from the struggle with Buddhism, was Gangeša-upādhyāya. His great work the Tattva-cintāmaṇi is analytical in its arrangement, following the example of Dignāga and Dharmakīrti. The old loose order of the aphorisms of Gotama is abandoned. The instructions in the art of debate are dropped. The main subject is logic. The adversary instead of the disappeared Buddhists is here very often Prabhākara and his followers.

The second school which professed realism and supported it by a realistic logic, the school of the Mīmāṃsakas, did not make proof of the same adamantine fidelity to realistic principles as the first. Under the influence of the Buddhist attacks it became split into two schools, one of which made very important concessions to the Buddhist point

---

1 E. g. the theory of a contact (*samikarṣa*) between an absent thing and the sense organ — *abhāva indriyeṇa gṛhyate.*

2 Cp. my Erkenntnisstheorie der Buddhisten, Appendix II (München, 1924).

3 Cp. on him Garbe, Der Mondschein, introd., and my article in Prof. H. Jacobi's Festschrift.

of view. These concessions did not go all the length of admitting the ideality, or nominality, of the Universals and denying the category of Inherence, but on a series of very important points they held back from the ultra-realism of the Naiyāyiks. The founder of the school was Prabhākara, a pupil of the celebrated Mīmāṃsaka teacher and antagonist of Buddhism Kumārila-bhaṭṭa.

The chief work of Kumārila, the Šlokavārtika, is an enormous composition of about 3500 stanzas entirely filled with a polemic against Buddhism. The information to be gathered from this work about the teachings of Buddhist logicians is, however, scanty and very often unclear. The author is an ardent controversialist and cares much more for brilliant repartees and witty retorts, than for impartial quotation of his enemy's opinions. His commentator Pārthasārathi-mišra very often fills up the gaps. He is also the author of an independent treatise, Šāstra-dīpikā, devoted mainly to the refutation of Buddhism.[1]

Prabhākara[1] is a real bastard son of Buddhism. Although a pupil of Kumārila and belonging to the same school, he revolted against the super-realism of his master and deviated from him in the direction of more natural views. According to Kumārila, time, space, the cosmic aether, motion and non-existence were perceived by the senses. Prabhākara denied this. The perception of non-existence,[2] according to him, was simply the perception of an empty place. In this point he fell in line with the Buddhists. He also agreed with them in the most important problem of illusion as due to a non-perception of difference.[3] He admitted introspection[4] as an essential character of all consciousness. He admitted the fundamental unity of subject, object and the act of cognition[5] and many others details in which he opposed his master, agreed with Buddhists, and thus was led to found a new branch of the realistic school of Mīmāṃsaka theologians. The logicians of the Nyāya school sided with the old Mīmāṃsakas and combated the followers of Prabhākara. The next centuries witnessed the decline and extinction of both the schools of Mīmāṃsakas. But a new and powerful adversary to realism arose in the shape

---

1 On Prabhākara cp. his Pañcapadārtha (Chowkhamba), Pārthasārathi-mišra's Šāstradīpikā *passim*, the article of G. Jhā in Indian Thought, and my article in Prof. H. Jacobi's Festschrift.

2 *anupalabdhi.*

3 *bheda-agraha = akhyāti.*

4 *sva-saṃvedana.*

5 *tri-puṭī = pramātṛ-pramāṇa-prameya.*

of reformed Vedānta with all its ramifications. One of the most typical agressors against realism from this side is the celebrated Šrīharṣa. In his Khaṇḍana-khaṇḍa-khādya he openly confesses that in his fight against realism he is at one with the Mādhyamika Buddhists, a circumstance which Šankara-ācārya carefully tried to dissimulate. Šrīharṣa maintains that «the essence of what the Mādhayamikas and other (Mahāyānists) maintain it is impossible to reject».[1]

After the disparition of Buddhism the schools were suspiciously accusing one another of having yielded to Buddhist influences. The Vedāntins accused the Vaišeṣikas of being Buddhists in disguise,[2] because that school admitted the momentary character of some entities, like motion, sound, thought etc. In their turn the Vaišeṣikas accused the Vedāntins of denying, like the Buddhists, the ultimate reality of the external world. Prabhākara was generally accused of being a «friend of Buddhists»[3] etc. etc.

When the followers of Gangeša-upādhyāya migrated from Durbhanga to Bengal and established their home in Nuddea, the fighting spirit of olden times seems to have given way to a more placid attitude. The new school concentrated all their attention on the problems of syllogism and was chiefly engaged in finding new and exceedingly subtle definitions of every detail of the syllogistic process. Logic in India rebecame what it essentially was at the start, a system of formal logic.

Thus the history of logic in India represents a development of more than 2000 years with a brilliant Buddhist intermezzo of more than 300 years and with a continual war against all sort of adversaries.

§ 16. Buddhist logic in China and Japan.

Pre-buddhistic ancient China possessed an original, very primitive teaching regarding some logical problems,[4] but it apparently did not enjoy great popularity, and is in no way connected with the Buddhist logic introduced at a later date by Buddhist missionaries and pilgrims.

---

[1] Cp. above p. 22, n. 2.

[2] *pracchanna-bauddha.*

[3] *bauddha-bandhuḥ.*

[4] Cp. Hu-shih, The development of the logical method in ancient China, Shanghai, 1922, and M. H. Maspero's article in T'oung-Pao, 1927, Notes sur la logique de Mo-tseu et son école.

This new logic was imported from India twice, the first time in the VIth century A. D. by the Indian missionary Paramārtha, the second time by the Chinese pilgrim Hsuen Tsang in the VIIth century. Paramārtha imported and translated three works ascribed to Vasubandhu, viz Ju-shih-lun (=tarka-šāstra), Fan-chih-lun (=paripṛcchā-šāstra?) and To-fu-lun (=nigraha-sthāna-šāstra).[1] They were entered into the Tripiṭaka collection as three separate items.[2] The collection contained at that time three further fasciculi of commentary upon these works, compiled by the same Paramārtha. The entries in later catalogues of the Tripiṭaka suggest that these three works in three fasciculi gradually dwindled away into one work in one fasciculus, and the commentaries became lost altogether. But this single fasciculus, although bearing the title of Ju-shih-lun (tarka-šāstra), contains mere fragments, most probably from all the three works.

We moreover can gather from the Chinese commentaries upon the translations of Nyāya-mukha and Nyāya-praveša compiled by the pupils of Hsuen Tsang that they knew three logical works of Vasubandhu, named Lun-kwei (=Vāda-vidhi),[3] Lun-shih (=Vāda-vidhāna) and Lun-hsin (=Vāda-hṛdaya). Some fragments of these works have apparently been preserved in the fasciculus which at present is entered in the catalogue of the Tripiṭaka under the title of Ju-shih-lun (=Tarka-šāstra).

To the same period must be referred the translations of the logical parts of Asanga's works.[4]

This first importation of logic had apparently no consequences. It did not produce any indigenous logical literature, neither in the shape of commentaries, nor in the shape of original works.[5] The fact that it gradually dwindled away into one single fasciculus, and that this single fasciculus which is preserved up to the present day consists of mere fragments, clearly shows that the work has been neglected.

The second introduction of logic into China and from that country into Japan is due to Hsuen Tsang.[6] On his return from India he brought with him and translated two logical works, the one is the

---

1 Cp. Boris Vassiliev, op. cit.

2 Cp. the Chung-ching-mu-lu catalogue, *Buniu Nanjio* № 1608 and Li-tai-san-pao-chi, ibid., № 1504.

3 But not Vāda-vidhāna as assumed by *Tucci*.

4 Cp. G. Tucci, IRAS, July 1929, p. 452 ff.

5 Cp. however ibid., p. 453.

6 Cp. S. Sugiura, Indian logic as preserved in China, Philadelphia, 1900.

Nyāya-mukha (=Nyāya-dvāra) by Dignāga, the other the Nyāya-praveša by Šankara-svāmin.[1] Both these works are very short tracts containing summaries of the formal part of the logic of Dignāga with unimportant changes and additions by his pupil Šankarasvāmin. The philosophic and epistemological part, as well as all controversies with non-Buddhist systems, are ignored in them. They bare the character of short manuals for beginners from which every difficult problem has been carefully eliminated. Pramāṇa-samuccaya, the fundamental work of Dignāga, as well as the seven treatises of Dharmakīrti, and the enormous literature of commentaries with their division in schools and subschools is quite unknown in China and Japan.[2] What may have been the reasons which induced Hsuen Tsang, who is believed to have studied the logical system of Dignāga in India under the guidance of the most celebrated teachers of his time, to choose for translation only two nearly identical, short manuals, it is difficult for us at present to decide. The most plausible explanation would be that he himself was much more interested in the religious side of Buddhism and felt only a moderate interest in logical and epistemological enquiries.

However, this second introduction of Buddhist logic in China did not remain without consequences. A considerable growth of commentaries and sub-commentaries on the manual of Šankara-svāmin has been produced. Among the disciples of Hsuen Tsang there was one, named K'wei-chi, who took up logic as his special branch of study. With Dignāga's manual on the one hand and the notes from Hsuen Tsang's lectures on the other he wrote six volumes of commentary on Šankarasvāmin's Nyāya-praveša. This is the standart Chinese work on logic. It has since come to be known as the «Great Commentary».[3]

From China Buddhist logic has been imported into Japan in the VIIth century A. D. by a Japanese monk Dohshoh. He was attracted by the fame of Hsuen Tsang as a teacher. He travelled to China and studied there logic under the personal guidance of the great master. On his return he founded in his country a school of logicians which afterwards received the name of the South Hall.

---

1 On the authorship of these works cp. the article of Prof. M. Tubiansky in the Bulletin de l'Acad. Sciences de l'URSS, 1926, pp. 975—982, and Tucci, op. cit.

2 Cp. however J. Tucci, JBAS, 1928, p. 10. B. Vassiliev thinks that the Chinese knew about Pramāṇa-samuccaya only from hear say.

3 Cp. Sugiura, p. 39. On Hsuen-Tsang's school of logic cp. also the information collected by B. Vassiliev, op. cit.

In the next century a monk named Gemboh brought from China the Great Commentary and other logical works. He became the founder of a new school of Japanese logicians which received the name of the North Hall.[1]

Of all this literature, which seems to be considerable, nothing as yet is known in Europe as regards the details of its contents and its intrinsic value.

§ 17. Buddhist logic in Tibet and Mongolia.

The fate of Buddhist logic in Tibet and Mongolia has been quite different. The earliest stratum, the three works of Vasubandhu, are not known in these countries, apart from a few quotations. They evidently have either never been translated or were superseded by the subsequent literature. But the chief works of Dignāga, the great commentary on Pramāṇa-samuccaya by Jinendrabuddhi, the Seven Treatises of Dharmakīrti, all the seven great commentaries on Pramāṇa-vārtika, the works of Dharmottara and many other Buddhist logicians, all this literature has been preserved in trustworthy Tibetan translations. The intercourse between Buddhist India and Buddhist Tibet must have been very lively after the visit of Šāntirakṣita and Kamalašīla to the land of snow. Every remarkable work of an Indian Buddhist was immediately translated into Tibetan. When Buddhism in India proper had become extinct, an indigenous independent production of works on logic by Tibetan monks gradually developped and continued the Indian tradition. The original Tibetan literature on logic begins in the XIIth century A. D. just at the time when Buddhism becomes extinct in northern India. Its history can be divided into two periods, the old one, up to the time of Tsoṅ-khapa (1357—1419), and the new one, after Tsoṅ-khapa.

The first author to compose an independent work on logic is Chaba-choikyi-senge[2] (1109—1169). He is the creator of a special Tibetan logical style on which some remarks will be made in the sequel. He composed a commentary on Dharmakīrti's Pramāṇa-vinišcaya and an independent work on logic in mnemonic verse with his own explanations. His pupil Tsaṅ-nagpa-tson-ḍui-senge has likewise written[3] another commentary on the Pramāṇa-vinišcaya. The classical

[1] Ibid., p. 40.

[2] Phyva-pa- chos-kyi-seṅ-ge, also written Cha-pa ...,

[3] Gtsaṅ-nag-pa-brtson-ḥgrus-seṅ-ge.

Tibetan work of this period has been produced by the 5-th grand lama of the Sa-skya territory, the celebreted Sa-skya-paṇḍita Kunga-gyal-mtshan (1182—1251). It is a short treatise in mnemonic verse with the author's own commentary. Its title is Tshadma-rigspai-gter (pramāṇa-nyāya-nidhi). His pupil Uyugpa-rigspai-senge composed a detailed commentary on the whole of Pramāṇa-vārtika. This work is held in very high esteem by the Tibetans.

The last writer of this period was Reñdapa-Zhonnu-lodoi[1] (1349—1412). He was the teacher of Tsoñ-khapa and the author of an independent work on the general tendency of Dignāga's system.

The literature of the new period can be divided in systematical works and school-manuals. Tsoñ-khapa himself has written only a short «Introduction into the study of the seven treatises of Dharmakīrti». His three celebrated pupils, Rgyal-thsab (1364—1432), Khai-ḍub (1385—1438) and Gendun-ḍub (1391—1474), composed commentaries almost on every work of Dignāga and Dharmakīrti. The literary production in this field has never stopped and is going on up to the present time. The quantity of works printed in all the monastic printing offices of Tibet and Mongolia is enormous.

The manuals for the study of logic in the monastic schools have been composed by Tibetan Grand Lamas mostly for the different schools founded by them in different monasteries. There is a set of manuals following the ancient tradition of the Sa-skya-paṇḍita monastery. In the monasteries belonging to the new sect founded by Tsoñkhapa there are not less than 10 different schools, each with their own set of manuals and their own learned traditions. The monastery of Ṭaśiy-lhuñpo[2] has alone three different schools[3] with manuals composed by different grand lamas of that monastery. The monastery of Sera[4] has two;[5] Brai-puñ[6]—two,[7] and Galdan[8]—three.[9] The schools of all other monasteries follow either the one or the other tradition

1 Ren-mdaḥ-pa-gzhon-nu-blo-gros.

2 Bkra-šis-lhuñ-po, founded in 1447, in Central Tibet.

3 Thos-bsam-gliñ grva-tshañ, Dkyil-khañ grva-tshañ, and Šar-rtse grva-tshañ.

4 Se-ra, in Central Tibet, founded in 1419.

5 Se-ra-byes grva-tshañ and Se-ra-smad-thos-bsam-nor-bu-gliñ grva-tshañ.

6 Hbras-spuñs, founded in 1416.

7 Blo-gsal-gliñ grva-tshañ and Sgo-mañ grva-tshañ.

8 Dgaḥ-ldan, founded by Tsoñ-khapa in 1409.

9 Byañ-rtse grva-tshañ, Šar-rtse grva-tshañ and Mñaḥ-ris grva-tshañ, the last school was founded in 1342 by the second Dalai-Lama.

and introduce the corresponding manuals. All Mongolia follows the tradition of the Goman[1] school of the Brai-puñ monastery, a school founded by the celebrated grand lama Jam-yañ-zhad-pa[2] (1648—1722). This extraordinary man, the author of a whole library of works on every department of Buddhist learning, was a native of Amdo in Eastern Tibet, but he studied in the Losaliñ school of the Brai-puñ monastery in Central Tibet. He dissented with his teachers, and retired to his native country, where he founded a new monastery, Labrang[3] in Amdo. It became celebrated as a seat of profound learning and as the spiritual metropolis of all Mongolia. It is interesting to note that Jam-yañ-zhadpa was exactly the contemporary of Leibniz.[4]

The course of logic in monastic schools lasts for about four years. During this time the 2000 odds mnemonic verses of Dharmakīrti's Pramāṇa-vārtika are learned by heart. They are the fundamental work (*mūla*) studied in this class and also the only work of direct Indian origin. The explanations are studied according to the manuals of one of the 10 Tibetan schools. The Indian commentaries, even the commentary of Dharmakīrti himself on the first book of his work, are ignored, they have been entirely superseded by Tibetan works.

The extraordinary predominance given in Tibet to one work of Dharmakīrti, his Pramāṇa-vārtika, is noteworthy. It is alone studied by everybody. His other works, as well as the works of Dignāga, Dharmottara and other celebrated authors, are given much less attention and are even half forgotten by the majority of the learned lamas. The reason for that, according to Mr. Vostrikov, is the second chapter, in the traditional order of the chapters of Pramāṇa-vārtika, the chapter containing the vindication of Buddhism as a religion. The interest of the Tibetans in logic is, indeed, chiefly religious; logic is for them *ancilla religionis*. Dharmakīrti's logic is an excellent weapon for a critical and dialectical destruction of all beliefs unwarranted by experience, but the second chapter of the Pramāṇa-vārtika leaves a loop-hole for the establishment of a critically purified belief in the existence of an Absolute and Omniscient Being. All other works of Dharmakīrti, as well as the works of Vasubandhu, Dignāga and Dharmottara incline

---

1 Sgo-mañ.

2 Hjam-dbyañ-bzhad-pa Nāg-dbañ-brtson-grus.

3 Bla-brañ.

4 The amazing intellectual activity of both these great men evoked the idea of their omniscience; Jam-yañ's title is «the omniscient (kun-mkhyen) lama», Leibniz is «der All-und Ganzwisser» (E. Du Bois-Reymond).

to a critically agnostic view in regard of an Omniscient Being identified with Buddha.

Substantially logic has hardly made any great progress in Tibet. Dharmakīrti had given it its final form. His position in Tibet can be compared with the position of Aristoteles in European logic. The Tibetan logical literature will then correspond to the European mediaeval scholastic literature. Its chief preoccupation consisted in an extreme precision and scholastical subtlety of all definitions and in reducing every scientific thought to the three terms of a regular syllogism. The form of the propositions in which the syllogism can be expressed is irrelevant, important are only the three terms.

The concatenation of thoughts in a discourse consists in supporting every syllogism by a further syllogism. The reason of the first syllogism becomes then the major term of the second one and so on, until the first principles are reached. The concatenation then receives the following form: if there is S there is P, because there is M; this is really so (i. e. there is really M), because there is N; this again is really so because there is O, and so on. Every one of these reasons can be rejected by the opponent either as wrong or as uncertain. A special literary style has been created for the brief formulation of such a chain of reasoning, it is called the method of «sequence and reason»[1] and its establishment is ascribed to the lama Chaba-choikyi-senge.

Thus it is that after the extinction of Buddhism in India three different seats remained in the East where logic was cultivated, 1) Nuddea in Bengal where the brahmanical Nyāya-Vaišeṣika system continued to be cultivated in that form in which it survived to the struggle with Buddhism, 2) China and Japan where a system founded on Šankarasvāmin's Nyāya-praveša was studied and 3) the monasteries of Tibet and Mongolia where the study of Dharmrkīrti's Pramāṇa-vārtika became the foundation of all scholarship.

Of these three seats the Tibetan is by far the most important. It has faithfully preserved the best achievements of Indian philosophy in the golden age of Indian civilisation.[2]

The analysis of this system based on Indian and Tibetan sources, as far as our limited knowledge of them at present goes, will constitute the main subject of this our work.

---

1 *thal-phyir.* An article on this method is prepared by A. Vostrikov.

2 For a more detailed review of the Tibetan literature on Logic, cp. B. Baradiin, The monastic schools of Tibet (a paper read at a meeting of our Institution).

PART I.

REALITY AND KNOWLEDGE.

(prāmāṇya-vāda).

§ 1. Scope and aim of Buddhist Logic.

«All successful human action is (necessarily) preceded by right knowledge, therefore we are going to investigate it».[1] By these words Dharmakīrti defines the scope and the aim[2] of the science to which his work is devoted. Human aims are either positive or negative,[3] either something desirable or something undesirable. Purposive action[4] consists in attaining the desirable and avoiding the undesirable. Right cognition[5] is successful cognition, that is to say, it is cognition followed by a resolve or judgment[6] which is, in its turn, followed by a successful action.[7] Cognition which leads astray, which deceives the sentient beings in their expectations and desires, is error or wrong cognition.[8] Error and doubt[9] are the opposite of right knowledge. Doubt is again of a double kind. It either is complete doubt which is no knowledge at all, because it includes no resolve and no judgment. Such doubt is not followed by any purposive action. But when it contains an expectation of some succes[10] or an apprehension of some failure,[11] it then is followed by a judgment and an action, just as right knowledge is. The farmer is not sure of a good harvest,

---

1 NB., transl. p. 1.

2 *abhidheya-prayojane.*

3 *heya-upādeya.*

4 *pravṛtti = artha-kriyā.*

5 *samyag-jñāna = pramāṇa.*

6 *adhyavasāya = niścaya.*

7 *puruṣārtha-siddhi.*

8 *mithyā-jñāna.*

9 *saṃśaya-viparyayāu.*

10 *artha-saṃśaya.*

11 *anartha-saṃśaya.*

but he expects it, and takes action.[1] His wife is not sure that she will not be visited by mendicant friars and obliged to give them the food which was intended for others, but she expects that perhaps none will come, and sets her pots on the hearth.[2]

As it runs the definition of Dharmakīrti is not very far from the one accepted in modern psychology. Psychology is defined as the science of mental phenomena, and mental phenomena are those which are characterized by «pursuance of future ends and the choice of means for their attainment».[3] The scope of this Indian science is but limited to an investigation of cognitive mental phenomena, of truth and error, and to human knowledge. The emotional elements of the mind are not investigated in this science. From the very definition of the phenomenon of knowledge it follows that there always is some, albeit very subtle, emotion in every cognition, either some desire or some aversion.[4] This fact has a considerable importance in the Buddhist theory of cognition, since the essence of what is called an Ego is supposed to consist of just that emotional part. But a detailed consideration of all emotions and of their moral value constitutes the subject matter of other Buddhist sciences[5] and is not treated in the context of an investigation of truth and error.

As has been stated in the Introduction, Buddhist Logic appeared as a reaction against a system of wholesale skepticism which condemned all human knowledge in general as involved in hopeless contradictions. The fundamental question with which it is concerned is, therefore, the reliability of our knowledge, that is to say, of that mental phenomenon which precedes all successful purposive action. It investigates the sources of our knowledge, sensations, reflexes, conceptions, judgments,

---

[1] TSP., p. 3. 5.

[2] *Ibid.*, cp. SDS., p. 4.

[3] W. James, Psychology, I. 8 (1890).

[4] This definition of right knowledge, which makes knowledge dependent upon the desire or aversion of man, provoked objections from the realists. They pointed to the fact that there is, e. g., a right cognition of the moon and of the stars which are not dependent upon the will of the observer, they cannot be included neither in the desirable nor in the undesirable class of objects, they are simply unattainable. This objection is answered by the Buddhist in stating that the unattainable class must be included in the undesirable one, since there are only two classes of objects, the one which is desirable and the one which there is no reason to desire, whether it be injurious or merely unattainable. Cp. Tātp., p. 15. 7 ff.

[5] A full classification of mental phenomena including all emotions is part of the *abhidharma*, cp. CC, p. 100 ff.

inferences and contains also a detailed doctrine of the syllogism and of logical fallacies. It then hits upon the problem of the reality of the cognized objects and the efficacy of conceptual thought. A series of questions arises. What is reality, what is thought? How are they related? What is bare reality [1] and what is mere thought? [2] What is causal efficacy? [3]

The subliminal part of consciousness is not a subject to be investigated. Buddhist logic professes to investigate only discursive thought, those cognitions which are the ascertainable source of the following purposive actions. It leaves out of account instinct and animal thought, the latter because it is always more or less instinctive and the purposive act follows upon the incoming stimulus directly, quasi automatically; [4] the existence of the intermediate members of the causal chain is unascertainable. The new born child and the animals are endowed with sensation and instinct [5] which is but prenatal synthesis, [6] but they do not possess full discursive inference. [7] Dharmottara delivers himself on this subject in the following way: [8] «Right knowledge is twofold, it either is (instinctive), as reflected in the right way of action (directly), or (discursive), directing our attention towards a possible object of successful action. Of these two only the last variety, that knowledge which stimulates purposive action, will be here examined. It always precedes purposive action, but does not directly appear (in the shape of such an action). When we acquire right knowledge we must remember what we have seen before. Memory stimulates will. Will produces action, and action reaches the aim. Therefore it is not a direct cause (viz, a cause without any intermediate chain of causation). In cases where purposive action appears directly and aims are attained straight off (knowledge is instinctive and) it is not susceptible of analysis».

Thus it is our discursive thought that is analysed in Buddhist logic. This subject is divided in three main parts devoted respectively

---

1 *sattā-mātra.*

2 *kalpanā-mātra.*

3 *artha-khiyā-samartha.*

4 *avicārataḥ = āpātataḥ.*

5 *vāsanā = bhāvanā.*

6 *prāg-bhavīyā bhāvanā=avicārita-anusandhāna.* Cp. upon instinct in animals and men NK., p. 252.

7 *pramāṇa = pramāṇa-bhūtā bhāranā.*

8 NBT., transl. p. 9—10.

to the origin of knowledge, its forms and its verbal expression. These three main subjects are called sense-perception, inference and syllogism, but they also deal with sensibility as the primary source of our knowledge of external reality, the intellect as the source producing the forms of this knowledge and syllogism as the full verbal expression of the cognitive process. They thus include epistemology as well as formal logic.

§ 2. A SOURCE OF KNOWLEDGE WHAT.

The definition of a source of right knowledge is but a natural consequence of the definition of the scope and aim of the science devoted to its investigation. A source of right knowledge is uncontradicted experience.[1] In common life we can call a man a source of right knowledge if he speaks truth and his words are not subsequently falsified by experience.[2] Just so in science, we can call a source of right knowledge, or right knowledge simply, every cognition which is not contradicted by experience, because right knowledge is nothing but a cause of successful purposive action.[3] Influenced by right knowledge, we take action and reach an aim. That is to say, we reach a point which is the point of application of our action. This point is a point of efficient reality[4] and the action which reaches it is successful purposive action. Thus a connection is established between the logic of our knowledge and its practical efficacy. Right knowledge is efficacious knowledge.[5]

To be a source of knowledge means literally to be a cause of knowledge. Causes are of a double kind, productive and informative.[6] If knowledge were a productive cause, in the sense of physical causation, it would forcibly compel the man to produce the corresponding action.[7] But it only informs, it does not compel, it is mental causation.

What strikes us, first of all, in this definition of right knowledge, is its seemingly empirical character. Right knowledge is every day right knowledge. It is not the cognition of an Absolute, the cognition

---

1 *pramāṇam avisaṃvādi*, cp. NBT., p. 3. 5.

2 NB., transl., p. 4.

3 *puruṣa-artha-siddhi-kāraṇa.*

4 *artha-kriyā-kṣamam vastu.*

5 NBT., p. 14. 21, *prāpakam jñānam pramāṇam.*

6 *kāraka-jñāpaka.*

7 NBT., p. 3. 8.

of the things as they really are, or the knowledge of the reality or unreality of the external world. Ordinary men in their daily pursuits perceive external objects by their senses, they are convinced of a necessary connection between these objects and their senses.[1] Or they perceive the mark of something desirable which is hidden in a remote place, they are convinced of the necessary connection between the perceived mark and the concealed aim, they take action and are successful.[2] The knowledge which these simple men are after, is characterized by logical necessity, it is just the knowledge which is investigated in science, says Dharmottara.[3]

It would be natural to expect that such a realistic general tendency should also produce a system of realistic logic. Indeed Candrakīrti represents to us the Buddhist logician as delivering himself in the following way.[4] «We are only giving a scientifical description of what just happens in common life in regard to the sources of our knowledge and their respective objects. The Naiyāyikas (are also realists, but) they are bunglers in logic, they have given wrong definitions of logical processes, and we have only corrected them». Candrakīrti remarks that this would have been a rather useless[5] and innocent occupation, if there really were no gap between the realism of the Nyāya school and Buddhist logic. However this is not the case. The Buddhist emendatory work in logic has led to the discovery of another world behind the world of naive realism, the world as it discloses itselt to a critical theory of cognition. Buddhist logic, when compared with Candrakīrti's standpoint of extreme skepticism, appears as a realistic system, but when compared with the consequent and uncompromising realism of the Naiyāyikas, it appears as critical and destructive. A deeper insight into what happens in our ordinary everyday cognition has led the Buddhists to establish behind the veil of empirical reality the existence of its transcendental source, the world of things as they are by themselves. According to Candrakīrti ultimate reality can be cognized only in mystic intuition.[6] He therefore condemns as useless every logic other than the simple logic of everyday life. But for Dignāga, as we shall see in the course of this our

---

1 NBT., p. 3. 12.

2 *Ibid.*, p. 3. 15.

3 *Ibid.*, p. 3. 24.

4 Cp. Candrakīrti, Madhy. vṛtti, p. 58. 14 ff., transl. in my Nirvāṇa, p. 140

5 *Ibid.*

6 *Ibid.*, (my Nirvāṇa) p. 44 ff.

analysis, logic has a firm stand upon a foundation of efficient reality, a reality however which is very different from the one in which naive realism believes.

§ 3. Cognition and recognition.

There is another characteristic of a right means of knowledge besides the characteristic of uncontradicted experience. Cognition is a new cognition,[1] cognition of the object not yet cognized. It is the first moment of cognition, the moment of the first awareness, the first flash of knowledge, when the light of cognition is just kindled[2]. Enduring cognition is recognition,[3] it is nothing but repeated cognition in the moments following the first flash of awareness. It certainly exists, but it is not a separate source of knowledge. «Why is that?» asks Dignāga,[4] and answers «because there would be no limit». That is to say, if every cognition is regarded as a source of right knowledge there will be no end of such sources of knowledge. Memory, love, hatred etc. are intent upon objects already cognized, they are not regarded as sources of knowledge. The cognitive element of our mind is limited to that moment when we get first aware of the object's presence. It *is followed* by the synthetical operation of the intellect which constructs the form, or the image, of the object. But this construction is produced by productive imagination,[5] it is not a source of cognition. It is recognition, not cognition.[6]

The Mīmāṃsakas have the same definition of what a source of knowledge is, viz, a source of knowledge is a cognition of the object not yet cognized,[7] but they admit enduring objects and enduring cognition. In every subsequent moment the object as well as its cognition are characterized by a new time, but substantially they are the same, they endure. The Naiyāyiks define a source of right knowledge as «the predominant among all causes producing cognition»,[8]

1 *anadhigata-artha-adhigantṛ = prathamam avisaṃvādi = gsar-du mi-slu-ba.*

2 NBT., p. 3. 11, *yenaiva jñānena prathamam adhigato 'rthaḥ... tad anadhigata-viṣayam pramāṇam.*

3 *pratyabhijñā*, cp. NBT., p. 4. 10—12 — *adhigata-viṣayam apramāṇam... anadhigata-viṣayam pramāṇam.*

4 Pr samucc., I. 3.

5 *kalpanā = vikalpa.*

6 *savikalpakam apramāṇam.*

7 *anadhigata-artha-adhigantṛ pramāṇam.*

8 *sādhakatamam jñānasya kāraṇam pramāṇam.*

such causes being sense-perception, inference etc. These definitions presuppose enduring, stable causes, enduring cognition and concrete universals, static objects endowed with their general and special characteristics which are apprehended by a mixed cognition through the senses with a great admixture of mnemic elements.[1] The Buddhist theory admits only objects as moments, as strings of events, and makes a sharp distinction between the senses and the intellect as two different instruments of cognition. The senses apprehend, the intellect constructs. Thus the first moment is always a moment of sensation, it has the capacity of kindling the action of the intellect which produces a synthesis of moments according to its own laws.[2] There is no concrete universal corresponding adequately to this synthesis in the external world. If an object is perceived, the first moment of awareness is followed by a vivid image.[3] If it is inferred through its mark, the latter produces also a first moment of awareness which is followed by a vivid image of the mark and the vague[4] image of the object invariably associated with it. But in both cases it is just the first moment of awareness which constitutes the source of right knowledge, the source of uncontradicted experience.

It is unthinkable that an object should produce a stimulus by its past or by its future moments of existence.[5] Its present moment only produces a stimulus. Therefore cognition *quà* new cognition, not recognition, is only one moment and this moment is the real source of knowledge, or the source of knowledge reaching the ultimate reality of the object.[6]

§ 4. The test of truth.

Since experience is the only test of truth, the question naturally arises whether the causes which produce knowledge also produce at the same time its reliability, or is knowledge produced one way and its reliability established by a subsequent operation of the mind?

This problem has been first faced by the Mīmāṃsakas wishing to establish the absolute authority of the Scripture. Four solutions have

---

1 *savikalpaka-pratyakṣa.*

2 TS., p. 390 — *avikalpakam api jñānam vikalpotpatti-śaktimat.*

3 *sphuṭābha.*

4 *asphuṭa.*

5 NK., p. 260. 4, *na santāno nāma kaścid eka utpādakaḥ samasti.*

6 The Naiyāyika and the Mīmāṃsaka, of course, reject this theory — *katham pūrvam eva pramāṇam nottarāṇy api*, cp. Tātp., p. 15. 6.

been given[1] and have for a long time remained a point at issue between different schools of Indian philosophy. According to the Mimāṃsakas all knowledge is intrinsically right knowledge, it is reliable by itself *quà* knowledge[2], since it is knowledge, not error. It can be erroneous only in the way of an exception, in two cases, either when it is counterbalanced by another and stronger cognition[3] or when its origin is proved to be deficient,[4] as for instance when a daltonist perceives wrong colours. The principle is laid down that knowledge is right by itself, its deficiency can be only established by a subsequent operation of the mind.[5] Kamalaśīla says,[6] «in order to establish the authority of Scripture the Jaiminīyas maintain that all our sources of knowledge in general are right by themselves, and that error is produced from a foreign cause».

The opposite view is entertained by the Buddhists. According to them knowledge is not reliable by itself. It is intrinsically unreliable and erroneous. It becomes reliable only when tested by a subsequent operation of the mind. The test of right knowledge is its efficacy. Right knowledge is efficient knowledge. Through consistent experience truth becomes established. Therefore the rule is laid down that the reliability of knowledge is produced by an additional cause, since experience by itself it is unreliable.[7]

The Naiyāyikas maintain that knowledge by itself is neither wrong nor right. It can become the one or the other by a subsequent operation of the mind. Experience is the test of truth and it is also the test of error.[8] Thus the rule is laid down that truth as well as error are not produced by those causes which call forth cognition, but by other, foreign causes, or by subsequent experience.[9]

Finally the Jainas, in accordance with their general idea of indetermination and of the dialectical essence of every entity,[10] maintain

1 Cp. ŚD., p. 74 ff.

2 *prāmāṇyam svataḥ.*

3 *bādhaka-jñāna*, e. g., when a piece of nacre mistaken for silver is subsequently cognized as nacre.

4 *kāraṇa-doṣa.*

5 *prāmāṇyam svataḥ, aprāmaṇyam parataḥ.*

6 TSP., p. 745. 1.

7 *aprāmāṇyam svataḥ, prāmāṇyam parataḥ.* This of course refers only to *anabhyāsa-daśā-āpanna-pratyakṣa*, not to *anumāna* which is *svataḥ pramāṇa*, cp. Tātp., p. 9. 4 ff.

8 *doṣo 'pramāyā janakaḥ, pramāyās tu guṇo bhavet.*

9 *ubhayam parataḥ.*

10 *sapta-bhangī-matam* = *syād-vāda.*

that every knowledge is by itself, without needing any test by a subsequent experience, both wrong and right.[1] It is always to a certain extent wrong and to a certain extent right.

The Buddhists insist that if an idea has arisen it is not at all enough for maintaining that it is true and that it agrees with reality.[2] There is as yet no necessary connection[3] between them and a discrepancy[4] is possible. At this stage[5] cognition is absolutely unreliable. But later on, when its origin has been examined,[6] when it has been found to agree with experience,[7] when its efficacy has been ascertained,[8] only then can we maintain that it represents truth and we can repudiate all objections to its being correct. As regards verbal testimony it must be tested by the reliability of the person who has pronounced the words.[9] Such a reliable person does not exist for the Veda, because its origin is supposed to be impersonal and eternal.[10] But since we meet in Scripture with such statements as, e. g., «the trees are sitting in sacrificial session» or «hear ye! o stones», such sentences as only could have been pronounced by lunatics, it is clear that their origin is due to persons quite unreliable and it is clear that Scripture, when tested by experience, has no authority at all.[11]

§ 5. Realistic and Buddhistic view of experience.

But although experience is the main source of our knowledge according to the Buddhists, and in this point they fall in line with the realistic schools, nevertheless the discrepancy between them in the way of understanding experience is very great. According to the Indian realists, Mīmāṃsakas, Vaišeṣikas and Naiyāyikas, the act of knowledge is something different from its content. The act of cognition, according to these schools, must be connected, as every other act indeed is,

---

1 *ubhayam svataḥ.*

2 ŠD., p. 76.

3 *aniścayāt.*

4 *vyabhicārāt.*

5 *tasyām velāyām*, ibid.

6 *kāraṇa-guṇa-jñānāt.*

7 *saṃvāda-jñānāt.*

8 *artha-kriyā-jñānāt.*

9 *āpta-praṇītatvam guṇaḥ.*

10 *apauruṣeya.*

11 ŠD., p. 77

with an agent, an object, an instrument and a mode of procedure.[1] When a tree is cut down in the forest by a wood-cutter, he is the agent, the tree is the object, the instrument is the axe, its lifting and sinking is the procedure. The result consists in the fact that the tree is cut down. When a patch of colour is cognized by somebody, his Soul or Ego is the agent, the colour is the object, the sense of vision is the instrument and its mode of procedure consists in a ray of light travelling from the eye to the object, seizing its form and coming back in order to deliver the impression to the Soul. The sense of vision is the predominant[2] among all these factors, it determines the character of the cognition, it is called the source of perceptive knowledge. The result for the realist is right cognition. But the Buddhists, keeping to their general idea of causation as functional interdependence,[3] repudiate the whole of this construction erected on the foundation of an analogy between an action and cognition. For them it is mere imagery. There are the senses, and there are *sensibilia* or sense-data, and there are images, there is a functional interdependence between them. There is no Ego and no instrumentality of the senses, no grasping of the object, no fetching of its form and no delivering of it to the Soul. There are sensations and there are conceptions and there is a coordination[4], a kind of harmony, between them. We may, if we like, surmise that the conception is the source[5] of our knowledge of the particular object falling under its compas. But it is also the result coming from that source. The same fact is the source and the result.[6] It is in any case the most efficient factor[7] determining the character of our cognition, but it is not an instrument realistically understood. Coordination of the object with its image and the image itself are not two different things, they are the same thing differently viewed. We may imagine this fact of coordination as a kind of source of our cognition, but we may also admit it as a kind of result.[8] There

---

1 This theory is found or alluded to almost in every logical treatise. It is clearly exposed and contrasted wit the Buddhist view by Udayana-ācārya in the extract from Pariśuddhi, translated in vol. II, Appendix IV.

2 *sādhakatama-kāraṇam = pramāṇam.*

3 *pratītya-samutpāda.*

4 *sārūpya*, cp. vol. II, Appendix IV.

5 *pramāṇam.*

6 *tad eva (pramāṇam)... pramāṇa-phalam*, cp. NB., I. 18.

7 *prakṛṣṭa-upakāraka*, cp. Tipp., p. 42. 3.

8 Cp. the remarks in NBT., I. 20—21 and vol. II, Appendix IV.

is only an imputed difference between a source of knowledge and its content when they are regarded from this point of view. In reality this kind of an instrument of knowledge and this kind of its result are one and the same thing.

We will revert to this interesting theory once more when considering the problem of the reality of the external world. It suffices at present to point out the difference between the realistic view of experience as real interaction and the Buddhistic one which only assumes functional interdependence.

§ 6. Two realities.

Non less remarkable than the definition of knowledge is the definition of Existence or Reality — both terms are convertible and mean ultimate reality — in the school of Dignāga and Dharmakīrti. Existence, real existence, ultimate existence is nothing but efficiency.[1] Whatsoever is causally efficient is real. The non-efficient is unreal, it is a fiction. Physical causation is first of all meant by efficiency. Existence, reality, being and thing are its names. They are all the opposite of fiction. Whether pure fiction or productive imagination, every vestige of thought construction is fiction, it is not ultimate reality.

A fire which burns and cooks is a real fire.[2] Its presence is physically efficient and it calls up a vivid image, an image whose degree of vividness changes in a direct ratio to the nearness or remoteness of the physical fire.[3] Even reduced to the shape of a remote point-instant of light, it produces a vivid image as long as it is real, i. e., present and amenable to the sense of vision. A fire which is absent, which is imagined, which neither really burns nor cooks nor sheds any light, is an unreal fire.[4] It produces a vague, abstract, general image. Even if intensely imagined, it will lack the immediate vividness of a real, present fire. The degree of vagueness will change in an inverse ratio to the force of imagination, and not in a direct ratio to its nearness or remoteness. Only the present, the «here», the «now», the «this» are real. Everything past is unreal, everything future is unreal, everything imagined, absent, mental, notional, general, every Universal, whether

---

1 NB., I. 15, *artha-kriyā-sāmarthya-lakṣaṇam vastu paramārtha-sat.*

2 *agni-svalakṣaṇa.*

3 NB., I. 13.

4 NBT., p. 14. 6.

a concrete Universal or an abstract one, is unreal. All arrangements and all relations, if considered apart from the terms related, are unreal. Ultimately real is only the present moment of physical efficiency.

Beside this ultimate or direct reality there is, however, another one, an indirect one, a reality, so to say, of a second degree, a borrowed reality. When an image is objectivized and identified with some point of external reality it receives an imputed reality. From this special point of view the objects can be distinguished in real and unreal substances, real and unreal attributes.[1] An example of a real substance is, e. g., a cow; of an unreal substance is, e. g., for the Buddhist, God, Soul and Matter as well, i. e., the primordial undifferentiated Matter of the Sāṅkhyas. An example of a real attribute is, e. g., blue; of an unreal attribute, e. g., unchanging and eternal, since for the Buddhist there is nothing unchanging and eternal. The fictions of our mind which do not possess even this indirect reality are absolutely unreal, they are mere meaningless words, as, e. g., the flower in the sky, *fata morgana* in the desert, the horns on the head of a hare, the son of a barren woman etc.

These objects are pure imagination, mere words, there is not the slightest bit of objective reality behind them. Directly opposed to them is pure reality in which there is not the slightest bit of imaginative construction. Between these two we have a half imagined world, a world although consisting of constructed images, but established on a firm foundation of objective reality. It is the phenomenal world. Thus there are two kinds of imagination, the one pure, the other mixed with reality, and two kinds of reality, the one pure and the other mixed with imagination. The one reality consists of bare point-instants,[2] they have as yet no definite position in time, neither a definite position in space, nor have they any sensible qualities. It is ultimate or pure reality.[3] The other reality consists of objectivized images; this reality has been endowed by us with a position in time, a position in space and with all the variety of sensible and abstract qualities. It is phenomenal or empirical reality.[4]

These are the two kinds of reality of the Buddhist logician, an ultimate or absolute reality reflected in a pure sensation, and a conditioned or empirical one, reflected in an objectivized image.

---

[1] Tātp., 338. 13, cp. transl., vol. I, App. V.

[2] *kṣaṇa* = *svalakṣaṇa*.

[3] *paramārtha-sat*.

[4] *saṃvṛtti-sat*.

Wherever there is an indirect connection with reality,[1] we have an uncontradicted experience,[2] albeit this experience is, from the standpoint of ultimate reality, an illusion.[3] Even a correct inference is, from this point of view, an illusion,[4] although it be correct. It is true indirectly, not directly.

§ 7. The double character of a source of knowledge.

In accordance with the just mentioned double character of reality, the direct, ultimate or transcendental one and the indirect or empirical one, a source of knowledge has likewise the same double character. A source of knowledge is either direct or indirect, it either means a source of cognizing ultimate reality or it is a source of cognizing conditioned reality. The direct one is sensation, the indirect one is conception. The first is a passive reflex,[5] the second is a conditioned reflex.[6] The last is strictly speaking a non-reflex, because it is a spontaneous construction or conception, it is not passive, but by way of compromise we may call it a circumscribed reflex.[7] The first grasps the object,[8] the second imagines[9] the same object. It must be carefully noted that there is no real «grasping» in a realistic or anthropomorphic sense in the Buddhist view of cognition, but according to the general idea of causation as functional interdependence there is only such dependence of sensation upon its object. The term to «grasp» is used only in order to differentiate the first moment of cognition from the subsequent construction of the image of the thing grasped. A single moment is something unique, something containing no similarity[10] with whatsoever other objects. It is therefore unrepresentable and unutterable. Ultimate reality is unutterable.[11] A representation and a name always correspond to a synthetic unity embracing a variety

---

1 TSP., p. 274.24 — *pāramparyeṇa vastu-pratibandhaḥ.*

2 *artha-saṃvāda*, ibid. (not *asaṃvāda!*).

3 *bhrāntatve'pi*, ibid.

4 NBT., p. 812 — *bhrāntam anumānam.*

5 *nirvikalpaka-pratibhāsa.*

6 *kalpanā.*

7 *niyata-pratibhāsaḥ* = *niyatā buddhiḥ* cp. Tātp., p. 12.27 = Tib. *bcad-śes* = *paricchinnam jñānam;* the term has a different meaning in NBT., p. 8. 8 ff.

8 *gṛhṇāti.*

9 *vikalpayati.*

10 *svam asādhāraṇam tattvam,* cp. NBT., p. 12. 14.

11 *anabhilāpya.*

of time, place and quality, this unity is a constructed unity, and that operation of the mind by which it is constructed is not a passive reflex.[1]

Dharmottara speaking of the double character of reality alludes at the same time to the double character of a source of knowledge. He says,[2] «The object of cognition is indeed double, the *prima facie* apprehended and the definitively realized. The first is that aspect of reality which appears directly in the first moment. The second is the form of it, which is constructed in a distinct apperception. The directly perceived and the distinctly conceived are indeed two different things. What is immediately apprehended in sensation is only one moment. What is distinctly conceived is always a chain of moments cognized in a construction on the basis of some sensation».

Every Indian system of philosophy has its own theory on the number of the different sources of our knowledge, on their function and characteristics. The Materialists, as already mentioned, admit no other source than sense-perception. The intellect for them is not different in principle from sensibility, because it is nothing but a product of matter, a physiological process. All other systems admit at least two different sources, sense-perception and inference. The Vaišeşikas remain by these two. The Sānkhya school adds verbal testimony, including revelation. The Naiyāyikas moreover distinguish from inference a special kind of reasoning by analogy[3] and the Mīmāṃsakas distinguish implication[4] and negation as separate methods of cognition. The followers of Caraka increase the number up to eleven different sources; among them «probability»[5] appears as an independent source of knowledge.

The Buddhists from the time of Dignāga[6] fall in line with the Vaišeşikas, they admit only two different sources of knowledge, which they call perception and inference. Verbal testimony and reasoning by analogy is for them included in inference. Implication is but a different statement of the same fact.[7] However, although the number of two

---

1 Tātp., p. 338.15.

2 NBT., p. 12. 16 ff.

3 *upamāna*.

4 *arthāpatti*.

5 *sambhava*, it is interpreted as a kind of knowledge by implication.

6 Guṇamati, Tanjur Mdo, v. 60, f. 79ª. 8, suggests that Vasubandhu accepted *āgama* as a third *pramāṇa*; cp. also AKB. ad II. 46 (transl. v. I, p. 226).

7 NBT., p.43.12.

different sources of knowledge is the same in both systems, the Buddhist and the Vaiśeṣika, their definititon and characteristics are different by all the distance which separates naive realism from a critical theory of cognition. In the course of our exposition we shall have several times the occasion to revert to this feature which is one of the foundation stones upon which the whole system of Dignāga is built, but we may mention already now that the difference lying between the two sources of cognition is, in the Buddhist system, a radical one, a real one, and it is moreover what we shall call in the sequel, a transcendental one. What is cognized by the senses is never subject to cognition by inference, and what is cognized by inference can never be subject to cognition by the senses. When a fire is present in the ken and cognized by the sense of vision, for the realist it is a case of sense-perception. When the same fire is beyond the ken and its existence cognized only indirectly, because some smoke is being perceived, fire is cognized by inference. For the Buddhist there is in both cases a part cognized by the senses and a part cognized by inference. The latter term is in this case a synonym of intellect, of a non-sensuous source of knowledge. Cognition is either sensuous or non-sensuous, either direct or indirect. In every cognition there is a sensible core and an image constructed by the intellect, one part is sensible, the other is intelligible. The thing itself is cognized by the senses, its relations and characteristics are constructed by imagination which is a function of the intellect. The senses cognize only the bare thing, the thing itself, exclusive of all its relations and general characteristics. The Buddhists will not deny that we cognize a present fire by perception and an absent one by inference, but apart from this obvious and empirical difference between the two main sources of our knowledge there is another, real, ultimately real or transcendental, difference. This difference makes it that every one of the two sources has its own object, its own function and its own result. The Buddhist view receives the name of an «unmixed» or «settled»[1] theory, a theory assuming such sources of knowledge which have settled and clear limits, the one never acting in the sphere of the other. The opposite theory of the realists receives the name of a «mixture»[2] or «duplication» theory, since according to that theory every object can be cognized in both ways, either directly in sense-perception or

---

[1] *pramāṇa-vyavasthā*, cp. N. Vārt., p. 5.5, Tātp., p. 12.15 ff.; cp. vol. II, App. II.

[2] *pramāṇa-samplava*, ibid.

indirectly in an inference. It is true that from the empirical point of view it is just the Buddhist theory which would deserve to be called a «mixture» theory, since the two sources are not found in life in their pure, unmixed condition. In order to separate them, we must go beyond actual experience, beyond all observable conscious and subconscious operations of the intellect, and assume a transcendental difference, a difference which, although unobserved by us directly, is urged upon us necessarily by uncontradicted ultimate reality. In that sense it is a theory of «settled» limits between both sources of knowledge. The whole of our exposition of Dignāga's philosophy can be regarded as a mere development of this fundamental principle. Not wishing to anticipate the details of this theory we at present confine it to this simple indication.

The doctrine that there are two and only two sources of knowledge thus means that there are two radically distinct sources of cognition, the one which is a reflex of ultimate reality and the other which is a capacity of constructing the images in which this reality appears in the phenomenal world. But it has also another meaning, a meaning which takes no consideration of ultimate reality. From the phenomenal point of view there are two sources or methods of cognition, perception and inference. In perception the image of the object is cognized directly, i. e., vividly.[1] In inference it is cognized indirectly, i. e., vaguely[2] or abstractly, through its mark. If a fire present in the ken is cognized directly, it is perception. If its presence is inferred through the perception of its product, the smoke, it is cognized indirectly, by inference. In both cases there is a sensuous core and a constructed image, but in the first case the function of direct cognition is predominant, the image is vivid, in the second the intelligible function is predominant, the image is vague and abstract.[3]

From this empirical point of view the two sources of cognition are considered in that part of Buddhist logic which deals with formal logic.

§ 8. The limits of cognition. Dogmatism and Criticism.

It is clear from what has been already stated, and it will be proved by the whole of our subsequent analysis, that Buddhist philosophy had a decidedly critical, anti-dogmatic tendency. Philosophy started

---

1 *viśadābha.*

2 *asphuṭa.*

3 NBT., p. 16. 12 ff.

in India, just as in other countries, by semipoetical flights of fancy embracing the whole of the Universe. During its infancy it is filled with dogmatical glib assertions regarding the sum total of existing things. Such was the character of Indian philosophy in the period of the Upanishads. Early Buddhism, in opposing their monistic tendency, manifested a spirit of criticism which resulted in a pluralistic system of existence dissected in its elements of Matter, Mind and Forces. Later Buddhism continued this critical spirit with the result that the ontology and psychology of the preceding period were entirely superseded by a system of logic and epistemology. It forsook the dogmatical method of mere assertions and turned its face to an investigation of the sources and limits of cognition. The sources, we have seen, are only two, and the limit which they cannot transcend, we have also seen, is experience, i. e., sensuous experience. What is super-sensuous, what transcends the limits of the empirical world is uncognizable.

It is true, we are in possession of an unsensuous source of knowledge, it is our understanding. But this source is not direct, not independent, it cannot go beyond sensuous experience. Therefore all super-sensuous objects, all objects which are «unattainable as to the place where they exist, as to the time when they exist, as to the sensible qualities which they possess»,[1] are uncognizable. Consequently all metaphysics is doomed. Such objects are «unascertainable».[2] Our understanding, or our productive imagination, may indulge in different kinds of constructions in the super-sensuous domain, but all such constructions will be dialectical, that is to say, self-contradictory. Non-contradiction is the ultimate test of reality and truth.

It cannot but strike the historian that the dogma of Buddha's Omniscience, which is so firmly established in another part, in the religious part, of Buddhism, is emphatically declared to be dialectical, it is an object regarding which we can «ascertain» nothing, neither in the way of an affirmation nor in the way of a denial.[3] The same applies, e. g., to the dogmatic idea of the Vaišeṣika school regarding the reality of the Universals. It is dialectical, since the reasons which are adduced in order to establish this objective reality are counterbalanced by other reasons of equal strength which may be adduced for its repudiation.

---

[1] *deša-kāla-svabhāva-viprakṛṣṭa* (*viprakṛṣṭa* = *atīndriya*) cp. NBT., p. 39. 21.

[2] *aniščita.*

[3] NB. and NBT., p. 39. 20; 75. 13 ff.; cp. the concluding passage of Santānāntara-siddhi.

We find in Dharmottara's work the following very characteristic statement.[1] «When an inference, says he, and the logical construction, on which it is founded, are dogmatically believed,[2] the foundation of the argument is dogma». Such arguments «are not naturally evolved out of (an unprejudiced consideration of real facts, but) they are produced under the influence of illusive (dialectical) ideas...»[3] «There are subjects which are the proper place for such arguments, viz, metaphysical[4] (super-sensuous) problems, problems unaccessible neither to direct observation nor to correct ratiocination, as, for instance, the problem of the reality of the Universals. When the investigation of these problems is tackled, dogmatical argumentation flourishes...» «It often happens that promotors of scientific[5] doctrines, being mistaken as to the real nature of things, ascribe to them features that are contradictory...» «But when the argument is founded on the properly observed real nature of real things,[6] when either a case of necessary succession or of necessary coexistence or of the absence (of an ascertainable object) is thus established, there is no room for contradiction». «Facts are established as logical reasons not by any (arbitrary) arrangement, but by their real nature. Therefore when the facts of coexistence, succession or absence are established as the real condition of real things, there can be no contradiction. An established fact is an ultimately real fact. Properly established is a fact which is established without trespassing (into the domain of fancy)... Such facts are not founded on imagination, but they stand as stands reality itself». An example of such a dogmatic assertion is the theory of the objective reality of Universals.

Kamalašīla[7] delivers himself to the same effect in the following remarkable passage. «Buddha himself was pleased to make the following statement: „O Brethren! he exclaimed, never do accept my words

---

1 NBT., p. 81. 19 ff. (text), transl. p. 223 ff.

2 *āgama-siddha.*

3 *avastu-daršana.*

4 *atīndriya.*

5 *šāstrakāra; šāstra* is here = *āgama*. The term *āgama* can have the meaning of revelation, it then = *āmnāyā* = *šruti* = *dharma* = *sūtra*, or it can mean dogmatic science, as, e. g., the system of the Vaišesikas. Its opposite in both cases will be *pramāṇa*. In TSP., p. 4 ff. it means Buddhist revelation.

6 This fundamental principle of criticism is expressed with special suggestivity in alliterative language — *yathā-avasthita-vastu-sthiti.*

7 In his Nyāya-bindu-pūrva-pakṣa-saṅkṣipti. Tanjur Mdo, vol. 112; the passage quoted begins fol. 114[a]. 8 of the Peking edition, cp. TSP., p. 12. 19.

from sheer reverential feelings! Let learned scholars test them (as goldsmiths are doing by all the three methods) of fire, of breaking (the golden object into pieces) and of the touching stone"».[1] In these words the Buddha has declared that there are only two (ultimate sources) of our knowledge, they constitute the essential principles of sense-perception and inference (i. e., sensibility and understanding). This he has intimated by the character of the examples chosen to illustrate (the methods of testing his own words). Sense-perception is suggested by the example of fire with which it is similar (by being a direct proof). Inference is suggested by the example of the touching stone with which it is similar (by being an indirect proof). The ultimate test is the absence of contradiction. This has been suggested (by the example of the jeweller whose ultimate test requires) the breaking up (of the golden object into pieces). This (last method), however, is (not an ultimately different third source of knowledge, it is nothing but a kind of) inference (114. b. 4). In accordance (with these three sources of knowledge) the objects cognized are also of three different kinds, viz, the present, the absent and the transcendental.[2] Thus when an object spoken of by Buddha is present, it must be tested by direct perception, just as the purity of gold is tested by fire. If the object is hidden (but its mark is present), it must be tested by a (sound) inference, just as the purity of gold when tested by the touching stone. But if the object is transcendental, it must be tested by the absence of contradiction, just as a jewel (when fire and touching stone are not appropriate) must be broken (in order to establish the purity of its gold). Thus even in those cases when we have a perfectly reliable sacred (Buddhist) text dealing with a transcendental subject of discourse, we will proceed (not by believing in the text), but by believing (in reason as the only) source of theoretical knowledge».[3]

The examples of objects transcendental are, first of all, Moral Duty and Final Deliverance, the laws of karma and of nirvāṇa. These objects are not experimentally known, but they are not contradictory, therefore Buddha's revelation of them can be accepted.

Morality and Final Deliverance, indeed, cannot be founded on experience. The law of karma as the mainspring regulating the world process

---

1 According to the Tibetans the passage is from the *Ghana-sūtra*, but we could not trace it.

2 = *pratyakṣa*, *parokṣa* and *atyanta-parokṣa* (= *mṅon-sum lkog-pa* and *śin-tu lkog-pa*).

3 = *savikalpaka-pramāṇa-bhāve śrad-dadhānāḥ pravartante.*

and the law of nirvāṇa as the ultimate aim of that process are assertions which regard the sum total of existence, but they are not dialectical, not contradictory, not «unascertainable as to place, time and quality», they are non-empirical, transcendental reality which a critical theory of cognition must nevertheless assume.

Besides, although all our knowledge is limited to the domain of possible experience, we must distinguish between this empirical knowledge itself and the *a priori* conditions of its possibility. The sharp distinction between sensibility and understanding as the two unique sources of knowledge leads directly to the assumption of pure sensibility, of pure object and of pure reason (or understanding).[1] These are things that are not given in experience, but they are not contradictory, they are even necessary as the *a priori* conditions of the whole of our knowledge, without which it would collapse. We must therefore distinguish between the metaphysical and transcendental objects. The first are objects «unascertainable neither in regard of the place where they are situated, nor in regard of the time when they exist, nor in regard of the sensible properties which they possess». The second are, on the contrary, ascertainable as to their presence in every bit of our knowledge, since they are the necessary condition of the possibility of empirical knowledge in general, but they by themselves cannot be represented in a sensuous image, they are, as Dharmottara[2] says, «unattainable by (knowledge)». Thus it is that metaphysical or transcendent things are constructed concepts, but they are illusions, dialectical and contradictory. Transcendental, or *a priori* things, as e. g., the ultimate particular, the ultimate thing as it is in itself, are not only real,[3] but they are reality itself,[4] although not given in a concept, since by its very essence it is a non-concept. More will be said on this subject at several places in the course of the progress of our investigation.

---

[1] *śuddham pratyakṣam, śuddha-arthaḥ, śuddhā kalpanā.*

[2] NBT., p. 12. 19 — *prāpayitum aśakyatvāt.*

[3] *kṣaṇasya = paramārtha-sataḥ*, ibid.

[4] *santāninaḥ = kṣaṇāḥ = sva-lakṣaṇāni vastu-bhūtāḥ*, ibid., p. 69. 2.

PART II.

THE SENSIBLE WORLD.

CHAPTER I.

THE THEORY OF INSTANTANEOUS BEING (KṢAṆIKA-VĀDA).

§ 1. The problem stated.

In the preceding chapter the importance has been pointed out which the Buddhists attach to their fundamental principle that there are two, and only two sources of knowledge, the senses and the understanding, and to the fact that they are utterly heterogeneous, so as to be the one the negation of the other. We thus have a sensuous and non-sensuous, or a non-intelligible and an intelligible source of knowledge.

In the opening words of his great treaty Dignāga makes the statement that in strict conformity with this double source of knowledge the external world is also double, it is either the particular or the general; the particular is the object corresponding to sensuous cognition, the general, or universal, is the object corresponding to the understanding or the reason. We thus have a double world, in India just as in Europe, a sensible one and an intelligible one, a *mundus sensibilis* and a *mundus intelligibilis*, a κόσμος αἰσθητός and a κόσμος νοετός. We will now proceed to examine the Buddhist ideas of the one and of the other.

The sensible world consists of *sensibilia* which are but momentary flashes of energy. The perdurable, eternal, pervasive Matter which is imagined as their support or substratum is a fiction of the Sānkhyas and other schools. All things without exception are nothing but strings of momentary events. «This their character of being instantaneous, of being split in discrete moments, says Kamalaśīla,[1] pervades everything. By proving this our fundamental thesis alone, we could have repudiated at one single stroke[2] the God (of the theists), the eternal Matter (of the Sānkyas) and all the wealth of (metaphysical) entities imagined by our opponents. To examine them one by one, and to compose elaborate refutations at great length was a perfectly useless trouble, since the same could have been done quite easily.[3] Indeed, no one of our opponents will admit that these entities are instantaneous, that they disappear as soon as they appear, that their essence is to disappear without leaving any trace behind.[4] We, indeed, are perfectly aware that by prooving the instantaneous character of Being in general, these (metaphysical) entities would have been *eo ipso* repudiated. We, therefore, will proceed to expatiate upon the arguments in proof of this theory in order (once more) to repudiate those entities which have already been examined, viz God, Matter (Nature, the Soul as it is established in different schools), up to the (half-permanent) «personality» of the Vātsīputrīya-Buddhists; and in order also to support the repudiation of those (enduring) entities which will be examined in the sequel, viz the Universals, Substance, Quality, Motion, Inherence, up to the (instantaneous) elements existing in «the three times» (as they are admitted by the Sarvāstivāda-Buddhists),[5] the (eternal) Matter as admitted by the Materialists,[6] the eternal Scriptures as admitted by the brahmins.[7] Thus (no vestige of an enduring entity will be left) and the theory of Instantaneous Being will be clearly established. A critical examination of the (supposed) stability of existence contains therefore the final outcome of all Buddhist philosophy». Such is the leading idea of Buddhism — there is no other ultimate reality than separate, instantaneous bits of existence. Not only eternal entities, be it God or be it Matter, are denied reality, because they are assumed to be enduring and eternal, but even the simple stability of empirical objects is something constructed by our imagination. Ultimate reality is instantaneous.

---

1 Cp. TSP., p. 131. 17 ff. (condensed).

2 *eka-prahāreṇa eva.*

3 *svalpa-upāyena.*

4 *niranvaya-nirodha-dharmaka.*

5 *trikāla-anuyāyino bhāvasya* (*dharma-svabhāvasya*), cp. CC., p. 42.

6 Lit. «the four great elements of the Cārvākas».

7 Lit. «the eternal sounds of the Scriptures of the Jaiminīyas».

§ 2. Reality is kinetic.

«It is natural, says the same Kamalašīla,[1] on the part of a normal human being[2] who is engaged in the pursuit of his daily aims to enquire about the existence or non-existence of everything[3] (he wants)... Not to do it would be abnormal.[4] Therefore, anything a man avails himself of, whether directly or indirectly, in whatsoever a place, at whatsoever a time, is called by him real...[5] Now, we (Buddhists) prove that such (real) things, viz things that are objects of some purposive actions,[6] are instantaneous, (they have a momentary duration). There is no exception to the rule that the capacity of being the object of a purposive action is the essential feature establishing reality. It is a feature conterminous with existence.[7] But a thing cannot be the object of a purposive action and cannot be efficient otherwise than by its last moment. Its former moments cannot overlap the moment of efficiency in order to produce the effect, still less can its future moments produce the preceding effect. «We maintain, says the same author,[8] that an object can produce something only when it has reached the last moment of its existence (which is also its unique real moment), its other moments are non efficient». When a seed is turned into a sprout, this is done by the last moment of the seed, not by those moments when it lay placidly in the granary.[9] One might object that all the preceding moments of the seed are the indirect[10] causes of the sprout. But this is impossible, because if the seed would not change every moment, its nature would be to endure and never to change. If it is said that the moment of the sprout is produced by a «totality» of causes and

---

1 TSP., p. 151. 19 ff.

2 *prekṣavān.*

3 *arthasya (= vastu-mātrasya) astitva-anastitvena vicāraḥ.*

4 *unmattaḥ syāt.*

5 *yad eva padārtha-jātam... tatraiva vastu-vyavasthā*; note the contrast between *padārtha* and *vastu*; among *padārthas* those alone are *vastu* which are efficient. The realists distinguish *svarūpa-sattā* from *sattā-sāmānya*, the Buddhists deny this distinction, cp. SDS., p. 26.

6 *arthā-kriyā-kāri-rūpa.*

7 *sādhyena (=sattayā) vyāpti-siddhiḥ.*

8 Ibid., p. 140. 19.

9 *kušūlādi-stho na janayati*, ibid.

10 *na mukhyataḥ*, ibid, p. 140. 22; the preceding moments are called *upasarpaṇa-pratyaya*, cp. NK., p. 126.8, 135.8 etc.

conditions,[1] the same applies to every moment, since every moment has its own totality of causes and conditions owing to which it exists. «This our moment (i. e., the moment which we consider to be real) is the moment when an action (i. e., the run of uniform moments) is finished».[2] But an action, in this sense, is never finished, every moment is necessarily followed by a next moment. The break in that motion which constitutes the essence of reality is nothing but the appearance of an outstanding or dissimilar moment.[3] It is outstanding for our practical requirements, because it is natural for us to disregard the uninterrupted change of moments and to take notice of it only when it becomes a new quality, i. e., sufficient to impress a new attitude on our behaviour or on our thought. The identity of the foregoing moments in the existence of a thing consists simply in disregarding their difference.[4] The break in this identity is not a break in their motion, it always is something imagined, it is an integration of moments whose difference we are not able to notice. «The essence of reality is motion», says Šāntirakṣita.[5] Reality indeed is kinetic, the world is a cinema. Causality,[6] i. e., the interdependance of the moments following one another, evokes the illusion of stability or duration, but they are, so to speak, forces or energies[7] flashing into existence without any real enduring substance in them, but also without intervals or with infinitesimally small intervals.[8]

This theory whose main lines are here briefly sketched, and which is supported by a series of arguments to be examined in the sequel of our analysis, is regarded by the Buddhists themselves, as well as by their opponents, as the keystone of the whole of their ontology.

The idea that there is no stability in the external world and that existence is nothing but a flow of external becoming, is familiar to us from the history of Greek philosophy where in the person of Hera-

---

1 *sāmagrī = hetu-kāraṇa-sāmagrī*; the totality of causes and conditions of a thing cannot be distinguished from the thing itself, — *sahakāri-sākalyam na prāpter atiricyate*, Tātp., p. 80.5.

2 AKB ad II.46 — *kriyā-parisamāpti-lakṣaṇa eva eṣo naḥ kṣaṇaḥ*; transl. vol. I, p. 232.

3 *vijātīya-kṣaṇa-utpāda.*

4 *bheda-agraha.*

5 TS., p. 138.9 — *cala-bhāva-svarūpa = kṣaṇika*; TSP., p. 117.17 — *cala = anitya*, cp. ibid., 137.22.

6 TS., p. 1 — *calaḥ pratītya-samutpādaḥ*, cp. TSP., p. 131.12.

7 *saṃskāra.*

8 *nirantara.*

cleitus it marks an episode in its early period, an episode which was soon forgotten in the subsequent development of Greek thought. We find it again in India as the foundation of a system whose roots go back into the VI-th century B. C. But here it is not an episode, it has an incessant development through a variety of vicissitudes, in a series of elaborate systems, and after an agitated life of 15 centuries it forsakes its native soil only to find a new home in other Buddhist countries. Since the same idea reappears in modern European speculation and is even partly supported by modern science, the historian will be interested to gain insight into the arguments by which it was established in India and into the forms in which it has there been shaped.

We are faced in India by two quite different theories of a Universal Flux. The motion representing the world-process is either a continuous motion or it is a discontinuous, although compact,[1] one. The latter consists of an infinity of discrete moments following one another almost without intervals. In the first case the phenomena are nothing but waves or fluctuations[2] standing out upon a back-ground of an eternal, all-pervading, undifferentiated Matter[3] with which they are identical. The Universe represents a *legato* movement.[4] In the second case there is no matter at all, flashes of energy[5] follow one another and produce the illusion of stabilized phenomena. The Universe is then a *staccato* movement. The first view is maintained in the Sānkhya system of philosophy, the second prevails in Buddhism.[6] We have here a case, not quite unfamiliar to the general historian of philosophy, of two contrary philosophical systems both apparently flowing from the same first principle.

The arguments brought forward by the Buddhists are the following ones.

---

1 *sāndratara.*

2 *vṛtti.*

3 *pradhāna.*

4 *pariṇāma-vāda.*

5 *saṃskāra-vāda = sanghāta-vāda.*

6 Both theories are rejected by the Realist; they are very pregnantly formulated by Udayana, Pariśuddhi, p. 171—172 — *na tāvat pratikṣaṇa-vartamānatvam Saugata-mata-vad vastunaḥ svarūpotpādaḥ, nāpi Sānkhya-vad vastu-svarūpa-sthairye'pi pariṇati-bheda eva Mīmāṃsakaiḥ svī-kriyate.* It must be added that the Sânkhyas nevertheless deny the visibility of *samavāya* and this fundamental feature distinguishes them also from the Vaišeṣikas and apparently also from the old Yoga school.

§ 3. Argument from the ideality of Time and Space.

The theory of Universal Momentariness implies that every duration in time consists of point-instants following one another, every extension in space consists of point-instants arising in contiguity and simultaneously, every motion consists of these point-instants arising in contiguity and in succession.[1] There is therefore no Time, no Space and no Motion over and above the point-instants of which these imagined entities are constructed by our imagination.

In order to understand the Buddhist conception of Time, of Space and of Motion we must confront them with the divergent conceptions established in the Indian realistic schools. To this method we will be obliged to recur almost at every step of our investigation. We begin with Time and Space.

According to the Indian Realists, Time is a substance. It is one, eternal and all-pervading.[2] Its existence is inferred from the facts of consecution and simultaneity between phenomena. Space is likewise a substance,[3] it is one, eternal and all-embracing. Its existence is inferred from the fact that all extended bodies possess impenetrability, they are beside each other in space. Prašastapāda adds[4] the very interesting remark that Time, Space and Cosmical Ether, being each of them unique in their kind,[5] the names given to them are, as it were, proper names,[6] not general terms.[7] Different times are parts of one and the same time. When Time and Space are represented as divided in many spaces and different times, it is a metaphor. The objects situated in them,[8] but not Space itself and not Time itself, are divided. They are, therefore, «not discursive or what is called general concepts».[9] They are representations produced «by a single object» only.[10]

---

1 *nirantara-kṣaṇa-utpāda.*

2 VS., 2.6 — 9, cp. Prašastp., p. 63.23 ff.

3 VS., 2. 10—16, cp. Prašastp., p. 67.1 ff.

4 p. 58.5 ff.

5 *ekaika.*

6 *paribhāṣikyaḥ sanjñāḥ.*

7 *apara-jāty-abhāve.*

8 *añjasā ekatvepi .. upādhi-bhedān nānātvopacāraḥ.*

9 It is curious that one of the principle arguments of Kant for establishing the unreality of Time and Space is found in an Indian realistic system, without drawing the same conclusion as Kant has done, CPR., p. 25.

10 Cp. N. Kandalī, p. 59.6 — *vyakti - bheda - adhiṣṭhāna.* Kant, CPR., p. 25, has concluded from this fact that time must be an intuition, because «a re-

It is clear that the Indian realists, just as some European rationalists considered Time and Space as two allembracing receptacles containing each of them the entire Universe.

The separate reality of these two receptacles is denied by the Buddhists. Real, we have seen, is a thing possessing a separate efficiency of its own. The receptacles of the things have no separate efficiency.[1] Time and Space cannot be separated from the things that exist in them. Hence they are no separate entities. Owing to our capacity of productive imagination we can take different views of the same object and distinguish between the thing and its receptacle, but this is only imagination. Every point-instant may be viewed as a particle of Time, as a particle of Space and as a sensible quality, but this difference is only a difference of our mental attitude[2] towards that point-instant. The point-instant itself, the ultimate reality cut loose from all imagination is qualityless, timeless and indivisible.

In the first period of its philosophy Buddhism admitted the reality of Space as one of the elements[3] of the universe. It was an empty space imagined as an unchanging,[4] eternal, allembracing element. But when later Buddhists were confronted by Idealism in their own home, they saw that the reality of external objects does not admit of a strict proof, and the reality of a substantial space was then denied. Substantial time[5] was likewise denied, but subtle time, i. e., the moment, the point-instant[6] of efficiency, was not only asserted, it was made, as we shall presently see, the fulcrum on which the whole edifice of reality was made to rest. The notions of substantial time and space were not attacked on the score that they were ***a priori*** intuitions whose empirical origine it was impossible to conceive, but they were destroyed dialectically on the score that the notions

---

presentation, which can be produced by a single object only, is an intuition». The Buddhists would never have said that, because for them a single object *(vyakti = svalakṣaṇa)* is only the point-instant and the intuition is only the pure sensation *(nirvikalpakam pratyakṣam)* corresponding to its presence.

1 They are not *artha-kriyā-kārin.*

2 *kālpanika*; cp. the remarks of the translators of Kathāvatthu, p. 392 ff.

3 Under the name of *ākāśa*, which name denotes in the Nyāya-Vaiśeṣica system the Cosmical Ether serving for the propagation of sound. Kamalaśīla says, TSP., p. 140.10, that the Vaibhāṣikas, since they admit the reality of this element, do not deserve to be called Buddhists — *na Śākya-putrīyāḥ.*

4 *asaṃskṛta.*

5 *sthūlaḥ kālaḥ*, in Kathā-vatthu — *mahākāla.*

6 *kṣaṇaḥ=sūkṣmaḥ kālaḥ.*

of duration and extention as they are used in common life covertly contain contradictions and therefore cannot be accepted as objectively real.

§ 4. Duration and extention are not real.

Indeed, if we assume that a thing, although remaining one, possesses extension and duration, we will be landed in a contradiction, so far we consider reality as efficiency. One real thing cannot exist at the same time in many places, neither can the same reality be real at different times. If that were the case, it would run against the law of contradiction. If a thing is present in one place, it cannot at the same time be present in another place. To be present in another place means not to be present in the former place. Thus to reside in many places means to be and at the time not to be present in a given place. According to the Realists empirical things have a limited real duration. They are produced by the creative power of nature or by human will or by the will of God out of atoms. The atoms combine and form real new unities. These created real unities reside, or inhere, in their *causa materialis,* i. e., in the atoms. Thus we have one real thing simultaneously residing in a multitude of atoms, i. e. in many places. This is impossible. Either is the created unity a fiction and real are only the parts, or the parts are fictions and real is only the ultimate whole. For the Buddhists the parts alone are real, the whole is a fiction,[1] for it were a reality, it would be a reality residing at once in many places, i. e., a reality at once residing and not residing in a given place.[2]

By similar considerations it is proved that a thing can have no duration. If a thing exists at a moment A, it cannot also exist at some moment B, for to exist really at the moment A means not to have any real existence at the moment B or at any other moment. If we thus admit that the same thing continues to exist at the moment B, this could only mean that it at once really exists and

---

1 Cp. Avayavi-nirākaraṇa by ācārya Ašoka in the «Six Buddhist Tracts» and Tātp., p. 269.3 ff., NK., p. 262.10 ff, N. Kandalī, p. 41.12 ff.

2 Cp. the words of Leibniz (Extrait d'une lettre 1693) — «extension is nothing but a repetition or a continued multiplicity of that which is spread out, a plurality, continuity and coexistence of parts»; and «in my opinion corporeal substance consists in something quite other than being extended and occupying place»; and «extension is nothing but an abstraction».

does not really exist at the moment A. If a thing could have real duration through several moments, it would represent a real unity existing at once at different times. Either is the enduring unity a fiction and real are only the moments, or the moments are fictions and real is only duration. For the Buddhists the moments alone are real, duration is a fiction, for if it were a reality, it would be a reality existing at different times at once,[1] i. e., existing and at the same time non-existing at a given moment.

Thus it is that ultimate reality for the Buddhist is timeless, spaceless and motionless. But it is timeless not in the sense of an eternal being, spaceless not in the sense of an ubiquitous being, motionless not in the sense of an allembracing motionless whole, but it is timeless, spaceless and motionless in the sense of having no duration, no extension and no movement, it is a mathematical point-instant, the moment of an action's efficiency.

§ 5. Argument from direct perception.

The momentary character of everything existing is further established by arguments from perception and inference. The first of them is an argument from direct perception.[2] That sensation is a momentary flash is proved by introspection. But a momentary sensation is but the reflex of a momentary thing. It cannot seize neither what precedes nor what follows. Just as when we perceive a patch of blue colour in a momentary sensation, we perceive just the thing which corresponds to that sensation, i. e., the blue and not the yellow, even so do we perceive in that sensation just the present moment, not the preceding one, and not the following one. When the existence of a patch of blue is perceived, its non-existence, or absence, is *eo ipso* excluded and hence its existence in the former and in the following moments is also excluded. The present moment alone is seized by sensation. Since all external objects are reducible to sense-data, and the corresponding sensations are always confined to a single moment, it becomes clear that all objects, as far as they affect us, are momentary existences. The duration of the object beyond the moment of sensation cannot be warranted by sensation itself, it is an extension of that sensation, a construction of our imagination. The latter constructs the image of the object, when stimulated by sensation, but sensation alone, pure sensation, points to an instantaneous object.

---

1 Cp. Tātp., p. 92.13 ff., translated in vol. II, App. I.; cp. NK., p. 125.
2 NK., p. 123. 14 ff; Tātp., p. 92. 15 ff.

§ 6. Recognition does not prove duration.

To this argument the Realist makes the following objection.[1] It is true, says he, that sensation apprehends only a blue coloured surface and that it does not apprehend at that time something different from it. But we cannot go all the length of maintaining that sensation apprehends the precise time of its duration and that this duration is momentary. Sensation itself lasts for more than a moment, it can last for two or three moments. It is not at all proved that it lasts only a single moment, and it is not at all impossible that a thing endures and produces gradually a series of sensations the one after the other.

The Buddhist answers.[2] Let us (for the sake of argument) admit that the momentary character of all existence is not reflected directly in our cognition, (but does duration fare any better? is duration reflected directly?). Yes it is! says the Realist. There is a consecrated fact, the fact of Recognition[3] which proves the stability and duration of things, it is a cognition of the pattern «this is the same crystal gem (which I have seen before»). This judgment, answers the Buddhist, does not at all prove the stability and duration of the crystal, it does not prove that its former condition is quite the same as its present condition. And if this is not proved, nothing lies in the way of our assuming that there is an imperceptible uninterrupted process of change even in the crystal gem. It will then be not an enduring substance, but a change of momentary existencies following one another. Indeed, the judgment «this is that same crystal» is an illicit association of two utterly heterogeneous elements which have nothing in common. The element «this» refers to the present, to a sensation and to a real object. The element «that» refers to the past, to something surviving exclusively in imagination and memory. They are as different as heat and cold. Their unity cannot be created even by the allmighty god Indra! If such things could be identical, there is no reason why the whole of the Universe should not be composed of identical things. Memory whose function is limited to the past cannot grasp the present moment, nor can sensation, whose function is limited to the present, apprehend the past. When there is a discrepancy in the causes, the effect cannot be identical, or else the result would be

---

1 NK., p. 123. 23 ff.

2 Ibid., p. 124. 7.

3 *pratyabhijñā bhagavatī*, cp. the same argument in NS., 111. 1. 2.

produced not by the causes, but at haphazard. Memory and sensation have each their respective field of action and their own result, they cannot mix up so as to work the one in the field of the other. Recognition is not to be distinguished from memory, and memory is produced by thought construction, it is not a direct reflex of reality. Therefore the contention of the Realist that recognition proves duration betrays only his desire that it should be so.[1]

§ 7. Arguments from an analysis of the notion of existence.

Although neither immediate perception, nor recognition can prove the stability of the objects of the external world, nevertheless let us, for the sake of argument, says the Buddhist,[2] concede the point and admit that immediate perception apprehends objects representing some stability. However, this perception is falsified. Stability is an illusion,[3] there are cogent arguments[4] against our admitting stability and duration.

The first argument consists in deducing analytically the fact of constant change from the conception of existence. Existence, real existence, we have seen, means efficiency, and efficiency means change. What is absolutely changeless is also absolutely unefficient; what is absolutely unefficient does not exist. For instance, the Cosmical Ether, even in the opinion of those who admit that it is a stuff, it is supposed to be motionless. But for the Buddhists, the motionless is causally unefficient and therefore does not exist. Motionless and unexistent are convertible terms, since there is no other means to prove one's existence than to produce some effect. If something exists without any effect at all, its existence is negligible. The Buddhists conclude that whatsoever does not change, does not exist.

The argument is thrown into the form of the following syllogism.[5]

Major premise. Whatsoever exists is subject to momentary change.

---

1 *manoratha-mātram*, cp. ibid., p. 124. 24.

2 Ibid., p. 127. 7 ff.

3 *samāropita-gocaram akṣaṇikam*, ibid.

4 Ibid., p. 123-34.

5 TS., p. 143. 17 ff.; this syllogism appears in a different form in SDS., p. 26, where it is quoted from Jñāna-śrī, and in NK., p. 127-9.

Example.[1] As, e. g., a jar (whose ultimate reality is but a point-instant of efficiency).

Minor premise.[2] But the Cosmical Ether is supposed to be motionless.

Conclusion. It does not exist.

That all existing objects are changing every moment is proved by a dilemma. Existing means efficient. The question then arises, is this efficiency perdurable or is it momentary? If it is perdurable, then all the moments the object is supposed to last must participate in the production of the effect. But that is impossible. The preceding moments cannot overlap the last moment in order to participate in the production of the effect. Perdurable means static and static means non efficient, i. e., not producing at the time any effect; unefficient means non existing. Every real object is efficient in producing the next following moment of its duration. The object must therefore produce its effect at once or it will never produce it. There is nothing intermediate between being static and not being static. To be static means to be motionless and eternally unchanging,[3] as the Cosmical Ether was supposed to be (by Indian realists as well as by some modern scientists). Not to be static means to move and to change every moment.[4] Things cannot stop and after taking rest begin to move again, as the naive realism of common life and realistic philosophy assumes. There is motion always going on in living reality, but of this motion we notice only some special moments which we stabilize in imagination.

The deduction of momentariness from existence is called an analytical deduction.[5] Indeed, the judgment «existence means efficiency» and «efficiency means change» are analytical, because the predicate is implied in the subject and is elicited by analysis. The same thing which is characterized as existent, can also be characterized as efficient and as changing. The terms existence, efficiency and change are connected by „*existential identity*“,[6] that is to say, they can be without

---

1 The example of Jñānaśrī is *yathā jaladharaḥ*, probably for metrical reasons.

2 The upanaya in NK. is *saṃś ca ... śabdādir* and in Jñānaśrī's formula *santaś ca bhāvā amī*. In the form quoted by Šāntirakṣita and Kamalaśīla the argument is a *prasanga-sādhana*, since the motionless Ether, as well as eternal time and eternal God etc. are assumed to exist by the opponents, they are therefore valid examples only for them.

3 *nitya* = *apracyuta-anutpanna-sthiraika-svabhāva*, Anekāntaj, f. 2. a. 10.

4 *anitya* = *prakṛtyā eka-kṣaṇa-sthiti-dharmaka*, ibid.

5 *svabhāvānumāna.*

6 *tādātmya.*

contradiction applied to one and the same point of reality, to a real fact. There are other characteristics which are connected with them by the same tie of Existential Identity, viz «whatsoever has an origin is always changing»,[1] «whatsoever is produced by causes is impermanent»,[2] «whatsoever is variable in dependence on a variation of its causes is subject to momentary change»,[3] «whatsoever is produced by a conscious effort is impermanent»[4] — all these characteristics, although they may have a different extension, are called «existentially identical», because they may without contradiction be applied to one and the same reality. A jar which is produced by the effort of the potter may also be characterized as variable, as a product, as having an origin, as changing, efficient and existent. In this sense the deduction of momentariness is an analytical deduction.

§ 8. Argument from an analysis of the notion of non-existence.

The foregoing argument in favour of the theory of Instantaneous Being was drawn from an analysis of the notion of existence as meaning efficiency. The present one is also analytical,[5] but it is drawn from the opposite notion of Non-existence[6] as meaning Annihilation.[7] What is annihilation to the thing annihilated? Is it the annihilated thing itself or it is something else,[8] a separate unity, being added to a thing in the course of its annihilation? Is the non-existence of a thing something real or is it a mere idea?

Here again in order to understand the Buddhist view we must contrast it with what it is opposed to, we must take into consideration the opinions of the Indian Realists. Just as Time and Space are for them real entities in which the things are residing; existence — something inherent in the existing things; efficiency is something additional to a thing when it becomes efficient; causality — a real relation uniting cause and effect; motion — a reality added to the thing when it

---

[1] NB., III. 12.
[2] Ibid., III. 13.
[3] Ibid, III. 15.
[4] Ibid.
[5] *svabhāva-anumāna*.
[6] *abhāva*.
[7] *vināśa*.
[8] *arthāntaram*.

begins to move; a Universal — a reality residing in the particular; the relation of Inherence — a reality residing in the members of that relation, — even so is Non-existence for the Realist something valid and real, it is something over and above the thing which disappears.

The Buddhist denies this, Non-existence cannot exist. He denies ultimate reality to all that set of hypostasized notions. They are for him mere ideas or mere names, some of them even pseudo-ideas. A mere idea, or a mere name, is a name to which nothing separate corresponds, which has no corresponding reality of its own. A pseudo-idea is a word to which nothing at all corresponds, as, e. g., «a flower in the sky». Thus existence is for the Buddhist nothing but a name for the things existing; efficiency is the efficient thing itself; Time and Space are nothing besides the things residing in them; these things again are nothing over and above the point-instants of which they represent an integration; Causality is dependent origination of the things originating, these things themselves are the causes, there is no real causality besides their existence; motion is nothing beyond the moving thing; a Universal is not a reality «residing» in the particular thing, it is a mere idea or a mere name of the thing itself; Inherence is an unreality of a second degree, since it is admitted in order to unite the particular thing with the Universal which itself is nothing but a name. Finally Non-existence or the annihilation of a thing is also a mere name, nothing over and above the thing annihilated.[1]

The controversy between Buddhists and Realists on this subject of Non-existence is a natural outcome of their different conception of reality. For the Buddhist the only reality is the efficient point-instant, all the rest is interpretation and thought-construction. The Realist, on the other hand, distinguishes between 3 categories of «existence» [2] (substance, quality, motion), and 4 categories of valid «meaning» [3] (universals, differentials, inherence and non-existence), which also have objective reality. Non-existence is valid since it is produced by its own causes. [4] The non-existence of a jar, e. g., is produced by the stroke of a hammer. It is not a mere name like a «flower in the sky».[5] But the

1 TS., p. 134. 25.

2 *sattā* = *astitva*.

3 *padārtha* = *bhāva*.

4 TSP., p. 135. 1, cp. NK., p. 142. 1-2.

5 According to Vātsyāyana, NBh., p. 2, existence and non-existence are two sides of reality. Everything can possess existence and non-existence as well. For this reason the amalgamated Nyāya-Vaišeṣika school has added a seventh category, non-

Buddhist answers that existence alone can have a cause, non-existence cannot be produced. [1] If we understand by the non-existence of a thing its replacement by another thing,[2] this non-existence will not be something different from the replaced thing itself. If we understand by it its simple non-existence, [3] then its cause will produce nothing and cannot be called a cause. To do nothing means not to do anything; to be a non-producer means not to be a cause. Hence non-existence will have no reality and no validity.

But then, the Realist asks again, what indeed is annihilation to the thing annihilated, is it something or is it nothing? If it were nothing, argues the Realist, the thing would never be annihilated and would continue to exist. It therefore must be something valid. If it is something separate,[4] added to the thing in the course of its annihilation, answers the Buddhist, it will remain separate, allthough added, and the thing will also remain unaffected,[5] notwithstanding the vicinity of such an uncomfortable neighbour. Let the «venerable gentleman»[6] of such a thing remain intact after destruction, retorts the Realist, it will be your «Thing-in-Itself»,[7] a thing deprived of all its general and special properties and efficiencies.[8] In so saying the Realist hints at the Buddhist theory of ultimate reality which is but a bare point-instant. This point, he says, will indeed remain even after the thing be destroyed. «This your realistic non-existence is empty and

---

existence, to the six categories of the old Vaišeṣika school. But this opinion did not prevail in the realistic camp without strong opposition. Prašastapāda among the Vaišeṣikas and Prabhākara among the Mīmāṃsakas rally in this point to the Buddhists, cp. Prāšast., p. 225. and ŠD, p. 322 ff. Šāntirakṣita, p. 135. 6 ff., simply accuses the realist of assuming that non-existence is an effect, like the plant produced by the seed. But Kamalašīla remarks, p. 135. 16, that this is not quite correct, since the Naiyāyiks and others do not assert that non-existence «exists» like a substance (*dravyādivat*), it is «a meaning» (*padārtha*), but not a substance (*dravya*).

1 TSP., p. 135 10.

2 Ibid., p. 135. 23.

3 Ibid., 136. 3 ff.; cp. NK. p. 132. 8 ff.

4 TSP., p. 133. 20 ff.; NK., p. 132. 3 ff.

5 NK., p. 139. 15—*asmin (pradhvaṃse) bhinna-mūrtau kim āyātam bhāvasya? na kiṃcit!* The realists who assume real non-existence, real relations, real annihilation are ridiculed by the Buddhist. If these things are real, they say, they should possess separate bodies, then we shall have «non-existence in person» — *vigrahavān abhāvaḥ, vigrahavān sambandhaḥ, bhinna-mūrtir vināšaḥ.*

6 *āyuṣmān bhāvaḥ*, ibid.

7 *svalakṣaṇa*, ibid.

8 *nirasta-samasta-arthakriya*, ibid.

nil, says the Buddhist to the Vaiśeṣika, because it is outside the disappearing thing», it has nothing of its own to support it in the external world. «Just the contrary, answers the Vaiśeṣika, your non-existence, i. e. nominalistic non-existence, is empty and nil, because it is included in the disappearing thing and does not represent any separate unity by itself».[1] That existence as well as non-existence must be separate unities added to some thing is clear, because there is between them a possessive relation which finds its expression in speech. The Genitive case in the expressions «existence *of* a thing», «non-existence *of* a thing» points to the fact that a thing can possess existence or non-existence. These expressions, answers the Buddhist, are nothing but perverse language, just as the expression «the body *of* a statue», while the statue itself is the body, there is nothing that possesses this body. The Genitive case «of» has here no meaning at all.[2] Existence and non-existence are not different appurtenances of a thing, they are the thing itself.

There are indeed two kinds of annihilation,[3] empirical annihilation called destruction[4] and a transcendental one called evanescence[5] or impermanence.[6] The first is the annihilation of the jar by a stroke of the hammer. The second is, so to speak, the destruction of the jar by time; an imperceptible, infinitely graduated, constant deterioration or impermanence which is the very essence of reality. Śāntirakṣita[7] therefore says «reality itself is called annihilation, viz, that ultimate reality which has the duration of a moment». It is not produced by a cause[8] like the stroke of a hammer; it arises by itself,[9] since it belongs to the essence of reality,[10] reality is impermanent. The fact that the annihilation of a thing always follows upon its previous existence[11] does not apply to such reality.[12] This reality is dynamic[13] in its

1 Cp. NBT., transl., p. 83 n. 4.
2 TSP., p. 138. 27, 142. 27 etc.
3 TSP., p. 137. 21, 156. 11.
4 *pradhvaṃsa.*
5 *vināśa = vinaśvaratva.*
6 *anitya = kṣaṇika.*
7 TS., p. 137. 26—*yo hi bhāvaḥ kṣaṇa-sthāyī vināśa iti gīyate.*
8 TSP., p. 138.2—*ahetuka,* cp. ibid., p. 133. 13.
9 TS., p. 132. 12; NK, p. 131. 23.
10 *vinaśvara-svabhāva=vastu=cala-vastu-svabhāva,* TSP., p. 138. 10.
11 *vastv-anantara-bhāvitva,* ibid., p. 138. 11.
12 *na . . . tādṛśi=na cala-svarūpe,* ibid., p. 138. 10.
13 *cala-bhāva-svarūpa,* ibid., p. 138. 9.

essence, it is indivisible,[1] it cannot be divided in parts so that non-existence should follow upon existence,[2] its evanescence arises simultaneously with its production,[3] otherwise evanescence would not belong to the very essence of reality.[4] Existence and non-existence are thus different names given to the same thing «just as a donkey and an ass are different names given to the same animal».[5]

§ 9. Šāntirakṣita's formula.

The formulation of the theory of Instantaneous Being as laid down by Šāntirakṣita in the dictum that «the momentary thing represents its own annihilation»[6] is remarkable in the highest degree. It shows us clearly the kind of reality we have to deal with in Buddhist logic. It is evidently not the empirical object that can be called its own annihilation. Nobody will deny that when a jar has been broken to pieces by a stroke of the hammer it has ceased to exist. But beyond this obvious empirical change there is, as stated above, another, never beginning and never stopping, infinitely graduated, constant change, a running transcendental ultimate reality. The creation of the jar out of a clump of clay and its change into potsherds are but new qualities, i. e., outstanding moments in this uninterrupted change. There is nothing perdurable, no static element in this process. An everlasting substantial matter is declared to be pure imagination, just as an everlasting substantial Soul. There is, therefore, as Šāntirakṣita says, in every next moment not the slightest bit left of what has been existent in the former moment. The moments are necessarily discrete, every moment, i. e., every momentary thing is annihilated as soon as it appears, because it does not survive in the next moment. In this sense everything represents its own annihilation. If something of the preceding moment would survive in the next moment, this would mean eternity, because it would survive in the third and following moments just in the same way as it did survive in the second. Static means eternal;[7] if matter exists, it necessarily is eternal, if it

---

1 *niraṃša*, ibid., p. 138. 10.

2 *yena tad-anantara-bhāvitvam asya bhavati*, ibid., p. 138. 11.

3 *nāšasya tan-niṣpattāv eva niṣpannatvāt*, ibid.

4 *anyathā .... (cala)-svabhāvam .... na syāt*, ibid., p. 138. 12.

5 TS., p. 139. 7.

6 TS., p. 137.26.

7 *nityatvam = avasthāna-mātram*. Tātp., p. 239. 24; cp. TSP., p. 140.24 — *yady utpāda-anantaram na vinašyet, tadā pašcād api.. tad-avasthaḥ (syāt)*.

does not exist, being is necessarily instantaneous. As already mentioned above, the first view is advocated in the Sānkhya system, the second in Buddhism. There can be nothing in the middle, there can be no eternal matter with changing qualities, as naive realism and the realistic systems assume. The transcendentalist, on the other hand, assumes that ultimate reality cannot be divided in substance and quality, it must be indivisible and instantaneous.

This kind of annihilation, transcendental annihilation, is not produced by occurrent causes.[1] Since existence itself is constant annihilation, it will go on existing, i. e., being annihilated and changing, without needing in every case any cause of annihilation. The elements of existence are automatically evanescent,[2] they do not want any additional circumstance [3] in order to produce that change which is going on always and by itself.

Just as the totality [4] of causes and conditions of every event is necessary followed by that event, because the totality is present,[5] nothing else is needed, the totality is the event itself,[6] just so everything is evanescent by its nature, no other cause of annihilation or change is needed. Reality has been characterized as efficiency, it can also be characterized as evanescence or annihilation.

§ 10. Change and annihilation.

The conception of a change[7] is a direct corollary from the conception of annihilation. Having repudiated the realistic view of annihilation, the Buddhist naturally also repudiates the realistic conception of a change. What is the exact meaning of the word «change?» It means, as already mentioned, either that one thing is replaced by another thing, or that the thing remains the same, but its condition, or quality, has changed, i. e., has become another quality. If it means the first, the Buddhist will not object.[8] But since there is a change at every moment, the thing will be at every moment replaced by another thing.

---

1 TSP., p. 140.25 — *kim nāśa-hetunā tasya kṛtam yena vinaśyeta.*

2 *svarasa-vināśinaḥ (sarve dharmāḥ).*

3 Ibid., p. 141.9 — *sarvathā akiṃcit-kara eva nāśa-hetur iti.*

4 *sāmagrī.*

5 TSP., p. 132.17.

6 Cp. Tātp., p. 80.5 — *sahakāri-sākalyam na prāpter atiricyate.*

7 *sthity-anyathātva* or *anyathātva*, cp. TSP., p. 110.25 ff.

8 *siddha-sādhyatā*, ibid., p. 137.23.

If it means the second, then a series of difficulties arise for the Realist. He assumes the existence of real substances along with real qualities. But ultimate reality cannot be so divided,[1] it cannot represent a stable stuff with real moving qualities situated upon it, as though it were a permanent home for passing visitors. This conception of naive realism cannot stand scrutiny. From the two correlative parts one alone must remain as ultimately real. It can be called a substance, but then, it will be a substance without qualities. Or it may be the qualities, but these qualities will be absolute qualities, without belonging to any substance. «Whatsoever exists, says Yaśomitra,[2] is a thing», it neither is a quality nor a substance. Reality, existence, thing and momentary thing are synonyms. If qualities are real, they are things. The categories of substance and quality are relative, they therefore do not reflect ultimate reality,[3] they are created by our intellect.

In this denial of a real substance-to-quality relation the Buddhists, as already mentioned, were at one with the Sānkhyas, but on the positive side both schools parted in opposite directions. The Sānkhyas assumed as ultimately real eternal matter alone, which itself is constantly changing, they denied the separate reality of its passing manifestations. The Buddhists, on the contrary, denied the separate reality of the perdurable matter and stuck to the reality of the passing qualities alone, thus converting them into absolute qualities, qualities not belonging to any substance.

Moreover, the Realist must face in regard of the reality of change the same difficulty with which he was confronted in regard of the reality of annihilation.[4] Does change represent something different from the thing changing or is it this thing itself? If it is nothing different, nothing will happen to the thing, the thing will remain as it was, there will be no change. If it is something apart, it will remain apart and there again will be no change. There is no other issue left than to assume that the words «the change of a thing» contain a perverse expression[5] and that in reality, in ultimate reality, there is another thing at every consecutive moment. When brass is changed from a solid into a liquid condition, the realist assumes that the matter is «the same», but its condition

---

1 Ibid., p. 134.3.

2 Cp. CC, p. 26 n., cp. TSP., p. 128. 17—*vidyamānam = vastu = dravya = dharma*.

3 *dharma-dharmi-bhāvo... na sad-asad apekṣate.* (Dignāga).

4 Cp. TSP., p. 141.2 ff.

5 Ibid., p. 142.27.

is other». The causes producing destruction, fire etc., cannot annihilate the matter, but they destroy its condition and produce a change.[1] The thing desappears not absolutely, but conditionally, in functional dependence upon causes which produce the change. But this is impossible. The thing must either remain or go, it cannot do both at once, changing and remaining. If it has changed, it is not the same.[2] The example of melted brass proves nothing. Melted brass and solid brass are «other» objects.[3]

§ 11. Motion is discontinuous.

Just as existence is not something added to the existing thing, but it is this thing itself, and just as annihilation, evanescence or change are not something real in superaddition to the thing changing or destroyed, but they are the thing itself,—just so is motion nothing additional to the thing, but it is the thing itself. «There is no motion, says Vasabandhu,[4] because of annihilation». Things do not move, they have no time to do it, they disappear as soon as they appear. Momentary things, says Kamalašīla, cannot displace themselves «because they disappear at that very place at which they have appeared».[5]

This statement, i. e. the statement that there is no motion, that motion is impossible, seems to stand in glaring contradiction with the former statement according to which reality is kinetic, everything is nothing but motion. Indeed when it is maintained that reality is kinetic, it is implied that everything moves and there is no real stability at all; and when it is maintained that there can be no real motion, it follows by implication that reality consists only of things stabilized and endurable. However these two apparently contradictory statements are only two different expressions of the same fact. The so called stability is the stability of one moment only,[6] and the so

---

1 Ibid., p. 140.27 — *anyathātvam kriyate.*

2 Ibid., p. 141.1 — *na hi sa eva anyathā bhavati*; p. 141.9 — *naikasya anyathātvam asti.*

3 Ibid., p.— 141.10 — *na asiddho hetuḥ*, i. e., the *hetu* of the realist is *asiddha.*

4 AK., IV. I — *na gatir nāšāt*; cp. Tātp., p. 383.13 — *karma-apalāpa-nibandhano hy ayaṃ kṣaṇika-vādaḥ.*

5 TSP., p. 232.90 *tasya (kṣaṇikasya) janma-deša eva cyuteḥ, nāšād, dešāntara-prāpty-asambhavāt.*

6 *eka-kṣaṇa-sthiti.*

called motion is nothing over and above the consecution of these moments arising without interruption in close contiguity the one after the other[1] and thus producing the illusion of a movement. Movement is like a row of lamps sending flashes the one after the other and thus producing the illusion of a moving light. Motion consists of a series of immobilities. «The light of a lamp, says Vasubandhu,[2] is a common metaphorical designation for an uninterrupted production of a series of flashing flames. When this production changes its place, we say that the light has moved, but in reality other flames have appeared in other contiguous places».

Thus the Buddhists by purely speculative methods came to envisage Motion in a way which bears some analogy with modern mathematical physics.

In order better to understand the position of the Buddhists in this problem we must here again, first of all, contrast the Buddhist views with the views of Indian Realists. This will lead us to another distinction, the distinction between motion considered empirically and motion considered transcendentally.

According to the realistic school of the Vaišeṣikas, motion is a reality, it is one of the three things in which the genus Existence inheres, the other two being Substance and Quality.[3] Motion is something different from the thing moving, it consists in the fact that the conjunction of the thing with its place has been destroyed and a new conjunction of it with a new place has been produced. Prašastapāda[4] defines motion as the real non-relative[5] cause, producing the change of position of a particle in space. It is instantaneous in the first moment and persistent, impressed motion or momentum,[6] in the following ones, up to the moment when the body is again at rest. The Vaišeṣikas accept one impressed motion as duration, lasting till the cessation of the motion.[7] For the Naiyāyiks,

---

1 *nirantara-kṣaṇa-utpāda.*

2 AK., IX, cp. my transl. in Soul Theory, p. 938.

3 The highest genus «existence», *sattā*, inheres, according to the Vaišeṣikas (VS., I. 2. 7—8), in things belonging to the categories of substance, quality and motion. The other categories are «meanings» *padārtha*, they have «*Geltung*» which sometimes is called *svarūpa-sattā*, but they do not «exist».

4 Prašastp., p. 290 ff.

5 *anapekṣa*, i. e., not merely relative to rest (?).

6 *saṃskāra.*

7 *bahūni karmāṇi... ekas tu saṃskāro'ntarāle*, ibid., p. 302.11.

on the contrary, impressed motion is also split into momentary motions, each generating the one that succeeds it. In this respect the Nyāya view falls in line with the Buddhist one. But the idea of an absolute moment as a single point-instant of reality was distasteful to all Realists; even in those cases where they accept constant change, they, as has been already mentioned, compose it of three-momentary or six-momentary durations. When a body falls to the ground, the force acting on it is gravity in the first instance and impressed motion in the succeeding moments, but gravity continues to operate.[1] This affords some explanation of the accelerated motion of falling bodies, as will be stated later on.

The Buddhist view is distinguished from these speculations by the fundamental theory which denies the existence of any substance. There is therefore no motion in the things, but the things themselves are motion. When Vasubandhu, therefore, declares that «there is no motion, because of annihilation», it is this realistic idea of a real motion which he denies. Motion exists empirically. If the Realists would simply maintain that this empirical motion has some cause behind it, the Buddhist would not object.[2] But this cause, according to his theory, consists of momentary fulgurations succeding one another in contiguous places without any abiding stuff in them. These flashes arise not out of the same stuff, but, so to speak, out of nothing,[3] since the foregoing flash is totally extinct[4] before the succeeding one arises. «There is, says Kamalaśīla,[5] not the slightest bit of some particle of a thing which survives» in the next succeeding moment.

The picture which the Buddhists made themselves of the real condition of the world is best of all elicited in the manner in which

---

1 *ādyam gurutvād, dvitīyādīni tu gurutva-saṃskārābhyām* ibid., p. 304.17. «Why do we not assume one movement in the interval between its beginning and its end»? asks Praśasta, p. 302.11, i. e., why do we not, like the Buddhists and Naiyāyiks, maintain that it is instantaneous? and answers «because of many conjunctions», i. e. motion being by its very definition conjunction-disjunction with a place, there are as many conjunctions as there are places through which, e. g., an arrow passes in its flight. Cp. H. Bergson's idea that such motion is indivisible. According to the Vaiśeṣikas motion is infinitely divisible, but the force (*saṃskāra*) or momentum is one.

2 The «existence» of the preceding moment is the cause: *sattaiva vyāpṛtiḥ*, TS. kār. 1772.

3 *niranvaya*.

4 *niruddha*.

5 TSP., p. 183—*na hi svalpīyaso'pi vastv-aṃśasya kasyacid anvayo'sti.*

they tried to explain the phenomemon of accelaration in a falling body[1] or the phenomenon of the rising smoke.[2] They found in these phenomena a striking confirmation of their idea that at every moment of its existence the falling body is really «another» body, because it is differently composed. Its weight is different at every moment. Every material body is a composition of four fundamental elements, which are conventionally called earth, water, fire and wind. Under the name of «earth» the solid element is understood, «water» is the name for the force of cohesion or viscidity, «fire» means temperature, and «wind» means weight or motion. All these elements or forces are present in whatsoever piece of matter, always in the same proportion. If the bodies are sometimes solid and sometimes liquid, sometimes hot and sometimes moving, this depends on the greater amount of intensity[3] in the energy representing the elements, not on its quantitative predominance. That the element of solidity is present in water is proved by its capacity of supporting a ship on its surface. That the «liquid» element is present in fire is proved by the fact that the particles of fire are holding together in a flame. It is clear that the fundamental elements of matter are rather forces or momentary quanta of energy than substantial atoms. They accordingly fall under the category of «cooperators» or «cooperating forces». The fourth element is called «motion», but also «lightness», i. e., weight.[4] Thus every material object is the meeting-point of the forces of repulsion, attraction, heat and weight. When a body falls, its movement in every point is accelarated, i. e., is «another» movement. It is also another weight and another quantum of the force of gravitation. The Buddhist philosopher concludes that the falling body is another body in every consecutive moment of its motion, because the quantum of energy is different in every moment and the material bodies in general are nothing over and above the quanta of energy which enter in their composition.[5]

---

[1] AKB., ad II.46, de la Vallée's transl. I, p. 229—230.

[2] Ibid.

[3] *utkarṣa*. It thus appears that ancient Indian had something in the kind of a dynamical theory of matter, as opposed to a mechanistic one, cp. below.

[4] *laghutva* = *īraṇātmaka*, cp. AKB., ad I. 12.

[5] On the motion in a falling body cp. NV., p. 420.

§ 12. Annihilation certain a priori.

Thus the argument which proceeds by an analysis of the notions of non-existence and annihilation leads to the establishment of the theory of momentariness just as the argument drawn from the analysis of the notion of existence as causal efficiency. We have pointed out that both arguments are analitycal, hence the conclusion appears with logical necessity. There is a third argument which differs but very slightly from the second. It starts from the fact that everything necessarily[1] must have an end. There is nothing at all that would have no end. This trivial truth which is known to every body, when minutely examined, cannot mean anything else than that evanescence is the very core of existence. If everything is evanescent, it is always evanescent, a thing cannot be severed from its own essence, there is therefore no duration at all. The evanescence of everything is *a priori* certain.

Thus it is that the momentary character of all existence is something which can be established *a priori.*[2]

Vācaspati-miśra[3] informs us that the early Buddhists deduced the idea of Momentariness by an induction from observation, it was for them an *a posteriori* idea. They at first noticed that such objects, as fire, light, sound, thought, were changing at every moment. A little more attention convinced them that our body is also changing constantly, so that at every consecutive point-instant it is «another» body. Then by a broad generalisation from observation, in an inductive way, they concluded, «just as this our body, so also the crystal gem»; it also is older of a moment in every succeeding point-instant. This way of reasoning was followed by the early Buddhists. But the later Buddhists did not prove momentariness by a generalisation from induction. They had found that annihilation, i. e., an end, was necessary, unavoidable, *a priori* certain, no need of proving it by observation. The realists answered by the following reasoning.[4] «Please, said they to the Buddhists, consider the following dilemma: does the continuity

---

1 *dhruva-bhāvi* = *avaśyam-bhāvi*, NK., pp. 132.14 ff.; Tātp., p. 383.19 ff; TS., p. 132.15 ff; NBT., 11.37.

2 *a priori* in the sense of non-empirical; literally *a priori* could be translated as *pratyañcaḥ pratyayāḥ*, cp. NK., p. 267.19, *parāñcaḥ* = *a posteriori*, Tātp., p. 84.18.

3 Tātp., p. 380 ff.

4 Ibid., 386.14 ff.

of existence of the potsherds necessarily follow upon the continuity of the existence of the jar, or not? If not, then the end of the jar is not at all necessary. We may indeed open our eyes as much as you like, we do not arrive at perceiving the end of the jar otherweise than at the moment of its change into potsherds.[1] Thus the necessary end of the jar is not really proved. Now let us admit that it is (*a priori*) necessary, nevertheless when it really happens, we observe that this necessary end depends upon the stroke of a hammer, that is to say, an adventitious cause, it is not necessary at all. The end is not concomitant with unconditional (*a priori*) necessity, you must prove that it does not depend upon a special circumstance. Therefore, since your proof of momentary change is thus repudiated, you really must admit that the recognition of the same jar in consecutive moments of its existence proves that it is one and the same jar (and not «another» jar in every moment)». But the Buddhist answers, «Whatsoever is not (*a priori*) necessary, depends upon special causes, just as the colour of a cloth depends upon the dye which has been applied; it is not necessary. If all existing things were likewise dependent for their end upon special causes, then we would have empirical objects which never would have an end, we would have eternal empirical objects. But this is impossible. The necessity of an end points to the fact that the things are so born that they go at the same moment as they are born, they go by themselves, without a special cause, they do not continue in the next moment. Thus it is proved that they change at every moment».

§ 13. MOMENTARINESS DEDUCED FROM THE LAW OF CONTRADICTION.

Whatsoever exists, exists separately [2] from «other» existing things. To exist means to exist separately. What exists really has an existence of its own; to have an existence of its own, means to stand out from among other existing things. This is an analytic proposition, since the notion of «apartness» belongs to the essential features of the notion of «existence».[3] If something is not apart from other existing things, if it has no existence of its own, if its existence coalesces with the existence

---

[1] NK., p. 139.21 ff.

[2] *sarvam pṛthak*, NS., IV. 1. 36.

[3] *bhāva-lakṣaṇa-pṛthaktvāt*, ibid.

of other things, it is a mere name for those other things, or a construction of our imagination. E. g., the whole does not exist separately from its constituent parts, time and space do not exist apart from point-instants, the Soul does not exist apart from mental phenomena, Matter does not exist apart from sense-data etc., etc. Since they are not apart, they do not exist at all.

Now, what is the thing which is really something quite apart from all other existing things, which is something quite unique?[1] It is the mathematical «point-instant».[2] Its only relation to other existents is «otherness». It is numerically other, not qualitatively. Every relation and every quality is something belonging to two realities at least, and therefore something unreal itself, as something having no existence of its own, apart from these two realities.

The formula of this «law of otherness» runs thus. A thing is «other», if united to incompatible properties.[3] Difference of quality involves a difference of the thing, if the qualities are mutually exclusive. Two qualities are not incompatible if the one is under the other, the one a part of the other, e. g. colour and red. But they are incompatible if they are both under the same determinable, as, e. g., red and yellow or, more properly, red and non-red. If the determinable is very remote or if there is no common determinable at all, the incompatibility is still greater.[4] It is obvious that this statement of the law of otherness is but a negative form of the law of contradiction as expressed in European logic by Aristoteles: nothing can possess at the same time, in the same place and in the same respect two mutually exclusive properties. This European formula of the law of contradiction presupposes the existence of the relation of substance and quality, or of «continuants and occurrents». In India we are faced, as mentioned above, by two systems which deny the objective reality of this relation. The Sānkhya admits a continuant only and the Buddhists admit merely the occurrents. A thing is then another thing whenever its determinations are other. These determinations are Time, Space and Quality.[5] A thing is other when its quality is other, e. g., the same thing cannot be at once red and yellow, i. e., red and non-red. It is other when its position in space is other, e. g., the radiance of a jewel in one place and its radiance in another place are two different things.

---

1 *sarvato vyāvṛtta, trailokya-vyāvṛtta.*

2 *kṣaṇa = svalakṣaṇa.*

3 NBT., p. 4—*viruddha-dharma-saṃsargād anyad vastu.*

4 Cp. below on the law of contradiction and on *apoha.*

5 *deśa-kāla-ākāra-bhedaś ca viruddha-dharma-saṃsargaḥ.* NBT., ibid.

Since an extended body involves position in at least two points of space, extension is not something ultimately real, in every point the thing is ultimately another thing. The same applies to time. The same thing cannot really exist in two different moments, in every instant it is a different thing.[1] Even the moment of sensation and the moments of a thing's apperception refer, in ultimate reality, to two different things. Their unity in the presentation is a constructed or imagined unity.

Thus every reality is another reality. What is identical or similar is not ultimately real. The real is the unique,[2] the thing in itself, the unrelated thing. All relations are constructed, relation and construction are the same. Ultimate reality is non-constructed, non imagined, non-related reality, the thing as it strictly is in itself, it is the mathematical point-instant.

We will revert to this problem when considering the Indian formula of the laws of Identity and of Contradiction. It is sufficient at present to point out the connection between the law of Contradiction and the theory of Instantaneous Existence. Many philosophers in Europe have laid down the dictum that identity implies difference. A is different from B even if they are identical, and *a fortiori*, when they are only similar. Buddhist philosophy operates with the (transcendental) notion of absolutely dissimilar and non-identical realities which are discrete point-instants.[3] Leibniz's principle that there are no two absolutely identical things in nature, the identity of indiscernibles being resolved in a continuity of qualitative change is, to a certain extent, comparable with the Buddhist view, with that capital difference that the discontinuous, unique and discrete thing is the limit of all continuity and is converted into an absolute ultimate existence of the mathematical point-instant.[4]

---

1 The example given NBT., p. 4. 6, is evidently chosen with the intention to be approved both by the Buddhist and the Realist, but the real meaning of the Buddhist appears from the remark, ibid., p. 4. 8 ff.

2 *svalakṣaṇam = paramārtha-sat.*

3 Cp. below on the history of the idea of *kṣaṇikatva*.

4 Among modern authors I find the «law of otherness» thoroughly discussed in W. E. Johnson Logic, I. ch. XII. The coincidences with Indian speculations are often striking. But the idea that «the real» must be «one» real, and that real being means one being is already familiar to the schoolmen who maintained that «*ens et unum convertuntur*»; it has been enlarged upon by Leibniz and lead him to the establishment of the ultimate reality of his Monads.

§ 14. Is the point-instant a reality? The differential calculus.

In the preceding exposition it has been sufficiently established that empirical Time and Space are, for the Buddhist, fictions constructed by our understanding on the basis of sensible point-instants which alone are the ultimate reality. Against this theory which reduces the reality to the «this», the «now», the «here», and converts all the rest of our knowledge into imaginative and relative differentiation, the Realists raised the very natural objection that the point-instant itself is no exception to the general rule, since it is also nothing but a construction in thought, a mere name without any corresponding reality. «In assuming, says Uddyotakara[1] to the Buddhist, that time itself is nothing but a name, you evidently also must assume that the shortest time, the time-limit, is likewise nothing but a name». The Buddhist retorts that the shortest time, the mathematical point-instant, is something real, since it is established in science.[2] The astronomer makes it the basis of all his computations. It is an indivisible time particle, it does not contain any parts standing in the relation of antecedence and sequence.[3] The Indian astronomers made a distinction between «time grossly measured»[4] and a «subtle time»,[5] measured with precision. The motion of a thing during a single moment they called instantaneous motion, or the «motion of just that time»,[6] i. e., not of another time, not of another moment. This time is nothing but the differential of a planet's longitude. Such a moment is no reality, says the Realist, it is a mere mathematical convenience.[7] «Just the contrary, says the Buddhist, we maintain that the instantaneousness of being is the ultimately real thing». The only thing in the universe which is a non-construction, a non-fiction, is the sensible point-instant, it is the real basis of all constructions.[8] It is true that it is a reality which cannot be represented in a sensuous image,[9] but this is just because it is

---

1 NV., p. 418. 15.

2 NVTP., p. 387. 1-*jyotir-vidyā-siddha.*

3 *pūrva-apara-bhāga-vikala.* Ibid., cp. NK., p. 127. 12.

4 *sthūla-kāla, kāla-piṇḍa.*

5 *sūkṣma-gatiḥ.*

6 *tat-kālikī gatiḥ.*

7 *sanjñā-mātram.*

8 *vāstavīkṣaṇikatā abhimatā.*

9 *kṣaṇasya (jñānena) prāpayitum aśakyatvāt,* cp. NBT., p. 12. 19 (*prāptiḥ = savikalpakam jñānam*).

not a thought-construction. The absolutely unique point-instant of reality, as it cannot be represented, can also not be named [1] otherwise than by a pronoun «this», «now» etc. Consequently it is not a mere name, it is no name at all, it has no name; ultimate reality is unutterable. What is utterable is always more or less a thought-construction. [2] Thus it is that the mathematical point-instant is a fiction for the Realist and a reality for the Buddhist, and *vice versa* empirical time or «gross time»,[3] «substantial time» [4] is a reality for the Realist and a fiction for the Buddhist. Just as the mathematician constructs his velocities out of differentials, so does the human mind, a natural mathematician, construct duration out of momentary sensations.

That space likewise contains no other ultimate reality than the momentary sensation has already been pointed out. [5] Dharmakīrti says: [6] «an extended form exists in the (real) object not (more) than in its idea. To admit that (the extended body) exists in one (unextended atom) would be a contradiction, and to admit that (the same extended body being one) is present in many (atoms) is an impossibility». The extended body being thus a fiction, there is no other issue left than to admit the ultimate reality of the point-instant.[7]

Whether the honour of having discovered the Differential Calculus must really be attributed to the Hindu astronomers we must leave it for others to decide,[8] but in any case they were unquestionally the discoverers of the mathematical zero. The idea of a mathematical limit, therefore, must have bean familiar to Indian scholars.[9] It is no wonder

---

1 TSP., p. 276.

2 *śabdā vikalpa-yonayaḥ, vikalpāḥ śabda-yonayaḥ* (Dignāga).

3 *sthūla-kāla.*

4 *kāla-piṇḍa.*

5 Cp. above, p. 85 ff.

6 Cp. NVTT., p. 425. 20—*tasmān nārthe na vijñāne...*

7 The Thing-in-Itself has been compared with a «Differential of Sensibility» by S. Maimon.

8 Dr. B. N. Seal asserts it and Mr Spottiswoode, the Royal Astronomer, to whom the facts have been submitted, admitted it with reservations, cp. P. G. Ray's Hindu Chemistry, v. II, p. 160 ff (where Dr. B. N. Seal's article is reprinted from his Positive Sciences of the Hindus).

9 M. H. Bergson asserts that the world of the mathematician is indeed an instantaneous world, it is also *kṣaṇika* as the world of the Buddhist. He says (Cr. Ev., p. 23—24)—«the world the mathematician deals with is a world that dies and is reborn at every instant, the world which Descartes was thinking of when he spoke of continuous creation». This idea is indeed quite Buddhistic, it sounds as if it were put in sanscrit—*ye bhāvā nirantaram ārabhyanta iti mahāpaṇḍita-śrī-*

that they applied it in the field of general philosophy, they were not the only school to do it.[1]

§ 15. History of the doctrine of Momentariness.

The origin of the theory of Instantaneous Being is most probably pre-Buddhistic.[2] Its vicissitudes in Buddhism are interwoven with the history of different sects. Since the literature of the majority of these sects is lost beyond recovery, we must be content to point out some salient features which will allow us tentatively to draw the main line of its development. We may at present distinguish between 1) the initial form of the doctrine when it was laid down with considerable precision, 2) a series of deviations and fluctuations in the schools of Hīnayāna, 3) a crisis of the doctrine in the schools of Mahāyāna when it seemed to be given up altogether, 4) its reintroduction in the school of Asanga and Vasubandhu, and 5) its final form in the school of Dignāga and Dharmakīrti.

This final form, we have seen, implies that ultimate reality belongs to the mathematical point-instant, to a time-unit which contains no parts standing in the relation of antecedence and sequence or, more precisely, to the infinitesimal differential points of reality, out of which our intellect constructs the empirical world as it appears to our understanding in manifold images. The theory is at that time founded on epistemological investigations. It is then the direct consequence of the theory of two heterogeneous sources of our knowledge, the senses which supply merely the detached point-instants of pure reality and the intellect which constructs of these infinitesimals a manifold and ordered world

At the opposite end of this historical process, at the starting point of Buddhism, we find a theory which is essentially the same, although

---

Dhekaratena vikalpitās, te sarve jyotir-vidyā-prasiddhāḥ pratikṣaṇam utpadyante vinaśyante ca. This being the precise rendering of Bergson's words, sounds like a quotation from an Indian text. It is also noteworthy that one of the synonyms for thought or constructive thought is computation *(sankalana)*. Thus thought, productive imagination and mathematics become closely related, cp. vol. II, p. 292 — *samākalayet* = *vikalpayet* = *utprekṣeta*.

[1] The Sānkhya-Yoga in this point, as in many others, comes very near to the Buddhist view, cp. Vyāsa on III. 52—*kālo vastu-śūnya-buddhi-nirmāṇaḥ sarva-jñāna-anupātī, kṣaṇas tu vastu-patitaḥ* ...., cp. B. N. Seal, op. cit., p. 80. Vijñāna-bhikṣu points out «time has no real, or objective, existence apart from the «moment», but the latter is real, being identical with the unit of change in phenomena»—*guṇa-pariṇāmasya kṣaṇatva-vacanāt*. Ibid.

[2] Cp. CC., p. 65 ff.

it is then bereft of its epistemological foundation. All reality is split in separate elements which are instantaneous. The theory of momentariness is implied in the pluralistic theory of the separate elements of existence. As soon as Buddhism made its appearance as a theory of elements, it was already a theory of instantaneous elements. Having arisen as a spirited protest against the Monism of the Upanishads[1] and of Sānkhya, it did not stop half the way, it asserted straight off the exclusive reality of the minutest elements of existence.[2] These elements were not mathematical points however, they were momentary sense-data and thought-data, linked together in an individual life only by the laws of causal interdependence. It would have been natural to assume that the Buddhists arrived at this precise formulation gradually, and that the starting point of the development was the general and very human consideration of impermanence as it naturally suggests itself to the mind in common life. However it seems that at the time when the fundamental principles of Buddhism were laid down, the formula «no substance, no duration, no other bliss than in Nirvāṇa» already referred not to simple impermanence, but to the elements of existence whose ultimate reality was confined to the duration of a single moment, two moments being two separate elements.[3]

---

[1] Just as in the history of Vedānta we have here mutual indebtedness. The early Buddhists were influenced by Sānkhya ideas, but later on the Pātañjala-Yogas were very strongly influenced by the formulas of the Sarvāstivādins, cp. my CC., p. 47.

[2] If we accept the highly ingeneous suggestion of the late M. E. Senart, that the term *satkāya-dṛṣṭi* is initially a corruption of *satkārya-dṛṣṭi*, we will see that the fundamental tenet of the Sānkhyas becomes a fundamental error for the Buddhists. The Sānkhyas (and Ājīvikas) maintain that everything, although constantly changing, exists eternally, nothing new appears in the world and nothing disappears; the Buddhists, on the contrary, maintain that everything exists instantaneously, it appears out of nothing and reverts at once into nothing, there is no *sub*-stance at all. Both these theories are radical (*ekānta*), they deny the categories of Inherence, Substance and Quality, deny the eternal atoms and maintain infinite divisibility, they are both opposed in these points by the Vaiśeṣikas. The central point at issue seems to have been the problem of Inherence. Vaiśeṣikas, and probably the early Yogas, admitted it, Sānkhyas and Buddhists rejected it, although from opposite sides. The «radical» standpoint of the Buddhists seems to have been their original view. The character of the deviations from it in the schools of the Vatsīputrīyas, Sarvāstivādins, Kāsyapīyas and others clearly shows that the «radical» view of separate and momentary elements lies at the bottom.

[3] CC., p. 38.

Now just in the middle between this initial and the final form of the doctrine it underwent a dangerous crisis.

The school of the Mādhyamikas bluntly denied the reality of the supposed point-instants of existence. Against the theory they appealed to common sense. Who is the man of sense, they thought, who will believe that a real thing can appear, exist and disappear at the same moment.[1] However this denial has no special bearing upon the theory of instantaneousness, since that school declared every separate object and every notion to be dialectical, relative and illusive.

The history of the theory of instantaneous reality during the first period prooves clearly how difficult it is for the human mind to grapple with the idea of pure change, i. e., the idea of a reality in which there is no *sub*-stance at all. The categories of an abiding substance with changing qualities is so deeply rooted in all our habits of thought that we always become reluctant to admit pure change, even when it is urged upon us by logic.

The school of the Vatsīputrīyas were the first among the early schools which admitted the existence of a certain unity between the elements of a living personality. Their position in this problem is highly instructive. They dared not readmit the spiritual substance of a Soul, so strong was the opposition against this idea in Buddhist circles. But they also were reluctant to deny any kind of unity between the separate elements of a personality and admit that the separate elements constituting a personality hold together only by causal laws. They therefore adopted an intermediate course. The personality was declared to be something dialectical, neither identical with its elements, nor different from them. It was not given the reality of an ultimate element, nor was that reality denied altogether.[2] This course of admitting dialectical reality and neglecting the law of contradiction reminds us of the dialectical method very popular among the Jains and consisting in assuming everywhere a double and contradictory real essence. It prooves at the same time that the doctrine of a radical separateness of all elements and their exclusive link in causal laws was anterior to the rise of the school of the Vatsīputrīyas.

Another attack against the theory of absolute change originated in the schools of the Sarvāstivādins and of the Kāšyapīyas. The theory

---

[1] Cp. Candrakīrti in the Madhy. vṛtti., p. 547.

[2] Cp. Vasubandhu's exposition of that theory, AK. IX, transl. in my Soul Theory.

of absolute change implies the idea that only the present exists. The past does not exist, because it exists no more, and the future is not real, because it does not yet exist. To this the Sarvāstivādins objected that the past and the future are real, because the present has its roots in the past and its consequences in the future. The Kāśyapīyas divided the past into a past whose influence has been exhausted and a past whose influence has not yet been exhausted. The second they maintained was real, the first was not real. This theory involved the danger of shifting into the pale of Sānkhya with its permanent stuff and its changing manifestations. In fact some Sarvāstivādins divided the elements in a permanent essence and momentary manifestations.[1] They nevertheless protested against the accusation of drifting into Sānkhya. All elements, they maintained, were instantaneous, they appeared and disappeared just at the same moment.[2]

Vasubandhu informs us[3] that the theory of the Sarvāstivādins was an innovation of the «exegetical literature», i. e., it was introduced by the ābhidharmikas, and it is not found, according to him, in the genuine Discourses of the Buddha. The school of the Sautrāntikas, that is to say, that school which proclaimed on its banner a return to the genuine doctrine of the Discourses, denied therefore the permanent essence of the elements and reestablished the doctrine that reality consists of momentary flashes, that the «elements appear into life out of non-existence and return again into non-existence after having been existent» for a moment only. «When a visual sensation arises, says Buddha in one of his discourses, there is absolutely nothing from which it proceeds, and when it vanishes, nought there is to which it retires».[4] But although arising «out of nothing» the elements are interdependent, i. e., connected by causal laws which evoke an illusion of their stability.

A further deviation from the principle of separate, momentary and equal elements consists in the division of Matter into primary and secondary elements and in the difference established between a central element of pure consciousness as separate from the secondary

---

1 Cp. Vasubandhu's exposition, transl. in CC., p. 76. ff.; cp. O. Rosenberg, Problems.

2 It is clear that the Sartāstivādins tackled the same problem which occupies our modern Geltungs-philosophie: the past, just as the universal, does not «exist», but it is real, since it is valid (es *gilt*, es *hat Bedeutung)*.

3 CC., p. 90.

4 Ibid., p. 85.

elements representing mental phenomena or moral forces. This decidedly was a back door for the categories of substance and quality partly to reenter into their usual position out of which they were ousted by Buddhism at its start.[1] Therefore the division of the momentary elements into primary and secondary did not remain without protest. Vasubandhu informs us that Buddhadeva did not admit neither the central position of pure consciousness among the mental elements of a personality nor the fundamental position of the tangibles among the elements of matter.[2]

The Ceylonese school preserved faithfully the original doctrine, viz, that every element is instantaneous, it cannot last even for two consecutive moments, because nothing survives in the next moment from what existed in the previous one. But in its mediaeval period this school invented a very curious theory according to which the moment of thought was much shorter than the momentary sense-datum.[3] A kind of preestablished harmony was supposed to exist between the moments of the external world and the moments of their cognition, a momentary sense-datum corresponding to 17 thought-moments. In order clearly to apprehend a momentary sense-datum thought must have passed through 17 consecutive stages, from the moment of being evoked out of a subconscious condition up to the moment of reverting into that condition. If the series for some reason were incomplete, the cognition would not attain clearness. These 17 moments are the following ones: 1) subconsciousness,[4] 2—3) first movement of thought and its desappearance[5], 4) choice of one of the 5 senses[6] (doors), 5) the sense chosen,[7] 6) sensation,[8] 7) presentation,[9] 8) its affirmation,[10] 9—15) emotions,[11] 16—17) two moments of reflexion,[12] after which the series corresponding to one moment of the external sense-datum is at an end.

---

1 Cp. my CC., p. 35 ff.

2 Cp. AK., IX, cp. my Soul Theory

3 Abhidhammatthasaṃgaho, IV. 8 (Kosambi ed., p. 18).

4 *atīta-bhavaṃga*

5 *bhavaṃga-calana, bhavaṃga-uccheda.*

6 *pañcadvārāvajjana-cittaṃ.*

7 *cakkhu-viññānaṃ.*

8 *sampaṭicchana-cittaṃ.*

9 *santīraṇa-cittaṃ.*

10 *voṭṭhapana-cittaṃ.*

11 *javanaṃ.*

12 *tadārammaṇaṃ.*

This theory seems to be quite unknown in all other schools. But the fundamental idea of no duration and no substance has evidently guided those who invented it.

In the first period of Mahāyāna the theory of Instantaneous Being lost every importance, since in the empirical plane the school of the Mādhyamikas had nothing to object against naive realism [1] and in regard of the Absolute it admitted only a cognition through mystic intuition.

However the theory of Instantaneous Being was reasserted in the second period of the Mahāyāna, in the school of the Yogācāras, in Buddhist Idealism. This school began by maintaining the reality of thought on the principle of *cogito ergo sum.*[1] The elements of thought were assumed as instantaneous, but the school at the same time aimed at maintaining the reality of the whole without denying the reality of the parts. The ultimate elements were divided in three classes: pure or absolute existence,[2] pure imagination [3] and a contingent reality between them.[4] The first and last class were admitted as two varieties of reality, the second, pure imagination, was declared to be unreal and non-existent. In this threefold division of the elements we have already the germ of that radical discrimination between sensible reality and imaginative thought which became later on, in the school of Dignāga, the foundation stone of his theory of cognition.

But although the theory of Instantaneous Being has been reintroduced by Buddhist Idealism, it did not enjoy an unconditioned sway. Just as in the Hīnayāna period the categories of substance and quality although officially banned, always tended to reappear through some back-door,[5] just so in the idealistic period the notion of a Soul, although it continued to be officially repudiated — Buddhists still remain the champions of Soullessness — nevertheless haunted the domain of Buddhist philosophy and tended to introduce itself in some form or other into the very heart of Buddhism. At first a «store house of consciousness» [6]

---

1 Cp. above, p. 12.

2 *pari-niṣpanna.*

3 *pari-kalpita.*

4 *para-tantra.*

5 Cp. CC., p. 35.

6 *ālaya-vijñāna.* On the rearrangement of the system of the elements of existence by Asanga cp. L. de la Vallée Poussin, Les 75 et les 100 dharmas, Muséon, VI, 2, 178 ff. The system of Asanga includes *ālaya-vijñāna* among the *saṃskṛta* and *tathatā* among the *asaṃskṛta-dharmas.*

was imagined to replace the cancelled external reality. All the traces of former deeds and all the germs of future thoughts were stored up in that receptacle. In compliance with Buddhist tradition this consciousness was also assumed as instantaneous, but it was evidently nothing but a Soul in disguise and as such was repudiated in the school of Dignāga and Dharmakīrti.[1] Saint Asanga, the founder of Buddhist Idealism, apparently fluctuated between this theory of a store of consciousness and the mystic idea of the Mādhyamikas, for whom the individual was but a manifestation of the Absolute or of the Cosmical Body of the Buddha. This manifestation under the names of «Buddha's progeny»,[2] «Buddha's seed»,[3] «Buddha's womb»,[4] the «element of Buddhahood»[5] was again nothing but a Soul in disguise corresponding to the *jīva* of the Vedāntins, just as the Cosmical Body of Buddha corresponds to their «Highest Brahma».

In the Sautrāntika-Yogācāra school of Dignāga and Dharmakīrti the theory of Instantaneous Being was finally laid down in the form and with the arguments which have been here examined, but it did not exclude the unity of the elements on another plane, from the stand-point of the highest Absolute, as will be explained later on.

§ 16. Some European parallels.

Leibniz declares in the preface to his Théodicée that one of the famous labyrinths, in which our reason goes astray, consists in the discussion of continuity and of the indivisible points which appear to be its elements. To reconcile the notion of substance as continuous with the contrary notion of discontinuous elements, he devised his theory of Monads which are not extensive, but intensive and perceptive units. Some remarks on the analogies between Leibnizian and Buddhist ideas will be made later on.

The similarity with the views of Heracleitus has already been pointed out. We have also had several occasions to draw the attention of the reader on some remarkable coincidences between them and the views

---

1 Cp. vol. II, p. 329, n.

2 *tathāgata-gotra.*

3 *sarvajña-bīja.*

4 *tathāgata-garbha.*

5 *tathāgata-dhātu.* On this problem as well as on the development of Asangas ideas cp. E. Obermiller's translation of Uttara-tantra.

of a modern philosopher, M. H. Bergson. It will perhaps not be amiss to reconsider this point once more, in order better to understand, by way of a contrast, the Buddhist point of view. There is indeed much similarity in the form in which the idea of an universal flux has taken shape in both systems, but there is also a divergence in the interpretation of this fact. There is an almost complete coincidence in some of the chief arguments used for its establishment, and there is a capital difference in the final aims of both systems.

The final aim of Bergson is to establish a real duration and a real time, he is a realist. The ultimate reality of the Buddhist is beyond our time and beyond our space, he is a transcendentalist.

The arguments for the establishment of the fact of a universal flux of existence are drawn on both sides 1) from introspection, 2) from an analysis of the notion of existence as meaning constant change and 3) from an analysis of the notion of non-existence as being a pseudo-idea.

«What is the precise meaning of the word „exist"», asks Bergson[1] and answers, «we change without ceasing, the state itself is nothing but a change»,[2] «change is far more radical as we are at first inclined to suppose».[3] The permanent substratum of these changes, the Ego, «has no reality»,[4] «there is no essential difference between passing from one state to another and persisting in the same state», it is an «endless flow».[5]

In these words Bergson makes a statement to the effect that 1) there is no Ego, i. e., no permanent substratum for mental phenomena, 2) existence means constant change, what does not change does not exist, 3) these changing states are not connected by a permanent substratum, ergo they are connected only by causal laws, the laws of their consecution and interdependence. The coincidence with the fundamental principles of Buddhist philosophy could not be more complete. Buddhism is called 1) the no-Ego doctrine,[6] 2) the doctrine of impermanence, or of Instantaneous Being,[7] and 3) the doctrine of

---

1 Creative Evolution (London, 1928), p. 1.
2 Ibid., p. 2.
3 Ibid., p. 1.
4 Ibid., p. 4.
5 Ibid., p. 3.
6 *anātma-vāda*.
7 *kṣaṇika-vada*.

Dependent Origination,[1] i. e., the doctrine which substitutes causal laws for the permanent substratum of passing phenomena.

The cause of growing old, continues Bergson,[2] are not the phagocytes, as the realist imagines, it must lie deeper, «properly vital in growing old is the insensible, infinitely graduated, continuance of the change of form in everything existing». «Succession is an undeniable fact even in the material world».[3] The Buddhist, we have seen, also directs his attention to the human body after having noticed the constant change which constitutes the quasi duration of a fire, of sound, of motion or of a thought. The human body is also nothing but constant change. He concludes, «just as the human body, so is also the crystal gem», existence is nothing but constant change; this is a general law, what does not change does not exist, as, e. g., the Cosmical Ether. The reason why our thought converts motion into stability is, according to Bergson, the fact that we are «preoccupied before everything with the necessities of action». Out of that duration which constantly «makes itself or it unmakes itself, but never is something made»[4] «we pluck out these *moments*[5] that interest us»,[6] thought prepares our action upon the things. The Buddhist, we have seen, likewise defines thought as a preparation to purposive action upon things, and reality as a thing, or a point-instant, which experiences this action.

But still more remarkable is the coincidence in the arguments which both the Buddhists and Bergson have drawn in favour of their theories from an analysis of the ideas of non-existence and annihilation. The idea of non-existence is closely related to the problem of the essence of a negative judgment. This problem has been solved in European logic by Ch. Sigwart: negation is but a special kind of affirmation.[7] This is exactly the Buddhist view, as will be shown in a later chapter. Bergson devotes some of his most eloquent pages[8] to the development of this theory. On this occasion he establishes that annihilation is a pseudo-idea, that «we speak of the absence of a thing sought for whenever we find (instead of it) the presence of another

---

1 *pratītya-samutpāda-vāda.*

2 Ibid., p. 19—20.

3 Ibid., p. 10.

4 Ibid., p. 287.

5 Ital. mine.

6 Ibid., p. 288.

7 Cp. Creative Evolution, pp. 304, 312.

8 Ibid., p. 287—314.

reality».[1] He establishes that annihilation is not something «in superaddition» to a thing, just as production is not something in superaddition to nothing. Bergson even maintains that the nothing contains not less, but more than the something.[2] Is it not the same as Sāntirakṣita declaring that «the thing itself is called annihilation?» [3] Both the Buddhists and Bergson reject as absurd the every day conception of change, of annihilation and motion. Change is not a sudden disaster ushered into the placidly existing thing, neither is annihilation something that supersedes existence, nor motion something added to a thing. Both systems deny the existence of an enduring substance. So far they agree. Bergson's dynamic conception of existence, his idea that existence is constant change, constant motion, motion alone, absolute motion, motion without any stuff that moves[4] — this idea which it is so difficult for our habits of thought to grapple with — is, on its negative side, in its stuff denial, exactly the same as the Buddhist contention. There are, we have seen, on the Indian side three different systems which maintain the theory of constant change; the Sānkhya system which maintains that matter itself is constant change; the Yoga system which maintains the existence of a perdurable stuff along a constant change in its qualities or conditions and the Buddhist system which denies the reality of an eternal matter and reduces reality to mere motion without any background of a stuff.

But here begins the capital divergence between both systems. Bergson compares our cognitive apparatus with a cinematograph[5] which reconstitutes a movement out of momentary stabilized snapshots.[6] This is exactly the Buddhist view. He quotes the opinion of Descartes that existence is continuous new creation.[7] He also quotes the paralogism of Zeno who maintained that «a flying arrow is

---

1 Ibid., p. 312.

2 Ibid., p. 291; and p. 302— «however strange our assertion may seem there is more... in the idea of an object conceived as „not existing", than in the idea of this same object conceived as „existing"». Bergson, p. 290, reproaches philosophers «to have paid little attention to the idea of the nought», but this by no means refers to Indian philosophers. Some Hegelians also thought that the Nothing is more than the Something; cp. Trendelenburg, Log. Untersuch I. 113.

3 Cp. above, p. 95.

4 Cp. especially his lectures on «La perception du changement».

5 Ibid., p. 322 ff.

6 Ibid., p. 322, 358.

7 Ibid., p. 24; cp. above p. 107, n. 9.

motionless, for it cannot have time to move, that is, to occupy at least two successive positions, unless at least two moments are allowed it».[1] Is it not just the same as Vasubandhu telling us that there is no motion, because (in the next moment) the thing is no more? [2] Or Šāntirakṣita telling that there is in the second moment not the slightest bit left of what existed the moment before?[3] But this instantaneousness, according to Bergson, is an artificial construction of our thought. He thinks that every attempt to «reconstitute change out of states» is doomed, because «the proposition that movement is made out of immobilities is absurd».[4] However the Buddhist, we have seen, when challenged to explain the construction of motion out of immobility, points to mathematical astronomy which also constructs the continuity of motion out of an infinite number of immobilities.[5] Our cognitive apparatus is not only a cinematograph, it also is a natural mathematician. The senses, indeed, even if continuity be admitted, can pluck out only instantaneous sensations, and it is the business of the intellect to reconstitute their continuity. Bergson thinks, that if the arrow leaves the point A to fall down in the point B, its movement AB is simple and indecomposable», a single movement is, for him, «entirely a movement between two stops».[6] But for the Buddhists there are no stops at all other than in imagination, the universal motion never stops, what is called a stop in common life is but a moment of change, the so called «production of a dissimilar moment».[7] In short, duration for the Buddhist is a construction, real are the instantaneous sensations, for Bergson, on the contrary, real is duration, the moments are artificial cuts in it.[8]

---

1 Ibid., 325.

2 AK., IV. 1.

3 TS., p. 173.27., cp. TSP., p. 183.12.

4 Op. cit., p. 325.

5 Cp. above, p. 106.

6 Op. cit., p. 326.

7 *vijātīya-kṣaṇa-utpāda*.

8 In order to complete the comparison in this point we ought to have considered the Bergsonian Intuition of the artist with the Buddhist theory of an intelligible, non-sensuous, mystic Intuition of the Saint, but this is a vast subject which deserves separate treatment.

CHAPTER II.

CAUSATION

(PRATĪTYA-SAMUTPĀDA).

§ 1. CAUSATION AS FUNCTIONAL DEPENDENCE.

„Among all the jewels of Buddhist philosophy its theory of Causation is the chief jewel", says Kamalaśīla.[1] It is marked by the name of Dependent Origination or, more precisely, «Combined Dependent Origination». This term means that every point-instant of reality arises in dependence upon a combination of point-instants to which it necessarily succeeds, it arises in functional dependence upon «a totality of causes and conditions» which are its immediate antecedents. In the preceding chapter the theory of Instantaneous Being was characterized as the foundation, upon which the whole of the Buddhist system is built. The theory of Dependent Origination is but another aspect of it. Reality, as ultimate reality, reduces to point-instants of efficiency, and these point-instants arise in functional dependence upon other point-instants which are their causes. They arise, or exist, only so far as they are efficient, that is to say, so far they themselves are causes. Whatsoever exists is a cause, cause and existence are synonyms.[2] An ancient text delivers itself on this subject in the following famous words — «All (real) forces are instantaneous. (But) how can a thing which has (absolutely) no duration, (nevertheless have the time) to produce something? (This is because what we call) «existence» is nothing but efficiency, and it is this very efficiency which is called a creative cause»[3]. Just as real existence is only a point-instant, just so a real cause is only this same point-instant. In other words, existence is dynamic, not static, and it is composed of a sequence of point-instants which are interdependent, i. e., which are causes.

Thus the Buddhist theory of Causation is a direct consequence of the theory of Universal Momentariness. A thing cannot be produced by another thing or by a personal will, because other things or persons are momentary existencies. They have no time to produce anything.

---

1 TSP., p. 10. 19.

2 *yā bhūtiḥ saiva kriyā*, an often quoted dictum.

3 TSP., p. 11. 5, the stanza is there ascribed to Buddha himself.

Not even two moments of duration are allowed them. Just as there is no real motion, because there is no duration, just so there can be no real production, because time is needed for that production. The realistic idea of motion, as has been pointed out, implies «a connection of contradictory opposed predicates, for instance, the being and not being of one and the same thing in one and the same place».[1] The realistic idea of causation, likewise, implies the simultaneous existence of two things of which the one operates or «works» in producing the other. Cause and effect must exist simultaneously, during some time at least, in order that the action of the one upon the other should take place. According to the realist the potter and the pot exist simultaneously. But for the Buddhist the potter is only a series of point-instants. One of them is followed by the first moment of the series called a pot. The run of the world-process is impersonal. There are no enduring Ego's who could «work». Therefore the cause can exist no more when the effect is produced. The effect follows upon the cause, but it is not produced by it. It springs up, so to speak, out of nothing,[2] because a simultaneous existence of cause and effect is impossible.

The Vaibhāṣikas[3] among the Buddhists admit the possibility of simultaneous causation, when two or more coexisting things are mutually the causes of, i. e., dependent on, one another. But this evidently is a misunderstanding, because of the following dilemma.[4] Does the one of the simultaneously existing things produce the other when it is itself already produced or before that? It clearly cannot produce it before having been produced itself. But if it is produced itself, the other thing, being simultaneous, is also produced, it does not need any second production. Efficient causation becomes impossible. Simultaneous causation is only possible if cause and effect are static and their causation is imagined as going on in an anthropomorphic way;[5] for instance, the pot can then exist simultaneously with the potter. But the cause does not seize the effect with a pincer,[6] and does not pull it into existence. Neither does the effect spring up into existence out of

---

1 CPR., of Time, § 5 (2 ed.), cp. above p. 86.

2 *abhūtvā bhavati.*

3 TSP., p. 175. 24. There are the *sahabhū-hetu* and *samprayukta-hetu*, cp. CC p. 30 and 106.

4 Ibid., p. 176. 1.

5 Ibid., p. 176. 6.

6 Ibid., p. 176. 12.

a tight embracement by its cause, just as a girl escaping to the tight embracement of her lover.[1] Neither the cause nor the effect really do any work, they are «forceless», «out of work», «unemployed».[2] If we say that a cause «produces» something, it is only an inadequate conventional[3] expression, a metaphor.[4] We ought to have said: «the result arises in functional dependence upon such and such a thing».[5] Since the result springs up immediately after the existence of the cause, there is between them no interval, during which some «work» could be done. There is no operating of the cause, this operating produces nothing.[6] The mere existence of the cause constitutes its work.[7] If we therefore ask, what is it then that is called the «operation» of a cause producing its effect, and what is it that is called the «dependence» of the effect upon its cause, the answer will be the following one: we call dependence of the effect upon its cause the fact that it always follows upon the presence of that cause and we call operation of the cause the fact that the cause always precedes its effect.[8] The cause is the thing itself, the bare thing, the thing cut loose of every extension, of every additional working force.[9]

§ 2. The formulas of causation.

There are three formulas disclosing the meaning of the term «Dependent Origination». The first is expressed in the words «this, being, that appears».[10] The second says — «there is no real production there is only interdependence».[11] The third says — «all elements are forceless».[12] The first and more general formula means that under such and such conditions the result appears, with a change of conditions

---

1 Ibid., p. 176. 13.

2 *nirvyapāram eva,* ibid.

3 *sanketa.*

4 *upalakṣaṇam.*

5 *tat tad āśritya utpadyate,* ibid., p. 176. 24.

6 *akiṃcit-kara eva vyāpāraḥ,* ibid., p. 177. 3.

7 *sattāiva vyāpṛtih,* TS., 177. 2.

8 TSP., p. 177, 11.

9 Ibid., p. 177. 3 — *vastu-mātram vilakṣaṇa-vyāpāra-rahitam hetuḥ,* ibid., p. 177. 23.

10 *asmin sati idam bhavati.* cp. CC., p. 28. ff.

11 *pratītya tat samutpannam notpannam tat svabhāvataḥ.*

12 *nirvyāparāh (akiṃcit-karāḥ) sarve dharmāḥ.*

there is a change in the result.[1] The full meaning and all the implications of these formulas disclose themselves when we consider that they are intended to repudiate and replace other theories which existed at the time in India and which Buddhism was obliged to fight. There were the theories of the Sānkhya school, of the Realists and of the Materialists. According to the Sānkhya school, as already mentioned, there is no real causation at all, no causation in the sense of new production, no «creative»[2] causation. The result is but another manifestation of the same stuff. The so called production is no production at all, because the result is identical, i. e., existentially identical, with its causes; it is a production out of one's own Self.[3] The Realists, on the other hand, consider every object as a separate whole,[4] a whole which is an additional unity to the parts out of which it is composed. When causation operates, this whole receives an increment,[5] produces an outgrowth, a new whole is produced. Between the two wholes there is a bridge, the fact of Inherence,[6] a link which again is a separate unity. Every case of causation is therefore not a causation out of its own Self, but a causation *ex alio*, out of another Self.[7] A third theory admitted haphazard production[8] and denied all strict causal laws. To these three theories the Buddhist answer is: «not from one's own Self, not from another Self, not at haphazard are the things produced. In reality they are not produced at all, they arise in functional dependence upon their causes».[9] There is no causation in the sense of one eternal stuff changing its forms in a process of evolution, because there is no such stuff at all, this stuff is a fiction. There is also no causation in the sense of one substance suddenly bursting into another one. Neither is there haphazard origination. Every origination obeys to strict causal laws. It is not a form of any abiding stuff, of any *sub*-stance, it is an evanescent flash of energy, but it appears in accordance with strict causal laws.

---

[1] *tad-bhāva-bhāvitva, tad-vikāra-vikāritva.*

[2] *ārambha.*

[3] *svata utpādaḥ.*

[4] *avayavin.*

[5] *atiśaya-ādhāna.*

[6] *samavāya.*

[7] *parata-utpādaḥ.*

[8] *adhītya-samutpāda = yadṛcchā-vāda.*

[9] *na svato, na parato, nāpy ahetutaḥ, pratītya tat samutpannam, notpannam tat svabhāvataḥ.*

It is clear that this theory of causation is a direct consequence of the No-Substance theory,[1] a theory which admits no duration and no extention as ultimate realities, but only a continual and compact flow of evanescent elements, these elements appearing not at haphazard, but according to laws of causation.[2]

The problem of a psycho-physical parallelism which led in the Sānkhya system to the establishment of two substances only, a Matter including all mental phenomena *minus* consciousness itself and a pure Consciousness separated from Matter by an abyss — this problem was very easily solved in Buddhism. Consciousness is a function of such and such facts. Being given a moment of attention, a patch of colour and the sense of vision, visual consciousness appears.[3] This interdependence is obvious, because if a change supervenes in one of the causes, a change in the result follows; if the eye is affected or destroyed, the visual consciousness changes or disappears.

The very much discussed question, in India as well as in Europe, whether light can be produced by darkness, whether the day is the effect of the preceding night, is very naturally solved on the Buddhist theory of causation: the last moment of the series called night is followed by the first moment of the series called day. Every moment is the product of the «totality» of its antecedents, it is always different from the preceding moment, but, from the empirical point of view, it can be both, either similar or dissimilar. The moments of the sprout are dissimilar to the moments of the seed. Experience shows that dissimilar causation is as possible as the similar one.[4] It is a limitation of our

---

1 *anātma-vāda.*

2 A mediaeval author thus summarizes the four main theories of Causation in a celebrated stanza (Sarvajñātamuni, in his Sankṣepa-šarīraka, 1. 4)—

ārambha-vādaḥ Kaṇabhakṣa-pakṣaḥ,
sanghāta-vādas tu Bhadanta-pakṣaḥ,
Sānkhyādi-pakṣaḥ pariṇāma-vādo
Vivarta-vādas tu Vedānta-pakṣaḥ;

which may be rendered thus:

Creative Evolution is the Realist's contention.
The Buddhist answers, «t'is a mass (of moments)»,
« One ever changing stuff», rejoins the Sānkhya,
Vedānta says: Illusion!

3 *cakṣuḥ pratītya rūpam ca cakṣur-vijñānam utpadyate.*

4 *vijatīyād apy utpatti-darśānāt.* Tipp., p. 30. 18.

empirical cognition[1] that we do not perceive the distinctness of «similar» moments[2] and assume that they represent substance and duration.[3]

Thus it cannot be doubted that we have in Buddhism a very sharply expressed theory of causation in the sense of Functional Interdependence.

§ 3. Causation and reality identical.

Thus it is that, according to the Buddhists, reality is dynamic, there are no static things at all. «What we call existence, they are never tired to repeat, is always an action».[4] «Existence is work» — says Šāntirakṣita. Action and reality are convertible terms. «Causation is kinetic».[5] It is an anthropomorphic illusion to suppose that a thing can exist only, exist placidly, exist without acting, and then, as it were, suddenly rise and produce an action. Whatsoever exists is always acting.

The conclusion that whatsoever really exists is a cause, is urged upon the Buddhist by his definition of existence quoted above. Existence, real existence, is nothing but efficiency.[6] Consequently what is non-efficient, or what is a non-cause, does not exist. «A non-cause, says Uddyotakara,[7] addressing himself to the Buddhist, is double, it is for you either something non-existing or something changeless». Kamalašīla[8] corrects this statement of Uddyotakara and accuses him of not sufficiently knowing the theory of his adversaries, «because, says he, those Buddhists who are students of logic[9] maintain that a non-cause is necessarily a non-reality».[10] This

---

1 *ajñādivad-arvag-dṛšaḥ*. NK., p. 133. 5.

2 *sadṛša-parāpara-utpatti-vilabdha-buddhayaḥ* (*na labdha-buddhayaḥ*), ibid.

3 To save the principle of «homogeneous causation» (*sajātīya-ārambha*), the schools of Vaišeṣika and Sānkhya, as well as the medical schools, in order to explain the formation of new qualities in chemical compounds, have devised very complicated and subtle theories. A very illuminating account of them is given by B. N. Seal, op. cit.

4 *sattaiva vyāpṛtiḥ*, TS., p. 177. 2.

5 *calaḥ . . pratītya-samutpādaḥ*, ibid., p. 1.

6 *artha-kriyā-kāritvam* = *paramārtha-sat*, NBT., I. 14—15.

7 NV., p. 416.

8 TSP., p. 140. 7.

9 *nyāya-vādino Bauddhāḥ*, ibid.

10 *akāraṇam asad eva*, ibid.

means that to be real is nothing but to be a cause, whatsoever exists is necessarily a cause. This discussion between the Realists and the Buddhists refers to the problem of the reality of space, whether it be an empty space or a *plenum*, a space filled up by the cosmical ether. The early Buddhists, those that were not students of logic, assumed an empty space[1] which nevertheless was for them an objective reality, an element, a *dharma*, an unchanging and eternal reality, similar to their unchanging and eternal Nirvāṇa. The realists filled this space with an eternal motionless and penetrable substance, the cosmical ether.[2] The later Buddhists, those that studied logic, discarded the reality of such an unchanging motionless and eternal stuff, on the score that what does never change, and does not move, does not exist; existence is change.

In this instance as in many others the historian of philosophy will, I believe, find it noteworthy that the Buddhists went through a course of argumentation that offers some analogy to modern physics.

§ 4. Two kinds of causality.

However, there are two different realities, a direct one and an indirect one. The one is ultimate and pure, — that is the reality of the point-instant. The other is a reality attached to that point-instant, it is mixed with an image artificially constructed by the faculty of our productive imagination. That is the reality of the empirical object. Consequently there are also two different causalities, the ultimate one and the empirical one. The one is the efficiency of the point-instant, the other is the efficiency of the empirical object attached to that point-instant. And just as we have pointed to a seeming contradiction between the two assertions that «reality is kinetic» and that «motion is impossible», just so are we faced by another contradiction between the two assertions that «every point of reality is efficient» and that «efficiency is impossible». Indeed, as has been stated above, all elements of reality are «inactive»,[3] because being momentary they have not the time to do anything. The solution of the contradiction lies in the fact that there is no separate efficiency, no efficiency in superaddition to existence, existence itself is nothing but causal

---

[1] AK., I. 5.

[2] *ākāśo nityaś ca akriyaś ca.*

[3] *nirvyāpāra.*

efficacy,[1] the cause and the thing are different views taken of one and the same reality. «The relation of an agent to the instrument and (to the object of his action) is not ultimately real, says Kamalašila,[2] because all real elements are momentary and cannot work at all». If we identify reality and causal efficiency, we can say that every reality is at the same time a cause. If we separate them, we must say that efficiency is impossible, because it involves us into a proposition with two contradictorily opposed predicates, since one thing then must exist at two different times in two different places, i. e. exist and not exist in the same time and place. A jar, e. g., is for the realist a real object consisting of parts, having extension and duration up to the moment when it is broken by the stroke of a hammer. There is causation between the clump of clay and the jar, between the jar and the potsherds, between the potter and the jar, between the hammer and the potsherds. But for the Buddhist a thing, i. e., a moment, which has vanished a long time since, cannot be the cause, cannot produce directly, a thing which will appear a long time hence. «An enduring object, says the Buddhist,[3] which should represent a unity (so compact that) its members would cease to be different moments owing to a unity of duration, (such a compact unity) is unthinkable as a producer of an effect». To this an objector remarks[4] that we cannot maintain that the efficiency of an object changes in every moment of its existence. Experience shows that a series of moments can have just the same efficiency. Otherwise, if the first moment of a blue patch would produce the sensation of blue, the following moments could not do it, they necessarily would produce different sensations. The image of the blue colour would not arise at all, if different moments could not possess together one and the same efficiency. The answer is to the effect that just as in every moment of the blue object there is an imperceptible change, just so there is a constant change in every moment of sensation and in every moment of the image. It is only by neglecting that difference that a seemingly uniform object and a seemingly uniform image are produced.[5]

---

1 *sattaiva vyāpṛtiḥ.*

2 TSP., p. 399. 12. — *na pāramārthikaḥ kartṛ-kāraṇādi-bhāvo'sti, kṣaṇikatvena nirvyāpāratvāt sarva-dharmāṇām.*

3 NK., p. 240, Vācaspati quotes here a Yogācāra Buddhist.

4 Ibid.

5 Ibid.

There are thus two causalities, the one real ultimately, the other real contingently or empirically, just as there are two realities, the transcendental reality of an instant and the empirical reality of a thing of limited duration. Dharmottara,[1] answering an objector who remarks that if causation is only imagined, it cannot be real, says, «Yes, but although serial existences, (i. e. objects having duration) are not realities, their members,[2] the point-instants, are ***the reality...***»[3] «When an effect is produced, we do not really experience causation itself as a sensible fact (separately from the effect). But the existence of a real effect presupposes the existence of a real cause, therefore (indirectly) the relation of causality is also necessarily a real one»,[4] i. e., empirical causality is contingently real.

§ 5. Plurality of causes.

A further feature of the Buddhist theory of causation consists in the contention that a thing never produces anything alone. It is followed by a result only if it combines with other elements which are therefore called co-factors.[5] Therefore the term «Dependent Origination» becomes synonymous with the term «Combined Origination».[6] This contention is expressed in the following formula,

> «Nothing single comes from single,
> Nor a manifold from single»,

or with a slight modification,

> «Nothing single comes from single,
> From a totality everything arises».[7]

This totality is composed of causes and conditions and different classifications of them have been attempted almost in every Buddhist school.

For the Realists causation consists in the succession of two static things. In this sense causation is for them a one-to-one relation,

---

[1] NBT., p. 69. 1 ff.

[2] *santāninas.*

[3] *vastu-bhūta.*

[4] Ibid., p. 69. 11.

[5] *saṃskāra.*

[6] *saṃskṛtatvam = pratītya-samutpannatvam = sambhūya-kāritva = dharmatā*

[7] *na kiṃcid ekam ekasmāt, nāpy ekasmād anekam*, or *na kiṃcid ekam ekasmā samagryāḥ sarva-sampatteḥ*, passim.

one unity produces the other. The Buddhist objects that a real unity, as experience shows, can never produce another unity. A single atom, for instance, is not «capable» of producing anything else than its following moment. A number of units is always needed in order that a «capacity» should be engendered. The realist does not deny that the seed is only the «matter», a material, i. e., passive cause.[1] There are acting or efficient, causes, whose «help»[2] or efficiency is needed, in order really to produce the effect. The Buddhist answers that if a cause is passive non-efficient, doing nothing,[3] it can safely be neglected. The other causes which alone are efficient should then be capable to produce the effect alone.[4] Thus moisture, heat, soil etc. should produce the sprout without the seed, since the seed is doing nothing.

The point of the Buddhist is that the whole conception of causality by the realist is anthropomorphic. Just as a potter takes a clump of clay and transforms it into a pot, just so are the causes of a sprout working. In order to be efficient they help one another.[5] This help is again imagined on the anthropomorphic pattern. Just as when a great weight does not yeild to the efforts of a number of persons, help is called in and the weight is then moved, —just so is it with the cooperating causes, they produce the effect when sufficient help is given them.[6] The material cause «takes them up in itself».[7] The efficient causes introduce themselves into the middle of the material cause, they destroy or annihilate the latter, and out of the material left they «create»[8] a new thing, just as masons pull down on old house and construct a new one out of the old bricks.

According to the Buddhist, there is no destruction of one thing and no creation of another thing, no influx of one substance into the other, no anthropomorphic mutual help between the causes. There is a constant, uninterrupted, infinitely graduated change. A result can indeed be compared with something produced by human cooperation. It is then called by the Buddhist «anthropomorphic» result.[9] But

---

1 *samavāyi-kāraṇa.*

2 *upakāra = kiṃcit-karatva.*

3 *akiṃcit-kara = anupakārin.*

4 SDS., p. 23.

5 *paraspara-upakārin.*

6 AK, II. 56.

7 *sahakāri-samavadhāna.*

8 *ārabbyate kiṃcid nūtanam.*

9 *puruṣa-kāra-phalam = puruṣeṇa iva kṛtam.*

instead of explaining every causation as a process resembling human cooperation, he regards even this human cooperation as a kind of impersonal process. All cooperating causes are convergent streems of efficient moments. They are called «creeping» causes[1] since there movement is a *staccato* movement. In their meeting-point[2] a new series begins. Material, static and passive causes do not exist at all. Cause, efficiency or *moment* are but different names for the same thing. When the soil, moisture heat and seed series of moments unite, their last moments are followed by the first moment of the sprout. Buddhist causality is thus a many-one relation. It receives the name of a «one-result-production» theory[3] and is contrasted with the «mutual-help», or «mutual-influence»[4] theory of the Realists.

Dharmottara[5] says: «Cooperation can be of a double kind. It either is (real) mutual influence or it is the production of one result (without real mutual influence). (In Buddhism), since all things are only moments, the things cannot have any additional outgrowth. Therefore cooperation must be understood as one (momentary) result produced by, (i. e., succeeding to, several simultaneous moments)». That is to say, cooperation which is indispensable in every act of causation must be understood as a many-one relation.

§ 6. Infinity of causes.

If causality is a many-one relation, the question arises whether these «many» are calculable, whether all the causes and conditions of a given event can be sufficiently known in order to make that event predictable. The answer is to the negative. As soon as we intend to know all the variety of causes and conditions influencing, directly or indirectly, a given event, causation appears so complicated that it practically becomes uncognizable. No one short of an Omniscient Being could cognize the infinite variety of all circumstances that can influence the production of an event. Vasubandhu says (quoting Rāhula):

---

1 *upasarpaṇa-pratyaya*, cp. NK., p. 135.

2 *sahakāri-melana.*

3 *eka-kārya-kāritva*, or *eka-kriyā-kāritva.*

4 *paraspara-upakāritva*; *upakārin* = *kiṃcit-kārin.*

5 NBT., p. 10. 11, transl. p. 26.

«Every variety of cause
Which brings about the glittering shine
In a single eye of a peacocks tail
Is not accessible to our knowledge.
The Omniscient knows them all».[1]

Nevertheless some fairly dependent regularities of sequence can be cognized by us in different lines of causation. Thus two sets of four main «conditions» and of «six causes» with «four kinds of result» have been established in the school of the Sarvāstivādins.[2] Among them there is a cause which is characterized as «cause in general»,[3] a cause which cannot be distinguished by a specific name, because it embraces all the active as well as all the passive (i. e., comparatively passive) circumstances conditioning a given event. The passive circumstances are not absolutely passive, they are also active in a way, viz, they do not interfere with the event, although they could do it. Their presence is a constant menace to it. Vasubandhu[4] gives a very characteristic example of what a passive cause is.[5] The villagers come to their chief and in making their obeisance they say: «Owing to you, Sir, we are happy». The chief has done nothing positive for the happiness of the villagers, but he has not oppressed them, although he could have done it, therefore he is the indirect cause of their happiness. Thus it is that every real circumstance in the environment of an event, if it does not interfere with its production, becomes its cause. An unreal thing, as e. g., a lotus in the sky, could not have any influence. But a real thing, existing at the moment preceding the production of the thing has always some, direct or indirect, near or remote, influence on it. Therefore the definition of a «cause in general» is the following one. «What is a cause in general?», asks Vasubandhu,[6] and answers with all the expressive force of the scientifical sanscrit style — «With the single exception of one's own self, all the elements (of the universe) are the general cause of an

---

[1] AK. IX, cp. my Soul Theory, p. 940.

[2] Cp. below, p. 138.

[3] *kāraṇa-hetur viśeṣa-saṃjñayā nocyate, sāmānyam hetu-bhāvam* (*apekṣya*) *sa kāraṇahetuḥ* (Yašomitra).

[4] AKB., ad. II. 50.

[5] Cp. Sigwart, op. cit., II. 162—«auch die Ruhe erscheint jetzt als Ausfluss derselben Kräfte, denen die Veränderung entspricht, sie ist in Bedingungen gegründet, welche keiner einzelnen Kraft eine Action gestatten».

[6] *svam vihāya sarve dharmāḥ-svato'nye kārana-hetuḥ* cp. AK., II. 50.

event». That is to say, there is no *causa sui*, but with that single exception all the elements of the Universe are the general cause of an event. As soon as the early Buddhists began to analyse existence into an infinity of discrete point-instants, they called them interrelated or cooperating elements.[1] The idea of their mutual interdependence was alive to them so as to convert the term «all» into a kind of technical term.[2] «All» means all the elements as classified under three different headings of «groups», of «bases of cognition», and of or «component parts of an individual life».[3] In the theory of causation this idea of the universe as an interconnected whole of discrete elements reappears. It reappears again in the idea of a «totality»[4] of causes and conditions. The actual presence of an event is a garantee that the totality of its causes and conditions is present. The effect itself, indeed, is nothing but the presence of the totality of its causes. If the seed and the necessary quanta of air, soil, heat and moisture are present in it, all other elements not interfering, the sprout is already there. The effect is nothing over and above the presence of the totality of its causes.[5] In this totality the «general cause» is included. That means that nothing short of the condition of the universe at a given moment is the ultimate cause of the event which appears at that moment, or that there is a constant relation between the state of the universe at any instant and the change which is produced in any part of the universe at that instant.[6]

Therefore it is that the inference of the existence of the cause when an event takes place is much safer than the inference from the existence of the cause to the possible advent of its result. The accomplishment of the result can always be jeopardized by some unpredictable event.[7]

§ 7. Causality and Free Will.

In connection with the theory of Causation the Buddhist attitude relating the great question of Liberty and Necessity must be breefly

---

1 *saṃskāra = saṃskṛta-dharma.*

2 CC., p. 5 and 95.

3 *sarvam = skandha-āyatana-dhātavaḥ.*

4 *hetu-kāraṇa-sāmagrī.*

5 Cp. Tātp., p. 80.5—*sahakāri-sākalyam na prāpter atiricyate.*

6 Cp. B. Russel. On the Notion of Cause, in Mysticism, p. 195.

7 Cp. the concluding passage of the second chapter of the NBT.

indicated. According to a tradition which we have no reason to disbelieve, the Special Theory of Causation[1] has been established by Buddha himself in defense of Free Will and against a theory of wholesale Determinism. This problem, which has always perplexed almost all the human race, was also vehemently discussed at the time of Buddha. He had singled out for special animadversion the doctrine of one of his comtemporaries, Gosāla Maskariputra, who preached an extreme determinism and denied absolutely all free will and all moral responsibility. According to him all things are inalterably fixed and nothing can be changed.[2] Everything depends on fate, environment and nature. He denied all moral duty and in his personal behaviour endulged in incontinence. Buddha stigmatized him as the «bad man» who like a fisherman was catching men only to destroy them. He rejected his philosophy as the most pernicious system. «Tbere is free action, he declared, there is retribution», «I maintain the doctrine of free actions».[3]

But on the other hand we are confronted by the statement that nothing arises without a cause, everything is «dependently originating». Vasubandhu, the second Buddha, categorically denies free will. «Actions, says he, are either of the body, or of speech or of the mind. The two first classes, those of the body and of speech, wholly depend upon the mind, and the mind wholly depends upon unexorable causes and conditions». We are thus at once landed in a full contradiction.

As against determinism the Buddhists maintain free will and responsibility. As against liberty they maintain the strictest necessity of causal laws. Buddha is represented in tradition as maintaining the paradoxical thesis that there is Liberty, because there is Necessity, viz, necessity of retribution which reposes on Causality.

The solution of the puzzle seems to lie in a difference of the conception of Liberty. For the Buddhist empirical existence is a state of Bondage comparable to a prison. Life by its own principle of kinetic reality is constantly moving towards an issue[4] in Final Deliverance. It is this movement which the Buddhist imagines as subject to strict causal laws. Movement or life is for him a process

1 The twelve membered *pratītya-samutpāda*.
2 Cp. Hoernle, art. Ajīvaka in ERE., cp. V. C. Law, Gleanings.
3 «*aham kriyāvādī*», cp. ibid.
4 *niḥsaraṇa* = *mokṣa*.

characterized in all its details by the strictest necessity, but it is a necessary movement towards a necessary final aim. Causality does not differ here from finality. For Gosāla necessity evidently means static necessity, a changeless reality, no Bondage and no Final Deliverance. For the Buddhist, on the contrary, necessity is a constant change, a running necessity, steering unavoidably to a definite aim. Thus interpreted the words of Vasubandhu are not in conflict with the declaration ascribed to Buddha.

But the Buddhists were always obliged to defend themselves against the stricture that there is in their outlook no place neither for Bondage nor for Deliverance, since the Ego, the Agent who could be bound up and then delivered does not exist at all. This the Buddhist concedes, but he maintains that the passing stream of events is the only Agent[1] which is required. «There is (free) action, there is retribution, says Buddha, but I see no Agent which passes out of one set of momentary elements into another one, except the Consecution of these elements.[2] This Consecution has it, that being given such and such points, such other ones will necessarily appear».

There is indeed not a single moment in the mental stream constituting the run of the individual's volitions which would appear at haphazard[3] without being strictly conditioned, i. e., «dependently originating». But volition which precedes every bodily action can be either strong or feeble. If it is feeble the action is *quasi*-automatical. It then will have no consequence, it will entail neither reward nor punishment. Such are our usual animal functions or our usual occupations.[4] But if the volition is strong, the following action will have an outspoken moral character, it will be either a virtuous deed or a crime. Such actions will be necessarily followed by retribution,

---

1 *kārakas tu nopalabhyate ya imān skandhān vijahāty anyāṃś ca skandhān upādatte*, cp. TSP., p. 11. 13.

2 *anyatra dharma-sanketam*, «other than the theory of dharmas».

3 In Sānkhya karma is explained materialistically, as consisting in a special collocation of minutest infra-atomic particles or material forces making the action either good or bad. In Hīnayāna the will *(centanā)* is a mental *(citta-samprayukta)* element *(dharma)* or force *(saṃskāra)* representing a stream of momentary flashes, every moment of which is strictly conditioned by the sum total *(sāmagrī)* or preceding moments. Apparent freedom consists in our ignorance of all the conditions of a given action. Garbe thinks that the Sānkhya doctrine contains a contradiction, but it probably must be explained just as the Buddhist one. Determinism means that it is impossible to escape retribution.

4 *airyapathika*.

either by reward or punishment. The law according to which a moral, resp. immoral, deed must necessarily have its fruition, is the law of *karma*.

If something happens as a consequence of former deeds,[1] it is not *karma*, that is to say, it will have no further consequence, it is *quasi*-automatical. In order to have a consequence the action must be free,[2] i. e., it must be produced by a strong effort of the will.[3]

The law of *karma* has been revealed by Buddha. It cannot be proved experimentally. It is transcendental.[4] But when critically examined it will be found to contain no contradiction and therefore it can be believed even by critical minds. The so called Free Will is nothing, but a Strong Will and the law of *karma*, far from being in conflict with causality, is only a special case of that causality.

Thus it is that the Buddhist Free Will is a freedom inside the limits of Necessity. It is a freedom to move without transgressing the boundaries of causation, a freedom inside the Prison of Dependent Origination. However this prison has an issue. Another postulate of Buddhism, besides the law of *karma*, seems to be the firm conviction that the sum-total of good deeds prevails over the sum-total of bad deeds. The evolution of the world process is an evolution of moral progress. When all good deeds will have brought their fruition, Final Deliverance will be attained in Nirvāṇa. Causation is then extinct and the Absolute is reached. Nāgārjuna says — «having regard to causes and conditions (to which all phenomena are subjected, we call this world) phenomenal. This same world, when causes and conditions are disregarded, (the world *sub specie aeternitatis*) is called the Absolute.»[5]

§ 8. The four meanings of Dependent Origination.

In all the phases of its historical development Buddhism remained faithful to its theory of Causation. But successive generations, in the

---

1 *vipāka* = *karma-phala*.

2 *savipāka* = *karma*.

3 Cp. AKB. ad II. 10 ff. Macrocosmically regarded, since we cannot know all causes and conditions of a given action, it seems as though it were free, but every single moment of the will *(cetanā)*, microcosmically regarded, cannot but appear in strict conformity to the totality of all preceding moments. Apparent freedom consists in our ignorance of all the minutest influences.

4 Cp. above, p. 77.

5 Cp. my Nirvāṇa, p. 48. On the difficult problem of vindicating the Moral Law in a phenomenal world. cp. ibid., p. 127 ff.

measure in which they strove to penetrate deeper into the idea of Interdependent Elements, arrived at different interpretations of it. We accordingly can distinguish between four main shapes of the theory of Dependent Origination, two of them belonging to the Hīnayāna and agreeing with its extreme Pluralism in philosophy, while the two others belong to the Mahāyāna and agree with its extreme Monism.

In early Buddhism there are two different theories of Interdependence, a special one and a general one. The generalized theory is a later development of the special one. That part of the literature of early Buddhism which goes under the name of the Discourses of the Buddha mentions only the special theory, the general theory is contained in the philosophic treatises which are appended to it and are of a later origin. This historical development was clear to the Buddhists themselves. Vasubandhu tells us[1] that the Discourses, because of their popular, intentional character, do not mention the general theory, although it is implied in them. Its clear statement is a creation of the doctors of the Small Vehicle, of the Abhidharmikas.[2] He accordingly treats the two aspects of the law of causation quite independently. The general laws of causation are expounded by him in the second book of his great compendium, as a conclusion to the detailed enumeration, classification and definition of all the elements of existence.[3] Having done with the explanation of all elements, it was natural for him to conclude by explaining their interdependence according to different lines of causation. But the special law of Dependent Origination, which has a special, mainly moral, bearing, is treated by him in the third book, where the different spheres of existence are described. The individual lives or, more precisely, the assemblages of elements, form themselves in these spheres according to the merit or demerit, acquired in former lives, and the special law of moral causation is developed in this context. Both doctrines, the general one and the special one, must be distinguished, and were distinguished even in the later Mahāyāna,[4] although the problem was tackled there from another side. However they were also often confounded, in olden as well as in more modern times. Anuruddha testifies that many masters of the doctrine (and Buddhaghoṣa seems to be in the number) have

---

1 AK., III. 25, cp. O. Rosenberg, Problems, p. 223, and my CC., p. 29.

2 Ibid.

3 AK., III.

4 Cp. my Nirvāṇa, p. 134 ff.

mixed them up, as though they were the same theory,[1] or the one a part of the other.

The special theory aims at explaining the notorious and puzzling fact that Buddhism assumes a moral law, but no subject of this law. There are good deeds and a reward for them, there are bad deeds and punishments. There is a state of Bondage and a state of Final Deliverance. But there is no one who commits these deeds, no one who abides in a state of Bondage and no one who enters into Final Deliverance; no Soul, no Ego, no Personality. There are only groups of separate elements, physical and mental, which are interrelated, which form themselves and which unform themselves. They are subject to a Moral Law, the law of a progressive development towards Final Eternal Quiescence. But a personal agent, an abiding spiritual principle, the subject of the moral law, is not at all necessary. «I declare, said Buddha, that there are voluntary deeds and there is a reward for them, but the perpetrator of these deeds does not exist at all.

---

1 Abhidhammatthasaṃgaho, VIII. 3. (D. Kosambi's ed.). Anuruddha evidently reproves those *ācāriyas* who have, like Buddhaghoṣa in the Visuddhimaggo, mixed up the *paticca-samuppāda-nayo* with the *paṭṭhāna-nayo.* Here the term *pratītya-samutpāda* is attached to the special theory, and the general goes under the name of *paṭṭhāna.* It is the reverse with Nāgārjuna who calls the general theory by the name of *pratītya-samutpāda* and indicates the special one by the name of the 12 *nidānas.* Šāntirakṣita (kar 544) apparently understands both theories by the term of *pratītya-samutpāda.* The SDS., p. 40 ff., basing upon some Yogācāra-sources, distinguishes between a *pratyaya-upanibandhana pr. s. utp.* in the sense of causes cooperating blindly, without any conscious agent, and a *hetu-upanibandhana pr. s. utp.* in the sense of an immutable order of causal sequence including the 12 *nidānas* of the Hīnayāna and the *dharmatā* of Mahāyāna, both theories implying also the denial of a conscious agent. The term thus implies 1) strict determinism, 2) cooperation, 3) denial of substance, 4) denial of an agent. Its synonyms are *pratītya-samutpāda = saṃskṛtatva = sambhūya-kāritva = saṃskāra-vāda = eka-kriyā-kāritva = kṣaṇa-bhanga-vāda = niḥsvabhāva-vāda = anātmavāda = pudgala-šūnyatā (Hīnayāna) = sarva-dharma-šūnyatā (Mahāyāna) = paraspara-apekṣā-vāda (Relativity).* — The opposite theory of the Vaišeṣikas is characterized by the following synonymic terms — *paraspara-upakāra-vāda = ārambha-vāda = sahakāri-samavadhāna-vāda = sthira-bhāva-vāda = asat-kārya-vāda = parata-utpāda-vāda.* The theory of the Sānkhyas is called *sat-kārya-vāda = svata-utpāda-vāda = prakṛti-vāda = pariṇāma-vāda.* The theory of the Vedāntins is called *vivarta-vāda = māyā-vāda = brahma-vāda.* The theory of the Materialists is called *adhītya-samutpāda-vāda = yadṛcchā-vāda.* The Buddhists deny the Sānkhya (*na svataḥ*), the Vaišeṣika (*na parataḥ*) and the Materialist (*nāpy ahetutaḥ*) theories. But the Mādhyamika theory can also be called *māyā-vāda.*

No one there is who assumes these elements, who is the bearer of them, who throws them off and assumes a new set of them».[1] They appear and disappear, according to the formulas, «This being, that appears». «They appear not out of one self, or out of another self, nor at haphazard, they are not really produced, they appear in interdependent apparitions».[2]

The whole of phenomenal life is represented as a wheel in twelve parts. It is conditioned, i. e., the whole series is conditioned, by the central element of our limited knowledge (1). When the element of absolute knowledge is developed, the mirage of phenomenal life vanishes and eternity is attained. In phenomenal life prenatal forces (2) produce a new life (3) which develops gradually its physical and mental constituents (4), its six senses (5), five outer and one inner sense, sensations (6) and feelings (7); a conscious life is produced in the full grown person with his desires (8), free actions (9) and occupations (10), after which comes a new life (11), a new death (12) and so on without interruption, up to the moment when the element of Ignorance which dominates the whole series is extinct, and Nirvāṇa is reached. There is no strictly logical proportion in the twelve stages into which scholasticism has framed the special theory of interdependent elements. One of them rules over the whole of the series (1), another (2) refers to a former, eight (3—10) refer to a present life and the two last (11—12) to a future life.[3] The present is attached to the former and is the source of the future, according to the laws of interdependence, without any necessity to assume an abiding principle in the shape of an eternal Soul or an Ego. Kamalašīla says:[4] «There is no contradiction at all between the denial of a real personality and the fact that former deeds engender a capacity of having a consequence», neither does it interfere with the fact that «there is not the slightest bit of reality which does survive in the next[5] moment; nothing survives, the next

---

1 TSP., p. 11. 13.

2 Cp. above, p. 133.

3 Two members of the series — *avidyā, saṃskāra* — refer to a former life, two — *jāti* and *jarā-maraṇa* to a future one, the remaining 8 members to a present life. In Mahāyāna the 12 *nidānas* are called *saṃkleša's* «great impediments» and are distinguished into three classes: three *kleša-saṃkleṣa — avidyā, tṛṣṇā, upādāna*, two] *karma-saṃkleša — saṃskāra, bhava*,— and the remaining seven members are styled *jāti-saṃkleša.*

4 TSP., p. 182. 19.

5 Ibid., p. 183. 12.

arises in mutual dependence on the former. The fact of memory is also sufficiently explained by causal laws without assuming a «store house» of former impressions. Neither are bondage and deliverance the properties of some one who is being bound up and then delivered. But the elements of ignorance, of birth and death produce the run of phenomenal life, they are called bondage; when these elements disappear in the face of an absolute knowledge, the ensuing pure consciousness is called deliverance, for it has been said «consciousness itself, polluted by passions and ignorance, is phenomenal life, that very consciousness when freed from them is called deliverance».[1]

The generalized theory of causation applies the same principles of denying the existence of any permanent element and of assuming exclusively an interdependence between separate impermanent elements to all phenomena in general, i. e., to all sense-data, to sensations, ideas and volitions. Every individual fact, every point-instant of reality is conditioned, according to this theory, by a sum total of causes and conditions; this totality can then be analysed in some special lines of causal dependence.

The different lines of such causal dependence are differently represented in the schools of the Hīnayāna. This alone could be a sufficient proof of the later origin of the doctrine. The school of the Sarvāstivādins distinguishes between **four conditions** and **six kinds of causes**. There is no hard and fast line of demarcation, at that stage of the doctrine, between what a cause and what a condition is. The list of six causes seems to be a later doctrine which came to graft itself upon the original system of four «conditions». These conditions-causes are the following ones:

1. Object-condition;[2] this cause embraces everything existing. All elements,[3] so far they can be objects of cognition, are object causes.

2. The immediately preceding and homogeneous condition;[4] it represents the immediately preceding moment in the stream of thought and is thus intended to replace the Ego or the inherent cause[5] of the Vaišeṣikas. It originally referred only to mental causation,

---

1 Ibid., p. 184.

2 *ālambana-pratyaya.*

3 *sarve dharmāḥ = chos. thams-cad (dmigs-rgyu).*

4 *samanantara-pratyaya.*

5 *samavāyi-kāraṇa.*

but later on, under the name of a «creeping cause» [1] *or causa repens*, it came to replace the *causa materialis* or the inherent cause in general.

3. The efficient, decisive or «ruling» condition,[2] as its name indicates, is the cause which settles the character of the result, e. g., the organ of vision in regard of visual sensation.

4. The «cooperating condition»,[3] such as light etc., in regard of visual sensation. With the preceding one they include together all things existing, since all elements are more or less interdependent.

The set of «six causes» is the following one:

1) The general cause;[4] it has already been explained above, it also includes all elements of existence.

2) and 3) «Simultaneous»[5] cause and «interpenetrating»[6] cause are defined as mutual causation. The second refers only to mental elements, viz, to the fact that the element of pure consciousness,[7] although a separate element, never appears alone, but always in company of other mental elements,[8] feelings, ideas and volitions. The first refers predominantly to the law according to which the fundamental elements of matter,[9] the tactile elements, although they are also assumed as separate elements, never appear singly and without the secondary elements [10] of colour etc. Both these causes are evidently intended to replace the category of inherence assumed by the Realists.

4) The «homogeneous cause» [11] with its corresponding «automatical result» [12] are intended to explain the homogeneous run of point-instants which evokes the idea of duration and stability of all objects.

5) «Moral cause» or Karma; [13] it refers to every deed having a pronounced, either good or bad, moral character. It works predominantly

---

1 *upasarpaṇa-pratyaya.*

2 *adhipati-pratyaya.*

3 *sakakāri-pratyaya.*

4 *kāraṇa-hetu.*

5 *sahabhū-hetu.*

6 *samprayukta-hetu.*

7 *vijñāna-citta.*

8 *caitta.*

9 *mahā-bhūta.*

10 *bhautika.*

11 *sabhāga-hetu.*

12 *niṣyanda-phala.*

13 *vipāka-hetu = karma.*

together with organic development or with the «cause of growth»[1] which constitutes the vanguard or the rampart, behind which the forces of merit or demerit influence the formation of life.[2]

6) Immoral or «all-powerful» cause;[3] under this name the different passions[4] and habitual ways of thought of the ordinary man are understood, which prevent him from seeing the origin and essence of empirical reality and thus prevent him from becoming a Saint.

The result can be of four different kinds, either «automatical»[5] or «anthropomorphic»,[6] or «characteristic»,[7] or «Final Deliverance».[8] The first two have already been explained, the third corresponds to our usual idea of a result, e. g., a visual sensation in regard or the organ of vision. The last is Nirvāṇa, as the final result of all life.

The Ceylonese school, as already mentioned, has mixed up the special form of the law of causation in twelve consecutive stages of a revolving life with the general law which distinguishes 21 different lines of causation. These 21 lines are easily reducible to the four and six lines of the Sarvāstivādins.

In the Mahāyāna period the doctrine of Dependent Origination is emphatically proclaimed as the central and main part of Buddhism. But its interpretation is quite different. Interdependence means here Relativity[9] and relativity means the unreality[10] of the separate elements. They are relative «as the short and the long»,[11] i. e., they are nothing by themselves. The doctrine of the twelve stages of life is declared to refer to phenomenal, unreal, life only.[12] The general theory of causation, the theory of the «four conditions», is denied likewise, as conditional and unreal.[13] But the idea of «Dependent Origination» itself which here means the idea of the Cosmos, becomes the central idea of the New Buddhism.

---

1 *upacaya-hetu.*

2 Cp. AKB., I. 37, cp. CC., p. 34.

3 *sarvatraga-hetu.*

4 *kleša.*

5 *nisyanda-phala.*

6 *puruṣakāra-phala.*

7 *adhipati-phala.*

8 *visamyoga-phala.*

9 *paraspara-apekṣatva = pratītya-samutpannatva = šūnyatā = dharmatā.*

10 *šūnyatva = svabhāva-šūnyatva.*

11 *dīrgha-hrasva-vat.*

12 Cp. my Nirvāṇa, p. 134.

13 Ibid. The doctrine of the «six causes» seems unknown to Nāgārjuna.

The meaning of the term «Dependent Origination» has changed once more in the latest, idealistic, school of Mahāyāna. It does no more refer to a motionless Cosmos the parts of which have merely an illusive reality. Dependent Origination, on the contrary, means here Motion,[1] a Cosmos which is essentially kinetic.

The contrast between the two interpretations of the principle of «Dependent Origination» in Manāyāna is clearly shown in the initial verses of the treatises of Nāgārjuna and Šāntirakṣita which can be viewed as the exponents of the ideas which prevailed in the first and in the second period of the Mahāyāna respectively. These initial verses contain, as usual, a reverential salutation to Buddha, and praise him as the creator of the doctrine of «Dependent Origination». This doctrine is at the same time shortly but pregnantly characterized. Nāgārjuna says[2] — «I salute the Buddha who has proclaimed the principle of Dependent Origination, according to which there is no plurality, no differentiation, no beginning and no end, no motion, neither hither nor thither». Šāntirakṣita says — «I salute the Buddha who has proclaimed the principle of Dependent Origination, according to which everything is kinetic, there is no God, no Matter, no Substance, no Quality, no (separate) actions, no Universals and no Inherence, but there is strict conformity between every fact and its result...»

§ 9. Some European parallels.

Although the Buddhist doctrine of causation has attracted the attention of scholars at the very outset of Buddhistic studies in Europe, its comprehension and the knowledge of its historical development have made till now but very slow progress. There is perhaps no other Buddhist doctrine which has been so utterly misunderstood and upon which such a wealth of unfounded guesses and fanciful philosophizing has been spent. We neither have any knowledge of its pre-Buddhistic sources, which are probably to be sought in Indian medical science, nor do we know much about the vicissitudes of interpretation it received in the schools of early Buddhism. Nay, although the literal translation of the Sanscrit and Pāli words which have been framed for its designation cannot be anything else than Dependent Origination, the majority

---

[1] *Calaḥ pratītya-samutpādaḥ*, TS., p. 1.

[2] For a more literal rendering cp. my Nirvāṇa, p. 69.

of scholars imagined for it every meaning, possible and impossible, except the meaning of dependent origination. The reason for this partly lies in the circumstance that it seemed highly improbable, too improbable beside sheer logical possibility, that the Indians should have had at so early a date in the history of human thought a doctrine of Causation so entirely modern, the same in principle as the one accepted in the most advanced modern sciences.

The framer of this theory in Europe S. Mach went through a course of reasoning somewhat similar to the Buddhistic one. When speculation is no more interested in the existence of an Ego, when the Ego is denied, nothing remains instead of it, said he, than the causal laws, the laws of functional interdependence, in the mathematical sense, of the separate elements of existence. Buddhism has pushed the separateness of these elements to its extreme limit, to the mathematical point-instants, but the formula of interdependence is always the same — «this being that appears».

Since the Buddhist theory of Causation is conditioned by its denial of the objective reality of the category of substance, it naturally must coincide, to a certain extent, with all those European theories which shared in the same denial. The objective reality of substance has been denied in Europe, e. g., by J. S. Mill, for whom substance is nothing but «a permanent possibility of (impermanent, i. e., momentary) sensation»; by Kant, for whom substance is but a mental Category; in our days by Bertrand Russel, for whom substances are not «permanent bits of matter», but «brief events», however possessing qualities and relations. For the Buddhist, we have seen, they are instantaneous events without qualities and relations in them. For the early Buddhists they are instantaneous flashes of specific energies, for the later Buddhists they are mathematical point-instants. There either is stability in the world or no stability, either duration or no duration. There cannot be both. A «short duration» is very simple from the empirical point of view, but from the point of view of ultimate reality it is an «unenduring duration». Things are evanescent by themselves, in their nature they can have no duration at all. This is the kind of an answer Dharmakīrti probably would have given to Mr. Russel.

Against the Kantian idea that substance is a category forced upon us by the general nature of our reason and constructed by the reason on the basis of a «manifold of sensibility» — against this the Buddhist would have probably nothing to object, since it implies the acceptance of a double reality, the ultimate reality of the things by themselves and the constructed reality (i. e., unreality) of empirical things. Empirical causation, but not the transcendental one, is a category.

The standpoint of J. S. Mill would probably have been shared, in the main, by the early Buddhists, since their moments are impermanent sense-data, sensible qualities without any substance. Stability and duration are for the Buddhist nothing but «chains of moments» following one another without intervals. The notion of a «chain of moments» corresponds very nearly to the modern notion of a «string of events». According to Mr. Russel the «string of events... is called one piece of matter»,[1] and the events are «rapid, but not instantaneous changes»,[2] they are separated by «small time like intervals».[3] «The common-sense thing, says he, is a character which I should define as the existence of a first order differential law connecting successive events along a linear route».[4] This reminds us of the Buddhist view, with that difference that the events are instantaneous and succeed without intervals or with infinitesimal intervals. If, as Kamalašīla[5] puts it, «not the slightest bit of what was found in the former moment is to be found in the next following moment», the change must be instantaneous.

The interpretation of causal laws as laws of functional interdependence, the principle «this being that becomes», we have seen, is also a direct consequence of the theory of «Instantaneous Being». Causality obtains between point-instants, not between stabilities or durations. This is likewise the opinion of Mr. Russel, although we would expect him to assert that they obtain between small pieces of stability and small bits of duration. In the doctrine of a plurality of causes, in the contention that causality is a many-one relation, and in the doctrine of the infinity of causes, the doctrine, namely, that to every particular change there is a corresponding state of the Universe of Being — in these two doctrines there is, it seems to me, an almost

---

1 Analysis of Matter, p. 247.

2 Ibid., p. 245.

3 Ibid. On p. 372 the possibility is admitted that the interval between two points of one light-ray is zero. The interval nevertheless remains for the realist «something mysterious and unaccountable», ibid., p. 375.

4 Ibid., p. 245.

5 TSP., p. 182. 12.

exact coincidence between Buddhist views and the views recently expressed by Mr. Russel.[1] The same must be said regarding the repudiation of a series of prejudices connected with the common-sense realistic idea of causation. The prejudice that causes «operate»,[2] that they «compell»[3] the result to appear, the inclination to consider a causal relation on the anthropomorphic pattern,[4] the prejudice, further, that the result must be «similar»[5] to the cause — in all these cases the coincidence is striking. On the negative side the coincidence is almost complete.

On the positive side there is all the difference which lies between a point-instant and a brief event. From the standpoint of ultimate reality there is but very little difference between a brief event and a long event, these characteristics are quite relative. But there is a great difference between duration and no duration. The point-instant is for Mr. Russel a mere «mathematical convenience». For the Indian realists of the Nyāya school it is also, we have seen, a mere idea or a mere name. But for the Buddhist it represents transcendental or ultimate reality. As a limit of all artificial constructions of our reason, it is real, it is *the reality*. There is no other reality than the point-instant, all the rest, whether brief or long, is constructed by our reason on this basis.

We must leave it to the general philosopher to appreciate the value and determine the place which these Buddhist speculations deserve to occupy in the general history of human thought, but we cannot refrain from quoting the eloquent words which the late Professor T. W. Rhys Davids has devoted to this subject. He thus summarizes the impressions of a life-long intimacy with Buddhist ideas: «Buddhism stands alone among the religions of India in ignoring the Soul. The vigour and originality of this new departure are evident from the complete isolation in which Buddhism stands, in this respect, from all other religious systems then existing in the world. And the very great difficulty which those European writers, who are still steeped in animistic preconceptions, find in appreciating, or even understanding the doctrine, may help us to realize how difficult

1 On the Notion of Cause, in Mysticism (1921), p. 187 ff.
2 Ibid., p. 192.
3 Ibid., p. 190.
4 Ibid., p. 189.
5 Ibid.

it must have been for the originator of it to take so decisive and so farreaching a step in philosophy and religion, at so early a period in the history of human thought... The doctrine of impermanence of each and every condition, physical or mental; the absence of any abiding principle, any entity, any *sub*-stance, any «soul», is treated, from the numerous points of view from which it can be approached, in as many different Suttas».[1]

---

[1] T. W. Rhys Davids. Dialogues, v. II, p. 242.

CHAPTER III.

SENSE - PERCEPTION (PRATYAKṢAM).

§ 1. The definition of sense-perception.

The definition of what a thing really is, according to the Buddhists, can never be given. «If the thing is known, they maintain, its definition is useless, and if it is not known, it is still more useless, because it is impossible».[1] This of course does not mean that the Buddhists themselves did not resort to definitions on every step of their investigations and did not strive to make them as sharp and clear cut as possible, but it means that what a thing is *in itself*, what its essence is, we never can express, we know only its relations. The Indian Realists, just as their European consorts, the schoolmen and Aristoteles their master, believed that the things possess «essences», which it is important to point out. The definition of the element fire, e. g., with them was — «the element which possesses fireness (or the essence of fire) is fire».[2] This «fireness» was for Indian Realists the essence[3] of fire and the definition an abridged syllogism which can be fully expressed in a mixed hypothetical form *modo tollente*,[4] as, for instance,

> Whatsoever does not possess the essence of fire, cannot be named fire, (e. g., water).
> This element possesses fireness,
> It is fire.[5]

The Buddhists contended that such definitions are useless, since the «essences» do not exist. For them the characteristic feature of all

---

1 N. Kandalī, p. 28. 22.
2 Ibid., p. 28. 15 where the definition of *pṛthivī* is given.
3 *svarūpa*.
4 *kevala-vyatireki-anumāna*.
5 For the Buddhists this will be a defective syllogism.

our conceptual knowledge and of language, of all namable things and of all names, is that they are dialectical. Every word or every conception is correlative with its counterpart and that is the only definition that can be given. Therefore all our definitions are concealed classifications, taken from some special point of view.[1] The thing defined is characterized negatively.[2] What the colour «blue» is, e. g., we cannot tell, but we may divide all colours in blue and non-blue. The non-blue in its turn may be divided in many varieties of colour, according to the same dichotomizing principle. The definition of blue will be that it is not non-blue and, *vice versa,* the definition of non-blue that it is not the blue. This Buddhist theory of names, which can be called Buddhist Nominalism[3] or the Buddhist Dialectical Method, will be treated later on. We mention it now, because the definition of sense-perception is framed with an evident reference to it.

What knowledge is in itself we never will know, it is a mystery. But we may divide it in direct[4] and indirect.[5] The direct will be the not indirect and the indirect will be not the direct. We may take a view of knowledge which reduces it to physiological reflexes,[6] we nevertheless will have a division into reflexes direct and indirect, simple and conditioned,[7] i. e., reflexes and non-reflexes.

The whole science of epistemology is built up on this foundation of a difference in principle between a direct and an indirect knowledge. We may call the direct source of knowledge sensibility and the indirect one—intellect or understanding, but the meaning of these terms will be that sensibility is not the understanding and that understanding is not sensibility.

After having stated that there are only these two kinds of knowledge,[8] which he conventionally calls perception and inference, Dignāga[9] turns to perception and says that this source

---

[1] *apekṣā-vaśāt.*

[2] *vyāvṛtti-vaśāt.*

[3] *apoha-vāda.*

[4] *sākṣāt.*

[5] *parokṣa.*

[6] *pratibhāsa (ādarśavat).*

[7] *niyata* — resp. *aniyata* — *pratibhāsa* (in the sense in which those terms are used in NBT., p. 8. 8 ff.).

[8] Pr. samucc., I. 2.

[9] Ibid., I. 3.

of knowledge is «non-constructive» which is only another way to state that it is direct, or not indirect. The name for inference in sanscrit means literally «subsequent measurement», it is indirect knowledge by its very name.[1] The existence of things can either be perceived directly or inferred indirectly, there is no other way of cognizing them. The exact measure of what is here direct and what is indirect must be established by the theory of cognition, but we will know it only when we have established what is direct without containing a bit of the indirect, and what is indirect without containing a bit of the direct, in other words, when we have established what is pure sensibility[2] and what is pure understanding.[3] «It is useless, says Dharmottara,[4] to mention such things as are unanimously admitted by everybody. There is no quarrel about understanding the term «sense-perception» as a direct cognition by an observer whose attention is aroused, of an object lying in his ken. But this simple and obvious fact has given rise to many different interpretations, and the right view will be established through a critique and rejection of the wrong views. Thus it will be established negatively, *per differentiam.*» The characteristics given to sense-perception by Dignāga and Dharmakīrti have thus a double aim, 1) to distinguish this source of knowledge from other means of cognition,[5] and 2) to distinguish the Buddhist conception of it from the conflicting views of other schools.[6] Thus sense-perception will be established negatively and this is the only way to define it.

The usual definition of sense-perception as that kind of cognition which is produced by the senses, or by a stimulus exercised by an object upon the senses,[7] is defective in many respects. It, first of all, takes no notice of the general feature of every real cognition *quà* cognition, that is to say, as a new cognition,[8] cognition of something new, not recognition. And such is only the first moment of

---

1 *anumāna*. There is an *anumāna-vikalpa* and a *pratyakṣa-vikalpa*, but as a contrast to *nirvikalpaka* = *kalpanā-apoḍha*, *anumāna* is the representative of *vikalpa*.

2 *śuddham pratyakṣam* = *nirvikalpakam*.

3 *śuddhā kalpanā*.

4 NBT., p. 6. 19. ff.

5 *anya-vyāvṛtty-artham*.

6 *vipratipatti-nirākaraṇārtham*.

7 *artha-indriya-sannikarṣa-utpannam*, NS. I. 1.4.

8 Cp. above, p. 64.

every cognition. Sense-perception, real sense-perception, or cognition by the senses, is only the first moment of perception. In the following moments, when the attention is aroused, it is no more that pure sense-perception which it was in the first instant. Moreover that usual definition contains a concealed confusion between the proper function of sense-perception and the function of other possible causes of it. For sense-perception has its own function, its own object and its own cause. Its function is to make the object present to the senses,[1] not of course in the sense of forcibly[2] attracting it into the ken, but by the way of knowledge. Its object is the particular thing,[3] since this alone is the real object which, being real and efficient, can produce a stimulus upon the senses. The cause, or one of the causes, is again the particular thing. The general feature of all knowledge is that one of the causes producing it is at the same time its object. How this cause is to be distinguished from other causes or, in other words, what is the fact of being an object, what is objectivity,[4] will be examined later on. Our main point at present is to determine the exact function of sense-perception. This function consists in signalizing the presense of an object in the ken, its mere presence and nothing more. To construct the image of the object whose presence has thus been reported is another function, executed by another agency, a subsequent operation which follows in the track of the first. Therefore the salient feature of sense-perception is that it is not constructive. It is followed by the construction of the image, but it is itself non-constructive. It is sense-perception shorn of all its mnemic elements. It is pure sense-perception. We would not call it sense-perception at all. It is sensation and even pure sensation, the sensational core of perception. Thus the function of sense-perception is sharply distinguished from the function of productive imagination. The first is to point out the presence of the object, the second — to construct its image. The full definition of sense-perception will accordingly account for this difference. It runs thus: perception is a source of knowledge whose function of making the object present in the ken is followed by the construction of its image.[5] This definition is very often repeated

---

1 *sākṣāt-kāritva-vyāpāra.*

2 *na haṭhāt*, NBT., p. 3. 8.

3 *svalakṣaṇa,* NBT., p. 12. 13.

4 *viṣayatā* (*tad-utpatti-tat-sārūpyābhyām*).

5 NBT., p. 3. 13; 10. 12.

and it amounts to the contention that only the first moment is really sense-perception, the subsequent image is mnemic. The final outcome of the Buddhist definition is something quite simple, viz, perception is sensation followed by conception, for conception is nothing but the image in a special context. The emphasis however is put on the word «followed», and this makes the definition not simple at all, since the implications of this «followed» are many and deep.

§ 2. The experiment of Dharmakīrti.

But, is not this single moment of pure sensation, just as its corollary the mathematical point-instant, a mere convention? Although produced by a stimulus coming from an external object, but from an absolutely propertyless pure object, is it indeed a reality? It is supposed to be absolutely stripped off from every vestige of an imaginative or constructive element. But is it not itself pure imagination? This question, as is well known, has been asked not only in India. The answer of the Buddhists is the same as their answer to the question regarding the reality of the mathematical point-instant. A single moment, just as an absolute particular, is not something representable in an image, it cannot «be reached by our knowledge»,[1] that is to say, it is not something empirically real. But it is the element which imparts reality to all the others. It is the indispensable condition of all real and consistent knowledge. It is transempirical, but it is not metaphysical, it is not a «flower in the sky».

It is not a metaphysical entity like the God of the Naiyāyiks, the Matter of the Sānkhyas, the Universals and the Inherence of the Vaišeṣikas, or the Soul of all these systems. Dharmakīrti proposes to prove its reality by an experiment in the way of introspection. The metaphysical entities are metaphysical just because they are pure imagination, just because there is no point of reality, no moment of pure sensation to which they could be attached. They are «unattainable as to place, time and sensible quality». But this point and this sensation are present, directly or indirectly, in every act of empirical reality and empirical cognition. This we can indirectly prove by introspection.[2] Dharmakīrti says—«That sensation

---

1 NBT., p. 12. 19.

2 *pratyakṣam kalpanāpoḍham pratyakṣenaiva sidhyati*, Pram. Vārt, III, 125; cp. Anekāntj, 207; cp. TS., p. 374. 7 ff.

is something quite different[1] from productive imagination — can be proved just by introspection.[2] Indeed, everyone knows that an image is something utterable (capable of coalescing with a name).[3] Now, if we begin to stare at a patch of colour and withdraw all our thoughts on whatsoever other (objects), if we thus reduce our consciousness to a condition of rigidity,[4] (and become as though unconscious), this will be the condition of pure sensation.[5] If we then, (awakening from that condition), begin to think, we notice a feeling (of remembering) that we had an image (of a patch of colour before us), but we did not notice it whilst we were in the foregoing condition, (we could not name it) because it was pure sensation».[6]

This experimemt of Dharmakīrti offers a remarkable coincidence with the one proposed by M. H. Bergson.[7] «I am going, says the French philosopher, to close my eyes, stop my ears, extinguish one by one the sensations... all my perceptions vanish, the material universe sinks into silence... I can even, it may be, blot out and forget my recollections up to my immediate past; but at least I keep the consciousness of my present, reduced to its extremest poverty, that is to say, of the actual state of my body». This consciousness, «reduced to its extremest poverty», is evidently nothing but Dharmakīrti's moment of pure sensation, the present moment. Bergson adduces it as a proof that the idea of a nought is a pseudo-idea. The Buddhists refer to it exactly for the same purpose.[8] But it is at the same time a proof that there is a minimum limit of empirical reality and empirical cognition, and this is just pure sensation.

---

1 There is concomitance (*tad-bhāva-bhāvitā*) between a point of external reality (*svalakṣaṇa*) and sensation (*pratyakṣa*). The concomitance is positive and negative: when there is a reality there is sensation, when there is no sensation there is no reality. The absence of sensation may be due to the absence of the object, or to its absolute unreality. The first is the case 1) when there is an intermediate space (*vyavadhāna*) preventing sight, i. e., when the object is not in he ken, 2) when the object is absolutely unreal, i. e., metaphysical, unaccessible in time, space and sensible quality (*desa-kāla-svabhāva-viprakṛṣṭa*),. cp. TSP., p. 378. 17—18.

2 *pratyakṣena=sva-saṃviditena.*

3 *vikalpo nāma-saṃśrayaḥ.*

4 *stimitena cetasā.*

5 *akṣa-jā matiḥ.*

6 *indriyād gatau.*

7 Creative Evolution, p. 293.

8 Cp. above, p. 93.

Kamalaśīla refers to the same experiment in the following passage.[1] «At the very first moment[2] when an object is apprehended and it appears in its own absolute particularity, a state of consciousness is produced which is pure sensation.[3] It contains nothing of that content which is specified by a name. Thereupon, at a subsequent moment, when the same object has been attentively regarded, the attention deviates[4] towards the conventional name with which it is associated. After that, after the object has been attentively regarded according to its name, the idea of its (enduring) existence[5] and other (qualifications) arise; we then fix it in a perceptual judgment.[6] Now, when these ideas, designating that same attentively regarded object by its name, are produced, how (is it then possible to deny that they) are nothing but mnemic... (since at that time the object has been not only perceived by the senses, but judged by the understanding). And where is the proof that the consecution of mental states which is here described is rightly observed?[7] It lies in the (known fact) that when our attention is otherwise engaged, we can cognize (only) the bare presence of something undifferentiated by any of its qualifications. Indeed, because the ideas of an (enduring) substance arise just in the manner here described, therefore, when the attention of the observer is otherwise engaged, when it is directed towards another object, when it is fully absorbed by another object, then, although he sees the object standing before him, but, since his attention is deturned from (the content) of the conventional name of the object he is facing, there is (at that time and) at the very first moment (of every perception) a mere sensation of something (quite indefinite), devoid of every possible qualification.[8] If this were not the case and if every conscious state would refer to an object containing (in itself) all the qualifications suggested by its name, how could it then happen that the observer who is absent-minded (and who apprehends the object by his senses only), sees a bare thing, a thing devoid of all qualities».

---

[1] TSP., p. 241. 5 ff.

[2] *prathamataram.*

[3] *akṣāśritam upajāyate.*

[4] *samaya-ābhoga.*

[5] *sad-ādi-pratyayāḥ.*

[6] *tad-vyavasāyitayā.*

[7] *ālakṣitaḥ.*

[8] *sarva-upādhi-vivikta-vastu-mātra-darśanam.*

Dignāga quotes from the Abhidharmasūtra a passage to the same effect.[1] «A man who is absorbed in the contemplation of a patch of blue, perceives the blue, but he does not know that it is the blue; of the object he then knows only that it is an object, but he does not know what kind of object it is». This quotation which is very often repeated by later authors would indicate that Dignāga had found the germ of his ideas of pure sensation already in the works of the Sarvāstivādins. However, that school admitted three kinds of constructive thought and one of them «natural construction»,[2] being a germ of constructive thought, was supposed by them to be present even in every rudimentary sensation or sense-perception.

§ 3. Perception and illusion.

The second characteristic feature of sense-perception, considered as one of the two sources of right knowledge, is that it must not contain any sense-illusion.[3] Indeed sense-perception can be reckoned as a source of trustworthy knowledge[4] only under the condition that the knowledge produced by a sensation does not represent an illusion of the senses. However it seems quite superfluous to mention this second characteristic of right sense-perception, because, according to the classification of the system, sense-perception is a variety of right, i. e., non-illusive, cognition. Dharmottara[5] says that the definition would then have the following meaning — «that consistent knowledge which is direct, is consistent,» a perfectly useless repetition of the term consistent through the term non-illusive.

But the term «illusion» is not univocal. There are different kinds of illusions. There is a transcendental illusion,[6] according to which all empirical knowledge is a kind of illusion, and there is an empirical illusion[7] which affects only some exceptional cases of wrong cognition. Knowledge can be empirically right, i. e., consistent, without being right transcendentally. E. g., when two persons are affected by the same

---

[1] Pr. samucc. vṛtti ad I. 4. The passage is very often quoted (with the variations — *saṃsargī, — samangī, — sangī*), cp. TSP., 11—12.

[2] *svabhāva-vitarka,* cp. AK., I. 33.

[3] *abhrānta.*

[4] *pramāṇa.*

[5] NBT., p. 7. 16.

[6] *mukhya-vibhrama.*

[7] *prātibhāsikī bhrāntiḥ.*

eye-disease, owing to which every object appears to them as double, their knowledge will be consistent with one another without being true, i. e., without being consistent with the knowledge of all other people. When one of them pointing to the moon will say, «there are two moons», the other will answer, «yes, indeed, there are two». Their knowledge is consistent with one another, although limited by the condition of their sense-faculties.[1] All empirical knowledge is just in the same position, it is limited by the condition of our sense-faculties.[2] If we would possess another intuition, an intelligible, non sensuous intuition which the Buddhas and Bodhisattvas alone possess, we would know everything directly and would be omniscient. But we cognize only the first moment of a thing directly, the operations of our intellect which thereupon constructs the image of the object are subjective. All images are thus transcendental illusions, they are not ultimate realities. In introducing the characteristic «non-illusive» Dharmakīrti had in view, according to Dharmottara, to indicate that in pure sensation, in that differential of all our knowledge, we are in touch with ultimate reality, with the uncognizable Thing-in-Itself.[3] The subsequent images, concepts, judgments and inferences

---

[1] Cp. Santānāntarasiddhi, my translation.

[2] The term illusion *bhrānti=vibhrama* is ambiguous, because it means both the transcendental *(mukhyā bhrantiḥ)* as well as the empirical one *(prātibhāsikī bhrantiḥ)*. Inference, e. g., is illusive from the transcendental point of view *(bhrāntam anumānam)*, but it is consistent *(saṃvādakam)* from the empirical one; cp. TSP., p. 390. 14 — *samvāditve'pi* (read so) *na prāmāṇyam iṣṭam*. But in TS., p. 394. 16 — *vibhrame'pi pramāṇatā* the term *pramāṇa* is used in the sense of *saṃvāda*. *avisaṃvāditva* means *upadarśita-artha-prāpaṇa-sāmarthya*. When sensation (*upadarśana*), attention (*pravartana*) and conception (*prāpaṇa*) refer to the same object, there is consistency (*saṃvāda*). The moon and the stars are *deśa-kāla-ākāra-niyatāḥ* and therefore efficient, real and consistent, *svocitāsu artha-kriyāsu vijñāna-utpāda-ādiṣu samarthāḥ*, but they are illusions from the standpoint of transcendental reality, when point-instants alone are real. Cp. NK., p. 193. 16 ff., and NBT., p. 5 ff. The laws of Identity, Contradiction and empiricl Causality are the necessary conditions of logical thought or consistent thought, but this logical consistency goes along with transcendental illusion (*bhrānti, aprāmāṇya*). No other problem has so deeply interested the Indian philosophers, as the problem of illusion. The theories relating to it are numerous and very subtle. Vācaspatimiśra has devoted a special work to that problem, the Brahma-tattva-samīkṣā, but it has not yet been recovered. An abridged statement of the principle theories is found in his Tātp., pp. 53—57.

[3] NBT., p. 7. 13— *pratyakṣam grāhye rūpe* (=*paramārtha-sati*) *aviparyastam*, *bhrāntam hy anumānam svapratibhāse anarthe* (= *saṃvṛtti-sati*)...

transfer us into the empirical, artificially constructed, subjective world and, in order to indicate this difference, Dharmakīrti has introduced the characteristic of non-illusive into his definition of sense-perception. In the light of this interpretation «non-illusive» will mean non subjective, non-constructive, non-empirical, transcendental, ultimately real.[1] The characteristic of being non-illusive would thus distinguish sense-perception from inference and the operations of the non-sensuous intellect, which are illusions from the transcendental point of view. The second characteristic would then become almost a synonym of the first. Pure sensation is passive or «non-constructive», therefore it is non-subjective, transcendentally true, non-illusive.

So far Dharmottara. His interpretation, however, is evidently in conflict with the examples of illusions given by Dharmakīrti. They are all examples of empirical illusions produced by an abnormal condition of the sense-faculties.[2]

The necessity of mentioning the characteristic of non-illusiveness was indeed controversial among the followers of Dignāga, in the «own herd» of the Master.[3] It was at first mentioned by Asanga, although we do not know with what intention;[4] it was dropped by Dignāga, then reintroduced by Dharmakīrti,[5] dropped again by some of his followers[6] and finally established for all the subsequent generations of Buddhist logicians by Dharmottara.

In dropping the characteristic of non-illusiveness Dignāga was led by three different considerations. First of all, illusion always contains an illusive perceptual judgment. But judgment does not belong to the sensuous part of cognition. If we think to perceive a moving tree on the shore when the tree is stable, the cognition «this is a moving tree» is a judgment, and every judgment is a construction of the

---

1 Dharmottara thinks that if the first characteristic, *nirvikalpaka*, is interpreted as contrasting with inference, the second, *abhrānta*, must be taken as repudiating misconceptions. But the contrary is also possible; *abhrānta* will then prevent confusion with inference and *kalpanāpoḍha* be directed against those who, like the Naiyāyiks, deny the fundamental difference between sensibility and understanding, cp. NBT., p. 7, cp. also TSP., p. 392. 9.

2 NB. and NBT., p. 9. 4 ff.

3 *sva-yūthyāḥ*, TSP., p. 394. 20.

4 Cp. Tucci, op. cit. It might have been a simple borrowing from NS., I. 1. 4.

5 Cp. NK., p. 192.

6 TSP., loc. cit.

intellect, not a reflex of the senses.[1] In criticizing the definition of sense-perception produced by the school of the Naiyāyiks, who included the characteristic of non-illusive into their definition of sense-perception,[2] Dignāga remarks that the «object of an illusive cognition is the object constructed by the intellect».[3] «Sense-perception, *quà* pure sense-perception, i. e., pure sensation, does not contain any judgment, neither the right one nor the wrong one, because it is non-constructive. Therefore it cannot contain any illusion at all. This consideration of Dignāga falls in line with the above interpretation of Dharmottara, but, according to Dignāga, it makes the mention of «non-illusiveness» superfluous, because non-illusive transcendentally, means nothing but non-subjective and non-constructive. The second characteristic would be a repetition of the first.

A further consideration of Dignāga for omitting non-illusiveness is the following one. He wanted his logic to be acceptable to both the Realists who admitted the reality of an external object and to the Idealists who denied the reality of an external world. He thought apparently, like some modern logicians,[4] that logic is not the proper ground to decide these metaphysical problems. The division of cognition into direct and indirect and the logical functions of judgment remain just the same in both cases, whether external reality is admitted or denied. Dignāga rejected Vasubandhu's definition formulated in the Vādavidhi, «sense-perception is that knowledge which is produced by the (pure) object itself»,[5] because it could be given a realistic interpretation. He, for the same reason, resolved to drop the characteristic of non-illusiveness; it could be interpreted as excluding the view of the Yogācāras for whom all empirical cognition was a hopeless illusion. The definition which means that pure sensation is passive, non constructive, is acceptable for both parties. Jinendrabuddhi[6] says, «Although convinced that there is no possibility of cognizing the external object in its real essence, (Dignāga) is desirous so to formulate his view of the problem of the resulting phase in the process of

---

1 According to Dharmottara the part «tree» is a right perception, the part «moving» is an illusion, cp. NBT., p. 7. 5 ff., and Tipp., p. 20. 14.

2 NS., I. 1. 4. (*pratyakṣam*)... *avyabhicāri*...

3 Pr. samucc. vṛtti, ad I. 19 — *yid-kyi yul ni ḥkhrul-pai yul yin* = *mano-viṣayo hi vibhrama-viṣayaḥ*.

4 Cp., e. g., Sigwart, op. cit., I, p. 106 and 409.

5 *tato arthād utpannam jñānam*, cp. Tātp., p. 99.

6 Cp. vol. II, p. 387 ff; cp. Tipp., p. 19, and TSP., 392. 6.

cognition that it should satisfy both the Realists who maintain the existence of an external world and the Idealists who deny it».

Kamalaśīla[1] contains a statement to the same effect, although he speaks of Dharmakīrti's definition which contains non-illusiveness. «The term non-illusive, says he, must be understood as referring to consistent knowledge,[2] not to that form which is the (ultimate) reality of the object. Because, if it were not so, since, according to the opinion of the Yogācāras, the external objects do not exist at all, the definition which is intended to satisfy both theories would be too narrow, (it would exclude the idealistic view)».

In order to satisfy both the Realists and the Idealists Dignāga dropped the characteristic of non-illusive, and Dharmakīrti, although he reintroduced it, gave it an interpretation which did not militate against the idealistic view.

Dignāga had a third and decisive consideration for avoiding the characteristic of non-illusiveness. Since this term admits of many interpretations, its introduction could in his opinion prove dangerous and even suicidal to the whole system.

The system is founded upon a sharp distinction between two heterogeneous sources of knowledge. The senses, according to this principle, cannot judge. But if illusions, or wrong judgments, are put on the account of the senses, there is no reason why right judgments should not equally be put on the same account, as the Realists indeed maintain. The foundation of the system then will be exploded. The perception of every extended body is a sense-illusion, because «extension is never a simple reflex».[3] The duration of a thing will likewise be an illusion, because only instantaneous reality corresponds to a simple reflex. The unity of a body, the unity of its parts consisting of a multitude of various atoms, will be an illusion,[4] just as the perception of one forest at a distance instead of the variety of trees of which it is composed is an illusion. If, on the contrary, these are declared to be right perceptions, where is the limit? Why should the perception of a double moon, of a firy circle when a firebrand is

---

[1] TSP., p. 392. 5 ff.

[2] *saṃvāditva.*

[3] NK., p. 194. 8 — *apratibhāso dharmo'sti sthaulyam.* Vācaspati explains — *pratibhāsa-kāla-dharmaḥ pratibhāsa-dharmaḥ,* i. e., a point-instant is not extended.

[4] Ibid., p. 194. 12.

being rapidly turned, of a moving tree by a passenger on a boat etc., etc., be alone illusions?[1] «The Master (Dignāga) has dropped the characteristic of non-illusiveness, says Vācaspatimišra, since that non-illusiveness is suicidal (for the whole system)».[2]

Dignāga, of course, does not deny that there are illusive or wrong perceptions, but they must be treated separately. Just as there are logical fallacies[3] or illicite inferences, just so are there fallacies of perception,[4] or cognitions illicitely put on the account of the senses, whereas they are produced not by the senses, but by the intellect. These would-be sense-perceptions are of four different kinds.[5] They are 1) illusions proper, as, e. g., *fata morgana,* they must be put on the account of the intellect, because they consist in mistaking by the intellect of some rays of light for water in the desert; 2) all empirical perception[6] is a transcendental illusion, for it consists in mistaking an objectivized image for external reality; 3) all inference and its result is illicitely treated as sense-perception; when we, e. g., say, «this is smoke, the mark of fire», «there is fire indicated by the presence of smoke», these judgments are really mnemic, though illicitely given the form of perceptual judgments; and 4) all memory and all desires, since they are called forth by former experience,[7] are produced by the understanding, though they often are illicitely given the form of sense-perceptions.

Dignāga thus generalizes the conception of an illusion and puts on the same line the empirical illusion, like *fata morgana*, and the transcendental one, represented by the whole of our empirical knowledge. His sense-perception is pure sensation laid bare of all mnemic elements. The characteristic of non-illusive in regard of pure sensation is out of place, because such sensation is neither wrong nor right. The real definition of Dignāga means that sensibility must be

---

1 Ibid., p. 194. 16.

2 Ibid., p. 194. 17 — *tad iyam abhrāntatā bhavatsv eva praharati ity upekṣitā ācāryeṇa.*

3 *hetv-ābhāsa.*

4 *pratyakṣa-ābhāsa.*

5 The kārikā Pr. samucc. I. 8. can be thus restored — *bhrāntiḥ saṃvṛtti-saj-jñānam anumānānumeyam ca; smṛtir abhilāṣaś ceti pratyakṣābham sataimiram,* cp. TSP., p. 394. 20, where *sataimiram* is explained as *ajñānam,* it is also explained as *taimirika-jñānam;* Jinendrabuddhi contains both explanations.

6 *saṃvṛtti-saj-jñāna.*

7 *pūrva-anubhava.*

distinguished from consistent thought-construction, which construction is the real guide of our purposeful actions.[1]

So far Dignāga. But Dharmakīrti diverges in this point from his master. He reintroduces the characteristic of non-illusiveness into the definition, and his reasons are the following ones.

We must distinguish between a sense-illusion and an illusion of the understanding. When we, e. g., mistake a rope for a snake, this illusion is produced by the wrong interpretation by the understanding of the matter presented to the senses. This illusion ceases, as soon as we have been convinced that the object is a rope and not a snake.[2] But if a man sees a double moon because, owing to an eye-disease he sees everything double, this illusion will continue, even if he be convinced that the moon is single.[3]

There are moreover hallucinations[4] and dreams where the visions are present with all that vividness which is the characteristic feature of direct sense-perception.[5] They lack that vagueness and generality which is the characteristic feature of conceptual thought.[6] They cannot be understood as a misrepresentation by the intellect of one thing for the other, because this thing is totally absent. If we stick to the definition that all conceptual thought is an illusion because it consists in mistaking one thing for the other, we must come to the absurd conclusion that hallucinations are right perceptions, because they do not consist in mistaking one thing for another.[7]

---

[1] *kalpanā-apoḍha = avisamvādi-kalpanā-apoḍha*, cp. TSP., 394. 21.

[2] TS., p. 392. 13 and TSP., p. 392. 23.

[3] Ibid., p. 394. 5 ff.

[4] *niradhiṣṭhānam jñānam = keśoṇḍrādi-vijñānam*, cp. NK., p. 192. 20, and TS., p. 392. 3.

[5] TSP., p. 392. 23.

[6] Ibid.—*na hi vikalpānuviddhasya spaṣṭārtha-pratibhāsatā*, cp. NK., p. 263. 13.

[7] Since the «constructiveness» (*kalpanā = yojanā*) which is the essence of the spontaneity of the understanding is defined as «the cognition of a real thing, i. e. of a particular, in the guise of a general image» (*sāmānya-ākārā pratītir vastuni kalpanā*), such constructiveness will be absent in a hallucination, because there the particular external thing is absent. It will then be «non-constructive», it will fall under the definition and will be a right sense-perception. The same may happen to the «flower in the sky» and to vivid dreams. They are not constructions on the basis of a real sensation, therefore as «non-constructive» they may fall under the definition of right sense-perceptions. To guard against these fatal consequences the addition of the qualification «non-illusive» is necessary, as thinks Dharmakīrti. But if this «non-illusiveness» is carried up to

It would lead us too far, if we would go into all the details of this exceedingly interesting discussion on the nature of illusion and hallucinations.[1] Dharmakīrti maintains that there are illusions which must be put on the account of sensibility and that the characteristic of being non illusive is not superfluous in the definition of sense-perception as a source of right knowledge. Dharmottara concludes the debate with the following statement.[2] «The causes of illusion are various. They may lie in the external object or in the observer; they may be called forth by a disease of the sense-organ, but they also may be entirely psychical,[3] as the visions of mentally diseased people. But in all cases of illusion the sense-faculties are necessarily involved, they are in an abnormal condition».

Thus it is true that the senses do not judge, they contain no judgment at all, neither the right one nor the wrong one, but the senses being in an abnormal condition can influence the faculty of judgment and lead the understanding astray.

This conclusion reminds us of Kant's view when he maintains[4] that «the senses cannot err, because there is in them no judgment at all, whether true or false. Sensibility, if subjected to the understanding as the object on which it exercises its function, is the source of real knowledge, but sensibility, if it influences the action of the understanding itself and leads it on to a judgment, is (can be?) the cause of error».

Dharmakīrti seems moreover to have disagreed with Dignāga in the appreciation of the understanding in our cognition. According to the latter the understanding is a source of illusion, sinee it constructs images of reality instead of a direct intuition of it. Although Dharmakīrti shares in this opinion, intuition is for him much wider in extension than sensation. Sensation or sensible intuition is not the only variety of direct cognition. The opposition is for him not between sensation and conception, but between direct and indirect cognition, or between intuition and conception. Sensible intuition is not the

---

its transcendental limit, it will be fatal for logic, as thinks Dignāga, cp. NK., pp. 191—194.

1 A summary of them is found in TS. and TSP., pp. 392—395, and by Jinendrabuddhi ad Pr. samucc., I. 8.

2 NBT., p. 9. 14. ff.

3 Ibid., p. 9. 18 — *vātādiṣu kṣobham gateṣu... adhyātmagatam vibhrama-kāraṇam.*

4 CPR., p. 239.

only way of direct knowledge, there is moreover an intelligible intuition.[1] A moment of it is present in every sense-perception.

§ 4. The varieties of intuition.

a) Mental sensation

(mānasa-pratyakṣa).

The Sanscrit term for perception therefore contains more in extension than sense-perception alone, it means direct knowledge or intuition, as contrasted with indirect knowledge or knowledge by concepts. Sense-perception is only one variety of intuition. There is another intuition, an intelligible one. Ordinary humanity does not possess the gift of such intuition, it is the exclusive faculty of the Saint who, according to theory, is not a human, but a superhuman being. A moment of this intelligible intuition is admitted to be involved in every perception in its second moment, the moment following on pure sensation.[2] It is evidently nothing more than the element of attention following upon the moment when the incoming stimulus has affected the sense-faculty. The theory of cognition, after having established a radical distinction between the two sources of knowledge, the senses and the intellect, was in need of some explanation of their collaboration. After having separated them, the theory felt obliged to reunite them. In early Buddhism the origin of a perception was explained as an interdependent appearance of three elements, e. g., one element of colour (external), one element of the organ of sight (internal and physical), and one element of the sixth sense (internal and mental). The three together produced the sensation, or sense-perception, of a coloured surface. By establishing the radical difference between sensibility and understanding Dignāga was led to abolish the sixth sense, and to replace the physical sense-organ by pure sensation. Thus the perception of a patch of colour was explained as a moment of pure sensation followed by the construction of an image by the intellect. It became the business of the understanding to find out for the given sensation a place in the range of colours and other impressions. But the first moment of this work of the

---

1 *mānasam yogi-jñānam*, TSP., p. 392. 17.

2 Cp. vol. II, Appendix III; this theory is not explained in detail in the TS. and TSP., but it is mentioned there, p. 396. 2.

understanding was imagined as analogous to pure sensation. It was also direct, intuitive, non-conceptive. The first moment of perception is thus, so to speak, a «sensuous sensation», the second an «intelligible sensation». We may call the first a moment of pure sensation and the second a moment of «mental sensation», in order to reserve the term of «intelligible intuition» for the mystic intuition of the Saint. Since this «mental sensation» is an intermediate step between pure sensation and the work of the understanding, it will be mentioned once more in the sequel, when dealing with the problem of judgment.

b) The intelligible intuition of the Saint (yogi-pratyakṣa).

Our intuition is all the while sensuous. It is limited to a moment of vivid and bright reality which is immediately followed by the understanding trying to explain it in vague and general images, or concepts, vague because general. If we would possess the other intuition, the intuition by the intellect, which would understand reality as directly as we feel it in the first moment of sensation, our knowledge would be illimited. We would know the remote as the near, the past and the future just as the present. We may imagine beings which are free from the limitations of our sensibility. Their cognition will not consist in a weary collaboration of two heterogeneous sources. They will have no need to cognize reality by a circuit of dialectical concepts, they will have only one method of cognition — direct intuition. Of their omniscience we cannot judge, because in order to judge of omniscience we must be omniscient ourselves, but we can imagine that this reality which we have such infinite pains of approaching in our limited constructions they would contemplate directly by an intelligible intuition. Productive imagination, we have seen, is a transcendental illusion, an illusion inherent in all our knowledge. Free from this illusion is only the intelligible intuition of the Saint.

It seems that the theory of the two sources of knowledge and of their limited character, the inanity of imagination and the blindness of the senses were in need, as a counterpart, of a free intuition, in order to characterize our limited cognition by an illuminating contrast. Such must be the logical value of the theory of an intelligible intuition. The agnostic attitude of Dharmakīrti is expressed with great decision and all logical sharpness. His Omniscient Being is the unapproachable limit of human cognition.

c) Introspection

(sva-saṃvedana).

It is a fundamental thesis of the Sautrāntika-Yogācāra school that all consciousness is self-consciousness.[1] Every cognition of an external object is at the same time a cognition of that cognition. Every feeling and every volition are, on the one side, connected with some object, but they also are, on the other side, self-conscious. We are thus possessed of «an awareness of our awareness». Knowledge is self-luminous.[2] Like a lamp which illumines the neighbouring objects and its own self at the same time, not being dependent on a foreign source of light for its own illumination, just so is knowledge self-luminous, since it does not depend on any other source of conscious light in order to be known. The Sānkhyas and the medical schools maintained that knowledge consists of something like physiological reflexes, unconscious in themselves, but receiving a borrowed consciousness from the Soul. For the Buddhists consciousness is not divided between a Soul and an inner sense; the inner sense, the «sixth» sense, is itself pure consciousness. The Sautrāntika-Yogācāra school brushes this «sixth» sense away, just as the Soul was brushed away by their predecessors of the Hīnayāna. They maintain, that «if we did not know that we perceive a blue patch, we never would have perceived it».[3] «All (simple) consciousness, as well as all mental phenomena, are self-conscious», says Dharmakīrti.[4] That is to say, simple consciousness,[5] the mere fact of our awareness of something quite indefinite in the ken, and all constructed, complicated mental phenomena,[6] images, ideas, as well as all feelings and volitions, in short all mental phenomena *quà* mental, are self-conscious in themselves.

This does not interfere with the fact that there are instinctive thoughts and actions.[7] Instinct, habit, *karma* retain in the Sautrāntika-

---

1 *jñānasya jñānam = jñāna-anubhava.*

2 *svayam-prakāša.*

3 Cp. SDS., p. 30, where Dharmakīrti's verse is quoted, *apratyakṣopalambhasya nārtha-dṛṣtiḥ prasidhyati.*

4 NB., I. 10, p. 11.

5 *citta = vijñānam = manas.*

6 *caitta = citta-samprayukta-saṃskāra.*

7 *vāsanā = saṃskāra = karma = cetanā.*

Yogācāra school all the importance which usually devolves upon them in Indian philosophy. Some actions are *quasi*-automatical, because the incoming stimulus is followed straight off by a purposeful action.[1] But this only seems so, because the intermediate complicated process, being habitual and very rapid, escapes discursive introspection. That does not mean that it is unconscious or not self-conscious altogether. The action of a new-born child when it stops crying and presses its lips on its mother's breast is self-conscious in that sense.[2] Self-consciousness in this sense is a synonym of life.

The full connotation of this theory of self-consciousness can be elicited only by contrasting it with the doctrines of other schools and after considering its history in India and Tibet. This however is a vast subject wanting special treatment. The following breef indications will be sufficient at the present place.

The standpoint of the Sānkhyas and the medical schools has been already mentioned. Self-conscious is only the Soul of the Individual, as a separate, eternal, unchanging substance. All the process of cognition, all its forms as well as feelings and volitions are unconscious in themselves. There are five outer senses and their respective objects, and there is an inner sense[3] with the threefold functions of an unconscious feeling of individuality,[4] an unconscious feeling of the desirable and undesirable[5] and an unconscious function of judgment.[6] These functions become conscious through the light thrown upon them by the Soul. Similarly the perception of external objects by the senses is a process unconscious in itself, but receiving consciousness through a reflection in the Soul. Introspection is thus explained on the pattern of external perception. The sixth or inner sense is the organ of the Soul for perceiving special objects, just as the five outer senses are also the organs of the Cognizer, or of the Soul, for perceiving external objects.

The triad of Soul, Organ and Object is retained in the realistic schools, as well as the principle of interpreting introspection on the pattern of external perception. They also assume a sixth organ or

---

1 NBT., p. 4. 17.
2 Ibid., p. 8. 12.
3 *antah-karaṇa.*
4 *ahaṃkāra.*
5 *manas.*
6 *buddhi.*

inner sense,[1] coordinated to the five organs of the outer senses. But the Soul is no more an unchanging substance consisting of pure consciousness. It possesses «qualities» which are passing mental phenomena inhering in the eternal Soul. They cannot, however, be cognized by the Soul directly, because cognition, being an action, cannot become its own object, just as the edge of a knife cannot cut its own edge. For the Mīmāṃsakas Soul and consciousness are synonyms, consciousness is not a quality of the Soul, but its essence.[2] In Nyāya-Vaišeṣika consciousness is only a passing phenomenon produced in the Soul through an interaction with the inner sense-organ. By itself it is unconscious «as a stone».[3] This difference in the conception of the Soul in the two realistic schools involves a difference in their respective explanations of introspection. For the Mīmāṃsaka self-consciousness is an inference, for the Naiyāyik it is a separate perception. When a jar is perceived by vision, the Mīmāṃsaka maintains, a new quality arises in the jar, the quality of «cognizedness».[4] The presence of this quality in the jar allows us to infer the presence of a cognition in the Ego.[5] In Nyāya-Vaišeṣika the rule that the Soul cannot cognize otherwise than through the medium of the senses holds good for the outer as well as for the inner objects.[6] When the perception of an external object, say, a jar is produced in the Soul in the form of the judgment «this is a jar», the perception of that perception, i. e., self-perception, follows in a new judgment[7] of the form «I am endowed with the perception of this jar». «When pleasure and pain, which are qualities inherent in the Soul, are grasped, the interaction between the inner organ and the quality of pleasure is the same as the interaction between the organ of vision and the quality of a colour inherent in the jar».[8] Nay, the

---

1 *manas*, which is here quite different from the *manas* of the Buddhists.

2 *jñāna-svarūpo, na tu jñāna-guṇavān ātmā.*

3 Cp. my Nirvāṇa, p. 54 ff.

4 *jñātatā*, cp. NK., p. 267. 12.

5 There is thus a remarkable coincidence between the extreme Realists of India and the American Neo-realists and behaviourists. On both sides images are denied (*nirākāram jñānam*) as well as introspection. B. Russel (An. of Mind, p. 112) thinks, just as the Mīmāṃsaka, that «the relation to the (inner) object is inferential and external». Prabhākara rallies to the Buddhists (*ātmā svayam-prakāšaḥ*).

6 Cp. NBh., p. 16. 2.

7 *anu-vyavasāya.*

8 Cp. Tarkabhāṣā, p. 28.

Ego itself is cognized in the same manner. When the cognition of the Soul is produced by the inner sense in the form of an Ego, this cognition is a new quality arising in the previously unconscious Soul.[1] In this process the organ is the internal organ, the object is the unconscious Soul, its cognition is a new quality produced in that Soul.

In Hīnayāna Buddhism the Soul as a substance, as well as its qualities disappear. But the triad of Consciousness, Organ and Object is retained, as well as the interpretation of self-perception on the pattern of external perception. There is also a «sixth» organ,[2] in regard of which all mental phenomena are its «objects».[3] It represents a passing stream of pure consciousness, it cognizes the mental phenomena as its own objects directly, and the external objects indirectly, in association with the five outer senses, according to the rules of Dependent Origination.

To all these doctrines Dignāga opposes an emphatic denial. He says,[4]

> No objects are the feelings,
> No (sixth) sense is the intellect.[5]

There was no universal agreement between the schools of the Hīnayāna in regard of the position of the sixth sense. Some of them, like the Sarvāstivādins, identified this sense with the intellect. For them pure consciousness, inner sense and intellect or understanding are the same thing.[6] But others, like the Theravādins, assume a sixth or inner sense[7] along with the element of consciousness. In his controversy on this point with the Naiyāyiks Dignāga calls attention to the fact that they themselves mention only five sense-organs in the aphorism in which the senses are enumerated.[8] But Vātsyāyana[9] sticks to the rule that the Cognizer, i. e., the Soul, cannot cognize otherwise than through the medium of an organ.

---

1 Ibid.

2 *mana-indriya* = *āyatana* No. 6.

3 *viṣaya* = *dharmāḥ* = *āyatana* No. 12.

4 On the theory of cognition in Hīnayāna cp. my CC., p. 54 ff.

5 Pr. samucc., I. 21, cp. NVTT., p. 97. 1. — *na sukhādi prameyam vā, manovāstīndriyāntaram.*

6 AK., II. 34— *cittam, mano, vijñānam ekārtham.*

7 *hadaya-dhātu.*

8 NS., I. 1. 12.

9 NBh., ad I. 1. 4, p. 16. 2 ff.

«In every case of sense-perception, says he, the Cognizer[1] judges[2] through the medium of a sense-organ, because if the sense-organ is destroyed, the corresponding subsequent judgment[3] (in the form «I am endowed with the cognition of this jar») does not arise». «But then, says an objector, you must explain the perception of one's own Self, and one's own feelings and ideas?» «This is done, answers Vātsyāyana, through the inner sense-organ, because the inner sense is surely an organ, although (in the aphorisms of Nyāya) it is reckoned separately, since it differs in some respects (from the other organs)... There is (in this aphorism) no special denial (of a sixth organ, and this silence) is the sign of approval». «But then, says Dignāga, if the absence of a statement to the contrary is a sign of approval, neither would it have been necessary to mention the (five outer) senses (since in regard of them there is universal agreement)».[4]

Dignāga denies the existence of an inner sense, and replaces it by his «mental or intelligible sensation».[5] All cognition is divided into subject and object, an apprehending part and an apprehended part. But the apprehending part is not further divided into another subject and another object. Consciousness is not split into two parts, the one watching the other. It is a mistake to interpret introspection on the pattern of external perception.

Dharmottara's argument in favour of a genuine and constant introspection is the following one. What is perception in the sense of direct sense-perception? It is a process in which the first moment of indefinite sensation is followed by the construction of an image of the perceived object.[6] «That form of the object, says he, in respect of which the direct function of sensation, that merely signalizes the presence of something in the ken, is followed by the construction of its image,[7] is sense-perceived». We have unquestionably a feeling of our personal identity, of our own Self. But is this feeling followed by the construction of an image of the Ego? Decidedly not. This feeling merely accompanies every state of our consciousness. When

---

1 *jñātṛ.*

2 *vyavasāya.*

3 *anu-vyavasāya.*

4 Pr. samucc., I. 21, cp. NVTT., p. 97. 28. — *aniṣedhād upāttam ced, anyendriya-rutam vṛthā.*

5 *mānasa-pratyakṣa.*

6 NBT., p. 11. 12.

7 *vikalpena anugamyate.*

we perceive a patch of blue and at the same time experience a feeling of ease, this feeling of ease is not the image corresponding to the sensation' produced by the patch of blue. But when some external object, e. g., a patch of colour, is perceived, we at the same time[1] are conscious of another thing, of something pleasant. This feeling is a feeling of the condition of our Ego». «Indeed, this form in which the Ego is felt,[2] is a direct self-perception,[3] consisting in being self-conscious. Thus at the time of experiencing a visual sensation we simultaneously experience something else, something additional, something accompanying every mental state, something different from the perceived external object,[4] something without which there is absolutely not a single mental state,[5] and this something is our own Ego.

There is therefore an awareness of knowledge. It is unquestionably a mental fact,[6] a feeling of the Ego; it is direct, it is not a construction[7] and not an illusion, it therefore falls under the definition of sense-perception, as one of its varieties.

In this connection the theory must be mentioned which denies the existence of indifferent, desinterested states of consciousness. The Ego is always emotional in some, be it very slight, degree. Objects are either desirable or undesirable, there are no indifferent ones. They are either to be attained or to be shunned. The indifferent which are assumed in realistic schools are only seemingly indifferent, they fall in the class of those that are to be shunned, since not to be desired means to be shunned. Neither are there interruptions in the stream of consciousness in a living being. Even in the state of deep sleep and in the cataleptic trance there is some kind of conscious life going on. Moreover consciousness is always a preparation for action,

---

1 *tulya-kālam*, NBT., p. 11. 9.

2 *yena rūpeṇa ātmā vedyate*, ibid., p. 11. 8; *ātmā* is here, of course, not the substantial *ātma* of the Spiritualists and Realists.

3 *tad rūpam ātma-saṃvedanam pratyakṣam*, ibid.

4 *nīlādy-arthād anyat*, ibid.

5 *nāsti sā kācit citta-avasthā yasyām ātmanaḥ saṃvedanam na pratyakṣam syāt*, ibid.

6 *jñānam eva*.

7 This self-consciousness is *nirvikalpaka* only in respect of *kalpanā* = *śabda-saṃsarga-yogyatā*, but evidently not in respect of the other primordial or transcendental *kalpanā* = *grāhya-grāhaka-kalpanā*. Some Tibetans on this score maintain that self-consciousness is already a construction of our imagination.

by its very essence it is such. It can consequently never be absolutely desinterested. The Ego as an element of interestedness accompanies every conscious state.

Thus the Ego of Indian philosophy after having been enthroned as the Highest Brahma in the Upanishads, is constituted as a pure substance in Sānkhya and as a qualified substance in the Realistic schools. It then descends in Hīnayāna to the position of a simple stream of thought with the functions of a sixth sense. It looses even that position in the logical school and becomes an accompanying element of every mental state, a kind of «transcendental apperception», transcendental because the bifurcation of consciousness into subject and object precedes every possible experience. It then belongs to the *a priori* conditions of a possible experience. However, as will be seen later on,[1] at the end of its career, in the reformed Vedānta, in the Mādhyamika school and the mixed schools of Mādhyamika-Svātantrika-Sautrāntika and Mādhyamika-Prasangika-Yogācāra it again soars up and reasserts its position of the Highest Brahma.[2]

§ 5. History of the Indian views on sense-perception.

The earliest systematical view of perception is represented by the theory of the Sānkhyas. According to this system, as already

---

[1] Cp. on this point E. Obermiller's translation of Uttara-tantra in the latest Acta Orientalia.

[2] This, of course, is only a very breef account of the Indian views in respect of what «ever since Hume's time has been justly regarded as the most puzzle in psychology» (W. James). It will be noticed however that the Hīnayānists, since they describe the self (*pudgala*) as an aggregate (*saṃskāra-samūha*), of which each part, as to its being, is a separate fact (*dharma*), fall in line with the Associationists in England and France and the Herbartians in Germany; Vedānta, Sānkhya and the Indian Realists favour a Spiritualist theory, compared with which the theory of the Buddhist logicians can be characterized as a kind of Transcendentalist theory. Kant, as is well known, had besides his theory of a Transcendental Apperception, a theory of an «inner sense», which can be stimulated by our internal objects («*der innere Sinn von uns selbst afficiert werde*»), just as the outer senses are stimulated by external objects. This part of Kant's theory coincides almost completely with the Nāiyāika view. Nay, even the perception of the Ego is on both sides produced through the inner sense — «*der Gegenstand des inneren Sinnes, das Ich*», (CPR., p. 472). This must be rendered in sanscrit as *ātmā āntarasya idriyasya arthaḥ*, and we find this stated exactly in the Tarka-Bhāṣā, p. 28.

mentioned above,[1] all the variety of changing perceptions are physiological reflexes, unconscious by themselves but receiving a borrowed consciousness from the light reflected upon them by the Soul. The Internal Organ[2] is one of the first evolutes of primordial matter; it is called the Great Principle,[3] because it is illimited in its action, it embraces everything cognizable. It is assisted by five outer senses, every one having its own respective limited field of objects. These agents assume in the act of cognition each its own part; the outer sense perceives, the internal organ judges, the Soul illumines.[4]

The medical schools likewise assume a Soul, an Internal Organ, and five outer organs of sense. The stuff, out of which these five organs are composed, corresponds to the five kinds of external matter. Every organ is active only in its own limited field, because of the principle that similar can be apprehended only by similars, a principle, as is well known, also assumed by the philosophers of ancient Greece. The organ of sight, e. g., can apprehend only colours, because both the organ and the colours are of the nature of the element fire, etc.[5] The internal organ is likewise physical, it consists of a single atom[6]

---

1 Cp. above, p. 164.

2 *buddhi = antah-karaṇa*, its function being *adhyavasāya* «judgment»; the functions of *ahaṃkāra* and *manaḥ* are associated with it.

3 *mahat.*

4 According to the definition of Iśvarakṛṣṇa, kār. 5, perception is perceptual judgment (*prativiṣaya-adhyavasāya*), but according to Varṣagaṇya (Tātp., p. 105. 10), it is mere sensation (*ālocanā-mātram*), produced by the senses «assuming the form of the object» (*indriyāṇām artha-ākāreṇa pariṇatānām*). The Sānkhya-sūtras assume both the indefinite sensation (*nirvikalpaka*) and the definite judgment (*savikalpaka*), with evidently only a difference of degree between them; the real perception is for them the definite one.

5 In the Sānkhya system the five sense-organs and the five corresponding elements of matter are produced in a parallel evolution from a rudimentary personality (*ahaṃkāra*), they are therefore called products of a personality (*ahaṃkārikāṇi indriyāṇi*). In the Nyāya-Vaiśeṣika, the early Yoga, the Mīmāṃsā and the medical schools this principle is dropped, and the sense-organs are composed of the same atoms as the corresponding elements of matter (*bhautikāni indriyāṇi*). The Buddhists assume as the seats of the five outer sense-faculties five special kinds of a translucent stuff (*rūpa-prasāda*).

6 *aṇutvam atha caikatvam dvau guṇau manasaḥ smṛtau*, cp. Cakrapāṇi ad I. 8. 5. The Realists therefore, just as the medical schools, denied the possibility of two simultaneous feelings or ideas since the internal organ could not at the same time be present in two different places.

of a special stuff. It moves with infinite speed inside the body from one seat of an organ to the seat of another organ, everywhere establishing a connection between the Soul and the organ of the outer sense. It may be therefore likened to a nervous current [1] imagined as something intermediate between the intelligent Soul and the physical organ.

Besides assisting the outer senses in apprehending external objects, this internal organ has its own special field of action. It is employed not only about external sensible objects, but also about the internal operations of our minds,[2] perceived and reflected on by ourselves. Internal or intelligible objects are: the Soul, the Judgment, the internal organ, and its special objects, feelings ideas, volitions etc.[3] They are apprehended by the internal organ directly.

We thus have the following arrangement. The outer senses assisted by the inner sense apprehend external objects. The inner sense [4] reflects upon the operations of our minds and instinctively [5] distinguishes between the desirable and undesirable objects. The judgment,[6] another internal organ, or another function of this organ, produces a clear and distinct perception, but the whole process wants to be illuminated by the light coming from the Soul which alone makes it conscious. This arrangement does not differ substantially from the Sānkhya theory. The Intellect is sometimes reckoned as a sixth organ, but sometimes only the five outer sense-organs are mentioned.[7] On this occasion Cakrapāṇi remarks [8] that this is not a contradiction. The medical science, says he, being the foundation of all other sciences,[9] can occasionally admit and approve of apparently conflicting opinions, for it does it always in a special context. In the chapter devoted to the sense-faculties their special features are indicated [10] and therefore they are distinguished from the intellect in its

---

[1] Prof. Garbe compares the *indriyas* of the Sānkhyas with our ideas of the functions of the nervous system, Sānkhya Phil., p. 235.

[2] *manasas tu cintyam arthaḥ*, ibid., I. 8. 16.

[3] *mano, mano'rtho, buddhir, ātmā ca ity adhyātma-dravya-guṇa-saṃgrahah* ibid , I. 8. 12.

[4] *manaḥ*, ibid.

[5] *ūha-mātreṇa = nirvikalpakena*, ibid., ad IV. 1. 20.

[6] *buddhi = adhyavasāya*, ibid.

[7] Ibid., IV. 1. 37 — 40.

[8] Ad I. 8. 3.

[9] *sarva-pāriṣam idam śāstram*, ibid.

[10] *adhika-dharma-yogitayā*, ibid.

own special sphere of a non-sensuous reflecting organ. But in other parts of his work Caraka includes the intellect among the sense-faculties and reckons, like the Vaišeṣikas and the Sānkhyas, six (resp. eleven) sense-faculties and organs.[1]

The realistic systems, the Nyāya-Vaišeṣika, the Mīmāṃsā, and the Jaina, likewise assume a Soul, an inner sense and five outer senses, but their parts in producing cognition are otherwise distributed.

The function of judgment, i. e., real cognition, is shifted from the internal organ to the Soul. According to the Nyāya-Vaišeṣika it is a property of the Soul occasionally produced on it by a contact with the internal organ.[2] According to the Mīmāṃsā it is consciousness itself.[3] Cognition is thus a judgment *by* the Soul *through* the organs. It is employed about external sensible objects through a double contact of the Soul with the internal organ and of the internal with the external one; and about internal objects, feelings, ideas and volitions, through the intermediate link of the internal organ. The internal organ loses here its function of judgment, but retains the functions of assisting the outer senses and perceiving, the operations of the mind itself. Sense-perception therefore includes a perceptual judgment. Indefinite sensation, although admitted, is but a feeble degree of perception.

The Hīnayāna Buddhists dropped the Soul altogether, but spiritualized the internal organ. The whole business of cognition was then thrust upon this internal organ. It was supposed to assist the outer senses in apprehending external objects and to cognize directly the internal operations of the mind. The intellect then became the sixth organ coordinated to the five external organs and having its own special objects in cognizing the internal world. «According to the Vaibhāṣikas the eye sees, says Vasubandhu, the intellect cognizes».[4]

---

1 In Sānkya *buddhi*, *ahaṃkāra*, *manas* are three different internal organs having each its own function. In Nyāya-Vaišeṣika *buddhi*, *upalabdhi*, *jñāna* (not *manas*) are synonyms, NS., I. 1. 15. In Buddhism *citta*, *manas*, *vijñāna* are synonyms denoting pure sensation, but *buddhi* = *adhyavasāya* = *niścaya* = *sanjñā* mean conception, which is then an object of *manas*. In the idealistic schools of Mahāyāna pure sensation is termed *pratyakṣa* and *vijñāna* becomes *sākāra*, i. e., an image or conception.

2 The *ātmā* of Nyāya-Vaišeṣika is *svato'cid rūpam nityam*, *sarvagatam*, *cetanā-yogād cetanam*, *na svarūpataḥ*, TS., p. 79—80.

3 The *ātmā* of the Mīmāṃsakas is *caitanya-rūpam*, *caitanyam buddhi-lakṣaṇam*, ibid., p. 94.

4 AKB., I. 42.

According to the principle of Dependent Origination, cognition is interpreted in early Buddhism as the compresence[1] of at least three elements: pure consciousness, an object and a sense-organ. This produces sensation.[2] An image, conception[3] or judgment are produced by the addition of the element of conception, but the element of pure consciousness is present in every cognition. It is entered into the system of elements as a sixth organ,[4] but Vasubandhu[5] remarks that it is not an organ at all in the sense in which the other organs are understood to be organs; nevertheless for the sake of symmetry the intellect is reckoned as a sixth organ, because there is an analogy between, e. g., the organ of sight apprehending a coloured surface and pure consciousness employed in watching the operations of our mind perceived by ourselves. These operations are the special objects of the «sixth sense», while in the perception of the external sensible objects it only assists the work of the other senses. We thus have in early Buddhism already that sharp division between pure sensation and conception which, although in another arrangement, is so an outstanding a feature of Buddhist logic. The «sixth sense», which replaces here the sixth sense of the Sānkhyas, of the medical and realistic schools together with their Soul, is entered into the system of elements as the «group of pure consciousness»[6] and distinguished from the «group of concepts»[7] and the other groups.

In Mahāyāna this arrangement is radically changed. The school of the Mādhyamikas must be left out of account, because of their negative attitude to logic in general.[8] But the early Idealists, Asanga and Vasubandhu, when denying the reality of an external world converted the whole of cognition into a process of watching the operations of our own minds. Instead of an external world they assumed a «store of consciousness».[9] This however was repudiated by

---

1 *sannipātaḥ.*

2 *sparšaḥ = trayāṇam sannipātaḥ.*

3 *sanjñā.*

4 *mana-āyatana = ṣaṣṭhendriya = indriyāntara,* cp. CC., p. 96.

5 AK. I. 16, cp. CC., p. 64.

6 *vijñāna-skandha.*

7 *sanjñā-skandha.*

8 Cp. my Nirvāṇa, p. 141, n.

9 *ālaya-vijñāna.*

Dignāga and Dharmakīrti as a Soul in disguise.[1] They then finally established in Buddhist logic the two heterogeneous elements of a non-constructive pure sensation and a constructive or conceptual synthesis. This together with the theory of introspection and the theory of images and names are the fundamental features of Buddhist epistemology.

The lesson to be derived from this historical development is that the idea of a pure, imageless consciousness has always been alive in Indian philosophy. We meet it in the «Soul» of the Sānkhyas and the medical schools, in the imageless cognition of the Realists, in the «group of consciousness» or the «sixth sense» of Hīnayāna, and in the «pure sensation» of the Logicians. But the latter alone maintain that «sense perception is pure sensation», devoid of every mnemic or every intelligible element. For all the other schools who have introduced into their doctrine the difference between an indefinite and a definite perception the difference is only one of degree, sensation is an incomplete perception, real cognition is produced by the definite perception. But for the Buddhists it is just the contrary, real cognition is pure sensation, because it is non-constructive and therefore not subjective, not artificial. It is the point where we come in touch with ultimate reality, with the Thing-in-Itself, with the pure object or pure existence. This is also the reason why the later Vedāntins rallied in this point to Buddhist logic. Utilizing a dictum of the Upanishads they defined sense-perception as the «not-indirect»[2] knowledge which, as we have seen, is the real meaning of the Buddhist definition. They identified it with the direct feeling of the Absolute, the One-without-the-Second, the undifferentiated pure Brahma.

The definition of the Realists mentions that sense-perception is produced by a sensory stimulus and that it includes the perceptual judgment.

The definition of Asanga is verbally the same as the one by Dharmakīrti, but it did not contain all its implications.

Vasubandhu apparently had produced two definitions. The first is the one he inserted in his «Vāda-vidhi». It states that «sense-perception is that cognition which is produced from the object itself». By this emphasis of «itself» the ultimately real object, the mere efficiency of a point-instant is meant. This definition has been severely

---

1 Cp. vol. II, p. 329, n.

2 *pratyakṣa*=*aparokṣa*, cp. my Nirvāṇa, p. 159, n. 2.

criticized by Dignāga, since it to closely resembles the first part of the definition of the realists, «produced from a contact between object and sense-organ», and is apt to be misinterpreted in a realistic sense. In a subsequent work, Vāda-vidhana, Vasubandhu probably corrected his definition and made it consonant with the one of Dignāga, but since the work is lost, we cannot know it exactly.

§ 6. Some European parallels.

We have seen that the main point at issue between the Buddhist theory of knowledge and its opponents in India is whether sense-perception in its strict meaning, *quà sense*-perception, includes also the perceptual judgment or not. This question can also be asked in the form: is pure sense-intuition, or pure sensation, a reality? And that question is intimately connected with the further question: are there really two and only two separate sources of knowledge, sensibility and understanding? We have seen that the doctors of the school of the Sarvāstivādins who were great masters in the psychology of trance had noticed that our senses may be intensely absorbed in the contemplation of a blue patch, absorbed to the exclusion of any other incoming stimulus, while our understanding does not know anything about it, and we are not able to assert the judgment «this is blue». We have seen that Dharmakīrti invites us to repeat an experiment in introspection which proves the reality of an element of pure sensation. We have also seen that the Indian realists concede the point to a certain extent, in so far as they admit a double sense-perception, an indefinite, confused one and a definite one which includes a perceptual judgment. The Buddhist point is that there is a pure sensation, or intuition, which is followed[1] by a perceptual judgment. The contrary point is that there is a confused as well as a definite sense-perception and that the latter includes[2] a perceptual judgment. The difference seems to be very slight, yet it is fundamental, the whole edifice of Buddhist philosophy stands and falls with it. It is intimately connected with Buddhist ontology, the theory of Instantaneous Reality. Pure sensation in the ordinary run has no duration, i. e., it lasts for one moment only and is therefore empirically uncognizable and unutterable,

---

1 *vikalpena anugamyate.*

2 *vyavasāyātmaka,* NS., I. 1. 4.

unutterability is its characteristic mark. We therefore have called it the transcendental element of our knowledge, since although uncognizable empirically in itself, uncognizable in a sensible image, it is the indispensable condition of every empirical perception, and of all real knowledge in general.

Others will be more competent to judge whether the history of European philosophy contains a doctrine partly or even completely coinciding with the Buddhist one. Our task is to represent the Indian theory also by the way of contrast in order to make it as clear as possible. Its fundamental principle seems to be quite clear, the senses and the understanding are different sources of cognition, different not in degree, but in substance, mutually the one the negation of the other. However both sources interact, and it is not always easy to disentangle their reciprocal parts in actual, i. e., empirical, cognition. Since the whole system is founded upon that distinction we shall have in the course of our investigation several occasions to revert to it and to point out the difficulties into which its consequences and implications are involved. Would European thought, in a similar juncture, appear to be involved in analogous difficulties, this indirectly would prove that the difficulties are essential and belong to the problem itself.

Among European philosophers Reid is prominent by his sharp distinction of sensation from perception and from ideal revival. The word «sensation» connotes with him only a subjective state without implying any awareness of an external object. To have a sensation is only to have a certain kind of feeling due to an impression on the organs of sense, pure sensation would be purely affective consciousness. On the other hand, to have a perception is to be aware of an object by means of a present sensation. When sensation conveys a meaning it is no more a pure sensation, it becomes perception. Its meaning comes not from sensation, but from another source which is the same as remembrance and imagination. This theory seems to come very near the Indian distinction of pure sensation — *nirvikalpakam pratyakṣam*, perception as a sensation coupled with imagination — *savikalpakam pratyakṣam*, and ideal revival or pure imagination — *kalpanā-matram*. However the distinction, though sharply formulated, did not lead in the hands of Reid to far reaching consequences and became half effaced in the hands of his successors.

Neither Locke's «idea», as a definite imprint made by outward things, nor the «idea» of Hume, which is a «feeling grown fainter», make any sufficient distinction in kind between pure sensation and full perception.[1]

Although Leibniz clearly saw that perception was inexplicable on mechanical grounds[2] and was puzzled to find its transcendental origin, nevertheless sensation was for him but a confused perception.

But Kant, at the beginning of his critical period, as is well known, reestablished the distinction. He thought that it had been «very much detrimental» for philosophy that this essential and «genetic» difference became almost fully abolished. Imagination is for Kant a necessary ingredient of empirical perception. In this point there is a coincidence of his theory with the one of Reid and with the Indian one. But the question of pure sensation and pure imagination presents difficulties. The first is complicated by Kant's distinction of sensation and intuition and the forms of an *a priori* pure intuition which are the forms of Time and Space. We have seen that, for the Buddhists, the forms of Time and Space are not an original possession of our mind, but are constructed by our faculty of productive imagination, just as all other sensible and abstract forms are. Sensibility as pure sensibility is by itself absolutely formless. As to productive imagination (*vikalpa*), it is in Buddhist logic a term which embraces everything which is not sensibility. It thus includes Kant's productive imagination together with his understanding, judgment, reason and inference. It could not be otherwise for the dichotomizing principle alone, since it divides all that is cognition in a sensible, purely affective consciousness and an intelligible, purely spontaneous and imaginative one. Sensation and imagination, says the Buddhist, have each of them their own object and their own function. The function of the senses is to make the object, the pure object, present, and nothing more. The function of imagination is to construct its image. The object of pure sensation is the pure object, the object of imagination is its image. Without sensation, says the Buddhist, our knowledge would be «empty of reality».[3] «Without intuition, says Kant,[4] all our knowledge would be without objects, and it would therefore remain entirely empty».[5] «If all thought (by means of categories) is taken away from empirical knowledge, no

---

1 On the contradictions to which Locke was led by his want of decision on this point cp. T. H. Green, Introduction to Hume's Treatise.

2 Monadology, 17.

3 *vastu-śūnya*.

4 CPR., p. 50 and 41.

5 Ibid., p. 50.

knowledge of any object remains, because nothing can be thought by mere intuition», says Kant. «Pure sensation, without any perceptual judgment, says Dharmottara, is as though it did not exist at all».[1] «Intuitions without concepts are blind,»[2] says Kant. «Without concepts, says the Buddhist, with pure sensation alone we would never know neither where to move nor where to abstain from moving». «These two powers or faculties cannot exchange their functions, says Kant.[3] The understanding cannot see, the senses cannot think. The same has been said and repeated hundreds of times by the Buddhists. «By their union only can knowledge be produced», says Kant.[4] «Both these (united) ways of cognition are right means of cognition, says the Buddhist, only in respect of successful purposive action (i. e., in the empirical field).[5] «Neither of these (two) faculties is preferable to the other», says Kant.[6] «Sense-perception, says the Buddhist, is not the predominant[7] among them. Both sense-perception and inference (i. e. sensation and understanding) have equal force».[8] «Pure intuitions and pure concepts are only possible a priori», says Kant.[9] Dharmottara[10] gives to this idea the following turn. «Pure sensation,[11] says he, is the source of our knowledge in that point[12] where the perceptual judgment,[13] neglecting (as it were) its own (conceptual) function, assumes the function of sensation, i. e., points to the presence of an object in the ken». The interpretation of such a pure sensation is then made over to concepts and judgments.

These coincidences in the fundamental principle as well as in some of its expressions must, for aught I know, be regarded as highly remarkable.

Modern psychology, as well as modern epistemology, have forsaken the standpoint of a «genetic» difference in kind between sensation and

---

1 *asat-kalpa*, NBT., p. 16. 6.

2 CPR., p. 41.

3 Ibid., p. 41.

4 Ibid., p. 41.

5 Cp. vol. II, p. 362.

6 Ibid., p. 41.

7 TSP., *pratyakṣam na jyeṣṭham pramāṇam.*

8 *tulya-bala* NBT., p. 6. 12.

9 Ibid., p. 41.

10 NBT., p. 16. 16.

11 *kevalam pratyakṣam.*

12 *yatrarthe.*

13 *pratyakṣa-pūrvako'dhyavasāyas.*

conception, and have reverted to a difference of degree and a difference of complexity. W. James delivers himself on this subject in the following way.[1] «It is impossible to draw any sharp line of distinction between the barer and the richer consciousness, because the moment we get beyond the first crude sensation all our consciousness is a matter of suggestion, and the various suggestions shade gradually into each another, being one and all products of the same machinery of association. In the directer consciousness fewer, in the remoter more associative processes are brought into play». James says, «the moment we get beyond the first crude sensation». The Buddhist would have rejoined that just this first moment of crude sensation is pure sensation. That all the rest is a matter of suggestion, does not contradict, but only corroborates the proposition that the first moment is not a matter of suggestion, it is pure sensation. Since the essence of reality is instantanecus, the circumstance that pure sensation lasts for a moment only, does not speak against its reality, on the contrary, it supports it. This reality is uncognizable in discursive thought and therefore unutterable, but such is the character of ultimate reality as revealed in sensation. «Therefore, as Plato long ago taught — though the lesson seems to require to be taught anew to each generation of philosophers — a consistent sensationalism must be speechless».[2]

According to B. Russel,[3] «theoretically, though often not practically, we can, in our perception of an object, separate the part which is due to past experience from the part which proceeds without mnemic influences out of the character of the object»; «sensation is a theoretical core in the actual experience, the actual experience is the perception». This would fall in line with the opinion of the Indian Realists for whom «definite perception» is the real sense-perception. B. Russel adds that «there are grave difficulties in carrying out these definitions». The fundamental difficulty is of course this, that when a momentary sensation is separated from every vestige of mnemic elements, it is, as Dharmottara says, no knowledge at all, «as if non-existent» (*asat-kalpa*); it is, as Kant thought and as the Indian Realists were forced to admit, not knowledge, but a «transcendental» *(atīndriya)* source of knowledge.

---

1 Psychology, II, p. 75.

2 T. H. Green, Introd. to Hume's Treatise, p. 36 (1898).

3 Analysis of the Mind, p. 131.

According to Sigwart, the perception of the form «this is gold» contains an inference, «*sobald ich sage „dies ist Gold", interpretiere ich das Phaenomen durch einen allgemeinen Begriff und vollziehe einen Subsumptions-Schluss*».[1] This would mean that every perception contains an inference, but Sigwart thinks that pure sensation *(das im strengsten Sinne injectiv direct Wahrgenommene, von jeder Interpretation losgemachte)*[2] conveys the perception of colours only, «who sees a rainbow can only tell that he sees colours arranged in a certain manner». The Buddhist maintains that by pure sensation «we really perceive the blue, but we do not know that it is blue» *(nīlam vijānāti, na tu «nīlam iti» vijānāti)*. As soon as we tell that it is blue, we have already compared it with the non-blue, and this the senses alone cannot achieve. A consistent sensationalism must be speechless.

Among modern philosophers H. Bergson has attempted to reestablish the barrier between the senses and the understanding. «The capital error, says he, consists in seeing but a difference of intensity between pure perception and memory instead of a difference in nature».[3] «There is in perception something that does not exist at all in memory, and that is an (ultimate) reality intuitively grasped».[4] This seems to coincide with the Buddhist theory, the theory, namely that pure sense-perception grasps the ultimately real.[5] The difference, however, is that for the Buddhist this ultimate reality is transcendental, it is only felt, it is unutterable and uncognizable by discursive thought, it is just the contradictorily opposed part of everything utterable.[6]

---

1 Logik, II, p. 395.

2 Ibid., p. 393.

3 Matière et Mémoire, p. 60.

4 Ibid., p. 71.

5 *nirvikalpakam pratyakṣam paramārthasat gṛhṇāti.*

6 That Bergson's perception is not at all pure, that discursive thought constantly intervenes in it, that in every empirical sensation conceptual relations are present, has been pointed out by O. Hamelin and R. Hubert, cp. Revue de Metaph., 1926, p. 347.

CHAPTER IV.

ULTIMATE REALITY

(PARAMARTHA-SAT).

§ 1. What is ultimately real.

The two preceding chapters and the introduction must have elicited with sufficient clearness the manner in which the Buddhists of the logical school have tackled the problem of Ultimate Reality.[1] Positively the real is the efficient,[2] negatively the real is the non-ideal.[3] The ideal is the constructed, the imagined, the workmanship of our understanding. The non-constructed is the real. The empirical thing is a thing constructed by the synthesis of our productive imagination on the basis of a sensation.[4] The ultimately real is that which strictly corresponds to pure sensation alone. Although mixed together in the empirical object, the elements of sensation and imagination must be separated in order to determine the parts of pure reality[5] and of pure reason[6] in our cognition. After this separation has been achieved it has appeared that we can realize in thought and express in speech only that part of our cognition which has been constructed by imagination. We can cognize only the imagined superstructure of reality, but not reality itself.

It may be not amiss to repeat here all the expressions with the help of which this unexpressible reality has nevertheless been expressed. It is—

1) the pure object,[7] the object cognized by the senses in a pure sensation, that is to say, in a sensation which is purely passive,[8] which is different in kind from the spontaneity of the intellect;[9]

---

1 *paramārtha-sat.*
2 *artha-kriyā-kārin.*
3 *nirvikalpaka.*
4 *vikalpena anugataḥ sakṣāt-kāraḥ.*
5 *sattā-mātram.*
6 *śuddhā kalpanā.*
7 *śuddha-arthaḥ.*
8 *sva-rasika.*
9 This spontaneity is called *jñānasya prāpako vyāpāraḥ*, cp. NBT., p. 15.2.

2) every such object is «unique» in all the three worlds,[1] it is absolutely separate,[2] i. e., unconnected in whatsoever a way with all the other objects of the universe;[3]

3) it is therefore an exception to the rule that every object is partly similar and partly dissimilar to other objects, it is absolutely dissimilar,[4] only dissimilar, to whatsoever objects;

4) it has no extension in space[5] and no duration in time;[6] although an indefinite sensation produced by an unknown object can be localized in time and space, but this localization is already the work of the understanding which locates the object in a constructed space and in an imagined time;

5) it is the point-instant of reality,[7] it has no parts between which the relation of preceding and succeeding would obtain, it is infinitesimal time, the differential[8] in the running existence of a thing;

6) it is indivisible,[9] it has no parts, it is the ultimate simple;

7) it is pure existence;[10]

8) it is pure reality;[11]

9) it is the «own essence» of the thing[12] as it is strictly in itself;

10) it is the particular[13] in the sense of the extreme concrete and particular;

11) it is the efficient,[14] is is pure efficiency, nothing but efficiency;

12) it stimulates the understanding and the reason to construct images and ideas;[15]

---

1 *trailokya-vyāvṛtta.*
2 *pṛthak.*
3 *sarvato vyāvṛtta.*
4 *atyanta-vilakṣaṇa.*
5 *deśa-ananugata.*
6 *kāla-ananugata.*
7 *kṣana = svalakṣaṇa.*
8 *pūrvāpara-bhāga-vikala-kāla-kalā = kṣaṇa.*
9 *an-avayavin = niraṃśa.*
10 *sattā-mātram.*
11 *vastu-mātram.*
12 *sva-lakṣaṇa.*
13 *vyakti.*
14 *artha-kriyā-kārin.*
15 *vikalpa-utpatti-śakti-mat.*

13) it is non-empirical, i. e., transcendental; [1]

14) it is unutterable. [2]

What is it then? It is something or it is nothing? It is just something, only something, something «I know not what». It is an X, it is not a zero. It could be at least likened to a mathematical zero, the limit between positive and negative magnitudes. It is a reality. It is even *the reality*, [3] the ultimately real element of existence. There is no other reality than this, all other reality is borrowed from it. An object which is not connected with a sensation, with sensible reality, is either pure imagination, or a mere name, or a metaphysical object. Reality is synonymous with sensible existence, with particularity and a Thing-in-Itself.[4] It is opposed to Ideality, generality and thought-construction.[5]

§ 2. The particular is the ultimate reality.

All objects of cognition are divided into general or universals and individual or particulars.

The particular alone is the real object, the universal is an unreal object [6] or a non-object,[7] a mere name.[8]

Familiar as this theory is to the student of logic from the times of Guillaume d'Occam who also maintained that «the only thing that exists is the individual», it has in Buddhist logic a special baring. The difference between individual and universal is here much more radical than it was assumed by the schoolmen. A man, a cow, a jar etc.

---

1 *na saṃvṛti-sat* = *paramārtha-sat, jñānena prāpayitum aśakyaḥ*. The idea of «transcendental» would be *atyanta-parokṣa*. The *mānasa-pratyakṣa* which is the next moment and equally *nirvikalpaka* is so designated, cp. vol. II, p. 333; it is not present to me that the term should be used with reference to *indriya-pratyakṣa*. But the Naiyāyiks, cp. Tarka-dīpikā, characterize the *nirvikalpaka-pratyakṣa* as *atīndriya*, and *atīndriya* = *atyanta-parokṣa*.

2 *anabhilāpya* = *avācya* = *anupākhya* = *anirvacanīya*; from those four terms which mean the same, the third is preferred by the Mādhyamikas and the last by the Vedāntins, they then carry corresponding connotation.

3 *vastu-bhūta* = *vastu eva*, cp. NBT., p. 69. 2.

4 *vastu* = *sattā* = *svalakṣaṇa* = *paramārtha-sat*.

5 *avastu* = *anartha* = *sāmānya* = *āropita* = *parikalpita*.

6 *avastu*.

7 *an-artha*.

8 *saṃjñā-mātram*.

will not be particulars, the particular is here only the underlying[1] sensible point-instant of efficient reality. The general image constructed by thought with reference to this point-instant is a universal. Only this sensible point-instant is the real particular, it alone represents the ultimately real Thing-in-Itself. «The particular which is (empirically) cognized, says the Buddhist,[2] is not the ultimately real thing». A fire which burns and cooks is a real fire, that is to say, its burning and cooking is real. But the fire, which we extend mentally to all fires, to all burning and to all cooking, represents its general shape, it is not at all real.[3] This general fire can neither burn, nor cook, it can only be imagined.

The Indian Realists assume a three-fold real existence expressible in words. A word can express an individual, a species or form and an abstract universal.[4] The two first classes, the individual and its form, correspond to the Buddhist particular,[5] but from the Buddhist standpoint they are not particulars at all, just because, as the Naiyāyiks maintain, they can all be expressed in speech by connotative names. From the Buddhist point of view, whatsoever can be expressed in speech by a name, is a universal. The particular is unexpressible,[6] since it is the ultimate pacticular, the Thing-in-Itself.[7]

Thus it is that the Particular and the Universal may be mutually defined as the negations of one another, they are correlated as the real and the unreal,[8] as the efficient and the non-efficient,[9] as the non-constructed and the constructed,[10] the non-artificial and the artificial,[11] the non imagined and the imagined,[12] the uncognizable and the cognizable,[13] the unutterable and the utterable,[14] the own essence and the gene-

1 *upādānam.*

2 *adhyavasīyamānam svalakṣaṇam na paramārtha-sat,* cp. Tātp., p. 341. 26.

3 Ibid., cp. vol. II, p. 424.

4 *vyakti-ākṛti-jāti,* cp. NS., II. 2. 63; cp. TSP., p. 281. 4 ff.

5 TSP., p. 282. 5.

6 *abhilāpa-saṃsarga-yogyasya anvayino (a)svalakṣaṇatvāt,* Tātp., p. 342. 9.

7 *svalakṣaṇam = paramārtha-sat.*

8 *vastu, avastu.*

9 *samartha, asamartha.*

10 *nirvikalpaka, kalpita.*

11 *akṛtrima, kṛtrima.*

12 *anāropita, āropita.*

13 *jñānena aprāpya, prāpya.*

14 *anabhilāpya, abhilāpya.*

ral essence,[1] the thing shorn of all its extensions and the thing containing albeit quite rudimentary extension,[2] the unique and the non-unique,[3] the non-repeated and the repeated[4] in space-time, the simple and the composite,[5] the indivisible and the divisible,[6] the transcendental thing and the empirical thing,[7] the essence unshared by others and the essence shared by others,[8] the external and the internal,[9] the true and the spurious,[10] the non-dialectical and the dialectical,[11] the significant and the insignificant,[12] the unformed and the form,[13] the Thing-in-Itself and the phenomenon.[14] Thus to exist means to be a particular or, as Leibniz expressed it, «to be a being is to be one being», to be a monad.

§ 3. Reality is unutterable.

Ideality or thought-construction, being by its very definition something that can be expressed in a name,[15] it is clear that reality, as pure reality, the contradictorily opposed thing to ideality, must be something that cannot be expressed in speech. A reality which is stripped off from every relation and every construction, which has neither any position in time and space[16] nor any characterizing quality, cannot be expressed, because there is in it nothing to be expressed, except the fact that it has produced a quite indefinite sensation. If a patch of blue has produced a visual sensation, we must distinguish in this mental occurrence two radically different facts.

---

1 *svalakṣana, sāmānya-lakṣaṇa.*

2 *sarvato vyāvṛtta, avyāvṛtta.*

3 *trailokya-vyāvṛtta, avyāvṛtta.*

4 *deśa-kāla-anugata, ananugata.*

5 *anavayayin, avayavin.*

6 *abhinna, bhinna.*

7 *paramārtha-sat, saṃvṛti-sat.*

8 *asādhāraṇa, sādhāraṇa-lakṣaṇa.*

9 *bāhyam, abāhyam.*

10 *analīkam, alīkam.*

11 *viruddha-dharma-adhyastam, anadhyastam.*

12 *atuccha, tuccha.*

13 *nirākāra, sākāra.*

14 *svalakṣaṇa = paramārtha-sat, saṃvṛti-sat = sāmānya-lakṣaṇa.*

15 Cp. NB., p. 7. 20 — *abhilāpa-saṃsarga-yogya-pratibhāsa-pratītiḥ kalpanā.*

16 Although the point-instant is the reality, but its position in time and space are constructed by our intellect.

In the first moment a sensation is produced, it is the real moment of a fresh cognition. We have cognized the blue, but we as yet do not know that it is the blue.[1] The sense of vision which alone has produced this cognition is by itself uncapable of imparting to it any definiteness. It therefore commits, so to speak, all further work to its associate, the understanding, which operates upon the material supplied by the senses and constructs with the help of mnemic elements a conception. This conception alone is capable of being expressed in speech. The thing as it is in itself, its unshared essence, can never receive such a name, it is unexpressible. A conception and a name[2] thus always refer to many moments. The pure reality of a single moment is unutterable. A reflex whose scope is strictly limited to the objective reality of one moment is susceptible neither of conceptual determination nor of linguistic expression.

To maintain that ultimate reality, the thing as it is in itself, can neither be conceived nor named means that it cannot be cognized by consistent logical methods, in this sense the Thing-in-Itself is uncognizable.

§ 4. Reality produces a vivid image.

A further characteristic of ultimate reality, whose mark is causal efficiency, also refers to the element present in the ken. It consists in the fact that it produces a sensation followed by a vivid image,[3] whereas only a vague image[4] is produced in memory by the thought of an absent object or by its name in speech. Moreover, according to another interpretation,[5] the degree of vividness changes in an inverse

---

1 TSP., p. 12—22 — *cakṣur vijñāna-sangi* (or *samangi*, or *saṃsargi*) *nīlam vijānāti, na tu nīlam iti,* already quoted by Dignāga in Pr. samucc. vṛtti from the Abhidharma-sūtra.

2 *dhī-dhvanī* cp. TS., p. 274 ff. 18.

3 *sphuṭa-pratibhāsa* = *sphuṭa-nirbhāsa* = *sphuṭābha* = *viśada* = *viśadābha* = = *spaṣṭa* not to be confounded with *spaṣṭa* in the sense of logically clear and distinct, it then = *niścita* = *niyata*.

4 *asphuṭa* = *aviśada* = *kalpita* = *niścita*.

5 Dharmottara's interpretation, NBT., p. 13. 2 ff., is probably wrong, for the same object cannot produce presentations vivid and vague, or else it must be understood as referring to the sameness of one consecutive line of existence. Vinitadeva's interpretation of *sannidhāna* as presence is preferable, cp. vol. II, p. 35., n. 1—2; cp. TSP., p. 169. 21, 510. 13, 176. 23 — *sannidhir sadbhāvaḥ*; cp. Tātp., p. 13. 8. — *saṃvādakam sad bhrāntam api... pramāṇam*.

ratio to the distance at which the object is situated. This obvious and simple fact, the fact namely that a present and near object produces a vivid image and that a remote or absent one produces a dim or vague one has received a special interpretation in the light of the theory of Instantaneous Being. According to this theory, we have at every moment «another» object. One and the same real object cannot produce a vivid image in one case and a vague one in another case. It would be a contradiction, for in the light of this theory this would mean that it produces both at once. The Realist contends that the vividness and vagueness are in the cognition, not in the object.[1] The same object can produce different impressions at different times in the same observer, or at the same time in different observers, because, says the Realist, images arise *a posteriori*, not *a priori*,[2] they correspond to external reality, for him they are not subjective creations superimposed upon a heterogeneous reality.

The vividness of the sensuous image, however, is something quite different from the clearness and distinctness of an abstract thought or of a mnemic representation.[3] It is apparently just the contrary of it. Vācaspatimiśra records an interesting controversy on the question of the origin of our representation of an extended body.[4] According to the Buddhist this representation is a construction of productive imagination, or of abstract thought,[5] and therefore illusive. Reality does not consist of extended and perdurable bodies, but of point-instants picked up in momentary sensations and constituting a string of events. Our reason then by a process of synthesis, so to speak, computes these moments and produces an integrated image, which is nothing but an imagined mental computation.[6] The Realist objects that a unity would never be produced in this way. He therefore maintains that the extended body exists really and is apprehended by

---

[1] *sphuṭatvam api jñeyatva-viśeṣa eva, na saṃvedana-viśeṣaḥ*, cp. NK., p. 267. 14.

[2] *parāñcaḥ pratyayāḥ, na pratyañcaḥ*, cp. NK., p. 269. 19. With the meaning of *paranc* and *pratyanc* in this context cp. Tātp., p. 84. 18, where *parāñ* is likewise used in the sense of *a posteriori* in a controversy with the Vaiyākaraṇas who assume that the names logically precede and give shape to ideas.

[3] *niyata-ākāra* = *niścita-ākāra* = *niyatā buddhiḥ* = *paricchinnam jñānam* = = *bcad-śes*.

[4] *sthūlatva*, cp. NK., p. 262. ff.

[5] *vikalpa*, ibid., p. 263. 9.

[6] *sankalanātmaka*, ibid., p. 263. 10.

the senses directly. In support of his view he refers to the Buddhist interpretation of the phenomenon of vividness. He quotes Dharmakīrti[1] and says that if the extended body would have been a thought-construction, it would never have produced any vivid representation, because, says he, «imagination (or abstract conceptual thinking)[2] cannot produce a vivid image of the object». The Buddhist then answers that there is here no direct vividness, the representation of an extended body is constructed by conceptual thought, it is vague, general and abstract. However it receives an indirect vividness through a simultaneous sensation, the vividness belongs to the sensuous substrate.[3] He apparently thinks that as long as conceptual abstract thought or productive imagination has not started to operate, the vivid reflex is a simple moment, the momentary object has neither extension, nor duration. But this again the Realist rejects. He says that the extended body, according to the Buddhist, has not been apprehended by sensation, and it is only in that case, viz, if it would have been apprehended by the senses directly, that it could have produced a vivid image.

The same problem is discussed by Šāntirakṣita and Kamalašīla.[4] We find in their work the following considerations. A vivid image and a non-vivid or vague one[5] are two quite different things, different in kind, as different as a visual sensation is from a gustatory one. If therefore a name, or a concept, refer to a vague and general image, it does not in the least refer to that genuine reality which is reflected in a pure sensation. A person who has one of his limbs burnt by fire, has of this fire quite a different representation than a person who knows fire only in the way of a general concept or a name. Just so is the sensation of heat vividly felt when it is an object of sensuous actual experience, whereas it is not felt at all, if nothing but the name of heat is pronounced, because the name can evoke only the general and vague idea of heat.[6]

---

1 Ibid., p. 263. 12, the passage has not yet been identified, but belongs most probably to Dharmakīrti.

2 *vikalpa-anubandha*, ibid.

3 *tad-upādhir*, ibid.

4 cp. TS. and TSP., pp. 280 — 281.

5 *spaṣta, aspaṣta.*

6 *svalakṣaṇam avācyam eva*, ibid., p. 280. 4; *avyapadeśyam svalakṣaṇam* ibid., p. 280. 9.

The vagueness is thus not a matter of degree, but it is an intrinsic property of all mental constructions which can never seize the object in its concrete vividness.[1]

§ 5. Ultimate reality is dynamic.

Dharmakīrti says[2] «the object cognized by sense-perception is the particular essence of that object». The particular essence, he then explains, is that essence which produces a vivid image.[3] The image is either vivid or vague. Only the vivid is produced by the presence[3] of the particular essence of the object. We cannot even say that it is an image, because we do not yet realize its features, it is simply a vivid impression which, as it fades away, will be replaced by a clear and distinct image. This clear and distinct image is the workmanship of the understanding which has been led to construct it by the impression, i. e., by a stimulus coming from the object. But the image is an internal, subjective construction called forth by a point-instant of external reality. This reality is by no means similar to the object, it is only the cause stimulating our intellect. Cause and effect, as has been sufficiently proved by our examination of the Buddhist theory of causation, need not at all to be similar.

The question is then raised, why is it that this «particular» alone, this essence which is not similar to the image, is nevertheless the exclusive object cognized in pure sense-perception?[4] Are we not firmly convinced in seeing a fire, that it is before us in the external world just as it is represented in our image internally?[5] No, says Dharmakīrti, the particular essence alone is in the external world, because it alone is the ultimately real element.[6] Why is that? Why is it that the particular essence is alone the ultimately real element? Because, says Dharmakīrti, it alone is efficient, the essence of

---

1 This also seems to be the opinion of B. Russel, when he says, Analysis of Mind, p. 222, «our images even of quite particular occurrences have always a greater or less degree of vagueness. That is to say, the occurrence might have varied within certain limits without causing our image to vary recognizibly».

2 NB., p. 12. 13.

3 Ibid., p. 12. 1. 3. We here accept the interpretation of Vinītadeva, according to which *sannidhāna* means presence in the ken.

4 NBT., p. 13. 8.

5 Ibid. *vahnir dṛśyātmaka eva avasīyate.*

6 NB., p. 13. 10.

reality is just only its capacity to be efficient.[1] Under reality we can understand nothing over and above the bare fact of efficiency.[2] The image is not efficient. The fire is not the flaming object of a definite shape and extension which we deem present before us, but it is merely a moment of caloric energy, the rest is imagination.[3] The jar is not the extended body having definite colour, shape, tactile qualities and duration, which is present in our imagination, but it is an efficient moment represented, e. g., in the fact of pouring water, the rest is imagination.[4] And again not the general picture of pouring water, but the particular fact.

When a leg is broken by the stroke of a stick, real is only the fact that it is broken; stick, stroke and leg are our interpretation of that fact by imagination,[5] they are extended, general and imagined; real is only the particular point.

External reality is only the force which stimulates imagination, but not the extended body, not the stuff, not the matter; the energy alone. Our image of an external thing is only an effect of,[6] it is produced by, external efficient reality.

Thus reality is dynamic,[7] all the elements of the external world are mere forces.

§ 6. The Monad and the Atom.

Since the ultimate particular is thus an infinitesimal external reality, how is it related to the atom which is also an infinitesimal external reality? The Buddhist theory of Matter has been mentioned above.[8] According to this theory, physical bodies consist of molecules and a molecule consists at least of eight atoms. They are divided in four fundamental and four secondary atoms. The fundamental are the solid, the liquid, the hot and the moving atoms. The secondary are the atoms of colour, smell, taste and touch. Secondary matter is

---

1 NB., p. 13. 15.

2 *yā bhūtiḥ saiva kriyā ,i,* cp. above.

3 *auṣṇyam eva agniḥ.*

4 *bauddhānam kṣaṇa-padena ghaṭādir eva padārtho vyavahriyate na tu tadatiriktaḥ kaścit kṣaṇa-nāmā kālo'sti* (Brahmavidyābharaṇa, ad II. 2. 20).

5 TSP., p. 134. 18.

6 Ibid. *upalambho eva kāryam.*

7 *sattaiva vyāpṛtiḥ, calaḥ pratītyaa-samutpādaḥ,* cp. above.

8 Cp. above p. 101, cp. my Soul Theory, p. 958, n. 11.

translucent. Every secondary atom wants four fundamental atoms for its support, so that the molecule consists really of twenty atoms, if the body does not resound. If it resounds, a secondary atom of sound is added. The molecule will then consist of nine or 25 atoms respectively. But these atoms are of a peculiar kind. First of all they are not indivisible. The Buddhists strongly object to the theory of the Vaišeṣikas who assumed indivisible, absolutely hard atoms. If two atoms are contiguous, they asked,[1] do they touch one another on one side only or totally, on all sides. In the latter case the two atoms will coalesce and all the universe will consist of a single atom. But if they touch one another on one side only, then every atom will be surrounded by at least six other atoms, four on every side of the horizon, one above and one beneath. It will then have at least six parts. A further characteristic of these atoms is that they are not particles of some stuff. The hard atom is not an atom of stuff characterized by hardness, and the fiery atom is not a stuff characterized by heat. The so called fiery atom is nothing but the energy of heat;[2] the atom of motion nothing but kinetic energy. The hard atom means repulsion and the liquid means attraction or cohesion. The term matter, *rūpa*, is by a fanciful etymology explained as meaning not stuff, but evanescence.[3] A further characteristic of these atoms is that all bodies consist of the same molecules. If a physical body appears as a flame, and another body appears as water or some metal, this is not due to the quantitative predominance of the corresponding element, but to its intensity.[4] We may thus call the Buddhist theory of matter a dynamic theory. This theory which was elaborated in the school of the Sarvāstivādins, was retained in the idealistic schools. It was opposed to the Sānkhya theory which can be characterized as a mechanical theory, because it assumed a ubiquitous uniform matter and a uniform principle of motion by which all changes, all evolution and all the variety of the empirical world were explained.

Both the Sānkhyas and the Buddhists were opponents of the atomic theory of the Vaišeṣikas, who assumed atoms of four kinds endowed with original, specific and real qualities. These atoms were possessed of a creative force producing the specific characters of

---

1 AK., I. 43, cp. SDS., 31. 1.

2 *vahnir auṣṇyam eva.*

3 Cp. CC., p. 11, n. 2.

4 *utkarṣa*, cp. AK., I ,CC., p. 29, n.

molecules and higher aggregates according to a canon of complicated rules.[1]

Thus the Buddhist theory of matter is in full agreement with its definition of reality as efficiency and with its theory of causation as kinetic. The ultimate reality is dynamic, pure existence is nothing but efficiency. The Thing-in-Itself is nothing but the way in which our sensitivity is affected by external reality.[2]

Dharmottara says,[3] «we apply the term „ultimately real" to anything that can be tested by its force to produce an effect... This indeed is the reason why purposive actions are realized in regard of objects directly perceived, not in regard of objects constructed (by imagination)... A really perceived object, on the other hand, produces purposive action. Consequently real is only the particular (i. e., the unique point of effiiciency,[4] the thing-in-itself), not the constructed (empirical) object».

§ 7. Reality is Affirmation.

Ultimate reality is also styled the affirmation or the essence of affirmation.[5] Dharmottara says,[6] «affirmation (viz, that affirmation which is the contrary of negation) is the thing», and «the thing is the synonym of ultimate reality»,[7] «ultimate reality is in its turn the ultimate particular»[8] or the thing as it is strictly in itself.

In order to understand this identification of a thing with a judgment, i. e., with a function of thought, especially in a system of logic whose leading principle is to establish a radical distinction between reality and every kind of thought-construction, we must bear in mind that for the Buddhist logician the fundamental act in cognition is not the concept, but the affirmation. There is consequently no difference between

1 Cp. the excellent analysis of Dr B. N. Seal, in Hindu Chemistry, II, p. 185 ff.

2 NB., I. 12 — 15, *vastu = paramārthasat = artha-kriyā-sāmarthya-lakṣaṇam.*

3 NTB., p. 13. 18, transl., p. 37.

4 «Cognition is an effect, just as the fetching of water in a jar, or the beaking of legs», cp. TSP., p. 134. 18.

5 *sva-lakṣaṇam vidhi-rūpam,* Tātp., p. 340. 13, 341. 16, cp. *bāhyam vidhi-rūpam apo-vyāvṛttam.*

6 NBT., p. 24.16 — *vastu-sādhanam = vidheḥ sādhanam.*

7 Ibid., p. 13. 18.

8 Ibid., p. 13. 11.

affirmation and what is affirmed, conception and concept, perception and percept, between cognition as an act and cognition as a content. The conception of a cow is understood as the judgment «this is a cow». In this judgment the essence of affirmation consists in the presence of a visual sensation produced by a point-instant of external reality, this sensation stimulates the intellect for the synthetic construction of a cow. In the judgment «this is a flower in the sky» there is no real affirmation, because there is no visual sensation which would not be an illusion or hallucination. The essence of affirmation consequently is not included in the concept of a cow or of a flower in the sky, but in a moment of sensation which is the direct reflex of external reality. In this sense Reality means Affirmation. Even the negative judgment «there is on this place no jar», although it is negative in its form, contains an affirmation, because it refers us to a visual sensation.[1] Concepts may attain to the highest degree of clearness and distinctness, they never carry the fact of existence in themselves. We can say «there is a cow» and «there is no cow». If the concept of a cow did imply existence, the judgment «the cow is» would be superfluous, it would contain a repetition, and the judgment «the cow is not», i. e., «there is here no cow», would contain a contradiction.[2] But a particular sensation, a point-instant, is existence. We cannot say «existence is», it would be a repetition, neither can we say «existence is not», this would be a contradiction. Thus the Buddhists have hit on the same problem which has occupied so long the European rationalists and their adversaries in their controversies on the validity of the ontological argument. Reality cannot be deduced from the clearness and distinctness of a conception. On the contrary, a clear and distinct conception is a guaranty for its being a thought-construction and, consequently, a non-reality, an imputation on reality.[3] The reality of every concept and of every judgment is a borrowed reality, it is taken from a corresponding sensation. In this sense it is said that affirmation, the essence of affirmation, is the Thing-in-Itself.

§ 8. Objections.

That the theory of a Thing-in-Itself was vehemently assailed by all non-Buddhist schools, and among the Buddhist themselves by the

---

[1] Ibid., p. 22. 18.

[2] Tātp., p. 340. 10 ff., 13. 2. ff.

[3] NBT., p. 48. 7 — *niścaya-ārūḍham rūpam-samāropitam = buddhy=avasitam*, ibid., p. 51. 8.

school of the **Mādhyamikas**, is quite natural. It could not be otherwise, since this theory summarizes as in a focus the doctrine of Buddhist Criticism. For the **Mādhyamikas** the repudiation of the theory was an easy work. For them not only our logical conceptions of finite and infinite, of divisible and indivisible etc. were dialectical and contradictory, but all conceptions without exception were relational, contradictory and therefore unreal. The «Thing-in-Itself» means that there is a thing which is characterized by its own self. If this relation were real, it would be similar to a knife cutting its own edge. But it is logical and therefore dialectical and unreal.[1]

The **Jains** assailed the theory of a Thing-in-Itself by arguments which did not substantially differ from the arguments of the Mādhyamikas in method, although the method was resorted to for a different aim.[2] According to them Relativity does not mean at all that the relative things are not real, they are real and relative at the same time. The nature of reality itself, not of logic alone, is dialectical. Reality is permanent and impermanent at the same time, it is finite and infinite, it is particular and universal simultaneously. This contradiction lies in the nature of reality itself and must be acquiesced in.[3]

The contention that the Thing-in-Itself is cut loose of every general feature as being the ultimate and absolute particular, is untenable. As every other thing it is particular and universal at the same time.[4] The notion of a Thing-in-Itself embraces all things in themselves, it is a universal.[5] Moreover every particular is distinguished from all other particulars, it possesses «otherness», and otherness is a category of the understanding. The supposed «purity» of the Thing-in-Itself is a phantom. It is as dialectical as every other logical notion, it is particular and general at the same time. But this feature does not interfere with its reality, because, the Jains maintain, reality itself is dialectical.[6]

---

[1] Cp. my **Nirvāṇa**, p. 142 ff.

[2] The argument of the Jains against the Thing-in-Itself is summarized by **Šāntirakṣita**, TS., p. 486 ff.

[3] Ibid., p. 486.23.

[4] Ibid., p. 486.25 ff. and 490.11.

[5] Ibid., p. 487.22.

[6] The reciprocal position of the **Mādhyamikas** and of the **Jains** in this problem can be, to a certain extent, likened to the reciprocal position of **Hegel's** idealistic dialectic and the dialectic of his materialistic followers, **Marx** and **Engels**, who also were ready to assume that reality itself is dialectical and contradictory.

A Jain philosopher surnamed Ahrīka[1] is reported to have adopted in this discussion a line of argument not unknown to the historian of philosophy. Everything, he maintained, includes at the same time some similarity and some difference, the similarity is the universal, the dissimilarity is the particular. If there were such a thing as the absolute particular, that would be unrelated and absolutely different from all other existing things, it would be non-existing, it would be nothing, a «flower in the sky».[2] And on the other hand, if it would not include some difference, it would coalesce with all other things and there would be no manifold altogether. It is wrong to maintain that an Ens must be a unity, an Ens is always double, it is existent and non-existent, moving and at rest, general and particular at the same time. The essence of reality is dialectical, i. e., always double. The Buddhist answers, that if the general and the particular are identical, then they will coalesce in the same unity and the unity will not be double. But if they are not identical, they will be different, and there will be two realities, the Ens again will not be double.[3] If it be assumed that the Ens is the same, but its conditions or qualities are different, the question will arise whether these qualities are real or imagined.[4] If they are imagined, the Buddhist will not quarrel. But the Jaina assumes real qualities, and real qualities cannot be contradictory, because an Ens is always a unity. If a thing could be another thing, it would loose its identity and become other. No one short of a lunatic[5] can deny the law of contradiction and this law, we have seen, establishes the reality of the ultimate particular or of the particular thing as it strictly is in itself.

§ 9. The evolution of the views on Reality.

All Indian systems of philosophy are at the same time doctrines of Salvation. The problem of Ultimate Reality has therefore a double aspect. It is either the ultimate element of life's evolution in Samsāra, or it is the eternal cessation of this evolution in Nirvāṇa.

In Sānkhya the ultimate elements of evolution are three kinds of infra-atomic Reals[6] whose different collocations create the manifold

---

1 Ibid., p. 486.25.

2 Ibid., p. 487.5, 487.20 and 495.12.

3 Ibid., p. 489. 7—10.

4 Ibid., p. 490.14.

5 Ibid., p. 491.9.

6 *guṇa*.

objects and their constant change, under the influence of a central force called *karma*. Nirvāṇa is the cessation of this evolution for ever.

In early Nyāya and Vaiśeṣika the ultimate elements are four kinds of atoms which, under the influence of *karma*, create [1] the worlds and their evolution. The cessation of that process in Nirvāṇa is Eternal Death, since consciousness becomes extinct as well as the world's evolution. In later Nyāya-Vaiśeṣika Eternity or Nirvāṇa consists in an eternal mystic and still contemplation of God.

In Hīnayāna the three kinds of Reals and the four kinds of atoms are replaced by three kinds of elements or energies.[2] Eternity is here also unconscious, a condition of Eternal Death as a consequence of the extinction of the force of *karma*.

In the first period of the Mahāyāna the force of *karma* becomes a Force of Illusion.[3] Eternity is the world *sub specie aeternitatis*, a condition attained through the destruction of this Illusion. The same position is accepted in Vedānta.

Finally in the second period of Mahāyāna the ultimate reality is the Thing-in-Itself. Its differentiation into subject and object [4] by the intellect under the influence of *karma* constitutes the world process. Its non-differentiation is Nirvāṇa. It. is an unspeakable Eternity of Pure Existence [5] and Pure Consciousness [6] where subject and object have coalesced.

Thus the Thing-in-Itself is, on the one hand, an external object, the ultimate cause of cognition. On the other hand, it is also the point where subject and object coalesce in the Final Absolute.

Jinendrabuddhi [7] says — «From the standpoint of «Thisness», (i. e., the absolute Reality or the Thing-in-Itself) there is no difference at all (between subject and object), but hampered as we are by Transcendental Illusion... all that we know is exclusively its indirect appearance as differentiated by the construction of a subject and an object».

The notion of «Own Essence», an essence which is strictly its own in every element, appears already in the Hīnayāna. The element of

---

1 *ārabhante.*

2 *dharma* = *saṃskāra.*

3 *māyā.*

4 *grāhya-grāhaka-kalpanā.*

5 *svabhava-kaya.*

6 *jñāna-kāya.*

7 Cp. vol. II, p. 396.

existence, the central conception of that period, is defined as the «bearer of its own essence».[1] However this notion differs from the later one in many respects. There is as yet no hard and fast line between reality and ideality, the elements of existence are divided into physical and mental, or into physical, mental and forces,[2] they all are equally real.[3] Reality is not defined as efficiency. All attention is concentrated upon the denial of the reality of every combination of elements. Matter, considered dynamically, is made so subtle and the elements of mind are so mutually exteritorialised that the difference between matter and mind almost dwindles away, both are forces.[4]

The schools of the Hīnayāna fluctuated in the definition of the «Own essence» as a point-instant. Each had its own list of elements. However the differences were not essential.

The distinction of all elements in the three classes of pure imagination,[5] pure reality[6] and the «interdependent»[7] class between them — this distinction which is characteristic for the early Yogācāra school — already implies a sharp demarcation between reality and ideality. Dharmakīrti gave to the theory its final shape by defining reality as efficiency and opposing it radically to every kind of ideality. The real then became synonymous with pure existence, with the extreme particular and the Thing-in-Itself.[8] It was distinguished and opposed to the «non-existence», ideality and generality of every mental construction.

The idea that the Absolute can be cognized as the Thing-in-Itself by pure sensation has been borrowed by the later Vedānta from the Buddhists. «Since the differentiation of objects is cognized by judgment,[9] and since without the cognition of that differentiation there are no

---

1 *sva-lakṣaṇa dharaṇād dharmaḥ*, cp. Yaśomitra ad AK. I. 3. and CC., p. 26, n. = *attano pana sabhāvān dharentī ti dhammā*, Atthasālinī, p. 39. § 94, cp. Mil. 205 & Netti 20.

2 *rūpa-jñāna-cittaviprayukta-saṃskāra.*

3 *bhāva = dharma = sat = anitya.*

4 Cp. CC., p. 84.

5 *pari-kalpita.*

6 *pari-niṣpanna.*

7 *para-tantra.*

8 *vastu = sattā = paramārtha-sat = svalakṣaṇa.*

9 *savikalpaka.*

individual objects, (but only the Whole or the Absolute, therefore the Vedāntins assume that pure sensation)[1] apprehends pure Existence[2] (or the Absolute Brahma)».[3]

§ 10. Some European parallels.

To summarize. The conception of Ultimate Reality as it is established in the critical school of Buddhism implies that it represents 1) the absolute particular, 2) pure existence, 3) a point-instant in the stream of existence, 4) it is unique and unrelated, 5) it is dynamic, not extended and not enduring, 6) it posseses the faculty of stimulating the intellect for the production of a corresponding image, 7) it imparts vividness to the image, 8) it constitutes the assertive force of judgments, 9) it is the Thing-in-Itself, unutterable and incognizable.

Philosophy in its more than bimillenary search for an ultimate reality has sometimes travelled on parallel lines, repeated, totally or partially, the same arguments, drawn from them the same or quite different conclusions, without however arriving at the same final result.

The term designating an ultimate reality in Buddhist logic literally means «Own Essence».[4] This «Own Essence», to a certain extent, coincides with Aristotle's First Essence. Its formulation as *Hoc Aliquid* coincides exactly with the term *kimcid idam* by which the «Own Essence» is explained. In Buddhism it is absolutely unrelated, since it is something strictly by itself. «Whether any Substance or Essence can be a *Relatum* or not, Aristotle is puzzled to say; he seems to think that the Second Essence may be, but that the first Essence cannot be so. He concludes however by admitting that the question is one of doubt and difficulty.»[5] The Indian denial is very categorical.

However «that which is most peculiar to Aristotle's Essence is, that while remaining *Unum et Idem Numero*, it is capable by change in itself of receiving alternately contradictory Accidents».[6] This, we

---

1 *nirvikalpaka.*

2 *sattā-mātra.*

3 Cp. ŚD., p. 126. Vedānta-paribhāṣā, p. 31 ff., explains «*tat tvam asi*» as *nirvikalpaka*, and Nyāya-makaranda, p. 153 ff. assumes a *tattva-sakṣāt-kāra* as a direct knowledge of the Absolute. The mystic Yogi only perceives every thing by *nirvikalpaka* directly, for him *mānasa-pratyakṣa* or intelligible intuition is the only *pramāṇa.*

4 *svalakṣaṇam = paramārtha-sat.*

5 Cp. Grote. Aristotle, p. 72.

6 Ibid., p. 69.

have seen, is quite different in Buddhism. Every change is here a change of essence. Moreover Aristotle assumes ten varieties of *Ens*, while the Buddhist «Own Essence» is the only *Ens*, all other categories are non-*Ens* by themselves. They can be indirectly an *Ens* only when a first Essence lies at the bottom, they then have a borrowed reality. This Aristotle seems to recognize by maintaining that his «First Essence is alone an *Ens* in the fullest sense». Just as the Buddhist «Own Essence» it is «indispensable as Subject or Substratum for all other Categories».

Passing by a multitude of comparisons which naturally suggest themselves in the course of examining the endless theories which have been formed by philosophers regarding the notions of Reality, Existence, Substance, Essence, etc., we may stop at Leibniz's Monadology since here the points of analogy are more numerous. We have already called attention to the analogy between the position of Leibniz and Dharmakīrti as against their monistic, mechanistic and atomistic adversaries. Just as Leibniz's dynamic reality denies 1) the Monism of Spinosa, 2) the Mechanism of Descartes and 3) the indivisible Ultimate Reality of the atomists — just so does Dharmakīrti deny 1) the Monism of Mādhyamika-Vedānta, 2) the Mechanism of the Sānkhya who regards all changes in nature as due to the variations of distribution of one constant quantity of moving matter, and 3) the atomic theory of the Vaišeşikas. The Own Essences just as the Monads are dynamic and instantaneous. «While motion, says Leibniz, is a successive thing, which never exists any more than time, because all its parts never exist together... force or effort, on the other hand, exists quite completely at every instant and must be something genuine and real». It is interesting in the highest degree that duration, extension and motion are denied reality by Leibniz exactly on the same grounds as in Buddhism, viz, because they cannot exist completely in a single point-instant. «Substances, says Leibniz, cannot be conceived in their bare essence without any activity, activity is of the essence of substance in general». This is exactly the Buddhist principle «existence is work», «efficiency is reality». A further, most remarkable, analogy consists in the contention that «as the Monads are purely intensive centres or (dynamic) units, each must be absolutely exclusive of all others, no Monad can influence another or produce any change in it. Just so the Buddhist units, we have seen, although they are nothing but efficiency, cannot really produce any thing, they are «unemployed». But here stops the analogy. The Monad, just as Aristotle's «First Essence», is an Entelechy, it is a Soul. In Buddhism it is an external point-instant.

Omitting a series of philosophers who have assumed a difference between the contingent reality of the empirically cognized object and its transcendental unknown source of final reality, we may be allowed to dwell somewhat longer on Kant, because here, as it would seem, we meet not only with some parallel lines and detached bits of similar argument, but with a similarity of the whole conception. The following points attract our attention.

1) Kant assumes, just as Dignāga, two and only two sources of our knowledge and a radical difference between them.

2) Although radically different and theoretically separable these two sources appear empirically always as mixed up. The difference between them is, consequently, not empirical, but transcendental.

3) In all other systems clear and distinct thinking has been assumed as a guaranty of truth. Through the senses phenomena alone are confusedly cognized, through the understanding, or the reason, ultimate reality, the things, as they really are in themselves, are clearly cognized. Kant, in his critical period, has reversed this relation. Clear and distinct cognition refers only to phenomena, but «that which in the phenomena corresponds to sensation, constitutes the transcendental matter of all objects, as Things by themselves (Reality, *Sachheit*)». According to the Buddhists, we have seen, the Thing-in-Itself is cognized in pure sensation. The things cognized clearly and distinctly are objectivized images.

4) The Thing-in-Itself is incognizable, says Kant, we cannot represent it in a sensuous image, it is the limit of cognition. The ultimate particular, says the Buddhist, cannot be reached by our cognition.

5) It nevertheless exists and is efficient, says Kant, it is nothing but the way in which our sensitivity is affected by external reality. The ultimate particular, says Dharmakīrti, is the ultimate reality, because alone it has efficiency.

6) There is a double reality and double causality, the ultimate reality-causality of the Thing-in-Itself and the indirect reality-causality of the empirical object. The thing-in-itself is but another name for ultimate reality-causality, it is nothing but the fact of this reality-causality. This point which is expressed by the Buddhists with sufficient precision, has puzzled the interpreters of Kant, because Reality is conceived by him as a synthetic Category, as a Reality

which is not ultimate, as an enduring and extended reality, *realitas phaenomenon.*[1]

The fundamental difference between the Kantian Thing-in-Itsef and Dharmakīrti's «Own Essence» consists in the clear identification of the latter with a single point-instant of Reality which corresponds to a moment of sensation. The Indian Thing is transcendental in the measure in which a single point-instant, as being outside every synthesis, cannot be empirically cognized.[2] Otherwise Kant's characteristic «what in the phenomena corresponds to sensation is the transcendental Thing-in-Itself»[3] fully applies to the Indian first Essence. A further difference may be found in the clear identification by the Buddhists of the Thing-in-Itself with pure existence.[4] This existence is not a predicate, not a category, it is the common Subject of all predication. In connection therewith is the logical use made of the conception of Ultimate Reality by the Buddhists. Ultimate Reality is also the Ultimate Subject[5] of all judgments and, as we shall see in the sequel, of all inferences. A further important difference between the Kantian Thing-in-Itself and the Buddhist «Own-Essence», consists in this, that Kant assumes an internal Thing-in-Itself behind every empirical Ego, just as he assumes an external Thing-in-Itself at the bottom of every external object. There are thus, it would seem, two sets of Things-in-Themselves, the one facing the other. This is different in Buddhist philosophy. The «Own-Essence»[6] is the external Thing as it is strictly in itself, shorn of all relations. The corresponding internal Thing is pure sensation shorn of all

---

1 This evidently must mean that there is another a non-synthetic, ultimate Reality, the reality, not of the continuum, but of the point-instant, cp. CPR., p. 137. It is just the Thing-in-Itself. The term «thing» already implies existence and is explained by Kant as meaning Reality *(Ding = Sachheit = Realität)*. Nevertheless a host of interpreters have accused him, and are still accusing him, of the most glaring contradiction by imputing him the theory of a thing which is not a thing, a thing which does nothing, although it is the ultimate thing, i. e., reality and efficiency itself, pure reality and «pure» efficiency.

2 *kṣaṇasya (jñānena) prāpayitum aśakyatvāt*, NBT., p. 12. 19.

3 CPR., p. 117 (Ch. on Schematism).

4 *sattā-mātra.*

5 *dharmin*, the common subject for all *dharmas*. Cp. Kant's words (in the same chapter) — «substance, if we leave out the sensuous conditions of permanence, would mean nothing hut a something that may be conceived as a subject, without being the predicate of anything else».

6 *sva-lakṣaṇa = bāhya-artha.*

construction.[1] But pure sensation and the corresponding pure object are not two things existing on equal terms of reality. They are one Ultimate Reality dichotomized into Subject and Object by that same faculty of constructive imagination[2] which is the architect of the whole empirical world and which always works by the dichotomizing or dialectical method. The external «Own-Essence» is the Ultimate Reality on the logical plane only. Since all philosophy must finally be monistic, there is in the very final translogical plane a Final Absolute in which Subject and Object coalesce. This is, as Dharmakīrti says, a Thing which we can neither cognize nor express in speech. That is to say, it is still more remote from the empirical plane than the incognizable pont-instant of external reality, it is the Final Absolute, personified as Buddha in his Cosmical Body.

The Buddhist Thing-in-Itself as pure sensation is a bit nearer the empirical world than the Kantian one. Kant protested against this half-empirical interpretation of the Thing-in-Itself which, according to him, is transcendental. As a single moment, the Buddhist Thing can hardly be said to be empirical.

That part of the Buddhist argument which consists in an identification of Existence with the essence of Affirmation strikes us by its similarity with some ideas expressed by Herbart. Existence means for this philosopher «absolute positing», «acknowledgment of that something which cannot be denied in thought», whose essence is not to admit negation.[3] The notion of existence is a sort of positing which means that it is the simple positing of something and nothing more. «Objects are being posited, says he, and they can be doubted so as to disappear completely. But they do not dissapear. The positing of something remains, it is only changed, it is directed towards something different from what it was directed to precedently. The quality (i. e., the general) is sacrificed to doubt, but that something which is posited (i. e., the extreme particular) is different, it is something incognizable».[4] «This Absolute Positing» is contained in every pure sensation, without being noticed by us.[5] Nobody will believe that the Nothing exists, since it would then become apparent. The characteristic of existence is to be

---

1 *nirvikalpaka.*

2 *grāhya-grāhaka-kalpanā.*

3 «Absolute Position, Anerkennung von dem, dessen Setzung nicht aufgehoben wird», cp. Met. II, § 201.

4 Ibid.

5 Ibid., § 204.

the ultimately simple. Existence is not liable to negation. This identification of pure existence with the sensible core of reality, its characterisation as the unknowable object, as the simple, i. e., the extreme particular, as the essence of affirmationn which allows of no denial, its contrast with the quality, i. e., with the general, which is no affirmation in itself,[1] but can be doubted, i. e., alternately affirmed and denied — all this argumentative speculation strikes us by its similarity with Buddhist ideas.[2]

That part of the Buddhist theory which compares the point-instant of Ultimate Reality with a Differential and the job of the intellect with mathematical computation[3] is also not left without a parallel in the history of European philosophy. The post-Kantian philosopher Solomon Maimon is known for his theory of «Differentials of Sensibility». «The Differentials of the Objects are the Noumena, says he, the Objects constructed out of them are the Phaenomena».[4]

---

1 We can say both «the cow is» and «the cow is not», but the *Hoc Aliquid* always is, it cannot be denied because its denial would be the affirmation of the Nothing, or, as Vācaspatimišra puts it, it would be «non existence in person», *vigrahavān abhāva;* cp. Tātp. 389. 22 — *na tv abhāvo nāmo kašcid vigrahavān asti yaḥ pratipatti-gocaraḥ syāt.*

2 Absolute Position = *vidhi-svarūpa* = *svalakṣaṇa* = *sattā-mātra* = *vastu-mātra* = *niramša-vastu* = *anavayavin.*

3 *samākalana.*

4 Cp. R. Kroner. Von Kant bis Hegel, I, p. 354.

PART III.

THE CONSTRUCTED WORLD.

CHAPTER I.

JUDGMENT.

§ 1. Transition from pure sensation to conception.

Having excluded from the realm of Ultimate Reality every bit of imagination, having reduced it to mere point-instants which include no synthesis, the Buddhist logicians were landed in the same difficulty which must befall every system endeavouring to establish a difference in kind between the two sources of our knowledge of the external world, the passive receptivity of the senses and the spontaneous productions of imagination. In Ultimate Reality, we have seen, there is no duration and no extension, no quality and no motion, no universals, no concrete individuals, etc. On the other side, in the imagined empirical world, there is an imagined time, there is a constructed space, there are manifold imagined qualities, motions, universals, particulars, etc. Both realms, the transcendental unimagined reality and the imagined or empirical one, are absolutely dissimilar.

There is between them no other connection than a causal one. The point-instants are points of efficiency, they possess the capacity of stimulating the understanding to construct in imagination illusive pictures which by ordinary men are mistaken for reality itself. This case of causality is a glaring challenge to the prejudice shared by all realistic systems that the effect must be similar to its cause. The effect is here absolutely dissimilar to its cause. There is between the point-instant and the image, or conception, constructed by imagination on its instigation, a «conformity»,[1] or correspondence, which we may,

---

[1] *sārūpya*, cp. vol. II, App. IV.

if we like, also call a kind of similarity, but it will be a «similarity between things absolutely dissimilar».[1] The Buddhist law of causation as Functional Interdependence does not militate against the dissimilarity between cause and effect. Given a point of reality and a receptive consciousness a sensation arises. The corresponding image likewise arises in functional dependence on a moment of sensation and a moment of objective reality.

However, some of the Buddhist logicians were puzzled to fill up the gap between pure sensation and the following mnemic image and thus to reestablish the unity of knowledge which they themselves have destroyed by assuming a radical distinction of the two sources of cognition. The solution of this fundamental problem, it is clear, would at the same time bridge over the abyss between ultimate and empirical reality and, since reality is nothing but efficiency and constructive imagination nothing but logic, it would also establish a link between logic and its efficacy.

Two explanations were propounded, a logical and a psychological one. The logical problem will be examined later on, on the occasion of Buddhist Nominalism and the Buddhist theory of Universals.[2] The psychologisal one is nothing else than the theory of attention or «mental sensation» already mentioned.[3]

The moment of pure sensation or sense-intuition is immediately followed by a moment of mental sensation or intelligible intuition. In one and the same stream of thought there are then two consecutive moments which are related as cause and effect. They are homogeneous in so far as they belong to the same stream of thought,[4] but they are heterogeneous in so far as the first is a sensation by the outer sense, the second a sensation by the inner sense or by the mind. From the standpoint of empirical psychology it is simply the moment of attention or of attending to the preceding moment of pure sensation. The mind which in early Buddhism was a special, sixth,[5] organ of cognition, and in the realistic systems identified with a nervous current, is here identified with a moment of attention[6] which is called «mental sensation» or sensation by the inner sense, in distinction

---

1 *atyanta-vilakṣaṇānām sālakṣaṇyam*, cp. NVTT., p. 340.17.

2 *apoha-vāda*.

3 *mānasa-pratyakṣa*, cp. above, p. 161, and vol. II, App. III.

4 *eka-santāna-patita*.

5 *mana-āyatana, āyatana* № 6, cp. CC., p. 8.

6 *manasi-kāra*, resp. *yoniśo-manasi-kāra*, cp. vol. II, App. III, p. 328, p. 3.

from «pure sensation» or sensation by the outer sense-organ. During this second moment of sensation the object is present in the ken, so that intelligible intuition is the joint product of the cooperation of the first moment of sensation with the second moment of the object.[1] In the next, third, moment of cognition the mnemic elements become aroused, the sensations fade away and the intellect constructs an abstract image according to its own laws.

This second moment of sensation, although it, from the empirical point of view, is nothing but a moment of attention, is, from the epistemoligical point of view, a direct, non-synthetical, unique moment, a moment which, although characterized as a moment of intelligible intuition, nevertheless lacks the most characteristic feature of being intelligible, it is as unimaginable and unutterable as the first, it is therefore half-intelligible, something intermediate between pure sensation and the corresponding intelligible image.

Only this kind of intelligible intuition, conditioned as it is by the presence of the object in the ken, is accessible to ordinary mankind.[2]

If we would possess real intelligible intuition not limited by a preceding moment of sensible intuition, we would be omniscient, we would not be what we are; we would cease to be human beings and become super-men.

The theory of the existence of a moment of intelligible intuition which follows on the mnemic image was first hinted by Dignāga in opposition to the theory of the Realists who imagined a Mind in the shape of a nervous current as a running atom establishing a connection between the organs of the outer senses and the Soul, the subject of cognition. It was developed by Dharmakīrti and received its final precision at the hands of Dharmottara. Pure sensation, according to Dharmakīrti, although it is also a necessary condition of all empirical knowledge, is a palpable reality, its existence is established, as we have seen, in the way ot an experiment in intro-

---

1 Cp. vol. II, App. III.

2 The Yogi and the Buddha cognize everything *sākṣāt*, they have only one *pramāṇa*. With the attainment of *dṛṣṭi-mārga* the man becomes *ārya* and that is a different *pudgala*, TS. and TSP., p. 901—902, cp. p. 396, 1—2. The Sarvāstivādins maintained that the Yogis omniscience proceeded by supernaturally clever inferences, since direct sense-perception applie's only to the present point-instant. But the Santrāntika school objected and maintained that the Yogis possessed intelligible (*mānasa*) intuition which cognizes the things in themselves (*svalakṣaṇa*) not by inference, but directly, cp. NB., p. 11, 17 ff.

spection.[1] But the moment of intelligible intuition is entirely transcendental.[2] There are no facts[3] and no possible experiments in order to prove its existence empirically. According to Dharmottara it is simply the first moment of the constructive operation of the understanding. It is a different moment, because its function is different. The function of pure sensation, we have seen, is to signalize the presence of the object in the ken, the function of intelligible intuition consists in «evoking the image of its own object».

Intelligible sensation is a middle term which is supposed to unite sensation with conception with a view to knowledge. But the Realist objects that it is impossible to unite two so absolutely heterogeneous things as a point-instant of sensibility with a clear image. If two such things could be made similar by something intermediate, says he, then «a fly could be made similar to an elephant through the medium of a donkey».[4]

Thus the objections against this theory of a moment of intelligible intuition came first of all from the side of the Realists who denied the sharp distinction between sensation and understanding and denied the theory of Instantaneous Existence. «The senses, says Vācaspatimiśra, do not reflect separate moments, therefore it is not possible that the intellect should grasp the moment following upon the moment which has produced the simple reflex; but, on the contrary, the intellect grasps just the same object as has been grasped by the senses».[5]

Among the Buddhist logicians themselves the theory has produced a variety of interpretations. The opposition against the hard and fast separation of sensation from the understanding as maintained by Dharmottara seems to have arisen in the school of Mādhyamika—Yogācāras who partly inclined towards a realistic logic and were partly steeped in the prejudice that the effect must be similar to the cause. Jamyan-zhadpa testifies[6] to the fact that the school of the Extreme Relativists, the Mādhyamika-Prasangika school, did not object against the possibility of a simultaneous cognition by the

---

1 Cp. above, p. 150.

2 *atyanta-parokṣa*, cp. vol. II, p. 333, n. 3.

3 NBT., p. 11.1 — *na tv asya prasādhakam asti pramāṇam.*

4 Tātp., p. 341. 25 — *hasti-maśakāv api rāsabhaḥ sārūpayet*, cp. transl., vol. II, p. 423.

5 Cp. vol. II., p. 321; NK., p. 122.

6 Cp. vol. II., p. 327.

senses and by the understanding at once. The commentator Prajñākara Gupta inclines towards the same view.[1] But Jñānagarbha and others maintained[2] that the theory of a moment of intelligible intuition was devised in order to have something intermediate between pure sensation and a corresponding conception. How could it otherwise happen that a pure sensation should be comprehended under a conception with which it has no point of connection, from which it is «absolutely dissimilar»? There must be some third thing, homogeneous, on the one side, with pure sensation, and, on the other, with the intelligible conception in order to render the application of the latter to the former possible. Such is the intelligible intuition. It is a pure intuition and this feature makes it homogeneous with pure sensation. On the other hand, it is an intelligible intuition, and this feature makes it homogeneous with the intelligible conception.[3] The transition from sensation to conception is thus facilitated and the principle of homogeneous causation saved.

However Dharmottara rejects this interpretation.[4] Causation as Functional Interdependence can exist between absolutely heterogeneous facts. Sensation can call forth an image directly, without any intermediate operation. The intellect begins to operate when the operation of the senses is finished. If that were not the case, there could be no sharp distinction between sensation and conception, there would be between them only a difference of degree, sensation would be a confused conception, in other words, there would be no pure sensation at all.[5]

To maintain the simultaneous existence of two pure intuitions, the one sensible, the other intelligible, is absurd, but on the principle of Functional Interdependence, the intelligible intuition arises just at the moment when the outer sensation having achieved its function disappears.[6] The hard and fast line between sensibility and understanding can be saved only on the assumption that the one has finished its task when the other begins.

---

1 Ibid., p. 315 ff.

2 Ibid.

3 Ibid., p. 314.

4 Ibid., p. 316. ff.

5 Cp. NBT., p. 10.22—*itarathā cakṣur-āśritātva-anupapattiḥ kasyacid api vijñānasya.*

6 *uparata-vyāpāre cakṣuṣi*, NBT., p. 10.21.

The moment of intelligible intuition is not empirically cognizable, because it is a moment; a single moment is always transcendental, it cannot be represented in an image, it is unutterable, but its assumption is urged upon us by the whole system which is built up on a radical distinction of the two sources of knowledge.[1]

§ 2. THE FIRST STEPS OF THE UNDERSTANDING.

The understanding is characterized as the active, spontaneous part of cognition. Its business is to construct the manifold of the empirical world out of that poor pure reality which is presented it by the medium of a merely receptive sensibility. It begins to give form to this material. The ultimate reality, the thing as it is in itself, is characterized as an external point-instant. But, strictly speaking, even that cannot be said, because in the first moment it is a simple sensation which is internal and nothing more. But as soon as the understanding is awaked, it at once dichotomizes this simple sensation in an internal something and its source. It is differentiated into subject and object; into a sensation proper and its external cause. This is the first mind-construction, a kind of «transcendental apperception», a feature owing to which every further cognition is accompanied by the consciousness of an Ego. According to early Yogācāras it is already a thought-construction.[2] According to the logicians, as we have seen,[3] it is still a

---

[1] Kant was also puzzled to find «a third thing homogeneous on the one side with the category, and on the other with the phenomenon»... This intermediate thing must be «intelligible on the one side and sensuous on the other». So far the problem is similar. But for Kant the gap to be filled lies between the empirical concept or image and the corresponding pure *a priori* concept. E. Caird (The crit. Phil. of I. Kant, v. I, p. 423, 2-d ed.), addresses to Kant's theory of schematism a criticism which *mutatis mutandis* could be applied to Dharmottara's views. «By taking thought as purely universal and perception as purely particular, says he, the middle term is made impossible; but if perception is taken as the apprehension of individual things (empirically), the middle term is unnecessary, for in such perception the individual is already a particularized universal». Dharmottara would have probably answered that a critical philosophy cannot abandon the principle of a difference in kind between sensibility and understanding, for to abandon it means either returning to the naive realism of the Naiyāyiks or to loose oneself in the wholesale skepticism of the Mādhyamikas.

[2] *grāhya-grāhaka-kalpanā.*

[3] Cp. above, p. 163.

direct sensation.[1] After that the mind begins to «murmur».[2] The sensation is either pleasant or unpleasant, and this engenders volition.[3] The external object becomes either desirable or undesirable. The mind then begins to «understand»,[4] and constructs the object according to the five fundamental notions or categories which are its own method of procedure.[5] It then forsakes the method of «murmur». It speaks, and says «this», i. e., this reality, is «something blue», a quality; «this is a cow», i. e., a species, etc.

Dignāga's table of categories will be examined later on. Here we call attention to the fact that the mind's spontaneity is described, just as some European philosophers describe it, as will associated to understanding.[6] But besides containing the double operation of volition and understanding, consciousness in the stage of awakening contains moreover the double operation of a searching[7] and a fixing[8] mind.

This double operation is, according to Vasubandhu, present in the subconscious, as well as in the state of full conscious, cognition. There is always, previously to the formation of a concept, some running of the mind through the manifold of sensuous intuition.[9] The Synthesis of Apprehension precedes the Recognition in a concept.

These two operations are already present in sub-consciousness. Under the threshold[10] of consciousness they are a «murmur« of the will. Emerging above the threshold of consciousness[11] they become understanding. Yašomitra[12] explains the double operation of a Synthesis of Apperception and a Recognition in a Concept by the following illustration. When a potter has manufactured a series of pots, he examines their quality by the pitch of the sound which they produce on being struck. He goes through the series in giving a slight

---

1 *jñāna-anubhava*, cp. NBT., p. 11.14.

2 *mano-jalpaḥ*.

3 *cetanā*.

4 *prajñā*.

5 *pañcavidha-kalpanā*.

6 *cetanā-prajñā-višeṣa*.

7 *anveṣako mano-jalpaḥ = vitarka*.

8 *pratyavekṣako mano-jalpaḥ = vicāra*.

9 *It is again absent in dhyāna = nirvitarka-nirvicāra-prajñā*.

10 *anatyūha-avasthāyām cetanā*; *ūha = nirvikalpaka*.

11 *atyūha - avasthāyām prajñā*; *atyūha* = über der Schwelle des Bewusstseins.

12 Ad AKB., II. 33.

stroke to each pot and when he thus finds out the defective one, he says, «there it is!». The examination of the pots is like the operation of the mind's running through the manifold of sensibility. The finding out of the defective pot is like the mind's fixation before the formation of a concept. The first operation is sometimes characterized as the mind's «grossness»[1] or primitivity, the second as its «subtility»[2] or «elaborateness».[3] Thus the Synthesis of Apprehension precedes the Recognition of the object in a concept.

§ 3. A JUDGMENT WHAT.

From among the two sources of our knowledge sense-perception has been defined above as the sensational core of perception, that part of it which remains when every bit of thought-construction and imagination has been eliminated. But this is only a transcendental source of knowledge.[4] Empirical perception is that act of cognition which signalizes the presence of an object in the ken[5] and is followed by the construction of an image of that object[6] and by an act of identification[7] of the image with the sensation. Such identification is made in a perceptual judgment of the pattern «this is a cow», where the element «this» refers to the sensational core incognizable in itself, and the element «cow» to the general conception expressed in a connotative name and identified with the corresponding sensation by an act of imputation. According to the Realists who do not admit any transcendental source of knowledge, this judgment is included in every sense-perception, it is sense-perceived, it is also a sensation.[8] But according to the Buddhists it is excluded from it, although it follows in its track. The senses alone could never arrive at a judgment.[9]

---

1 *audarikatā.*

2 *sūkṣmatā.*

3 The medical schools have carried the analysis of the subconscious mind into further details, cp. Caraka, IV. 1. 18 ff.

4 *atīndriyam nirvikalpakam.*

5 *sākṣāt - kāritva - vyāpāra.*

6 *vikalpena anugamyate.* Therefore the seemingly conflicting statements TSP., p. 399. 16 — *sākāram eva pramāṇam,* and ibid., p. 390. 14 — *saṃvāditve'pi* (sic) *na pramāṇyam.*

7 *ekatra-adhyavasāya.*

8 *adhyavasāyātmakam pratyakṣam = savikalpakam.*

9 *yebhyo hi cakṣurādibhyo vijñānam utpadyate na tad-vaśāt taj-jñānam... śakyate avasthāpayitum* (*= avasātum*). NBT., p. 15. 17.

This judgment of perception is the fundamental act of the understanding. All the operations of the understanding can be reduced to judgments, the understanding may be defined as the faculty of judging, but its fundamental act is that which is included in the negative definition of pure sense-perception;[1] it is a non-sensation, it is a thought-construction,[2] it is the perceptual judgment of the pattern «this is a cow». Since the element «this»,[3] the sensational core, has been characterized above as referring us to the incognizable Thing-in- Itself, such a judgment can be expressed in the formula $x = a$. The judgment is thus a mental act uniting sensation with conception with a view to knowledge. For neither sensation alone, as pure sensation, affords any knowledge at all; nor conception alone, i. e., pure imagination, contains any real knowledge. Only the union of these two elements in the judgment of perception is real knowledge. Sensation, we have seen, imparts to knowledge reality,[4] particularity,[5] vividness[6] and efficient affirmation.[7] Conception, or the constructed image, on the other hand, imparts to it its generality,[8] its logic,[9] its necessity,[10] its clearness and distinctness.[11]

The sanscrit term which we thus translate as judgment means, in its common application, a decision.[12] It is just a judgment, a verdict, a volitional act, it is rendered it Tibetan as «volition».[13] More especially it is a decision regarding the identification of two things.[14] It is also used as a technical term in another very developed Indian science, the theory of poetical figures.[15] These are divided into simple comparisons and identifications. Identification means there a poetical assertion of identity of two things which are by no means identical,

---

1 *kalpanāpoḍha.*
2 *kalpanā = adhyavasāya.*
3 *idaṃtā.*
4 *vāstavatva.*
5 *svalakṣaṇatva.*
6 *sphuṭābhatva.*
7 *vidhi-svarūpatva.*
8 *sāmānya-lakṣaṇa = sārūpya.*
9 *saṃvāditva.*
10 *niścaya.*
11 *niyata-ākāratva.*
12 *adhyavasāya.*
13 *zhen-pa.*
14 *ekatvādhyavasāya.*
15 Cp. Alaṃkāra-sarvasva, p. 56 and 65.

as, e. g., of the moon with a damzel's face. Just so is the perceptual judgment here characterized as an assertion of similarity between two things absolutely dissimilar.[1] This judgment is synthetical in so far it brings together two parts which are quite different. The point-instant of reality receives in such a judgment its place in a corresponding temporal series of point-instants, it becomes installed in concrete time and becomes a part of an object having duration.[2] Owing to a special synthesis of consecutive point-instants it becomes an extended body[3] and owing again to a special synthesis of these moments it gets all its sensible and other qualities, it becomes a universal.[4]

§ 4. Judgment and the synthesis in concepts.

Besides the synthesis examined above, the synthesis, namely, which consists in referring an image to a sensation, there is in every perceptual judgment another synthesis[5] which consists in bringing under the head of a synthetic image, or of a general conception, of a manifold of single impressions, sensations and experiences. «What is a judgment?» asks a Buddhist in the course of a discussion regarding the reality of the external world.[6] That is to say, what is the volitional act by which I decide that an image must be identified with a point-instant of external reality? He answers, «to judge means to conceive».[7] Both inference and sense-perception contain judgments, but an inference deals with conceptions (directly), it is «in its essence an act of conceiving»,[8] whereas perception, or a perceptual judgment, is an act of conceiving (indirectly), because it is a sensation which «calls forth a conception».[9] Now, if a judgment, besides being a judgment, i. e., a decision, is also an act of conceiving, what does the term «conception» properly mean? The answer is that to conceive means to imagine, or to construct an object in imagination. The object conceived is an object imagined. To imagine productively means to produce unity in

---

1 *atyanta-vilakšaṇānām sālakṣaṇyam = sārūpyam.*

2 *santāna.*

3 Cp. Prašast., and N. Kandalī, p. 63 ff. where time and space are represented as realities, but their parts as constructed in imagination.

4 *sāmānya-lakṣaṇa = ekatva-adhyavasāya.*

5 *ekatva-adhyavāsāya.*

6 NK., p. 257.

7 *vikalpo adhyavasāyaḥ.*

8 *anumānam vikalpa-rūpatvāt tad-viṣayam.*

9 *pratyakṣam tu vikalpa-jananāt.*

difference, to synthesize in a (fictitious) unity a variety of time, place and condition.[1] The expression of this synthesis is the judgment of the form «this is that»,[2] in which the non-synthetic element «thisness»[3] is coupled with the synthetic element of «thatness».[4]

Consequently there is no substantial difference between a perceptual judgment and a conception, on the one hand, and between a conception, an image, productive imagination and a general notion on the other. Particular conceptions, images and notions do not exist. There are images referred to particulars and they may be metaphorically called particulars, but in themselves they are always general.

The cognizing individual has indeed a faculty of sense-perception and a faculty of imagination. Vācaspatimišra[5] makes a following statement of the Buddhist view regarding this subject: «When the cognizing individual thinks that he perceives by his senses an image which he has really constructed himself, he simply conceals as it were his imaginative faculty and puts to the front his perceptive faculty. This imaginative faculty is the mind's own characteristic, its spontaneity, it has its source in a natural constructive capacity by which the general features of the object are apprehended (i. e., constructed). Since the image is called forth by a reflex, he naturally thinks that he perceives the image as present in his ken, but it is really constructed by his own productive imagination».

§ 5. Judgment and namegiving.

However not every kind of the conceiving activity of the mind is taken into account when the two sources of knowledge are characterized as the non-conceptive and the conceptive. Some of the fundamental varieties of this differentiating and uniting activity are left alone. The original differentiation of sensation into subject and object,[6] the initial stage of the synopsis in the chaos of manifold impressions, the operation of running through[7] these impressions and

---

1 *sa* (sic) *ca vikalpānām gocaro yo vikalpyate, deša-kāla-avasthā-bhedena ekatvena anusandhīyate*, cp. Tātp., p. 338, 15.

2 *„tad eva idam" iti*, ibid.

3 *idamtā.*

4 *tattā.*

5 Tātp., p. 88, 8, transl. in vol. II, App. I, pp. 260 ff. (lit. transl. ibid., p. 261 n. 8).

6 *grāhya-grāhaka-kalpanā.*

7 *vitarka.*

stopping[1] at some of them as long as they are not yet stabilized enough in order to be definitely fixed by receiving a name — have no importance in a system of logic.[2]

That conceiving activity which comes directly into play when a perceptual judgment is formed can be clearly distinguished by its mark; this mark consists in the capacity of being expressed in speech. Conceptions are utterable, just as sensations are unutterable. A mental construction which implies a distinct cognition of a mental reflex which is capable of coalescing with a verbal designation — this variety of the spontaneous activity of the mind is meant when sensation is contrasted with conception, says Dharmakīrti.[3] Thus the Indian «conception» coincides more or less with the European, since its association with a name and its generality are assumed as its principal characteristics on both sides. Just as the European science[4] establishes a mutual influence, of conceptions on the formation of names and *vice versa* of names on the formation of conceptions, just so, says Dignāga, «the names have their source in concepts and the concepts have their source in names.[5]

Pure sensation and its corresponding Thing-in-Itself have been characterized above[6] as being unutterable. It follows from it that conception and judgment can be defined as that element which is utterable, which receives a name.

Thus it is that conception comprehends every thought capable of being expressed in words[7] and excludes pure sensation whose content cannot be so expressed. Thus the predicate in the normal type of a judgment is always a concept. A predicate is just a predicate; it is, as

---

1 *vicāra*.

2 Cp. TSP., p. 367. 8 ff.

3 *abhilāpinī pratītiḥ kalpanā*, TSP., pp. 369. 9, 371. 21; cp. NB. I. 5.

4 Cp.. Sigwart, Logik, I, p. 51.

5 *vikalpa-yonayaḥ śabdāḥ, vikalpāḥ śabda-yonayaḥ.*

6 Cp. p. 185.

7 *jātyādi-yojanā=kalpanā* is admitted by some adversaries. The true opinion of. Dignāga (*sva-prasiddha*) is *abhilāpinī pratītiḥ kalpanā=nāma-yojanā kalpanā*. He nevertheless in Nyāya-mukha (TSP., p. 372. 22 ff., cp. Tucci, transl., p. 50), and in the Pr. samucc. I. 2, has expressed himself so as to satisfy both opinions. Cp. TSP., p. 368. 25 ff. This has been criticized by Śankarasvāmin and others, ibid., p. 367. 4 ff. But if we interpret the passage of Dignāga as meaning *namnā jāti - guṇa - kriyā - dravya - kalpanā* the criticism will be cleared away, since *kalpanā* will then be *nāma - kalpanā* in general, and the other 4 *kalpanās* will be its subordinate varieties, cp. ibid., p. 369, 23 ff.

the name indicates, predicable or utterable. It is contrasted with the non-predicate, the subject, which is always, *quà* pure subject, unutterable. If all thinking reduces to judgments and all judgments are, directly or indirectly, perceptual judgments, our cognition can be characterized as the union of an utterable element with an unutterable one, or as a reference of a conception to its corresponding pure object. And just as the reality of pure sensation is established by Dharmakīrti in the course of an experiment in introspection, just so the narrow association of conceptions with words is also proved by introspection.[1] On such occasions when we freely indulge in fancy and allow our imagination a free play,[2] when we are engaged in pure imagination, we notice that the play of our visions and dreams is accompanied by an inward speech. «Nobody can deny that imagination is interwoven with speech», says Śāntirakṣita.[3] Pure imagination is an imagination without reality; pure reality is reality without imagination. A judgment, or cognition, is imagination with an objective reference to reality and, this is always something utterable associatively referred to something unutterable.

§ 6. Categories.

A classification of judgments is therefore a classification of names. Since all cognition reduces to judgment and a judgment is an (illicite) combination of a non-synthetic element with a synthetic one, of an unutterable element with a name or a predicate, the question arises, what are the ultimate kinds or categories of predicates or of names? It is not a question about the categories of all namable things, since there is only one ultimate thing and that is the Thing-in-Itself. This ultimate reality cannot be dichotomized or classified, it is essentially one. Neither can it be named, it is a non-name, a non-predicate, it is the necessary subject in every judgment, for every description of predicates. However the manner of conceiving it and its names can be various, since all names are, directly or indirecly, names of its different attributes. Thus the most general relation, that which is conterminous with judgment or cognition in general, is the substance-to-quality relation, in the sense of the relation of a First Essence to all other categories of attributes.

1 *pratyakṣataḥ*, cp. TSP., p. 368, 1.

2 *cintotprekṣādi - kāle sā (kalpanā) śabdānuviddhā*, cp. TS., p. 368. 2—3.

3 Ibid.

The categories of the Buddhists are therefore very different from the categories of the Realists. The Nyāya-Vaišeṣika system establishes (finally) a Table of Categories containing 7 items: Substance, Quality, Motion, Universals, Differentials, Inherence and Non-existence. These are 7 kinds of Being or of Meaning expressed by names (*pada-artha*). In answer and in replacement of this table of Categories, Dignāga establishes a table of a five-fold «arrangement» or «construction» (*pañca-vidha-kalpanā*) of reality, which is but a classification of names (*nāma-kalpanā*).[1] They are — Proper Names, Classes, Qualities, Motions and Substances. They are nothing but names, mere names, not things.[2] The table really means, Proper Names, Class Names, Quality Names or Adjectives, Motion Names or Verbs, and Substance Names or Substantives. Just as Aristotle, Dignāga gives no definitions of them, but he illustrates them by examples. He says[3] — «a thing can be named by some sound at random, i. e., by a non-connotative proper name, e. g., «Diṭṭha» (a meaningless sound). In class-names it is given the name of a class, e. g., «a cow». In quality-names it is given the name of a (sensible) quality, e. g., «white». In verbs it is given the name of an action, e. g., «he cooks». In substantives it is characterized by (another) substance, e. g., «stick-possessor», «horn-possessor», «horny».

This table calls forth the following remarks. Its fundamental principle is a division of cognition into the non-synthetic and the synthetic principle in knowledge. The synthetic element is the same as the general, conceptual, predicable element, or the name. The names are then divided in five kinds, following mainly the division which was already established in Indian grammar. The proper names are not really names of individuals, they are, strictly speaking, also general names. Kamalašīla[4] says — «although the words like «Ḍiṭṭha» are generally admitted to be proper names, but, since they refer to a (continued) existence, from birth up to the moment of death, they are not capable of designating (a real individual) which changes every moment and is a real thing (in itself) having nothing in common with other things. The object they are intent upon and which they designate is (also) a class, inhering in a thing which is characterized by the limits of an enduring (lapse of) time». But since they contain

---

[1] Pr. sammucc., I. 2 ff.; cp. TSP., p. 369. 23 ff.; cp. Tātp., p. 52. 5 ff. and 102. 2 ff.

[2] *svasiddhaiva kevalā kalpanā (nāma-kalpanā)*, cp. TS., p. 369. 21.

[3] TSP., p., 369. 23 ff.

[4] Ibid., p. 370. 17 ff.

no connotation,[1] they are entered into the system as a separate item. «Besides the words like cow are generally known in common life as class names, but such words as *Citrangadā* are known in life as proper names».[2] Therefore, because not everybody knows that all names are general and that the proper names are no exception to the rule, they have been distinguished from the others.

Consequently the category of names, as understood by Dignāga, includes all other categories. We must conceive his fivefold division, according to the Indian method of counting only the final items in a classification, as a division into names and non-names, and then as a division of the names in four different kinds of names.

The category of substances is illustrated by the examples of «the possessor of a stick», «the possessor of horns» or «horny». We would call them possessive adjectives.[3] They are indeed secondary substances, such substances as characterize other substances. Only the First Essences of things can never become predicates, all other substances can become attributes in regard of other objects. They are thus not substances in their essence, but secondary or metaphorical substances, they can be both substance or attribute. Substance then means the possessor of an attribute. The ultimate and real possessor of all attributes is the Thing-in-Iself. All constructed objects, being attributes in regard of it, can be metaphorically called substances when they are characterized as possessing other substances.

Compared with the categories of the Vaišeṣikas we find in the table of Dignāga, with the *proviso* that they are not realities (*sattā*), but mere names (*nāma-kalpanā*), the three fundamental categories of Substance, Quality and Action. The category of Universals has disappeared from the list as a separate item, because all categories are Universals. The category of Differentials, in the sense of ultimate Differentials, has also disappeared, because it is a non-category, the unutterable element at the bottom of every object.[4] Inherence and Non-existence are also not to be found in this table of Dignāga.

---

1 Ibid., p. 370. 27 — *ta eva bhedā avivakṣita-bhedāḥ sāmānyam iti.*

2 Ibid., p. 370. 2 ff.

3 *daṇḍī, viṣāṇī.*

4 J. S. Mill, Logic, I. 79 calls attention to the fact, that «all the attributes of bodies which are classed under Quality and Quantity are grounded on the sensations which we receive from those bodies». This could mean that all classes are nothing but sensation differently interpreted by our imagination in its function of name-giving or judging.

We will find them, or their corresponding functions, in another table of categories, which owes its origin not to the perceptual judgment, but to the inferential judgment. It will be examined in connection with the theory of inference.

§ 7. Judgment viewed as analysis.

The same sanscrit term which has been interpreted above as meaning synthesis in a conception means, curiously enough, also analysis or division in the same conception. It is a *vox media*. The uniting tie of these both meanings seems to have been the idea of construction which is also the meaning, of the verbal root from which the world is derived.[1] The idea of construction naturally developped into the idéa of mental construction, of putting together in imagination.[2] It was then admirably suited to express the idea of rationalism, i. e., a consciousness which itself constructs the images of objects and projects them into the external world. It then began to connote the idea of artificiality, unreality, wrong imputation and illusion. On the other hand, another word derived from the same root, received the meaning of binary construction, division in two, dilemma, the dialectic tendency of thought in general, and finally analysis.[3] Both terms coalesced in the meaning of conception which represents a unity in difference.[4] When the unity is put to the front it is a synthesis; when its component parts are attended to, it is an analysis. Viewed as a judgment referring a constructed image to a point of reality, the conception contains both the elements. When we consider the movement of thought from the point to the image, we have a differentiation or analysis of the unity to a plurality. But when we consider the judgment as the reverse movement, from the image to the point to which it is being referred, we have a movement from plurality to unity, i. e., synthesis. The first step of conceptive thought, productive imagination or judgment — all three terms mean here the same — is the division of the original unity of the moment of sensation into a subject and an object, the construction in this original unity of the part «grasped» and the part «grasping».[5] But when the initiative of

---

1 √ kḷip.

2 *kalpanā* = *yojanā* = *ekīkaraṇa* = *ekatrādhyavasāya.*

3 *kalpanā* = *vikalpa* = *dvaidhīkaraṇa* = *vibhāga.*

4 *ta eva bhedā avivakṣita-bhedāḥ sāmānyam*, TSP., p. 370, 27.

5 On the dichotomizing, dialectical movement of thought in general cp. the words of Candrakīrti, Mādh. vr., p. 350, 12 ff. The difference between the

thought in our cognition was interpreted in Buddhist Logic as the faculty of judgment uniting a point-instant of ultimate reality with a constructed image, a judgment of which the subject corresponds to reality and the predicate to its image — then this kind of a conceiving or judging attitude of the mind was represented as a dispersion of the original reality into so many views that can be taken of it. The intellect indeed can take of the same reality an infinite variety of views, it can interpret the object called «jar» as an extended body, a solid body, a thing, a substance, possessing such and such colour and shape etc. etc., while the real core of these constructions is a moment of efficiency, it is always the same. The fire likewise may give rise to an infinite variety of interpretations and theories, while its ultimate reality is but a point-instant of heat-sensation. These views may be represented as so many rays dispersed by a single point of the real object. The thing as it is in itself becomes then the lively play of the fancy of our productive imagination. The Buddhist says:[1] «the indivisible Thing-in-Itself is then analysed, or imagined, as being such and such». It then receives all its general and special features. «That is the field of thought-construction which is (differently) constructed,[2] or differently imagined». Then the dispersed rays are as it were made to converge in the same thing as their focus. Thus the function of the understanding in judgments may be described as analytic-synthetic and likened to the dispersion of the rays from, and collecting them in, the same thing which is this focus.

§ 8. Judgment as objectively valid.

When the perceptual judgment of the pattern «this is a cow» is characterized as the mental act of uniting an extreme concrete and particular thing with a general conception, or of bringing a momentary sensation under the head of a constant conception, the Buddhist logician does not deny that such a definition contains a contradiction. It consists in establishing «a similarity between two things absolutely dissimilar». What is general and internal cannot be assimilated to

---

Mādhyamikas and the Yogācāras is that for the latter there is a foundation of reality in itself upon which the dialectical, artificial constructions of our mind are erected, whereas for the Mādhyamikas there is only relativity, nothing real in human cognition cp. Tsoṅ-khapa's Legs-bšad-sñiṅ-po.

[1] Tātp., p. 89, 12. — *evam avibhāgam svalakṣaṇam... tathā tathā vikalpayanti.*

[2] Tātp., p. 338. 15. *sa ca vikalpānām gocaro yo vikalpyate.*

what is external and singular. This is one of the reasons why the realistic schools denied the existence of images. They transferred the image into the external world and made of it a reality. They preferred this conceptual realism to the incongruity of uniting an internal image with an external thing. They objected to those realists who maintained the reality of both the image and its external pattern. They answered that in this case we must cognize in the judgment «this a blue patch» a double patch, we must perceive two blue patches at once, an internal one and an external one.[1] The difficulty is solved by the Buddhist by pointing to the fact that absolute similarity does not exist in the world; on the contrary, all things are absolutely dissimilar. They can however be made similar to a certain degree by neglecting their difference. Then all things will be similar to that amount to which their difference will be neglected. This is the Buddhist corollary from the law of Identity of Indiscernables. All cows are absolutely dissimilar with each another, but if we neglect this their dissimilarity, they will appear as similar when compared with horses and lions. The image of a thing is identified with an external point-instant only so far as the difference is neglected. The judgment thus becomes a necessary projection of an image into the external world, its necessary identification with a corresponding point-instant of external reality. The judgment «this is a cow» necessarily brings the synthesis of our understanding into objective reality.

Now what is this necessary objectivisation contained in every judgment? asks the Buddhist. Dharmottara[2] answers — to judge «means to deal with one's own internal reflex, which is not an external object, in the conviction that it is an external object». This identification is neither a «grasping» of an external object by its image, nor a converting of the image into an external object, nor is it a real uniting of two things, nor a real imputation, or placing of one thing in the place of another one.[3] It is our illusion, a wrong imputation.[4] The image is internal, but owing to an intrinsic necessity of our understanding the image is projected into the external world. Dharmottara[5] says «that form of the object, which is cognized by productive imagination

---

[1] *dve nīle iti syāt* cp. TSP., p. 574.17.

[2] NB., p. 7. 13, cp. NVTT., p. 339. 8.

[3] *na grahaṇam, na karaṇam, na yojanā, nāpi samāropaḥ*, cp. NVTT., p. 339, 10.

[4] *alīka eva*, ibid., p. 339, 21 ff.

[5] Ibid., p. 339, 22 ff.

as non-different from its counter-part (the thing as it is in itself), is our idea, it is not external».

The verbal expression of this externalisation consists in the copula «is», the *verbum substantivum*. It means to distinguish the objective unity of given representations from the subjective.[1] The verb «is» refers directly to a point-instant of external reality, to the bare thing as it is in itself. «If I consider, says Kamalašīla,[2] the meaning of the verb „is", no other meaning enters the province of my understanding than the meaning of the Thing as it is in itself».

To summarize: the judgment is first of all —

1) a judgment, i. e., a decision of our understanding,

2) this decision consists in giving an objective reference to a conception,

3) it does not differ from a conception, in as much a conception *quà* real knowledge must also contain an objective reference,

4) it contains a double synthesis, the one between the thing and the image, and another between the varieties of sensation which are brought to unity in conception,

5) it can be viewed also as an analysis, in as much as the concrete unity of the thing appears in it in the different aspects of its predicates,

6) it is an illusive, allthough necessary, objectivisation of the image.

As regards quantity, this judgment is always singular, it is even the extreme singular in its constant subject, which is the element «this». Its predicate is on the other hand, always a universal.

As regards quality, it is affirmative. The negative and illimited judgments are founded on a special principle. They belong to a later derivative stage of thought and cannot be coordinated to the perceptual judgment. As regards relation it is categorical. The hypothetical and disjunctive judgments are also derivative and will be examined in another context. As modality it is apodictic. The assertory is not distinguished from the apodictic and the problematic is no judgment at all. For expressing this necessity Dharmakīrti resorts to the same term[3] which expresses also the necessary connection of subject and predicate in an analytical judgment. «In every judgment which

---

1 CPR., p. 752 (§ 19).

2 TSP. p., 287, 17 — *svalakṣaṇādi-vyatirekeṇa anyo asty-artho nīrupyamāno na buddher gocaratām avatarati.*

3 *niščaya.*

is affirmed with full consciousness the necessity of its affirmation is included».[1] Vācaspatimiśra[2] quotes the Buddhist maintaining that «judgment (or decision), conception (or synthesis) and necessity (or apodictic necessity) are not different things».

A judgment has thus been described. Now what is a non-judgment? Dharmakīrti says,[3] it is a reflex.[4] «Sensation, says he, does not carry any necessity (of knowledge) for anybody. If it apprehends an object, it does it not in the way of a categorical necessity, but in the way of a (simple) reflex. In so far the sensation is capable of producing a subsequent categorical assertion, in so far only can it assume (the dignity) of a source of right cognition».

§ 9. History of the theory of judgment.

Sensation and conception are always present on the stage of Indian philosophy, but at different times, in different systems, they appear as different *dramatis personae* in the drama of cognition. The sharp distinction between pure sensation and the act of judgment, the idea that the judgment is a volitional act of decision, and that the whole of our cognition consists in an illicite connexion[5] of pure consciousness and semi-unconscious reflexes — these features belong already to the earliest stratum of philosophy in India. We meet them in the Sānkhya system and the medical schools.[6] Indeed, pure sensation appears there in the rôle of a separate spiritual substance,[7] whereas all mental phenomena and, the foremost among them, the judgment as a decision,[8] are reduced to the rôles of physiological reflexes, unconscious by themselves, but «mirrored» in the pure motionless Ego.

---

[1] Sigwart, cp. cit., I, 236.

[2] NVTT., p. 87, 25.

[3] Cp. Anekāntaj, p. 177.

[4] *pratibhāsa.*

[5] *sārūpya*, cp. CC., p. 64.

[6] Caraka, IV. 1. 37 ff.

[7] CC., p. 63 ff.

[8] *buddhi* «cognition» is here the Great Principle *(mahat)*, because it embraces everything cognizable. It is the first evolute of the Chief Principle *(pradhāna)* which is Matter *(prakṛti)* and at the same time it is the internal organ whose function is described as «decision» *(adhyavasāya)*. But this «decision» is by itself nothing but a special momentary collocation of infra-atomic particles of matter and energy. They become *quasi* conscious when «mirrored» in the pure light of the Soul.

The rôles are otherwise distributed in Hīnayāna Buddhism. The dualism of two substances is replaced by a pluralism of separate elements connected only by causal laws, and therefore appearing in «mutually dependent originations».[1] Pure sensation is an element[2] and conception (or judgment) is another element.[3] They represent two streams of momentary thought fulgurations running parallel, never acting upon each other, but appearing together.

The medical schools, the Sānkhya and Yoga systems, the Jains and the Hīnayāna Buddhists, all made their contributions to Indian psychology, especially in connexion with the phenomenon of trance. They watched the first steps of awakening consciousness and followed its development from the sub-conscious states through all degrees of concentration up to the condition of a cataleptic trance.[4] They established and described a series of mental faculties and states. We cannot, in the present condition of our knowledge, distinguish between the original contributions of each school to this common stock of knowledge. But the philosophical explaination is always the same. In Sānkhya and its dependent schools all mental phenomena are explained materialistically, their consciousness comes from a foreign substance. In Buddhism they are separate mental elements united by no enduring substance, but only by causal laws.[5]

In the realistic schools, Nyāya-Vaišeṣika and Mīmāmsā' there is, properly speaking, no separate perceptual judgment at all. Sensation is but a confused perception and a perceptual judgment is but a clear perception. That is a difference in degree, not in kind. Cognition in those systems resides in the Soul. All the variety of objects reside in the external world. They are contemplated by the Soul through the senses. Soul is itself imageless[6] and motionless, just as in the Sankhya system.

---

1 *pratītya-samutpanna.*

2 *vijñāna = prativijñaptiḥ.*

3 *sanjñā.*

4 *asanjñi-samāpatti.*

5 All mental elements are brought in early Buddhism under the four heads of feeling, conception (judgment), volition and pure consciousness (*vedanā-sanjñā-saṃskāra-vijñāna-skandha*), a classification, which, leaving alone the category of pure consciousness, is the same as the one at which European science arrived at a very recent date, cp. CC., p. 6 and 96 ff.

6 *nirākāra.* Since all the general and special qualities of the object are in these systems external realities, they are picked up by the Soul through the senses, but the *nirvikalpaka* cognizes the qualities by themselves (*svarūpataḥ*),

In Mahāyāna the theory of the perceptual judgment is the natural counterpart of the theory of sense-perception. The extreme idealists of the Mādhyamika school join hands with the extreme realists of Nyāya-Vaišeṣika in equally repudiating, although on contrary grounds, the theories of pure sensation and of the perceptual judgment.[1] The Sautrāntika school seems the first to have made the important departure of converting pure consciousness into a consciousness filled with images.[2] The external world *pari passu* had lost a part of its reality and became a hypothetical cause of our images.[3] Since the whole literature of this school, the works of Vasumitra, Kumāralābha and others, are lost, it is difficult to assign them their share in the development of the Buddhist theory. The same must be said of the Svātantrika school whose works, although partly extant, have not yet been investigated.

With the advent of the idealistic Yogācāras the hypothesis of an external world was dropped altogether. Asanga at the same time was the first to establish the difference between an unconstructed and a constructed element in knowledge.[4] He thus opened the path to the theories of pure sensation and perceptual judgment. The school of Dignāga and Dharmakīrti reverted in logic to the Sautrāntika standpoint. They admitted the reality of the extreme concrete and particular, of the Thing-in-Itself,[5] and converted the perceptual judgment into a link between ultimate reality reflected in a pure sensation and the images constructed by our intellect.

Among the followers of Dignāga the discussion on the proper formulation of this theory of a perceptual judgment continued. Some of his followers insisted that the special job of the intellect is conception or judgment, it must not be characterized as the subsumption

---

whereas the *savikalpaka* cognizes them as related (*mitho višeṣaṇa-višeṣya-bhāva-avagāhitvena*, cp. NVTT., p. 82. 8). In this sense the *savikalpaka* of the realists is also a kind of judgment.

1 Cp. my Nirvāṇa, p. 156 ff.

2 *sākāram vijñānam.*

3 *bāhyārtha-anumeyatva.*

4 Tucci, op. cit.

5 *svalakṣaṇa.* On the controversies which raged between the different schools round this problem of a point of ultimate reality as not being relative (*šūnya*), cp. my Nirvāṇa, p. 142 ff. Very interesting details on the same question are contained in Tsoṅ-khapa's work Legs-bšad-sñiṅ-po, commented upon by Khaiḍub.

of sensuous reality under one of the categories,[1] but simply as the faculty of names-giving.[2] The categories are but a further detail of naming. The phrasing of Dignāga admits both interpretations.[3] Dharmakīrti, Dharmottara and their followers rallied to Dignāga's own opinion. They define the constructive intellect, or the perceptual judgment, as the capacity of apprehending an utterable image.[4] Utterability is thus made the characteristic mark of the act of judging. The judgment becomes, to a certain extent, an «outspeaking»; but not a simple outspeaking, it is an outspeaking establishing the necessary connection between logical thought and transcendental pure reality.

In post-Buddhistic Indian logic, the theory of judgment naturally disappears,[5] since it is a corollary from the theory of pure sensation. Prof. H. Jacobi[6] in giving an account of this system rightly remarks that it has no doctrine of judgment, as something different, on the one hand, from sense-perception and, on the other hand, from inference.

Just as the Buddhist logic itself, its theory of judgment appears as an intermezzo in the history of Indian philosophy.

§ 10. Some European parallels.

When the student of Indian philosophy is faced by the task of finding an equivalent for a conception which is familiar to him, because he meets it often used in his texts, he may nevertheless be often quite perplexed about how to render it in translation because there is no corresponding term available. In philosophy and logic all European languages form common stock, because they have a common ancestor in the writings of Aristotle. But Indian philosophy has developped independently from this influence. It has its own Aristotle and its own Kant. It constitutes an independent line of development which runs parallel to the European one. It is therefore of the highest historical interest to note the cases when both currents agree on a common conception or a common theory. It may be an indirect, partial proof of its truth, because truth is one, and error is many. When the subject of dis-

---

1 *jātyādi-kalpanā = klpti-hetuḥ*, cp. TS; p. 366. 24 ff.

2 *nāma-kalpanā = artha-śūnyaiḥ śabdair eva viśiṣṭā*, Pr. Samucc. Vṛ., I. 3.

3 TSP., p. 368. 25 ff.

4 NB., 1. 5.

5 Cp. however above, p. 224 n. 6.

6 In his article in GGN, quoted above.

course consists in a deduction of one proposition from two or several others, all containing only three terms, we have no doubt that it is a syllogism. But when we are faced by the necessity of deciding whether a characteristic act of our understanding is to be rendered as judgment, we must know what a judgment is. And here we find an illimited variety of opinions. Suffice it to consult a dictionary of philosophic terms in order to be astonished by the amazing contradictions on this problem between the leading philosophers in Europe. The majority thinks that judgment is a «predicative connexion between two concepts», but Brentano emphatically denies this. He thinks that judgment is something quite different from conception. However Schuppe decidedly asserts the contrary[1]. According to the majority the judgment is an act of synthesis, according to Wundt it is, on the contrary, an act of separation, etc. etc. The problems of the existential, the perceptual and the impersonal judgments are admittedly so many puzzles. However in examining the Buddhist descriptions of the act of judging, and its different characteristics from different points of view, we cannot but recognize in them some of the features which we find scattered piecemeal in different European doctrines. Thus we apparently find in Locke's Essay some of our perceptual judgments under the name of simple ideas. The perceptual judgments «this is white», «this is round» are interpreted as a reference of a present sensation to a permanent object of thought.[2]

The chief difference between the Buddhist and all European views of judgment consists in the circumstance that the latter founded their analysis on the pattern containing two conceptions without any regard to their objective reference, whereas the Buddhist analysis starts with the pattern containing only one conception and its objective reference. The judgment with two conceptions, as will be shown later on, is an inferential judgment, or an inference. The judgment proper is the

---

[1] Erkenntnisth. Logik, p. 123 «*beide sind dasselbe, und nur vor den genannten verschiedenen Standpunkten der Reflexion aus verschieden*».

[2] These «ideas» «in the reception whereof the mind is only passive» (II, 12, § 1) contain nevertheless distinction from other ideas and identity with themselves. Although instantaneous, «each perishing the moment it begins» (II, 17, § 2) they contain a comparison «of the thing with itself». They moreover are self-conscious, since «it is impossible for any one to perceive without perceiving that he does perceive» (ibid., § 9). This corresponds exactly to Dharmakīrti's *apratyakṣopalambhasya nārtha-dṛṣṭiḥ prasidhyati*, which he puts on the account of passive sensation (*anubhava*). However generally Locke identifies sensation with perception and thus falls in line with the Naiyāyiks.

perceptual one. In this connexion an interesting remark of Prof. Sigwart[1] deserves to be mentioned. He calls attention to the fact that, as a rule, only the predicate of a judgment must be named, the subject or «the subject-presentation can be left without any expression in speech». It can be expressed by a mere demonstrative pronoun or by a gesture. «It is with such judgments, says he, that human thought begins. When a child recognizes the animals in a picture book and pronounces their names, it judges». From the Buddhist point of view this statement must be generalized. All judgments consist in connecting an element which cannot be named at all with another element which is necessarily capable of being named. Thus the impersonal judgment is the fundamental form of all judgments.

As to Kantian ideas, the coincidence with his view of the understanding as a non-sensuous source of knowledge and of judgment as the function of the understanding has already been mentioned. Kant has moreover repudiated the definition of his predecessors who maintained that a judgment is a relation between two concepts, because, says he, «we are not told in what that relation consists».[2] The judgment, according to him, is «nothing but the mode of bringing given cognitions into the objective unity of apperception; this is what is intended by the copula „is"». That definition points to a synthesis and a projection of our images into the external world as the most characteristic features in a judgment. If we add the theories of a synopsis of sensuous intuition[3] and of the fixation[4] of it on one point, which theories correspond to Kant's Apprehension in intuition and Recognition in concepts, we can hardly deny that there is a strong analogy between some Kantian ideas and the Buddhist theory, although Kant's examples, following the Aristotelian tradition, are always given in the form of a judgment with two concepts.

The essential feature of a decision, assent or belief contained in every judgment, has been first pointed out in European philosophy by the Mills, father and son, and Brentano following on them. According to James Mill it is «necessary to distinguish between suggestion to the mind of a certain order among sensations or ideas...... and the indication that this order is an actual one».[5] «That

---

1 Logik, I, p. 64; cp. ibid. I, p. 142.

2 CPR., § 19.

3 *vitarka.*

4 *vicāra.*

5 Anal. of the Phen. of the Human Mind, I, p. 162 (2-d ad.).

distinction, says J. S. Mill, is ultimate and primordial.» «There is no more difficulty in holding it to be so, than in holding the difference between a sensation and an idea to be primordial».[1] We have seen that according to the Buddhists the real «primordial distinction» is between pure sensation and pure understanding and the jugment is a decision to connect both these elements with one another. Therefore the real act of judgment contains only one conception and its objective reference. This is also the opinion of Brentano. «It is not right to maintain, says he, that every judgment contains either a connection or a separation of two representations...... A single representation can be also the object of belief or disbelief.» Brentano moreover thinks that the copula «is» represents the most important part in every judgment. It therefore can always be reduced to the form of an existential judgment, «A is». «This man is sick» reduces to the form «this sick man is». Such a judgment however does not consist in establishing a predicative connexion between the element A (the conception) and the notion of Existence,[2] but, Brentano insists, «A itself is believed to exist».[3] For the Buddhist, we have seen, all judgments must be reduced not to existential, but to perceptual judgments. Existence is never a predicate, it is the necessary Subject in all real cognition. Existence is just the Non-Predicate,[4] «Pure Position»[5] the Thing as it is in itself, shorn of all predicative characteristics or relations.

---

[1] Ibid., p. 412.

[2] According to Sigwart (Logik, I, p. 92) the existential judgment and the perceptual judgment are two different classes of judgments, distinguished by the inverted position of their subject and predicate. The judgment «this is a cow» is perceptual or namesgiving. The judgment the «cow is» represents an existential one. Both classes exist in their own equal rights. Existence is the subject in the one, it is the predicate in the other. In both cases the judgment asserts a relation between two concepts. From the Buddhist standpoint this is quite wrong. Existence is never a predicate, never a name, it is unutterable. The judgment «the cow is» differs from «this is a cow» only grammatically.

[3] Psychol., II, p. 49. «*Nicht die Verbindung eines Merkmals Existenz mit «A», sondern «A» selbst ist der Gegenstand den wir anerkennen*».

[4] In this respect there is some similarity between the subject of the Buddhist perceptual judgment and Aristotle's category of First Substance, the *Hoc Aliquid*. The *Prima Essentia* is indispensable, we are told, as a Subject, but cannot appear as a Predicate, while all the rest can and do so appear. The Second Substance or Essence, when distinguished from the First, is not Substance at all, but Quality. (Grote, p. 91). Therefore all knowledge is nothing but a process of ascribing an infinite number of Predicates to Reality, or to First Substance.

[5] Cp. above, p. 192.

But from all European theories of judgment Bradley's and Bosanquet's analysis of the perceptual judgment comes perhaps nearest to the Buddhist view. For these scholars that fundamental variety of judgment also consists in connecting together pure reality with a constructed conception. The subject represents something «unique, the same with no other, nor yet with itself», but alone in the world of its fleeting moment»,[1] something that can merely be expressed by the pronoun «this».[2] The predicate is «an ideal content, a symbol», or a conception.[3]

---

1 Bradley, Logic, p. 5.

2 Bosanquet, Logic, p. 76; cp. 13. Russell, Outline, p. 12, «all words, even proper names, are general, with the possible exception of «this».

3 It is interesting to note that, according to the opinion of Hegel (Geschichte der Phil., II. p. 143), the idea that sensation or «thisness» (das Diese) is nnutterable and that the Universal alone can be expressed in speech, this idea which he found in Greek philosophy, possesses a high philosophic value. « This is a consciousness and an idea, says he, to which the philosophic development of our own times has not yet arrived».

CHAPTER II.

INFERENCE.

§ 1. Judgment and Inference.

From the perceptual judgment or judgment proper, we must distinguish another variety of judgment, the inferential one.[1] Since all real cognition, i. e., all cognition of reality, reduces to judgments, i. e., to interpretation of sensations in concepts, and since cognition can be distinguished as a direct and indirect one, the judgment can also be divided in a direct and an indirect one. The direct one is perception, the indirect one is inference. The direct one, we saw, is a synthesis between a sensation and a conception, the indirect one is a synthesis between a sensation and two concepts. The direct one has two terms, the indirect one has three terms. The direct one reduces to the form «this is blue» or «this is smoke». The indirect one can be reduced to the form «this is smoke produced by fire», or «there is some fire, because there is smoke». The smoke is perceived, the judgment «this is smoke» is perceptual and direct. The fire is hidden, the judgment «there is here fire» is inferential and indirect. All things may be divided in perceived and unperceived. The cognition of a non-perceived through a perceived is called inference. It is an indirect cognition, a cognition, so to speak, round the corner, a cognition of an object through its «mark». The hidden object has a mark, and this mark is, in its turn, the characteristic, or the mark of a point of reality. The cognition of a point of reality, as possessing the double mark, as possessing the mark of its mark, is inference — *nota notae est nota rei ipsius*. In a perceptual judgment we cognize the object X through its symbol which is the conception A. In an inferential judgment we cognize the object X through its double symbol A and B.

The symbols A and B are related as reason and consequence. When one of them, the element A, is cognized, the cognition of the other, of the element B, necessarily follows. Since the element X, the Substratum of the Qualities A and B, or the Subject of both these Predicates, is indefinite, always the same, its expression can be dropped;

---

[1] *svārthānumāna*.

its presence will be necessarily understood without any formal expression. In that case the two interrelated elements or qualities A and B will represent the whole inference or the whole inferential judgment. This judgment will then apparently consist of two conceptions only, but related as reason and consequence, the one being the necessary ground for predicating the other.

The inferential judgment will then become a judgment of concomitance.[1] Inference, or the object cognized in an inference, says Dharmottara, is either «a complex idea of the substratum together with its inferred property, or, when the invariable concomitance between the reason and the inferred attribute is considered (abstracly), then the inferred fact appears as this attribute (taken in its concomitance with the reason)».[2] In the first case we just have an inferential judgment, in the second case a judgment of concomitance. The first corresponds to a combination of the minor premise with the conclusion, the second corresponds to the major premise of the Aristotelian syllogism.[3] Indian logic treats them as essentially «one cognition», the cognition, e. g., of the fire as inferred through its mark.

The judgment «fire produces smoke» or «wherever there is smoke there is fire», or «there is no smoke without fire», just as the judgments «the *śimśapā* is a tree», or «the blue is a colour», «the cow is an animal», so far they are cognitions of the real and have a hold in reality, must be reduced to the form «there is *here* a fire, because there is smoke», «*this* is blue which is a colour», «*this* is a tree because it is a *śimśapā*», «*this* is an animal, since it is a cow», etc. Without the element «this» or «here», either expressed or understood, they would not be cognitions of reality.

However not every cognition containing three terms of which one is the substratum for the two others, will be an inference. Only such

---

[1] *vyāpti* = *sāhacarya* = *avinābhāva*.

[2] NBT., p. 20. 16 ff.; transl., p. 58.

[3] It is clear that those European logicians who explain the relation of subject and predicate in a normal judgment as the relation of reason and consequence, like Herbart and others, especially N. O. Lossky, reduce the normal judgment to a judgment of concomitance. But it is also clear that the judgment of concomitance belongs rather to inference, than to judgment proper, it is the major premise according to the first figure. The subject of such judgments is always the reason of the inference. The judgment «smoke is produced by fire» is reduced in India to the form «wheresoever there is smoke, there necessarily is some fire», the judgment «the *śimśapā* is a tree» means «if something is characterized as *śimśapā* it is necessarily also characterized as a tree», etc. They are hypothetical judgments.

a combination of them, where the two attributes are necessarily interrelated, the one deducible from the other, represents an inference. The judgment «there is a fiery hill» contains three terms, however they are not necessarily interrelated. But the judgment «there is here a fire, because there is smoke» «there is no smoke without a fire» are inferential, since smoke is represented as necessarily connected with its cause, the fire.[1]

Of what kind this necessary relation is — will be told later on.

§ 2. The Three Terms.

Every inference therefore contains three terms which are the logical Subject, the logical Predicate and, between them, the Reason or Mark, which unites them.

The Subject can be the ultimately real Subject or the metaphorical one. The ultimately real is always nothing but a point-instant of pure reality. It represents that substratum of reality which must underlie all thought-construction. It is the element «this», that «thisness» which we already know from the theory of the perceptual judgment. It is the non-subsistent substance with regard to wich all other categories are qualities.

The metaphorical or secondary Subject is itself an inferred entity, a quality, with regard to the ultimate subject. But it serves as a substratum for further inference, and appears therefore as an enduring thing possessing qualities, as a substitute for the ultimately real Subject. In the inference «this (place) possesses fire, because it possesses smoke», the element «this» represents the real Subject. In the inference «the mountain possesses fire, because it possesses smoke», the

---

[1] The difference between a judgment of perception and a judgment of inference is, to a certain extent, similar to the difference which Kant draws between a judgment of perception and a judgment of experience, cp. Proleg., § 20. The observation that the «sun warms a stone» is not yet a judgment of experience. But the universal and necessary synthesis between sun's rays and the calefaction of the stone is what Kant calls experience. It is an inference of the form «this stone is warm, because it is sunlit», or «whatsoever is sunlit becomes warmed, this stone is sunlit, it becomes warmed». Generally speaking it seems better logic to treat cognition under the heads of perception and inference, or sensibility and understanding, than to treat it under the heads of judgment and syllogism, as the Aristotelian tradition does A judgment of concomitance surely belongs much more to the process of inference — it is its major premise — than to the process of simple judgments.

subject «mountain» replaces the real subject or substratum, it is itself partly inferred.

«The subject of such inferences, remarks Dharmottara,[1] consists of a particular place actually perceived and of an unperceived (inferred) part. It is a complex of something cognized directly and something invisible, (something inferred)... The word «here» (or «this») points to the visible part». The subject (or the substratum) of an inference is thus a combination of a part perceived directly and a part not actually perceived also in all cases where the conclusion represents not a singular, but a universal judgment. E. g., when it is being deduced that all sound represents a compact series of momentary existences, only some particular sound can be directly pointed to, others are not actually perceived... The subject of an inference represents a substratum, an underlying reality, upon which a conception corresponding to the predicate is grafted and this has been shown to consist (sometimes) of a part directly perceived and a part unperceived (i. e. inferred).[2]

Thus the subject of an inference corresponds to Aristotle's Minor Term. As ultimate Subject it corresponds ontologically, to his First Substance or First Essence, «which is a Subject only; it never appears as a predicate of anything else. As *Hic Aliquis* or *Hoc Aliquid* it lies at the bottom (either expressed or implied) of all the work of predication».[3]

According to Dignāga, says Vācaspatimiśra,[4] sense-perception (the true voucher of reality) does not refer to an extended place upon which the smoke is situated. According to his theories, there is no such thing called mountain as a whole consisting of parts (having extension). Such a mountain is a construction of our imagination. Therefore the true or ultimate Subject in every inference, whether expressed or merely understood, just as in every perceptual judgment, is «thisness», the point-instant, the First Essence, the *Hoc Aliquid*, which is the Subject by its essence, and never can be a Quality or a Predicate.

The second Term of an inference is the logical Predicate otherwise called the *probandum* or the logical Consequence.[5] It represents that

---

1 NBT., p. 31. 21.

2 Ibid.

3 Grote, Aristotle, p. 67.

4 NVTT., p. 120. 27 ff. Vācaspati says that the mountain must be substituted by atoms. But atoms are also denied by Dignāga, they must be understood as dynamical point-instants, *Kraftpunkte*.

5 *sādhya*.

quality of the subject which is cognized through the inference, the quality which is inferred. It may be expressed as a substantive by itself, e. g. «fire», but with respect to the subject it is its quality, the «fireness» of a given place. Together with the subject this quality represents the «object» cognized through the inference.[1] Dharmottara says,[2] that the object cognized through the inference may be 1) either the substratum[3] whose quality it is intended to cognize or 2) the substratum together with that quality,[4] or 3) that quality alone, when its relation to the logical reason, from which it is deduced, is considered abstractly, e. g., «wheresoever there is smoke, there also is fire», or, more precisely, «wheresoever there is smokeness, there also is fireness». «All inferential relation, says Dignāga,[5] is based upon a substance-to-quality relation, it is constructed by our understanding,[6] it does not represent ultimate reality».

Indeed the Reason as well as the Consequence must be regarded in respect of their substratum of ultimate reality as its constructed qualities.[7] Taken abstractly the quality deduced through inference, or the logical Predicate, corresponds to Aristotle's Major Term.

The third term is the logical Mark of the Reason already mentioned. It is also a Quality or a mark of the Subject and is itself marked off by the Predicate. It corresponds to the Middle Term of Aristotle and represents the most important part of the inference. The inference can thus be represented in the formula «S is P, because of M», «here there is fire, because there is smoke», «here there are trees, because there are *śiṃśapās*». It has been already mentioned that in common life the expression of the real subject is usually omitted and these inferences appear in the form of judgments of concomitance, such as «the *śiṃśapā* is a tree», «the presence of smoke means presence of fire», or «smoke is produced by fire.»

---

1 *anumeya.*

2 NBT., p. 20. 16.

3 *dharmī.*

4 *dharma.*

5 Cp. NVTT., p. 39. 13 and 127. 2.

6 *buddhy-ārūḍha.*

7 Cp. Bradley, Logic, p. 199 — the categorical judgment S—P (which is also the conclusion of inference), «attributes S—P, directly or indirectly, to the ultimate reality», whereas the major premise which expresses a necessary connection is hypothetical, «it is necessary when it is, *because* of something else». Necessity is always hypothetical. We will see later on that this is also the opinion of Sigwart, cp. Logic 3, I. 261 and 434.

§ 3. The various definitions of inference.

Thus inference can be defined as a cognition of an object through its mark.[1] This definition, says Dharmottara,[2] is a definition not of the essence of an inference, but of its origin. The cognition of the concealed fire is revealed by its mark. The mark produces the cognition of the object which it is the mark of. The origin of the cognition lies in its mark.

Another definition takes inference from the objective side. Inference is the cognition of an inferred, i. e., invisible, concealed object. All objects can be divided in present and absent. The present are cognized by perception, the absent by inference.[3]

A third definition lays stress upon the inseparable connexion which unites the mark with the inferred object and defines inference as a consequence or an application of an inseparable connexion between two facts by a man who has previously noticed that connexion.[4] Thus in our example, the cognition of the concealed fire is a consequence of that inseparable causal tie, which unites smoke with its cause, the fire, and which has been cognized in experience.

A further definition takes it as the most characteristic feature the fact that inference cognizes the general, whereas the object of sense-perception is always the particular.

This is, in a certain respect, the most fundamental definition, since Dignāga opens his great treatise by the statement that there are only two sources of knowledge, perception and inference, and, corresponding to them, only two classes of objects, the particular and the universal. The universal is thus cognized by inference, whereas the particular is grasped by the senses.

However it is clear that the fire whose presence is inferred is as much a particular fire as the one whose presence is perceived by vision. Without the general features which constitute the object fire and are the property of all fires in the world, the particular fire never

1 It is always said «through its threefold mark», i. e., through its concomitant mark, through the mark which is concomitant with the *probandum*. This is the definition of Dignāga, Pr. samucc., II. 1. and NB. II. 1.

2 NBT., p. 18.

3 Cp. the passage from Kamalašila quoted above, p. 18. 2.

4 This is the definition of Vasubandhu in the Vāda-vidhi «*anantarīyaka-artha-daršanam tad-vido'numānam*».

would have been cognized as fire. Nor would the inferred fire without having been referred in imagination to a certain point-instant of reality ever been cognized as a reality. But still, there is a difference in the generality of the features which are attended to in ratiocination and the particularity of the object which is present to the senses.

According to Dharmottara, inference has an imagined object, e. g., an imagined fire, as its own object, since inference is a cognition of an absent thing which cannot be grasped, which only can be imagined. But its procedure consists in referring this imagined object to a real point and thus its final result is just the same as in sense-perception, the cognition of a point of reality through a constructed symbol.[1] The difference consists in the movement of thought which is the one the opposite of the other. In perception cognition grasps the particular and constructs the symbol. In inference it grasps the symbol and constructs the particular. In this sense only is the general the object of inference, and the particular the object of sense-perception. Otherwise there is no difference in this respect between a perceptual and an inferential judgment. Both, as the Buddhist says, are «one cognition», representing a synthesis «of sensation and non-sensation, conception and non-conception, imagination and non-imagination.»[2] That is to say, it contains a sensible core and its interpretation by the understanding. The difference between sense-perception and inference at this depth of Buddhist investigation is the same as between sensibility and understanding. We are told that there are two sources of knowledge, perception and inference. But the deeper meaning is that the two sources are a sensuous one and a non-sensuous one. It is clear from what has been said that inference is not regarded as a deduction of a proposition or judgment, out of two other propositions or judgments, but as a method of cognizing reality which has its origin in the fact of its having a mark. What really is inferred in an inference is a point of reality as possessing a definite symbol, e. g., a mountain as possessing the unperceived, inferred fire. «There are some, says Dignāga, who think that the inferred thing is the new property discovered in some place, because of its connection with a perceived mark of that property. Others again maintain that it is not this property itself, but its connection with the substratum that is cognized in inference. Why not

[1] NBT., 19. 20; transl., p. 56.

[2] NK., p. 125.

assume that the inferred part consists in the substratum itself as characterized by the inferred quality?» That is to say, the thing cognized in an inference is neither the major term nor the connection of the major with the minor, but it is that point of reality which is characterized by its deduced symbol. The definition is the same for Dignāga and Dharmakīrti. The definition of Vasubandhu is not materially different, but its phrasing in the Vādavidhi is severely criticized by Dignāga.[1]

§ 4. Inferring and Inference.

Since inference is represented as one of the sources of our knowledge, we are again faced by the problem of a difference between a source and its outcome, between the act of cognition and its content.[2] What is the difference between inferring as the act, or the process, of cognition and inference as its result? Just as in sense-perception the Buddhist denies the difference. It is the same thing differently viewed. Inference means cognition of an object through its mark. This cognition is «one cognition»,[3] i. e., one act of efficient knowledge which can be followed by a successful action; on analysis it contains an image and its objective reference. Just as in sense-perception there is «conformity»[4] or correspondence between the subjective image and the objective reality. We may, if we like, consider the fact of this conformity as the nearest cause producing knowledge. Conformity will then be the source of cognition and its application to a given point of reality the result. But the conformity of knowledge and knowledge itself are just the same thing, only regarded from different standpoints.

The realistic schools admitted no images and consequently no conformity between the image and external reality. The act of cognition, as every act, is inseparable from an agent, an object, an instrument, its method of procedure, and a result. In inference the result is the conclusion. The procedure and the instrument, according to one party, consist in the knowledge of concomitance between the Reason and the Consequence. According to others, it consists in the cognition

---

1 Pr. samucc., II. 25 ff.

2 *pramāṇa* and *pramāṇa-phala*.

3 *anumānam ekam vijñānam*, cp. NK., p. 125.

4 *sārūpya*.

of the Mark as present on the Subject of the inference. This step coincides partly with the Minor Premise.[1] It çontains more, since it is described as containing the concomitant mark, i. e., a combination of the minor with the major premises. It is the step upon which the conclusion immediately follows. According to Uddyotakara,[2] both these steps represent the act of inferring, they are both the immediately preceding, proximate cause producing the conclusion. The Buddhist, of course, does not deny the existence and improtance of these premises. But for him they are cognitions by themselves. What he denies is the difference of *noëma* and *noësis* inside every knowledge. The intentness of knowledge upon its object and the knowledge of this object are the same thing. Dharmottara says that supposing we have cognized through an inference the presence somewhere of a patch of blue colour, the result in this respect will be the same as if we had cognized it through sense-perception. «This (imagined) image of the blue, says he,[3] arises (at first indefinitely); it is then settled as a definite self-conscious idea of a blue patch, (by the way of its contrast with other colours which are not blue). Thus the coordination of the blue (its contrast with other colours which are not blue, may be regarded) as the source of such a (definitely circumscribed image), and the imagined distinct representation will then appear as its result, because it is through coordination (and contrast) that the definite image of the blue is realized.»

Thus «the blue» and «the coordination of the blue» are just the same thing. The blue means similarity with all the things blue in the universe and it means also dissimilarity with all the things not-blue in the universe. Both these similarity and dissimilarity constitute the intentness of our knowledge upon the blue and the cognition of the blue. Whether the presence of the blue patch is perceived or inferred, that makes no difference. There is no difference between the act and the content of knowledge.

§ 5. How far Inference is true knowledge?

A source of knowledge has been defined[4] as a first moment of a new cognition which does not contradict experience.[5] It must

1 Cp. Tātp., p. 112.

2 NV., p. 46. 6.

3 NBT., p. 18. 11 ff.; transl., p. 51.

4 Cp. above, p. 65.

5 *prathamam avisaṃvādi* = *gsar-du mi-slus-pa*.

therefore be free from every subjective, mnemic or imaginative feature.[1] We have seen that in sense-perception only its first moment, which is pure sensation, satisfies to that condition. But such sensation alone, since it is quite indefinite,[2] cannot guide our purposeful actions. Therefore imagination steps in and imparts definiteness to the crude material of sensation.

The perceptual judgment[3] is thus a mixed product of new and old cognition, of objective reality and subjective interpretation. It assumes the dignity or a source of right new cognition, although, strictly speaking, it has not the full right to do it. Inference is still more remote from pure sensation. If the perceptual judgment is not quite new cognition,[4] inference has still lesser rights to pose as a source of right knowledge. Dharmottara therefore exclaims, «Inference is illusion![5] It deals with non-entia which are its own imagination and (wrongly) identifies them with reality!»

From that height of abstraction from which pure sensation alone is declared to represent ultimate right knowledge attaining at the Thing-in-Itself, the perceptual judgment is, intermingled as it is with elements mnemic, subjective and imaginative, nothing but half-knowledge. Inference which is still more steeped in thought-constructions—two thirds, so to speak, i. e., two of its three terms being imagination — certainly appears as a kind of transcendental illusion. The fact that Dignāga begins by stating that there are only two sources of knowledge and only two kinds of objects, the particular and the universal, as if the two sources existed in equal rights and the two kinds of objects were real objects, i. e., objective realities, this fact is to be explained only by the might of tradition coming from the Nyāya and Vaišeṣika schools. For after having made this statement at the beginning of his work, Dignāga is obliged to retract step by step all its implications. The universals are, first of all, no realities at all, but pure imagination and mere names. Inference, obliged to manipulate these constructed conceptions, becomes, not a source of right knowledge, but a source of illusion. Nay, even the perceptual judgment is right only at a half, for although it reaches the Thing-in-Itself directly, it is obliged to stand still, powerless before its incognizability. Men must

1 *nirvikalpaka.*
2 *aniścita.*
3 *savikalpaka = adhyavasāya.*
4 *savikalpakam na pramāṇam.*
5 *bhrāntam anumāṇam*, cp. NBT., p. 7. 12.

resort to imagination in order to move in a half-real world. Inference from this point of view is a method subservient to sense-perception and to the perceptual judgment. Its office is to correct obvious mistakes. When, e. g., the momentary character of the sound has been apprehended in sensation and interpreted in a perceptual judgment, the theory of the Mimāṃsakas must be faced according to which the sounds of speech are enduring substances, manifesting themselves in momentary apparitions. Inference then comes to the front and deduces the instantaneous character of these articulate sounds, first from the general character of Instantaneous Being, and then from the special rule that whatever is the outcome of a conscious effort is not enduring.[1] Thus inference is an indirect source of knowledge when it serves to correct illusion. Dharmakīrti says,[2] «Sensation does not convince anybody. If it cognizes something, it does it in the way of a passive reflex, not in the way of judgment. In that part in which sensation has the power to engender the following right judgment, in that part only does it assume (the dignity) of a right knowledge.[3] But in that part in which it is powerless to do it, owing to causes of error, another source of knowledge begins to operate. It brushes away all wrong imagination and thus we have another source (viz. inference) which then comes to the front.»

We find the same train of reasoning with Kamalaśīla.[4]

A source of knowledge has indeed been declared to consist in uncontradicted experience. But from that experience its sensational core has at once been singled out as the true source of the knowledge of ultimate reality. The rest, although representing also uncontradicted experience, appears to be a transcendental illusion. «Although it is uncontradicted (empirically), says Kamalaśīla,[5] we do not admit that it represents (ultimate) truth». As soon as a sensation[6] has been produced by an external object which in the sequel will be sensed, conceived and named, as, e. g., a fire, attention is aroused and the understanding, after having determined its place in the time and space order, produces a dichotomy. The whole universe of discourse is

---

[1] *prayatna-anantarīyakatvād anityaḥ śabdaḥ.*

[2] Cp. the reference in Anekāntaj, p. 177, a part of which has been quoted above, p. 223.

[3] *prāmāṇyam ātmasāt-kurute.*

[4] TSP., p. 390. 10 ff.

[5] TSP., p. 390. 14.

[6] *nirvikalpakam.*

divided into two classes of objects, fire-like and fire-unlike. There is nothing in the middle [1] between them, both groups are contradictorily opposed to each another. The laws of Contradiction and Excluded Middle begin to operate. Two judgments are produced at once, a judgment of affirmation and a judgment of negation, viz. «this is fire», «this is not a flower etc.», i. e., it is not a non-fire.

In inference the operation of the understanding is more complicated. When we infer the presence of fire from the presence of smoke, the universe of discourse is dichotomized in a part where smoke follows on fire and a part where non-smoke follows upon non-fire. Between these two groups there is nothing intermediate, no group where smoke could exist without having been produced by fire.

This dichotomizing activity of the mind belongs to its every essence and we will meet it again when analysing the Buddhist theory of Negation, [2] its theory of Contradiction [3] and its doctrine of Dialectic. [4]

§ 6. The Three Aspects of the Reason.

Although there is no difference between the process of inferring and its result, nor is there any difference between the perceptual and the inferential judgments, since both consist in giving an objective reference to our concepts, nevertheless there is a difference in that sense that the inference contains the logical justification of such an act of reference. When, e. g., we unite a given point-instant with the image of a fire, which is not perceived directly, we are justified to do it, because we perceive smoke. Smoke is the certain mark of the presence of fire and justifies the conclusion.

This justification, or the Reason, is thus the distinguishing, outstanding feature which points to the difference between a perceptual and an inferential judgment. Nevertheless in both cases cognition is a dichotomy.

Cognition in so far as it is the function, not of passive sensation, but of the constructing intellect, is a dichotomizing act. It always begins by dividing its object into two parts, the similar and the dissimilar. It always operates by the method of argeement with the

---

[1] *tṛtīya-prakāra-abhāvaḥ.*

[2] *anupalabdhi.*

[3] *virodha.*

[4] *apoha-vāda.*

similar and disagreement with the dissimilar, i. e., by the Mixt Method of Agreement and Difference. If the method of agreement alone is expressed, the method of difference is also understood. If the method of difference is expressed, the method of agreement is also understood. For the sake of verification and precision both can be expressed.

What is a similar case in an inference? and what a dissimilar case? Dharmottara[1] says — an object which is similar to the object cognized in the inference «by the common possession of a quality which is the logical predicate represents a similar case». In our example all cases possessing «fireness» will be similar cases. «It is the predicate, the thing to be proved, the *pvobandum*, continues the same author, since as long as the inference is not concluded it is not yet proved; and it is a quality, because its existence is conditioned by a substratum, from which it differs. It is thus a predicated (or derived) quality». Dharmottara adds, «No particular can ever make a logical predicate. It is always a universal. That is the reason why it is stated that the thing to be cognized in an inference is a common property. It is a predicated property and it is general. The similar case is similar to the object cognized through an inference, because both are comprehended in the universality of the predicated quality».

It follows from this statement that a particular predicate can never enter into an inferential process otherwise than by an unnatural and perverse method of expressing it.

What is a dissimilar case? The dissimilar is the non-similar, it is the reverse of the similar. All instances in which the property cognized in the inference cannot be present, e. g., water in which fire cannot exist, are dissimilar cases. They are either the simple absence of that property, or the presence of something different, or of something contradictorily opposed. Thus absence, otherness and opposition constitute together the dissimilar cases; absence directly, otherness and opposition by implication.[2]

The relation of the logical Reason to the Substratum of the inference, on the one side, and to the similar and dissimilar cases, on the other side, is expressed in the three rules of Vasubandhu, which have been endorsed by Dignāga and Dharmakīrti. They constitute the celebrated Three Aspects of the Logical Reason as

---

[1] NBT., p. 21 . 1; transl., p. 59.

[2] NBT., p. 21 . 10; transl., p. 60.

taught by the Buddhists and rejected by all other schools of Indian logicians except the reformed Vaišeṣikas.

This threefold aspect of the Reason is:

1. Its presence on the Subject of the Inference.

2. Its presence in Similar Instances.

3. Its absence in Dissimilar Instances.

In order to give to this formulation more precision Dharmakīrti utilises a remarkable feature of the Sanscrit language which consists in putting the emphasizing particle «just» either with the copula or with the predicate. In the first case it gives to the assertion the meaning of the impossibility of absence,[1] in the second case it means the impossibility of otherness.[2] The three aspects then are thus expressed:

1. The presence of the Reason in the Subject, its presence «just», i. e., never absence.

2. Its presence in Similar Instances, «just» in similars, i. e., never in dissimilars, but not in the totality of the similars.

3. Its absence from Dissimilar Instances, its absence «just», i. e., never presence, absence from the totality of the dissimilar instances.

It is easily seen that the second and the third rule mutually imply each the other. If the reason is present in the similar instances only, it also is absent from every dissimilar case. And if it is absent from every dissimilar case, it can be present in similar instances only, although not necessarily in all of them. Nevertheless both rules must be mentioned, because, although in a correct inference the application of the one means the application of the other, in a logical fallacy their infringements carry sometimes different results. Dharmakīrti moreover adds the word «necessary» to the formulation of each rule. Their final form will thus be:

1. The necessary presence of the Reason in the Subject's totality.

2. Its necessary presence in Similars only, although not in their totality.

3. Its necessary absence from Dissimilars in their totality.

Expressed with all the pregnant laconicity of the Sanscrit and Tibetan tongues:

1. In Subject wholly.

---

1 *ayoga-vyavaccheda.*

2 *anya-yoga-vyavaccheda.* A third case would be *atyanta-yoga-vyavaccheda*, cp. NVTT., p. 213.

2. In Similar only.
3. In Dissimilar never.

If the reason were not present in the totality of the Subject, a fallacy would result. E. g., the Jaina inference «trees are sentient beings, because they sleep» is a logical fallacy, since the sleep which is manisfested by the closing of the leaves at night is present in some trees only, not in their totality.

If the rules of inference required that the reason should be present in all similar cases, then one of the arguments directed against the Mīmāmsakas viz. «the sounds of speech are not eternal entities, because they are produced at will», would not be correct, since produced at will are only a part of the non-eternal things, not all of them.

The same argument when stated in a changed form, viz. «the sounds of speech are produced at will, because they are impermanent» will contain an infringement of the third rule since «the mark of impermanence is present in one part of the dissimilar cases, such as lightning etc., which, although impermanent, are not voluntarily produced.

If the third rule would have been formulated in the same phrasing as the second, i. e., if it would require the absence of the reason from the dissimilar instances only, then the inference «the sounds of speech are non eternal, because they can be produced at will» would not be correct, since voluntary production is absent not in dissimilar instances only, but also in some of the similar, non eternal, instances, such as lightening etc.

It is easy to see that the second and third rule correspond to the major premise of Aristotle's first and second figure, and the first rule is nothing but the rule of Aristotle's minor premise.

The order of the premises is inverted, the minor occupies the first place and this corresponds to the natural procedure of our understanding when engaged in the process of inference. Inference primarily proceedes from a particular to another particular case, and recalls the general rule only in a further step of cognition. The general rule is here stated twice in its positive and negative or contraposed form, as will be stated later on when examining the Buddhist theory of the syllogism.

§ 7. Dharmakīrti's tract on relations.

We have so far established that inference consists in a) a necessary connection between two concepts or two facts and b) in the reference of the so connected facts to a point-instant of objective reality. The first corresponds to the major premise in the Aristotelian syllogism, the second to a combination of its minor premise with its conclusion. From that point of view from which the Buddhists deal with inference, the problem of relations receives a capital importance, since inference is nothing but the necessary interrelation between two facts and their necessary reference to a point of reality. The interrelation of the three terms of an inference has been settled by the theory of the Three Aspects of the Logical Reason. They are the formal conditions to which every logical reason must necessarily satisfy. But we are not told neither in what the interrelation consists, nor whether the relations themselves are real, as real as the objects interrelated; or whether they are added to the objects by our productive imagination. What indeed are relations to the things related? Are they something or are they nothing? If they are something, they must represent a third unity between the two unities related. If they are nothing, the two things will remain unrelated, there will be between them no real relation at all. The Buddhist's answer to the question is clear cut. Relations are contingent reality, that is to say no ultimate reality at all. Ultimate reality is unrelated, it is non-relative, it is the Absolute. Relations are constructions of our imagination, they are nothing actual.[1] The Indian Realists, however, kept to the principle that relations are as real as the things and that they are perceived through the senses. Uddyotakara says[2], «the perception of the connection of an object with its mark is the first act of sense-perception from which inference proceeds». According to him connection is perceived by the senses as well as the connected facts.

---

1 Cp. Bradley, Logic, p. 96 — «If relations are facts that exist between facts, then what comes between the relations and the other facts? The real truth is, that the units on one side, and on the other side the relation existing between them, are nothing actual». This sounds quite as a Buddhistic idea which could be rendered in Sanscrit thus, *yadi sambandhinau madhye sambandho kaścid vastutaḥ praviṣṭaḥ tat-sambandhasya sambandhinoś ca madhye kòpy aparaḥ sambandhaḥ praviṣto na vā (ity anavasthā); athāyam paramārthaḥ, sambandinau ca sambandhās ca sarve mithyā, mānasas te, kalpanikāḥ, atad-vyāvṛtti-mātra-rūpāḥ, anādi-avidyā-vāsanā-nirmitāḥ, aropita-svabhāvāḥ, niḥ-svabhāvāḥ, śūnyāḥ.* According to the Indian Realists, a relation between two facts is a third unit possessing reality and existence, but the further relation between this third unity on both its sides and the two facts connected by it, has no separate existence, it possesses *svarūpa-sattā = viśeṣaṇa-viśeṣya-bhāva*, but no *sattā-sāmānya*.

2 NV., p. 468.

Dharmakīrti attached so much importance to this problem that, besides incidentally treating it in his great work, he singled it out for special treatment in a short tract of 25 mnemonic verses with the authors own commentary, under the title of «Examination of Relations».[1] In a sub-comment on this work Šankarānanda, surnamed the Great Brahmin, thus characterizes its aim and content — «This work considers the problem of Reality. By one mighty victorious stroke, all external objects whose reality is admitted (by the Realists) will be repudiated, and, in contrast to it, that ultimate reality which the author himself acknowledges will be established». Indeed, if all relations are cancelled, the Unrelated alone emerges as the Ultimate Reality. In the first stanza Dharmakīrti states that conjunction or relation necessarily means dependence. Therefore «all relations in the sense of ultimate (or independent) reality do not really exist.» Vinītadeva, in another sub-comment, states that the expressions «related to another», «dependent on another», «supported by another», «subject to another's will» are convertible. Causality, Contact, Inherence and Opposition are not realities by themselves. There are no «possessors» of these relations otherwise than in imagination. A reality is always one reality, it cannot be single and double at the same time. Dharmakīrti states,[2]

Since cause and its effect
Do not exist at once,
How can then their relation be existent?
If it exists in both, how is it real?
If it does not exist in both, how is it a relation?[3]

Therefore Causality is a relation superimposed upon reality by our understanding, it is an interpretation of reality, not reality itself.[4] Vācaspatimišra[5] quotes a Buddhist who remarks that these relations considered as objective realities are, as it were, unfair dealers

---

1 Sambandha-parīkṣā, to be found in the Tanjur with the commentaries of the author and two subcommentaries of Vinītadeva and Šankarānanda. The Buddhist theory of relations is analysed by Vācaspatimišra, in his NK., p. 289 ff., where a *saṃsarga-parīkṣā* is inserted.

2 Sambandha-parīkṣā, VII.

3 A similar line of argument is found in Pr. samucc., II. 19.

4 This, of course, refers to empirical causation alone, a causation between two constructed objects is itself constructed. Ultimate causation of the point-instant, we have seen, is not a relation, since it is synonymous with ultimate reality.

5 NK., p. 289. The same comparison, but in another connection, is quoted by the same author in Tātp., p. 269.9.

who buy goods without ever paying any equivalent. They indeed pretend to acquire perceptiveness, but possess no shape of their own which they could deliver to consciousness as a price for the acquisition of that perceptiveness. If a thing is a separate unity, it must have a separate shape which it imparts to consciousness in the way of producing a representation. But relation has no shape apart from the things related. Therefore, says Vinītadeva,[1] a relation in the sense of dependence cannot be something objectively real. Neither, says the same author, can a relation be partially real,[2] because to be partially real means nothing but to be real and non-real at the same time, «because reality has no parts; what has parts can be real empirically, (but not ultimately)».

Thus there is nothing real apart from the ultimate particular,[3] or the point-instant which, indeed, is also a cause, but an ultimate cause. It alone is unrelated and independent upon something else.

§ 8. Two lines of dependence.

However inference has nothing to do with this ultimate independent and unrelated reality. Inference is founded upon relations which are a superstructure upon a foundation of ultimate reality. «All inference, says Dignāga, (all relation between a reason and its consequence) is based upon relations constructed by the understanding between a substrate and its qualities, it does not reflect ultimate reality or unreality.»[4]

Since ultimate reality is non-relative and independent, its counterpart, empirical or imagined reality, is interrelated and interdependent. But a relation is not a fortuitous compresence of two facts, it is a necessary presence of the one when the other is present. There is therefore in every necessary relation a dependent part and another upon which it depends. One part is tied up to the other. There is a part which is tied up and another part to which it is tied up.[5] All empirical existence is dependent existence. Now, there are two and only two ways in which one fact can be dependent upon another fact. It either is a part of the latter, or it is its effect.

1 Ibid.
2 Ibid.
3 Cp. Sambandhap., Kār. XXV.
4 Cp. Tātp., p. 127, 2.
5 NBT., p. 25.

There is no third possibility. The division is founded on the dichotomizing principle, and the law of excluded middle forbids to assume any third coordinated item. This gives us two fundamental types of reasoning or of inference. The one is founded on Identity. We may call Identity the case when of the two necessarily related sides the one is the part of the other. They both refer to the same fact, their objective reference is identical. The difference between them is purely logical.

The other type of reasoning is founded on Causation. Every effect necessarily presupposes the existence of its cause or causes. The existence of the cause can be inferred, but not *vice versa*, the effect cannot be predicted from its causes with absolute necessity, since the causes not always carry their effects. Some unpredictable circumstance can always jeopardize their production.[1]

The first type of reasoning may be exemplified by the following inferences —

> This is a tree,
> Because it is a *śiṃśapā*,
> All *śiṃśapās* are trees.

Another example —

> The sound is impermanent,
> Because it is produced at will.
> Whatsoever is produced at will is impermanent.

Impermanence and willful production are two different characterstics which refer to the same objective point, to the sound. The *śiṃśapā* and the tree likewise refer to the same reality. The difference between them is a difference of exclusion.[2] The tree excludes all non-trees, the *śiṃśapā* excludes in addition to all non-trees moreover all trees that are not *śiṃśapās*. But the real thing to which both terms refer is the same. We therefore can say that they are related through Identity, or by an identical objective reference.

An example of the other type is the often quoted —

> There is here some fire,
> Because there is smoke.
> There is no smoke without fire.

---

1 Cp. NBT., p. 40.8.

2 *vyāvṛtti-bheda*.

Smoke and fire are not related by Identity, since there objective reference is different. They refer to two different, though necessarily interdependent, points of reality. Since causality, we have seen, is nothing but Dependent Origination or dependent existence, there can be no other real relation of dependence than causation. Dependence, if it is not merely logical, is Causation.

Thus we have a division of inference, or of inferential judgments, into those that are founded on Identity and those that are founded on non-Identity. The first means Identity of Reference, the second means Causation. The division is strictly logical as founded on a dichotomy.

Dharmottara[1] says, «The predicate (in a judgment) is either affirmed or denied.... When it is affirmed (through a mark, this mark) is either existentially identical with it, or when it is different, it represents its effect. Both possess the three aspects», i. e., in both cases there is a necessary dependence.

§ 9. Analytic and synthetic judgments.

It becomes thus apparent that the Buddhist Logicians, while investigating inference, have hit upon the problem of the analytic and the synthetic judgments. That inferential judgments, founded on experience, or on the law of Causation, are synthetic — has never been disputed. Neither has it been disputed, that there are other judgments which are not founded on Causation, judgments in which the predicate is a part of the subject, in which the mere existence of the subject is sufficient to deduce the predicate. Whether this division is exhaustive and the line of demarcation sufficiently clear cut, whether the problem coincides more or less completely with the Kantian one, we need not consider at present. The problem appears in India under the head of inference. That the Indian inference is an inferential judgment, a judgment uniting two fully expressed and necessarily interdependent concepts has been sufficiently pointed out. The two interdependent concepts have either one and the same objective reference or they have two different, but necessarily interdependent, objective references. Between one and two — there is nothing in the middle. At the first glance the division seems to be logically unimpeachable.

---

[1] NBT., p. 21.18, transl., p. 60.

Strictly speaking both kinds of judgment are synthetic, because understanding itself, and its function the judgment, is nothing but synthesis. The conception of a *śiṃśapā* is synthesis, the conception of a tree is synthesis, their union is likewise a synthesis. The same refers to the conceptions of smoke, of fire and of their union. The intellect can dissolve only where it has itself previously united.[1] But in one case the predicate is a part of the subject and is seemingly extracted out of it by analysis. In the other case it is not a part of it, it must be added to it, and can be found out by experience only.

The so called synthetic judgment is always experimental. The so called analytic judgment is always ratiocinative. The use of the understanding is double, it either is purely logical and consists in bringing order and system into our concepts, or it is experimental and consists in establishing causal relations by observation and experiment. Causality in this context, says Dharmottara,[2] «is a conception familiar in common life. It is known to be derived from experience of the cause wherever the effect is present, and from the negative experience of the absence of the effect when its cause is absent». The Identity upon which the so called analytic judgment is founded is not a familiar concept. Therefore its definition is given by Dharmakīrti. He says,[3] «Identity is a reason for deducing a predicate when the subject alone is by itself sufficient for that deduction», i. e., when the predicate is part of the subject. It is therefore not absolute Identity, it is, as some European philosophers have called it, a partial Identity. Dharmottara explains,[4] «What kind of logical reason consists in its merely being contained in its own predicate? This predicate possesses the characteristic of existing wheresoever the mere existence of the reason is ascertained. A predicate whose presence is dependent on the mere existence of the reason, and is dependent on no other condition beside the mere existence of the fact constituting the reason, such is the predicate which is inseparable from the reason (and can be analytically deduced from it)». Some remarks on the difference between the European, Kantian, treatment of the problem of synthetic and analytic judgments and the Buddhist conception will be made in the sequel.

---

1 Cp. CPR., § 15 (2-d). The perceptual judgment is analytic also (Sigwart, I. 142.)
2 NBT., p. 24 . 11; transl., p. 67.
3 Ibid., p. 23 . 16; transl., p. 65.
4 Ibid.

§ 10. THE FINAL TABLE OF CATEGORIES.

From what has been said above it is easy to represent to one self the final table of Buddhist categories, a table which corresponds to both the Aristotelian and the Kantian tables.

The synthesis which is contained in every act of the understanding, as has been pointed out, is double. It is first of all a synthesis between a particular sensation and a general concept, and it is also a synthesis of the manifold gathered in that concept. This last synthesis, we have seen, is fivefold. The five kinds of the most general predicates correspond, more or less, to the ten Aristotelian Categories, if the partial correspondencies and inclusions are taken into account. This table contains also the logical aspect of Ontology which analyses Ens into a common Subject and its five classes of Predicates. It finds its expression in the perceptual judgment in which the five classes of names are referred to this common Subject. It contains in addition to the five classes of names, or namable things, one general relation, just the relation of all these Predicates to a common Substrate.

But the synthesis of the understanding not only contains the manifold of intuition arranged under one concept and its reference to a common Subject, it moreover can connect two or several concepts together. This synthesis is no more a synthesis of the manifold of intuition, it is a synthesis between two interdependent concepts or facts. Thus in addition to the table of the most general names, we shall have a second table of the most general relations. This second table is directly connected with inference, since inference is a method of cognizing founded upon necessary relations between two concepts, of which one is the mark of the other. This point constitutes the principal difference between the Buddhist and the European tables of categories. The table of names and the table of relations are two different tables in Buddhist Logic, while in both the European tables relations and names are mixed up in one and the same table. The relation of Substance to Quality, or, more precisely, of the First Essence to all Predicates, is the most general relation which, being conterminous with judgment and the understanding itself, includes in itself all the other items of both tables. This relation covers all the varieties of connection whether it be the connection of one concept with its objective reference or whether it be the connection of two different concepts.

We shall thus have two different tables of Categories, a table of the Categories of namable things and a table of the Categories of Relations between two concepts.

First Substance is not entered into the list, because, as has been explained, it is the common substratum for all categories, it is not a Category, it is a non-Category. Neither is Quality in general to be found in it, because Quality in general embraces all categories, it is coextensive with the term Predicate or Category. Simple qualities are ultimate sense-data, as appears in the perceptual judgment «this is blue» or, more precisely, «this point possesses blueness». Complicated qualities are classes; e. g., in the perceptual judgment «this is a cow» which means as much as «this point of reality is synthesized as possessing cowness». Second Substances are metaphorical First Substances. On the analogy of a reality «possessing cowness», the cow itself appears also as a substance when it is conceived in its turn as something possessing attributes, e. g., «horn-ness». As an example of such substances Dignāga gives «the possessor of horns» or «horny», which for us would be a possessive adjective. We thus arrive at the following two Tables of judgments and their corresponding Categories.

TABLE OF JUDGMENTS

I

Pepceptual judgment (*savikalpaka-pratyakṣa*).

1. *Its Quantity* — Extreme Singular (*svalakṣaṇam adhyavasiyamānam*).
2. *Its Quanlity* — Affirmation-Reality (*vidhi = vastu*).
3. *Its Relation* — Conformity (*sārūpya*).
4 *Its Modality* — Apodictic (*niścaya*).

II

Inferential judgment (*anumāna-vikalpa*).

1

Quantity.

Universal (*sāmānya-lakṣaṇam adhyavasīyamānam*).

2

Quality.

Affirmation (*vidhi*).
Negation (*pratiṣedha*).

3

Relation.

Synthetic = Causal (*kārya-anumāna*).
Analytic = non-Causal (*svabhāvānumāna*).

4

Modality

Apodictic (*niścaya*).

TABLE OF CATEGORIES

I

Categories or kinds of synthesis under one Concept or one Name (*pañcavidha-kalpanā*)

1. Individuals — Proper Names (*nāma-kalpanā*).
2. Classes — Class Names (*jāti-kalpanā*).
3. Sensible Qualities — Their Names (*guṇa-kalpanā*).
4. Motions — Verbs (*karma-kalpanā*).
5. (Second) Substances — Substantives (*dravya-kalpanā*).

II

Categories of Relations (between two concepts).

1
Affirmations (of necessary defendence).
(*vidhi*)

2
Negation (of an assumed presence)
(*anupalabdhi*)

Identity (= non-Causality)
(*tādātmya*).

Causality (= non-Identity of the underlying reality)
(*tadutpatti*)

According to the Indian method of counting the ultimate items in a classification, there are only three Categories of Relation, viz. Negation, Identity and Causality. The subordinate and derivative kinds are not counted, neither is that Affirmation which embraces both Identity and Causality counted.

§ 11. Are the items of the table mutually exclusive.

Does this table of Categories satisfy to the principles of a correct logical division? Are its parts exclusive of one another? Does it not contain overlapping items? Is the division exhaustive?[1] We know that both classifications of Aristotle and of Kant have been found to contain flaws in this respect. Does the Buddhist table fare any better? Dharmottara asks[2] with respect to the three ultimate items of the division which are Identity, Causality and Negation — «These are the

[1] On the problem of *tādātmya* and *tadutpatti* cp., besides Pr. vārt. first chapter, and NBT. second chapter, Tātp., p. 105 ff., and N. Kandalī, p. 206 17 ff.

[2] NBT., p.24, 13; transl., p. 68.

different varieties of those relations upon which inference is founded. But why do we reckon only three (final) items? The varieties may be innumerable?» To this the answer of Dharmakīrti is the following one — «Inferential cognition is either Affirmation or Negation, and Affirmation is double, it either is founded on Identity or on Causality.» This answer means that, since the division is made according to the principle of dichotomy, the parts are exclusive of each another, there can be nothing between them, the law of Excluded Middle precludes any flaw in this respect. Indeed the fact that all judgments are divided in Affirmation and Negation is firmly established in logic since the times of Aristotle who even has introduced this division into his definition of the judgment. It is therefore wrong to coordinate the parts of this division with other items, belonging to other divisions, because the parts will then necessarily be overlapping.

The affirmative judgment again can either be analytic or synthetic, in other words, either founded on Identity or on non-Identity. The latter, i. e. the interdependence or the synthesis of non-identical facts, is nothing but Causality. Thus the division into Identity and Causality or, which is the same, the division of all judgments into analytic and synthetic is also founded upon the dichotomizing principle and must be deemed logically correct in accordance with the law of Excluded Middle, provided analytic and synthetic are understood in the sense which is given to this division in Buddhist logic. Dharmottara insists[1] that the division is strictly logical. He says, «The predicate in judgments is sometimes positive and sometimes negative. Since affirmation and negation represent attitudes mutually exclusive, the reasons for them both must be different. Affirmation again can only be either of something different or of something non-different. Difference and non-difference being mutually opposed by the law of contradiction, their justifications (in judgments) must also be different».

We must not forget that what is here called Identity is an identity of objective reference, the union of two different concepts which may be identical in extension or the one possess only a part of the extension of the other, but both referring to the same objective reality. Two concepts may be different, yet the objective reality to which they are referred may be the same. E. g., the concepts of a tree and of a *śiṃśapā* are different, yet the particular thing to which they refer is identical,

---

[1] NBT., p. 24. 19, transl., p. 69.

it is just the same. On the other hand, a concept may be the same, or the difference between them undiscernible, yet the real thing to which they refer will be different. E. g., this same *śiṃśapā* at two different moments of its existence. According to the Buddhists, two moments of the *śiṃśapā* are two different things, causally related. In the concepts of fire and smoke both the concepts and the real things are different. But the same relation of causality obtains between two consecutive moments of smoke as between the first moment of smoke and the preceding moment of fire. Thus the term synthetic refers to a synthesis of two different things, the term analytic to a synthesis of two different concepts.

Thus interpreted synthetic and analytic judgments are exclusive of each another and we cannot maintain, as has been done in European logic, that a synthetic judgment becomes analytic in the measure in which its synthesis becomes familiar to us.

It is thus proved that the Buddhist table of categories possesses order and systematical unity, since its parts are exclusive of one another. It remains to examine whether the table is exhaustive.

§ 12. Is the Buddhist table of relations exhaustive?

Dharmottara asks,[1] «Are there no other relations representing valid reasons?» «Why should only these three relations (viz. Negation, Identity and Causality) represent valid reasons?» The answer is that, according to Dharmakīrti, relation means here dependence. «One thing can convey the existence of another one only when it is essentially dependent on the latter,»[2] i. e., such relations which are reasons, which are the foundation of inference, are relations of necessary dependence. Dharmottara explains,[3] «When the cause of something is to be (synthetically) deduced, or an essential quality is to be deduced (analytically), the effect is essentially dependent on its cause (and the analytically deduced) quality is by its essence dependent upon the conception from which it is deduced. Both these connections are Essential Dependence.» Leaving alone Negation which is founded on a special principle to be examined later on, there are only two relations of necessary Dependence. They are either the logical interdependence of two conceptions having one and the same objective reference,

---

1 NBT., p. 25. 3; transl., p. 69.

2 NB. II.20, transl., p. 69

3 Ibid.

or, if the objective reference is not the same, it is an interdependence of two real facts of which the one is the effect of the other. The effect is necessarily dependent upon its cause. Causality is for the Buddhist nothing but Dependent Origination. Apart from these two kinds of necessary dependence, the one logical, the other real, there is no other possible interdependence.

The Indian Realists reject both these Buddhist contentions, viz., they reject that there are analytical judgments which are founded on Identity, and they reject that all necessary synthetical judgments are founded on Causality. The classification according to them is not exhaustive. The analytical judgment founded on Identity, first of all, does not exist at all. When two conceptions are identical, the one cannot be the reason for deducing the other, the deduction will be meaningless. If it be objected that the reality is the same, but the superimposed conceptions alone are different, the Realist answers that if the conceptions are different, the corresponding realities are also different. «If the concepts were not real, says he, they would not be concepts».[1] The judgment *taru* is *vṛkṣa* (which both terms mean a tree) would be founded on Identity, but not the judgment «*śimśapā* is a tree», because *śimśapā* and tree are for the Realist two different realities, both cognized in experience which teaches their invariable concomitance and the inherence of the tree in the *śiṃśapā*.

Nor are all real relations traceable to Causality. There are a great number of invariable concomitances ascertained by uncontradicted experience which are not reducible neither to Identity nor to Causation. E. g., the rising of the sun is invariably connected with its rising the day before; the appearance of a lunar constellation on one side of the horizon is always accompanied by the disappearance of another constellation on the opposite side; the rising of the moon is concomitant with high tide in the sea, etc. All these are examples of invariable concomitance which is not founded on causation.[2] When we experience the flavour of some stuff we can infer the presence of its colour,[3]

---

[1] Tātp., p. 108. 24 — *kālpanikasya avāstavate tattva-anupapatteḥ.*

[2] Cp. Prašast., p. 205, and Tātp., p. 107.

[3] Prof. A. Bain is inclined to admit that Causality is the only relation of uniformity among real units. He says, Logic, II, p. 11, «Of Uniformities of Coexistence, a very large number may be traced to Causation. It remains to be seen whether there be any not so traceable»... «they are all results of causation starting from some prior arrangement». «In conjoined Properties of Kinds, he further states, ibid., p. 52, there may be laws of Coexistence without Causation». The

because we know from experience that this kind of flavour is invariably concomitant with a definite colour. This invariable connection cannot be treated as founded on causality, because both phenomena are simultaneous, whereas causality is a relation of necessary sequence. To this the Buddhists answer that all these relations are traceable to causality, if causality is rightly understood. Indeed, every instant of a gustatory sense-datum is dependent on a preceding complex of visual, tactile and other data of which alone this stuff consists. The colour which exists simultaneously with the flavour is related to the latter only through the medium of the preceding moment in which visual, tactile and other sense-data represent that complex of causes, in functional dependence on which the next moment of colour can arise. What the realist calls a stuff is for the Buddhist a complex of momentary sense-data. Thus the inference of colour through flavour is really founded on simultaneous production by a common cause. The Buddhist considers causality microscopically, as a sequence of point-instants. Every real thing is resolvable into a stream of point-instants, and every following instant arises in necessary dependence upon a complex of preceding moments. To this Ultimate Causality, or Dependent Origination, every real thing is subject. Vācaspatimiśra[1] seems indirectly to concede this point «The inference of colour from the presence of a certain flavour, says he, is made by ordinary people. They have eyes of flesh (i. e., coarse sensibility) which cannot distinguish the mutual difference between point-instants of ultimate reality. Nor is it permissible for critical philosophers to transcend the boundaries of experience and to change the character of established phenomena in compliance with their own ideas,[2] because, if they do it, they will cease to be critical philosophers».[3] This sounds like an indirect confession that for a philosopher all real interdependence must be ultimately traceable to Causality. The Buddhist concludes that because one fact can convey the existence of

---

«conjoined properties» is similar to «coinherent properties» or to «identical reference» of two concepts. Thus Prof. A. Bain appears to accept, though in a timid way, the theory of the two exclusive modes of relation, Identity of Reference and Causation (*tādātmya-tadutpatti*). He also quotes, ibid., p. 52, an example of coexistence of scarlet colour with the absence of fragrance (= *gandhābhāvād rūpānumānam*) which is similar to the Buddhist explanation of *rasād rūpānumānam*; cp. Tātp., p. 105. 18 ff.

1 Tātp., p. 107. 18 ff.

2 Or «in compliance with the theory of the Thing-in-Itself», the term *svalakṣaṇa* having here probably a double meaning.

3 Ibid., p. 108. 14. *teṣām tattva* (= *parīkṣakatva*) *anupapatteḥ*.

the other only when they are necessarily interdependent, and because all real necessary interdependence is Causation, there can be no other synthetical and necessary judgment than the one founded on Causation. The division of necessary relations into those founded on Identity and those founded on Causality is thus an exhaustive division, «because, says Dharmakīrti, when a fact is neither existentially identical with another one, nor is it a product of the latter, it cannot be necessarily dependent upon it».

Dharmottara[1] adds — «A fact which is neither existentially identical nor an effect of another definite fact, cannot be necessarily dependent upon this other fact, which is neither its cause nor existentially the same reality. For this very reason there can be no other necessary relation than either Identity or Causality. If the existence of something could be necessarily conditioned by something else, something that would neither be its cause nor essentially the same reality, then only could a necessary connection repose on another relation, (besides the law of Identity of Reference and the law of Causation). Necessary, or essential connection, indeed, means Dependent Existence. Now there is no other possible Dependent Existence, than these two, the condition of being the Effect of something and the condition of being existentially (but not logically) Identical with something. Therefore the dependent existence of something (and its necessary concomitance) is only possible on the basis either of its being the effect of a definite cause or of its being essentially a part of the same identical essence».

Thus the division of judgments into synthetical and analytical, and of relations of Necessary Dependence into Causality and Existential Identity, is exhaustive, if we understand the synthetical judgment as causal or empirical, i. e., if we exclude from under the concept of synthesis every *a priori* connection.[2]

---

1 NBT., p. 26. 22. ff., cp. transl., p. 75.

2 Out of Kant's three Categories of Quality, two — Reality (=Affirmation= *vidhi*) and Negation (*anupalabdhi*) — are found in the Buddhist table directly. Out of his Categories of Relation, Causality is found directly. The Category of Inherence-Subsistence is either the relation of a substratum to its predicates which is conterminous with the synthesis of the understanding in general, or it is a synthesis of Identical Reference. Time and Space, which for the Buddhists are also synthetic, have no separate place in the table, since time is a synthesis of consecutive moments which is included under Causality, and Space is a synthesis of simultaneous moments which is included under Identical Reference. Neither does Quantity appear in the table as a separate mode of synthesis, since all quantity is

§ 13. Universal and Necessary Judgments.

«Experience, positive and negative,[1] says Dharmakīrti,[2] can never produce (a knowledge) of the strict necessity of inseparable connection.[3] This always reposes either on the law of Causality[4] or on the law of Identity.[5]» That is to say, experience, positive and negative, furnishes to our understanding all the materials for the construction of concepts. But by itself sensible experience is but a chaos of disordered intuition. The understanding, besides constructing the concepts, arranges them so as to give them order and systematical unity. It arranges them, so to speak, either along a vertical line in depth or along a horizontal line in breadth. It thus produces synthesized bits of reality arranged as cause and effect along a vertical line, and it produces a system of stabilized concepts deliminated against one another, but united by the law of Identical Reference. The law of Contradiction is not mentioned by Dharmakīrti in this context, but it evidently is implied as the principle of all negative judgments. Thus the laws of Contradiction, of Causality and of Identical Reference are the three laws which are the original possession of the Understanding. They are not derived from experience, they precede it and make it possible. They are there-

a synthesis of units, and all understanding is either consciously or unconsciously a synthesis of units. Thus the Buddhist table is made according to Kant's own principle that «all division *a priori* by means of concepts must be dichotomy» (CPR., § 11). For the same reason Similarity or Agreement as well as Dissimilarity or Difference are not Categories, as some philosophers have assumed. They are coextensive with thought or cognition. They are active principles even in every perceptual judgment. They are just the same in Induction. The first aspect of a logical reason, viz., its presence in similar cases, or cases of agreement, corresponds to the Method of Agreement. Its third aspect corresponds to the Method of Difference. Prof. A. Bain, Logic, II, p. 51, says, «The Method of Agreement is the universal and fundamental mode of proof for all connections whatever. Under this method we must be ready to admit all kinds of conjunctions, reducing them under Causation when we are able and indicating pure coexistence when the presumption inclines to that mode». This sounds like Dharmottara, p. 21. 18, transl., p. 60, telling us that «Relations are either Causation or Identity and that both possess the three marks», i. e., the methods of Agreement and Difference serve to establish both Causation and Coinherence.

1 *darśana-adarśana.*

2 Quoted from Pram. vārtika, I. 33 in Tātp., p. 105. 13, N. Kandalī, p. 207. 8.

3 *avinābhāva-niyama.*

4 *kārya-kāraṇa-bhāvo niyamakaḥ.*

5 *svabhāvo niyamakaḥ.*

fore in safety against the accidents of experience, they are necessary and universal truths.

All this is denied by the Realists. They deny all strict necessity and universality in knowledge and they deny that the understanding can be dissected into a definite number of its fundamental and necessary principles. All knowledge comes from experience which must be carefully examined. It then can yield fairly reliable uniformities, but we are never warranted against a new and unexpected experience which can come and upset our generalizations. Since all our knowledge without exception comes from experience, we cannot establish any exhaustive table of relations. Relations are innumerable and various as life itself.[1] «Therefore, says Vācaspatimišra,[2] we must carefully investigate whether (an observed uniformity of sequence) is not called forth by some special (additional) condition, and if we dont find any, we conclude that it does not exist. (This is the only way) to decide that (the observed uniformity) is essential».

We thus find in India a parallel to the discussion which so long occupied the field of philosophy in Europe, on the origin of necessary truths. The great battle between Realism and Idealism raged round the problem whether our understanding represents by itself, as pure understanding, a *tabula rasa*, a sheet of white paper upon which experience inscribes its objects and their relations, or whether it is not rather an active force having, previously to all experience, its own set of principles which constitute its necessary modes of connecting together the manifold of intuition. In Indian phrasing the question is asked, whether right cognition in general and inference in particular represents a pure light, comparable to the light of a lamp,[3] which is in no way necessarily connected with the objects upon which it accidentally happens to shed its light; or whether cognition, and the logical reason in particular, are necessarily connected with the cognized object. In the latter case the understanding must consist of some definite principles, which are not accidental as all sensible experience is; they must precede that experience and must make it possible. Our knowledge in that case will have a double origin. Its frame work will be due to the understanding and will consist of a definite set of fundamental principles; its contents will be due to all the accidents of sensible experience. The Indian systems of Nyāya, Vaišeṣika, Mīmāṃsā, Jaina

---

1 *sambandho yo vā sa vā*, cp. Tātp., p. 109. 23.

2 Tātp., p. 110. 12.

3 *pradīpavat*, cp. NBT., p. 19. 2, 25. 19, 47. 9; cp. Vātsyāyana, p. 2.4.

and Sānkhya share in the realistic view that the understanding represents initially a *tabula rasa*, comparable to the pure light of a lamp, that it contains no images and that there are no principles in the intellect before accidental experience comes to fill it up with more or less accidental facts and rules.

The Buddhists, on the other hand, maintain that there is a set of necessary principles which are not revealed by the lamp of experience, but represent, so to say, this lamp itself. The law of Contradiction, the law of Identity and the law of Causality are the three weapons with which our understanding is armed before it starts on the business of collecting experience. If we were not sure, before every experience, that the smoke which we see has necessarily a cause, or, more precisely, that every moment of smoke depends upon a set of preceding moments, we never could infer the presence of fire from the presence of its effect. No one short of an Omniscient Being could then make inferences. If, as the Realist maintains, the *śiṃśapā* and the tree are two different realities whose simultaneous inherence in a common substrate has been revealed by an accidental, though uncontradicted, experience, no one again, short of an Omniscient Being, could maintain that the *śiṃśapā* is necessarily and always a tree.[1] That the same object being blue cannot also be non-blue is certain before any experience, albeit the blue and the non-blue are known to us by accidental experience.

Thus the fact that we possess Universal and Necessary truths is intimately connected with the fact that we possess principles of cognition preceding every experience and that we possess a definite number of Categories of them, neither more nor less.

§ 14. The limits of the use of pure understanding.

But although the laws of Contradiction, of Identical Reference and of Causality are the original possession of our understanding and

---

1 Or to take another example, no one could maintain that the straight line is necessarily and always the shortest distance between two points. Subject and Predicate in this universal judgment are united not, of course, by Causality, but by the law of Identical Reference. All mathematical judgments are judgments founded on the principle of Identical Reference. A straight line and a shortest distance are known to us from sensible experience, but the judgment «this is the shortest distance, because it is a straight line» is necessary and not subject to the accidents of experience. It is analytical in this sense that it is not founded on Causation.

although they are independent in their origin from any sensible experience, they cannot extend their sway beyond the limits of experience. Those objects which by their nature lie beyond every possible experience, which are metaphysical, which are «unattainable neither as to the place in which they exist, nor as to the time at which they appear, nor as to the sensible qualities which they possess», — such objects are also uncognizable by the pure intellect. «Their contradiction, says Dharmottara,[1] with something else, their causal dependence upon something else, their subalternation (or identical reference) to something else, it is impossible to ascertain. Therefore it is impossible to ascertain what is it they are contradictorily opposed to, and what are they causally related to. For this reason contradictory facts, causes and effects are fit to be denied (as well as affirmed) only after their (positive and negative) observation has been recurrent... Contradiction, Causation and Subalternation of (interdependent) concepts are (in every particular case) necessarily based upon non-perception of sensibilia», i. e., upon positive and negative experience, upon perception and non-perception.

As to causal relation every particular case of it is known when it is established by five consecutive facts of perception and non-perception,[2] viz. —

1) the non-perception of the result, e. g. of smoke, before its production,

2) its perception, when —

3) its cause, the fire, has been perceived;

4) its non-perception, when —

5) its cause is not perceived.

There are thus: a) in respect to the result two cases (1 and 4) of non-perception and one case (2) of perception; b) in respect of the cause — one case (3) of perception and one case (4) of non-perception The facts which constitute a causal relation we cognize through sense-perception or through the perceptual judgment, but that they are indeed causally related we cognize only in an inferential judgment or a judgment of concomitance, because causality itself, the causal relation, cannot enter into our mind through the senses, it is added by the understanding out of its own stock. Dharmottara[3] says «when an effect is produced, we do not really experience causality

[1] NBT., p. 28. 20 ff.; transl., p. 105.
[2] Cp. N. Kandalī, p. 205.22 ff.
[3] NBT., p. 69, 11; transl., p. 192.

itself (as a sensible fact), but the existence of a real effect always presupposes the existence of its cause. Therefore this relation is real (indirectly)», i. e., it is constructed by the intellect on a basis of reality. But the principle of Causality itself is an original possession of the understanding.[1] This Dharmakīrti has expressed in his celebrated and often quoted stanza translated above.[2]

§ 15. Historical sketch of the views of Inference.

The Science of Logic (*nyāya-śāstra*) developped in India out of a Science of Dialectics (*tarka-śāstra*). Inference appears in the latter as one of the methods of proof, but its part is insignificant, it is lost in a multitude of dialectical tricks resorted to in public debates. Its gradual rise in importance runs parallel with the gradual decrease in the importance of dialectics.[3] During the Hīnayāna period the Buddhists seem to know nothing about either syllogism or inference. But with the advent of a new age, at that period of Indian philosophy when the teaching of the leading schools were put into systematical order and their fundamental treatises composed, inference appears in the majority of them as one of the chief sources of our knowledge, second in order and in importance to sense-perception. At the right and at the left wings of the philosophical front of that period we have two schools which, although for contrary reasons, deny inference as a source of real knowledge. The orthodox Mīmāṃsakas deny it because neither sense-

---

1 Of course that Causality, or efficiency, which is synonymous with existence itself, with the Thing-in-Itself, is not a category of the understanding, it is the non-category, the common substrate for all predicates or for all categories of the understanding.

2 Pram. vārt., I. 33, cp. above, p. 260.

3 The origin of the Indian doctrine of inference and syllogism must be indigenous. I find no unmistakable proofs of its foreign descent. Its whole conception as one of the «sources of knowledge» (*pramāna*) gives it from the start an epistemological character. S. C. Vidyabhusana, Indian Logic, p. 497 ff., assumes the influence of Aristotle «whose writings were widely read in those days». But he also thinks that the introduction of different parts of the Greek Prior Analytics «must needs have been gradual, as these had to be assimilated into and harmonized with Indian thought and language». Although an intercourse between Greek and Indian scholarships is highly probable, the Indian doctrine seems to me to have followed its own line of development. The similarities are easily explained by the subject-matter and the divergence must be explained by the originality of the Indian standpoint.

perception nor inference is a source of cognizing religious duty.[1] The Materialists, on the other side, deny it because direct sense-perception is for them the only source of knowledge.[2] Between these two extremes we have the schools of Nyāya, Vaiśeṣika and Sānkhya which in the period preceding Dignāga framed their definitions of inference as the second source of our knowledge of the empirical world. With Vasubandhu the Buddhists enter into the movement and produce in the Vādavidhi their own first definition. All these definitions, beginning with the definition of his Master Vasubandhu, the definitions of the Nyāya, the Vaiśeṣika and the Sānkhya schools, as well as the negative attitude of the Mīmāṃsakas, are mercilessly criticized and rejected by Dignāga. The Nyāya school defines inference as a cognition «preceded by sense-perception».[3] This is interpreted as meaning a cognition whose first step is «a perception of the connection between the reason and its consequence».[4] The Sānkhyas maintain that «when some connection has been perceived the establishment (on that basis) of another fact is inference».[5] The definition of the Vaiśeṣikas simply states that inference is produced by the mark (of the object).[6] Finally Vasubandhu in the Vādavidhi defines it as «a knowledge of an object inseparably connected (with another object) by a person who knows about it (from perception)».[7]

Dignāga, besides severely criticizing every word of these definitions[8] from the standpoint of precision in expression, opposes to them the general principle that «a connection is never cognized

---

1 Mīm. Sūtra, I, 1. 2. Later Mīmāṃsakas, Kumārila etc., define inference as a step from one particular case to another one.

2 A certain Purandara attempted to justify the position of the Materialists by maintaining that they deny only the supra-mundane use of inference in metaphysics and religion, but the Buddhists retorted that they also admit inference as a source of empirical knowledge only, cp. TSP., p. 431. 26.

3 NS., I. 1. 5.

4 NV., p. 46. 8.

5 This definition is quoted by Dignāga in Pr.-samucc.-vṛtti ad I. 35, and repeated in NV., p. 59. 17.

6 VS., IX. 2. 1. *laingikam=rtags-las ḥbyuñ-ba.*

7 Quoted in Pr. samucc. and NV., p. 56. 14 ff.

8 In the second chapter of. Pr. samucc. the stanzas 25—27 are directed against the Vāda-vidhi view, the stanzas 27—30 against the Nyāya, the stanzas 30—35 against the Vaiśeṣikas, the stanzas 35—45 against the Sānkhyas and 45 ff. against the Mīmāṃsakas.

through the senses».[1] Inference deals with concepts, i. e., with the general and «the general cannot be seen»;[2] it cannot enter into us through the senses. This view is a direct consequence of the definition of sense-perception as pure sensation. Sense-perception is not the «eldest» or chief source[3] of knowledge, in regard of which inference would be a subordinate source, second in order and in importance. Both sources have equal rights.[4] Inference in this context means understanding in general as contrasted with sensibility.[5] The senses alone yeild no definite knowledge at all. Jinendrabbuddhi says that the «non-Buddhists alone think that the senses can yeild definite cognition». On the other hand, the understanding alone is powerless to produce any knowledge of reality. Both sources are equally powerless alone, and equally efficient together. But the understanding or inference with its own principles which exist in it previously to all experience contains the possibility of our knowledge of necessary truths. This seems to have been the view of Dignāga, a view which he did not succeed to formulate definitely and which was later formulated by Dharmakīrti. Dignāga objects to the contention of the Naiyāyiks that the results are predictable when we know the causes, and that we can infer the future result[6] from the presence of its causes. «The result is not established by the presence of the cause, says he, the cause may be present, but an impediment may interfere, and another (secondary) cause can fail, and then the result will not appear».[7] He also objects to the theory of the Sānkhyas when they

---

1 Pr. samucc., II. 28 — *hbrel-pa dbaṅ-bas gzuṅ-bya-min*=*na sambandha indriyeṇa gṛhyate*. This coincides almost verbatim with Kant's words, CPR., § 15, «the connection (*conjunctio*=*sambandha*) of anything manifold can never enter into us through the senses (=*na indriyeṇa gṛhyate*)».

2 Ibid., II. 29 — *spyi mthoṅ-ba yaṅ min*=*na sāmānyam dṛśyate*.

3 *pratyakṣam na jyeṣṭham pramāṇam*, TSP., p. 161. 22.

4 *tulya-balam*, cp. NBT., p. 6. 12.

5 Cp. NB., I. 12—17, where the principle is laid down that the senses apprehend the individual, i. e., the thing as it is strictly in itself, shorn of all its relations, whereas inference apprehends, resp. constructs, the general, cp. Pr. samucc. II. 17, as well as the *vṛtti* and the remarks of Jinendrabuddhi, op. cit., f. 115. b. 2 ff

6 From this standpoint the future is altogether uncognizable, cp. Viśālāmalavatī, fol. 124. a. 3, cp. NBT., p. 40. 8; transl. p. 108. When we deem to predict the future it is only an indirect consequence of the law of Causation, the law namely that every thing depends on its causes. The result necessarily depends on its causes, but the cause does not necessarily carry its result, since an unexpected impediment can always interfere.

7 Pr. samucc., II. 30 — *rgyu-las ḥbras-bu ḥgrub-pa min*=*na kāryam kāraṇāt sidhyati*.

establish a relation of «mutual extermination»[1] which allows us, e. g., to infer the absence of snakes in a place where ichneumons are abundant. The snake, says he, may be a victor in the struggle with the ichneumon and the inference will be a failure. But the inference of impermanence from the fact of causal origin[2] is certain, because it is founded on Identity, just as the inference of the preceding moment in the existence of a thing is certain because it is founded on causal necessity.

Apart from this fundamental divergence, the Vaišeṣikas, from among all non-Buddhist schools, come the nearest to the Buddhists, both in their definition of inference and in their classification of relations.[3] They acknowledge 4 kinds of relations, viz. Causality, Coinherence in a common substrate, Conjunction (or simple concomitance) and Opposition or Negation. If Coinherence is understood as Identical Reference and the category of Conjunction dropped altogether, the classification will not differ substantially from the one of Dharmakīrti. Conjunction is either superfluous itself or makes the three other categories superfluous. The aim of the fourfold division however, as Vācaspati thinks, was to be complete and exhaustive with members mutually exclusive of one another.[4] Dignāga records[5] that at his time the Vaišeṣikas explained the generalizing step which the understanding makes when it moves from a particular case to a universal premise as a supernatural intuition, evidently because it was unexplainable from experience. The idea of a fixed number of relations was nevertheless dropped by them in the sequel. Prašastapāda says,[6] «If the Aphorisms mention Causality etc. (as the categories of Relation), they do it by the way of examples, not in order to have an exhaustive table. Why? because experience proves that other relations are possible. E. g., when the *adhvaryu*-priest pronounces the syllable Om!, it is an indication that the chief priest is present, even when he is not seen; the rising of the moon is a token of the

---

[1] *ghātya-ghātaka-bhāva*, cp. ibid.

[2] Ibid.

[3] The threefold classification of the Nyāya (*pūrvavat, šeṣavat, sāmānyato-dṛṣṭa*) was differently interpreted by the Naiyāyiks themselves, cp. Vātsyāyana, p. 18; it is rejected by Dignāga in Pr. samucc. II. 26 ff. The sevenfold division of the Sānkhyas is mentioned in the vṛtti on the same work ad II. 35 and in Tātp., p. 109. 21. It is entirely fortuitous and is not recorded in the works of the classical period of this system.

[4] Tātp., p. 109. 12 — *cāturvidhyam tv iṣyate.*

[5] Pr. samucc. vṛtti, II.

[6] Prašastap., p. 205. 14.

high tide in the sea...; the clear water in the ponds in autumn is simultaneous with the rise of the planet Agastya, etc. etc. All these instances fall under the aphorism which mentions the four kinds of relations, (although they are not included under one of them in particular), because its meaning (is not to give an exhaustive classification of relations), but to indicate (and exemplify) concomitance in general».

The natural tendency to give an exhaustive table of relations has thus been abandoned as soon as it was realized that experience which is always to a certain extent accidental, cannot furnish by itself neither any necessary truths, nor a definitely fixed number of them.

The words of Prašastapāda are likewise an indirect indication that at the time of Dignāga the question was already debated whether there are any real relations not traceable to Causality.

But although Dignāga seems to have had in his head the system of relations which we find clearly stated in the works of Dharmakīrti, he was not sufficiently categorical in expressing it and it was left to his great follower to give to this theory its final formulation. In the time between the two masters there was a fluctuation in the school. Išvarasena, the pupil of Dignāga, denied the possibility of strictly necessary and universal principles in our knowledge. According to him,[1] no one short of an Omniscient Being could possess a knowledge strictly universal and necessary. He in this point rallied to the Vaišeṣikas. He evidently was convinced that the works of Dignāga did not contain the theory which was found in them by Dharmakīrti and so it was left to the latter to clear up all doubt in this respect and finally to establish the Buddhist table of the Categories of Relations.[2]

---

1 Mahāpaṇḍita Išvarasena's opinions are referred to in the commentary of Šākya-buddhi and he is quoted by Rgyal-tshab in his Thar-lam. He maintained that ordinary men (*tshur-mthoṅ-ba-rnams=arvag-daršinaḥ*) can never know that the reason is totally absent in the dissimilar cases; exceptions to the general proposition are always possible. This was rejected by pointing out six cases in which this opinion conflicts with different passages of the Nyāya-mukha and Pr. samucc.—*hgal-ba-drug-gi sgo-ṇas pan-chen Dban-phyug-sde-la thal-ba phans-thsul-ni*. The commentator Prajñākara Gupta however seems to have reverted to the view that necessary truths are discovered by supernatural intuition, cp. vol. II, p. 130 n.

2 It is therefore clear that the *svabhāvānumāna* which already appears in the Uttaratantra and other writings of Asanga cannot have the same meaning as with Dharmakīrti.

§ 16. Some European Parallels.

What the Buddhist Logic treats as inference, the European Logic treats partly as judgment, resp. proposition, and partly as syllogism. Dignāga has established a hard and fast line between inference, or reasoning «for one self» and syllogism, or inference «for others». The latter, as will be seen later on, is a fully expressed form of inductive-deductive reasoning. It is not at all a process of cognition, it can be called a source of knowledge only by the way of a metaphor.[1]

On the other hand much of the material which is treated in Europe as immediate, incomplete or apparent inference (*enthymema*) is treated by the Buddhists as inference proper. The Conditional proposition which in the first instance applies to cause and effect is treated in Europe either as a judgment or a Hypothetical Syllogism, or as an immediate inference. If there is an effect, there necessarily is a cause, if the cause is absent, the effect is necessarily absent. De Morgan thinks that «this law of thought connecting hypothesis with necessary consequence is of a character which may claim to stand before syllogism, and to be employed in it, rather than the converse». As will be shown later on, this is exactly the Buddhist view. The reason for this lies just in the fact that syllogism gives a deductive formulation to every observation of a causal sequence. One half of our inferential thinking is founded on the law of Causality and the respective judgments are always inferential in the part in which they are not directly perceptual. Prof. A. Bain remarks that «the same conditional form holds when one thing is the sign of another», i. e., not only when the effect is the sign of the existence of a cause, but also when another sign than the effect is «constantly associated with that other object». Since all inference and all syllogism reduces to the fact that «one thing is the sign of another» (*nota notae*), we can interpret the remark of Prof. Bain as a hint to the fact that all inference is either causal or non-causal and this, as we have seen, is just the Buddhist view. The cognition of an object through its sign or mark is treated in European Logic as the axiom upon which the syllogism is founded, *nota notae est nota rei ipsius*. Axiom here evidently means that essential character which our thought possesses in every inferential cognition. It would consequently have been more proper to call it not the axiom,

---

[1] NBT., III. 2.

but the definition of inference and to separate it from syllogism, as Dignāga has done in India.

As to the line of demarcation between Judgment and Inference, it is settled in India on altogether different lines from what it is in the majority of European systems. Since Judgment, Synthesis and Understanding are equivalent terms, all inference is contained under the head of judgment. But the judgment can either contain the statement of one fact, or the statement of a necessary interdependence between two facts. The first is always reducible to a perceptual judgment, the second is an inference. Dignāga, whose leading principle is a difference between Sensibility and Understanding, distinguishes between pure sensation, perceptual judgment and inference. His real aim is to distinguish sensibility from the understanding, but in compliance with tradition he treats of them under the heads of sense-perception and inference. That the synthesis of the manifold of intution in one concept and the synthesis of two interdependent concepts are two quite different operations of the understanding is occasionally hinted by Kant, when he says that there is a synthesis in all acts of the understanding, «whether we connect the manifold of intuition or several concepts together».[1]

The usual form of a judgment which is defined in European Logic as a predicative relation (i. e. synthesis) between two concepts applies, from the Indian standpoint, to inferential judgment or syllogism. In fact it is always the major premise of a syllogism in which the interdependence of two concepts (the middle and the major terms) are expressed. The common substrate for both these concepts, or the minor term, when it is not expressed, is understood, it is the common Subject of all Predicates, the First Essence of all things. Thus the major premise can really contain the whole inference. This is just the opinion of Prof. A. Bain[2] when he says that «in affirming a general proposition, real Inference is exhausted». «When we have said „All men are mortal" we have made the greatest possible stretch of inference. We have incurred the utmost peril of inductive hazard». This hazardous step of a universal judgment is explained, we have seen, by the Vaišeṣikas, to whom Īšvarasena seems to have rallied, as a super-human intuition. But Dignāga and Dharmakīrti have offered another explanation.

---

1 CPR., § 15 (2-d ed.).

2 Logic, I, p. 209.

Remains the problem of the synthetical and the analytical judgments The term which we translate as «analytical judgment» following Kant's terminology, literally means «own-essence inference». This term implies that the predicate of the judgment belongs to the «own essence» of the subject and can be inferred «from the existence of the subject alone», i. e., the subject alone, without betaking oneself to another source, viz., to experience, is sufficient for inferring the predicate. The predicate can be easily inferred from the subject, because it already is contained in it. The judgment «a *śiṃśapā* is a tree» would certainly have been characterized by Kant as an analytical one. As a matter of fact it means that «the *śiṃśapā*-tree is a tree».

Since all acts of the understanding in general and all judgments in particular are synthesis, an analytical judgment seems to be a *contraditio in adjecto.* In fact Kant does not treat it as a new cognition.[1] It is a secondary act of dissolving what we ourselves have connected and then reuniting it in a judgment which has no cognitional value at all.[2] «Analytical affirmative judgments, says Kant, are therefore those in which the connection of the predicate with the subject is conceived through Identity, while others, in which the connection is conceived without Identity, may be called synthetical». Compare with this statement the words of Dharmottara[3] «Affirmation (i. e., the predicate that is affirmed) is either different (from the subject) or it is identical with it». The so called analytical judgments are synthetical, but founded on Identity. The purely synthetical contain a synthesis without Identity. The coincidence between the Indian and the European view extends here even to terminology.

However the connotation of the term Identity with Kant seems to be not at all the same as the meaning of this term in Buddhist Logic, and the importance given to the so called analytical judgment on the Indian side is quite different from the negligible part it plays in European Epistemology. Kant believed in the preexistence or ready concepts[4] which can be dissolved by us in their component parts.

---

[1] According to the Indian terminology a purely analytical judgment would not be a *pramāṇa* in the sense of *anadhigata-artha-adhigantṛ*. Indeed the *svabhāvānumāna* in the writings of Asanga is not coordinated with *kāryānumāṇa.*

[2] As B. Russell puts it, no one except a popular orator preparing his audience to a piece of sophistry will resort to an analytical judgment, cp. Problems, p. 128.

[3] NBT., p. 24. 20, transl., p. 63.

[4] Although he says that «we cannot represent to ourselves anything as connected in the object, without having previously connected it ourselves» (CPR., § 15 (2-d ed.).

If something new is added to such a concept, the judgment will be synthetical, e. g., the judgment «all bodies are heavy», because heaviness is not contained in the old concept of a body and has been added as a result of some new experience. But for the Buddhist all ancient features and all new characteristics which may be added to a ready concept are united by the Identity which is contained in that unity of the concept. The Identity of two non-identical concepts consists in the identity of their objective reference. The *šiṃšapā* and the tree are not two identical concepts, but the real thing to which both these concepts refer is identical. One and the same thing which is called *šiṃšapā* may also be called a tree. The judgment which we have, because of its partial analogy with Kants terminology, called analytical, is really meant to be a judgment of Identical Reference. «Even in those cases, says Dharmottara,[1] where inference is founded on Identity (i. e. on identity of objective reference), (there is a dependent and an independent part). It is the dependent part that possesses the power to convey the existence of the other. The independent part, that part to which the other part is subordinated, is the deduced part».

The *šiṃšapā* and the tree, although they both refer to the same identical object, are not identical by themselves. They are interdependent, so that where one of them, the dependent part, is present, the other part, the independent one, is necessarily present also, but not *vice versa*. The tree is not dependent on the *šiṃšapā*. There can be trees which are not *šiṃšapās*, but all *šiṃšapās* are necessarily trees.[2]

The judgment «all wich happens has its cause» is according to Kant synthetical, because «the concept of cause is entirely outside that concept (of something that happens)» and is «by no means contained in that representation». This is quite different on the Indian side. It has been sufficiently established above that all that happens, i. e., all that exists is necessarily a cause, the non-cause does not exist; reality is efficiency, efficiency is cause. The judgment will be

---

1 NBT., p. 26. 3, transl., p. 72.

2 Kant says «in every analytical proprosition all depends on this, whether the predicate is really thought in the representation of the subject». The criterion is psychological. Dharmakīrti would have said (cp. NB., II) «in every analytical proposition all depends on this, whether the predicate must or can be thought in the representation of the subject, as logically flowing out of the latter». The criterion is logical necessity, and its establishment sometimes very complicated.

analytical in the sense that it will be a judgment of Identical Reference, because the same identical thing which is called existent is also called a cause.[1]

The judgment $5+7=12$ would certainly be regarded by Dharmakirti as analytical, or founded on Identity of Reference, since it means that the same thing which we call twelve as an aggregate can also be called $7+5$ or in any other distribution of that collective unity.

The judgments «everything is impermanent, there is nothing eternal», we have seen, are also analytical in this sense. The predicate is not at all «really thought» in the representation of the subject, but it is logically contained in it, although the proof may be very elaborate. This so called analytical judgment far from being negligible in the whole compass of our cognition occupies nearly one half of it.[2] If a Necessary Conjunction is not founded on Causation, it is founded on Identity. There is no other possibility. Necessary Conjunction, if not founded on Identity, is founded on Causality. Causality is Necessary Dependence of one thing upon others.

The judgment «in which the connection of the predicate with the subject is conceived without Identity may be called synthetical», says Kant. Dharmakirti calls them causal, because connection means here dependence of a thing on something else, on something non-identical. Such a necessary dependence is causation. Thus the division of all inferential judgments, affirming the necessary connection, or dependence, of one thing upon another, their division in those that are founded on Identical Reference and those that are founded on Non-Identical, but interdependent, Reference is exhaustive, since it is founded upon the principle of dichotomy.[3]

---

[1] This Kant seems indirectly to admit in saying «In the concept of something that happens I, no doubt, conceive of something existing preceded by time, and from this certain analytical judgments may be deduced».

[2] The judgment «all men are mortal», according to J. S. Mill's interpretation, adds the characteristic of mortality to the concept of a man as a consequence of our assent to the empirical judgment that all men are mortal, because John, Jack etc. have been found to be mortal. This would mean that although John, Jack etc. have been found to be mortal, it is by no means sure that Alfred may not be found to be immortal. According to the Buddhist, the judgment is founded on Identity, since everything that exists and has a cause is necessarily perishable. Immortal means unchanging (*nitya*) and unchanging means non-existing.

[3] Kant also says that «generally all division *a priori* by means of concepts must be a dichotomy» (CPR., § 11, 2-ded.). He was puzzled by the fact that his own table was not so.

The division of all judgments into synthetical and analytical is, therefore, on the Indian side, an integral part of the system of all Categories of necessary relations, while in Kant's system this division stands completely outside his table of Categories which includes synthetical judgments only.

It is not our business at present to make a detailed statement and a comparative estimate of the Indian and European achievements in this part of the science of logic. More competent pens will no doubt do it some time. We however could not leave without notice a remarkable partial coincidence, as well as the great difference, in a special point of epistemological logic, between India and Europe. It is more or less unanimously admitted that Kant's table of Categories and his manner of treating the analytical and synthetical judgments have proved a failure. But Kant's system still stands high as the Himalaya of European philosophy. A host of respectable workers are trying to undermine it, without as yet having been successful neither in pulling it down completely, nor, still less, in replacing it by another system of the like authority. Although Kant's table of Categories is a failure in its details, nevertheless his obstinate belief 1) that our understanding must have principles of its own before any experience, 2) that these principles are the foundation of universal and necessary judgments and 3) that there must be an exhaustive table of such principles, neither more nor less, — this his obstinate belief which induced him to introduce his twelve-membered table even where there was absolutely no need for it, — this belief finds a striking support in the parallel steps of Indian philosophy. As regards the problem of analytical and synthetical judgments the perusal of the more than hundred pages of Vaihinger's Commentary devoted to a mere summary of the amazing variety and mutual contradictions in the views of post-Kantian philosophers, will convince the reader that the problem has been merged in a hopeless confusion. Although it remains a problem, it has not been neither solved nor removed and Kant must still be credited with the merit of having first approached it in European logic. We must now wait till some professional philosopher will enlighten us as to the relative value of its Indian solution.[1]

---

[1] There are thus according to Dharmakīrti two different Necessities (*niścaya* = *avinābhāva-niyama*) or two kinds of *a priori* certainty, the one is concerned about the necessary conjunction of two concepts coinherent in one and the same substrate of reality, the other about two concepts inhering in two different, but necessarily interdependent, concepts. The first can be called analytical, the second is evidently

CHAPTER III.

SYLLOGISM
(PARĀRTHĀNUMĀNAM).

§ 1. Definition.

The aim of Buddhist logic is an investigation of the «sources» of our knowledge with a view to finding out in the cognized world its elements of Ultimate Reality and of separating them from the elements of Imagination, which in the process of cognition have been added to them. Syllogism is not a source of knowledge. It consists of propositions which are resorted to for communicating ready knowledge to others. It is therefore called by Dignāga an inference «for others». When an inference is communicated to another person, it then is repeated in his head and in this metaphorical sense[1] only can it be called an inference. Syllogism is the cause which produces an inference in the mind of the hearer. Its definition is therefore the following one[2] — «a syllogism consists in communicating the Three Aspects of the Logical Mark to others».

What the so called Three Aspects of the Logical Mark are — we know from the theory of Inference. They correspond to the minor

---

synthetical. We may contrast with this attitude the views of Aristotle and all Rationalists, according to whom every *a priori* necessary knowledge is analytical, and of Kant for whom it is always synthetic, (the analytical judgments being mere identical explanations). By a quite different definition of the Category of Identity (*tādātmya*) Dharmakīrti succeeds in giving to the propositions of pure logic and pure mathematics an altogether different basis from the propositions of pure physics. By keeping separate these two specific kinds of knowledge Dharmakīrti comes nearer to Hume, but he differs from him and comes nearer to Kant by establishing the *a priori* necessity of causal relations. The terms analytical and synthetical are very much misleading. First of all synthesis and analysis in the perceptual judgment should be distinguished from those of the inferential (with two concepts). They are confounded, e. g., by Sigwart. Logik, I. 141 ff. It would have been better to contrast the two Necessities as static and dynamic. That the really primordial division of the procedure of the human mind must be established in the way of a dichotomy (as every division of concepts *a priori*) dawned upon Kant in the second edition of his Critique (§ 11). He then calls the one class dynamical, the other — mathematical. The dynamical evidently corresponds to Causation, the mathematical — to Coinherence or Identity (of substrate). Kant's attempt to force his twelve-membered division into this double one is by no means clear.

1 *upacārāt*.

2 NB., III. 1; transl., p. 109.

and major premises of Aristotle's syllogism and to its conclusion. They are virtually the same in syllogism, but their order is different. An inference is essentially a process of inferring one particular case by its similarity to another particular case. The general rule uniting all particular cases and indicated by the quotation of some examples, intervenes subsequently as a uniting member between the two particular cases. A syllogism, on the contrary, starts by proclaiming the general rule and by quoting the examples which support it, and then proceeds to a deduction of the particular from the general. The order of the premises in the Buddhist syllogism is therefore the same as in the Aristotelian First Figure. It begins with the major premise and proceeds to the minor one and the conclusion.[1]

The difference between the inference «for one self», or, more precisely, «in one self» and the inference in the sense of a cause which produces an inference in the head of a hearer, is thus considerable. The first is a process of cognition containing three terms. The second is a process of communicating a ready cognition and consists of propositions.

In order to understand the position of Dignāga in this point, we must keep in mind his idea of what a source or right knowledge is. It is the first moment of a new cognition, it is not recognition.[2] Therefore only the first moment of a fresh sensation is a right cognition in the fullest sense. A perceptual judgment is already a subjective construction of the intellect. Inference is still more remote from that ultimate source of right knowledge. When knowledge is communicated to another person, the first moment of a new cognition in his head can, to a certain extent, be assimilated to a fresh sensation whose source, or cause, are the propositions of which a syllogism consists.

The following three examples will illustrate the difference as it appears in the three types of the inference «for one self» and in the corresponding three types of the inference «for others».

---

1 Cp. with this the indecision of Prof. B. Erdmann (Logik³, p. 614) regarding this very point. In the last edition of his Logic he made the important step of changing the Aristotelian order of premises and putting the minor premise on the first place. He found that this order renders more faithfully the natural run of our thought, i. e., he envisaged syllogism as an inference «for one self». Sigwart thinks that the order in real life can be the one or the other, both are equally possible.

2 *pramāṇam=prathamataram vijñānam=anadhigata-artha-adhigantṛ*, cf. above, p. 65.

Inference for one self —

1. The sounds of speech are impermanent entities.
   Because they are produced at will, just as jars etc.

This is an inference founded on Identical Reference of two concepts, «impermanence» and «production».

2. There is fire on the hill.
   Because there is smoke, just as in the kitchen etc.

This is an inference founded upon a Causal Relation between two facts.

3. There is no jar on this place.
   Because we do not perceive any, just as we perceive no flower growing in the sky.

This is an inference founded on Negation.

The corresponding three types of a syllogism will have the following form.

1. Whatsoever is produced at will is impermanent, as, e. g., a jar etc.
   And such are the sounds of our speech.
2. Wheresoever there is smoke, there must be some fire, as in the kitchen etc.
   And there is such a smoke on the hill.
3. Whenever we dont perceive a thing, we deny its presence, as, e. g., we deny the presence of a flower growing in the sky.
   And on this place we do not perceive any jar, although all the conditions of its perceptibility are fulfilled.

The difference between Inference and Syllogism is thus a difference between that form of the Inferential Judgment which it usually has in the natural run of our thinking and acting process, and another form which is most suitable in science and in a public debate. In a public debate the universal proposition is rightly put forward as the foundation of the reasoning to which should follow the applying proposition, or the minor; whereas in the actual thought-process the universal judgment is never present to the mind in its necessity, it seems hidden in the depths of our consciousness, as though controlling the march of our thought from behind a screen.

Our thought leaps from one particular case to another one, and a reason seems to suggest itself to the mind. Its universal and necessary connection with the predicate lies apparently dormant in the instinct and reveals itself only when duly attended to.[1] We have retained the name of Inference for the individual thought-process, because it more closely corresponds to the natural process of transition from one particular case to another one. We have given the name of Syllogism to inference «for others» because of its outward similarity with Aristotle's First Figure. As a matter of fact it is very difficult always to distinguish between what belongs to inference as a thought-process and what to its expression in speech, since we cannot deal with the thought-process without expressing it in some way. The problem is solved in practice so, that the definition of the inferential process, its «axioms», its canon of rules and the capital question of those fundamental relations which control the synthetic process of thought are treated under the head of inference «for one self». On the other hand, the problem of the Figures of the syllogism and the problem of logical Fallacies are dealt with under the head of «inference for others». But even this division of problems cannot be fully carried through. Dharmakīrti[2] treats the important problem of the Figures of a Negative Syllogism under the head of inference «for one self», because, says he, the repeated consideration of Negation through all its different aspects and formulations brings home to us the essence of the Negative Judgment itself.

But although it seems quite right to put in the first place the general proposition as the foundation of the reasoning, nevertheless that form of the syllogism which has survived in the practice of all monastic schools of Tibet and Mongolia belongs rather to the abbreviated form of inference «for one self». The debate, whether didactic or peirastic, does not begin by putting forward the universal proposition, nor are propositions as such used at all. The Respondent begins by stating his three terms, the Subject, the Predicate and the Reason (or Middle term), without caring to put them in the form of propositions. The Opponent then considers two questions, 1) is the Reason (R) really present in the Subject (S) wholly and necessarily, and 2) is the Reason (R) necessarily and universally present in the Predicate (P). Thereupon begins the debate. The two questions if reduced to the phrasing of modern English formal logic will mean, 1) is the Middle distributed in the Minor,

[1] This psychological fact is probably the real cause why some European logicians, as J. S. Mill and others, have characterized the major premise as a kind of collateral notice which helps the mind in its transitions from one particular case to another, cp. Sigwart, op. cit., I. 480.

[2] NB., II. 45 and NBT., p. 37, 11 ff., transl., p. 100 ff.

and 2) is the Middle distributed in the Major. This form of stating the Syllogism has been found through centuries of assiduous practice to be the most convenient for detecting fallacies. The real work of logic begins only when the three terms are clearly and unambiguously singled out. In the diffuse propositional form the real terms are often so concealed as to be difficult of detection.

§ 2. The members of a syllogism.

As is seen from the above examples, the syllogism consists of two propositions only. When Dignāga started on his logical reform he was faced by the theory of a five.-membered syllogism established in the school of the Naiyāyiks. This syllogism was supposed to represent five interrelated steps of an ascending and descending reasoning. It started by a thesis and ended in a conclusion which was nothing but a repetition of the thesis. The members were the following ones:

1. Thesis. There is fire on the hill.
2. Reason. Because there is smoke.
3. Example. As in the kitchen etc.; whereever smoke, there fire.
4. Application. And there is such smoke on the hill.
5. Conclusion. There is fire on the hill.

From these five members Dignāga retained only two, the general rule including the examples, and the application including the conclusion. Indeed the main point in every syllogism, just as in every inference, is the fact of the necessary interrelation between two terms as it is expressed in the major premise. The second point consists in the application of the general rule to a particular case. This is the real aim of an inference, i. e., the cognition of an object on the basis of the knowledge of its mark. When these two steps are made, the aim of the syllogism is attained, other members are superfluous. It thus consists of a general rule and its application to an individual case.[1]

But the syllogism of the Naiyāyiks contains much more details. It first of all contains a separate thesis and a separate conclusion, although by its content the conclusion is nothing but the repetition of the thesis at the end. The syllogism thus resembles a mathematical demonstration, it begins by proclaiming the *probandum* and concludes by stating that its demonstration has been made. Dignāga

---

[1] Cp. Bain. Logic, I. 146. — «The essential structure of each valid deduction is 1) a universal ground-proposition, affirmative or negative, and 2) an applying proposition which must be affirmative».

and Dharmakīrti enlarge upon the definition of a correct thesis. Evidently this was a point at issue between the schools of their time. They maintain that a thesis in a public debate should be correctly formulated. But they at the same time maintain that the thesis is not at all an indispensible member of every deduction. It can be safely dropped even in a debate when in the course of debating it is clearly understood without special mention. A thesis according to them cannot be something absurd or contradictory, something which it is not worth the while of proving, and it must be a proposition which the disputant himself believes, which he *bona fide* really intends to prove. It would be bad logic if a philosopher attempted to make capital out of ideas which he does not share himself. Vācaspati remarks that if a philosopher who is known to be an adherent of Vaiśeṣika principles would suddenly take for his thesis the theory of his adversaries, the Mīmāṃsakas, regarding the eternity of the sounds of speech, if he would do it at a public meeting in the presence of authorized judges, he would not be allowed to go on, his defeat would be pronounced at once, before listening to his arguments.

Thus a series of rules were established to which an acceptable thesis must satisfy.[1] But later on this chapter on a correctly formulated thesis gradually sunk into insignificance, since all fallacies of a thesis became merged in the doctrine of false reasons.

According to Dignāga and Dharmakīrti, real members of a syllogism, the necessary members of the logical process, are thus only two, the general rule and its application to an individual instance. The first establishes a necessary interdependence between two terms, the second applies this general rule to the point in question. The first is called Inseparable Connection.[2] The second is called Qualification of the Subject (by the fact of this Inseparable Connection).[3] Its formula, accordingly, is the following one—

R possesses P,
S possesses R + P.

The conclusion, indeed, as has been noticed also by some European logicians,[4] cannot be separated from the minor premise in the same

1 Cp. my notes to the transl., v. II, p. 160. 6 ff.

2 *avinābhāva=anantarīyakatva=avyabhicāra=vyāpti.*

3 *pakṣa-dharmatā*, also called *pakṣa* simply, cp. N. mukha, p. 12.

4 Sigwart. Logik, I. 478 n.

degree, as the major premise from the minor. If we give it the rank of a separate member, there is no sufficient reason to deny this rank to the thesis, i. e. to the repetition of the conclusion at the beginning in the guise of a *probandum*, as the Naiyāyiks indeed maintain. «I refute the theory of those logicians, says Dignāga,[1] who consider the thesis, the application and the conclusion as separate members of the syllogism».

Dharmottara[2] says, «There is no absolute necessity of expressing separately the conclusion. Supposing the reason has been cognized as invariably concomitant with the deduced property, (we then know the major premise). If we then perceive the presence of that very reason on some definite place, (i. e., if we know the minor premise), we already know the conclusion. The repetition of the deduced conclusion is of no use».

Thus the real members of the syllogism are the same as the Three Aspects of the Logical Reason which have been established in the inference «for one self», but their order in the inference «for others» is changed.

They are:

1. In Similars only,
2. In Dissimilars never, } = Inseparable Connection.
3. In Subject wholly = Application.

The first two aspects, as will be established presently, represent only a difference of formulation, essentially they are equipollent.

§ 3. Syllogism and Induction.

«But then, says Dignāga,[3] (if neither the thesis, nor the application, nor the conclusion are separate members), the formulation of the example does not represent a different member, as it merely declares the meaning of the reason?» The answer of Dignāga is to the effect that «it is necessary to express separately the positive and the negative examples», (in order to show that the reason possesses its two other conditions, besides the condition of being present on the subject of the minor premise). But the example is not to be separated

[1] N. mukha, Tucci's transl., p. 45.
[2] NBT., 53. 16; transl., p. 150.
[3] N. mukha, transl., p. 45.

from the major premise, it is not a separate member, it is inherent in the general rule and in fact identical with it.

The Indian syllogism indeed is not only the formulation of a deductive reasoning, it also contains an indication of that Induction which always precedes Deduction. The general rule, or major premise, is established by a generalization from individual facts which are «examples», they exemplify and support it. An example is an individual fact containing the general rule in itself. Without the examples there is no general rule, nor can the individual facts be considered as examples if they do not contain the general rule. Thus example and general rule, or major premise, are practically the same thing. In order to safeguard against incomplete Induction the examples must be positive and negative. That is to say, that the joint method of Agreement and Difference must be applied. When either no positive examples at all, or no negative ones can at all be found, no conclusion is possible, the result can then be only a fallacy. But the Naiyāyiks regard the example as a separate member of the syllogism, as a separate premise, and give its definition. This, according to Dharmakīrti, is perfectly superfluous. Because if the definition of the Logical Reason is rightly given, the definition of what an example ought to be is also given, they cannot be given separately. The Logical Reason is something that is present in similar instances only and absent in dissimilar instances always. These instances and the reason are correlative, as soon as the reason is defined they also are defined by their relation to the reason. Dharmakīrti delivers himself on this point in the following way.[1] «The essence of a logical reason in general has been defined by us to consist in its presence only in similar cases, and its absence from every dissimilar case. Further, we have specified that the Causal and the Analytical Reasons must be shown to represent, the first an effect (from which the existence of its necessary cause is inferred), (the second a necessarily coexisting attribute) which alone is sufficient for deducing (the consequence). When the reasons are so represented, it is then shown that 1) e. g., whereever smoke exists, fire exists also, like in the kitchen etc.; there is no smoke without fire, like (in the pond and in all) dissimilar cases; 2) wheresoever there is production, there is change, like in a jar etc.; if something is changeless, it is not a product, like Space. It is, indeed, impossible otherwise to show the existence of the reason in similar

[1] NB., III. 123; transl., p. 131.

and its absence from all dissimilar cases .... (it is impossible to exhibit these general features otherwise than by showing) that 1) the causal deduction of the existence of a cause necessarily follows from the presence of the effect, and that 2) the analytically deduced property is necessarily inherent in the fact representing the analytical reason. When this is shown, it is likewise shown what an example is, since its essence includes nothing else».

§ 4. The Figures of the Syllogism.

Since the syllogism is nothing but the expression of an inference in propositions, it is clear that there will be as many different kinds of syllogism as there are kinds of inference. Inference has been defined as the cognition of an object through its mark, and the mark, or the so called Three-Aspected Logical Mark, is nothing but a case of necessary interdependence between two terms. There can be, accordingly, as many varieties of syllogism as there are varieties of conjunction between two terms. We have seen that there are three, and only three, varieties of necessary relation between two terms which allow us to cognize one thing through its necessary connection with the other. We can either cognize a thing through its Effect, or through its being an Inherent Property, or through its Negative Counterpart. There will be accordingly three kinds of syllogism, the Causal, the Analytical and the Negative. They have been exemplified above.

These differences however are founded on the content of the syllogism, not on its form. They are founded upon a difference of logical relations of which a strictly definite table of Categories has been established by Dharmakīrti. There is another difference which affects the mere form of the syllogism. The same fact, the same cognition of an object through its logical mark can be expressed in two different ways. We can call this difference a difference of Figure. Every logical mark indeed has two main features, it agrees with similar instances only and it disagrees with all dissimilar ones. Dignāga insists that it is one and the same mark, not two different ones.[1] A mark cannot be present in similar cases only, without at the same time being absent from all dissimilar cases. But practically, just because the mark is the same, we may attend to its positive side and understand the negative one by implication, or we may attend to the negative side and understand

---

[1] Cp. N. mukha, transl., p. 22.

by implication the positive one. The mixt method of Agreement and Difference controls the whole domain of cognition, but since there is an equipollency between the positive and the negative part of it, it becomes quite sufficient to express one side alone, either the agreement or the difference. The counterpart of it will necessarily be implied. This is the reason why we have two figures of every syllogism. Figure in this context does not mean a twisted, unnatural and perverse verbal arrangement of the terms of an inference, where the real core of every inference, the universal and necessary interdependence of two terms, becomes quite obliterated; but it means two universal and equipollent methods of cognizing truth on the basis of a necessary interdependence between two terms. We have seen that the perceptual judgment «this is fire» is nothing but a cognition of an object as similar with all fires and dissimilar with all non-fires. The cognition of an invisible fire through its mark, the smoke, is likewise a cognition of its similarity with all places possessing the double mark of smoke and fire, and its dissimilarity with all places where this double mark is always absent. Nay, even the negative judgment «there is here no jar», notwithstanding it is a negative, or, according to Indian phrasing, an inference through «non-perception», can be expressed according to both these methods, the positive and the negative one. Indeed, we may express this judgment in the following way —

> Whatsoever, all conditions of perceptibility being fulfilled, is not perceived, is absent.
> On this place no such jar is perceived.
> It is absent.

Or we may express the same idea by the method of Difference. We then will obtain the following propositions —

> Whatsoever is present, all conditions of perceptibility being fulfilled, is necessarily perceived.
> But on this place no such jar is perceived.
> It is absent.

The absence of a jar on a definite spot is cognized either through its similarity with other instances of negation, or through its difference from the positive instances of its presence. The same two methods can be naturally applied to inductions and deductions founded on Causality and to those founded on Identity of objective reference.

An analytical deduction expressed according to the method of Agreement is, e. g., the following one—

Whatsoever is variable in functional dependence on a variation of its causes is non-eternal, like jars etc.
The sounds of speech are variable,
They are non-eternal.

The same deduction expressed according to the method of Difference will be thrown in the following syllogistic form—

Whatsoever is eternal is never variable in functional dependence on a variation of its causes, like, e. g., Space.
But the sounds of speech are variable,
They are non-eternal.

There are likewise two different figures of every Causal deduction. Expressed according to the method of Agreement is the following causal syllogism—

Wherever there is smoke, there is fire, as in the kitchen.
Here there is smoke,
There must be some fire.

The same expressed according to the method of Difference—

Wherever there is no fire, there neither is smoke, as in water.
But here there is smoke,
There must be some fire.

The methods of Agreement and Difference are thus in Indian Logic not only «the simplest and most obvious modes of singling out from among the circumstances which precede a phenomenon those with which it is really connected by an invariable law»,[1] but they are the universal methods for establishing every kind of connection, and even every kind of judgment.[2] The one consists «in comparing together different instances in which the phenomenon occurs», the other consists in comparing them with instances in which it does not occur.[3] Dignāga insists that these are not two different methods, but one mixt method of Agreement and Difference, which can either be expressed by attending to its positive or to its negative side. The

[1] J. S. Mill, Logic, I, p. 448.
[2] Cp. A. Bain, Logic, I. 8 and II. 46.
[3] J. S. Mill, Logic, I, p. 448.

presence of fire on a remote hill where only smoke is perceived can be established either by its agreement with the places where both phenomena have been observed to occur, or by its difference from all places where both phenomena have never been observed to occur. The method of Agreement will be then expressed in the major premise of the syllogism, the method of Difference in its Contraposition. They are the two aspects of the Logical Mark as it appears in the syllogism. The first aspect of the Logical Mark in a syllogism is expressed in the positive form of the major premise, its second aspect is expressed in the Contraposition of that premise. But there is no necessity of expressing both figures, because, as already mentioned, «from a formula of Agreement the corresponding formula of Difference follows by implication».[1] Dharmottara[2] says, «When a formulation directly expresses agreement (or the necessary concomitance of the reason with its consequence), their difference, i. e., the contraposition (or the general proposition) follows by implication». «Although the contraposition is not directly expressed, when the concomitance is expressed in its positive form, it nevertheless is understood by implication», «because, says Dharmakīrti,[3] if that were not so, the reason could not be invariably concomitant with the consequence». Both methods equally establish the same circumstance of a necessary tie of dependence between two facts or notions. «And it has been established, says Dharmakīrti,[4] that there are only two kinds of dependent existence, whatsoever the case may be. The dependent part represents either a reference to the same identical thing, or the effect (of another thing which is its cause)». The contraposed general proposition always expresses the same necessary interdependence of two facts following one another, or the necessary connection of two notions referring to one and the same fact. This interdependence (causal or analytical) is «nothing but the general proposition in its positive form». «Thus it is that one single general proposition, either directly or in its contraposed form, declares that the logical mark is present in similar and absent in dissimilar cases».[5]

Thus it is that every syllogism can be expressed in two figures, the one of which corresponds to the «axiom» *nota notae est nota rei*

---

1 NB., III. 28; transl., p. 142.
2 NBT., p. 51. 4; transl., p. 143.
3 NB., III. 29; transl., p. 143.
4 Ibid., III. 33.
5 Ibid., III. 34.

ipsius, the other to the second axiom *repugnans notae repugnat rei ipsi*. These are the only real logical figures.

That the particular judgments have no place in the syllogism follows from the definition of inference as founded on a necessary and universal connection between two terms, and on the necessary presence of the logical mark in the whole compass of the Subject. As to the negative syllogism, so far Contraposition is not to be regarded as negative in substance, they will be treated and their figures analyzed separately, in a subsequent chapter, together with an analysis of the Law of Contradiction.

§ 5. The value of the syllogism.

It is clear from what has been stated above that the syllogism is a valuable method only for a correct formulation and communication of ready knowledge to another person. It is not a genuine source of knowledge, its value for the acquisition and expansion of new knowledge is nil. This is first of all quite clear in the syllogism of Causality. «We can assert that the effect represents the logical reason for deducing its cause, says Dharmakīrti,[1] only when the fact of their causal relation is already known». By no effort of ratiocination can we arrive at a deduction of the cause producing an observed smoke, if we do not already know that it is fire. But «in the kitchen and similar cases it is established by positive and negative experience, that there is between smoke and fire a necessary invariable connection representing a universal causal relation». The inference proper consists in applying this general rule to a particular point, and the syllogism communicates this fact to another person. But the essential part of what is communicated by a syllogism is the fact of a necessary dependence[2] of the effect upon its causes. How the principle as well as the particular content of this relation, how its empirical and its *a priori* parts are established, has been explained in the theory of inference,[3] and a syllogism adds nothing but its correct formulation in two or three propositions.

All human knowledge is of relations, and necessary relations, we have seen, are only two, Identity and Causation. The negative relation is here left out of account. Relation, as has been explained, is here

---

1 NBT., transl., p. 137.

2 Ibid., p. 129.

3 Cp. above, p. 260 ff.

used it the sense of necessary dependence of one term upon another and a necessary interdependence can exist either between two coexisting or two consecutive facts. A necessary coexistence of two different things, we have seen, is always traceable to a necessary consecution or causality between them, so that coexistence proper, coexistence not reducible to causality, coexistence not between two different facts is a coexistence of two necessary conceptions inside the compass of a single fact. It is coexistence, or coinherence, reposing on the Identity of the common substrate of two different concepts. Now the empirical content of this necessary coexistence of two concepts in one substrate, coexistence founded on Identity, is also established by experience, but not by a syllogism. The offices of the latter even in ratiocination are limited to correct formulation and communication. «Indeed a logical reason, says Dharmottara,[1] does not produce cognition of some fact accidentally, as, e. g., a lamp (producing knowledge of such objects which it accidentally happens to illumine). But it produces knowledge by logical necessity, as an ascertained case of invariable concomitance. The function of a logical reason is, indeed, to produce a cognition of an unobserved fact, and this is just what is meant by ascertainment of the reason's invariable concomitance with the latter. First of all (as a preliminary step) we must be certain that the presence of our logical reason is necessarily dependent upon the presence of the predicated consequence, we must do it (in an analytical judgment founded on Identity) by applying the law of contradiction[2] which excludes the contrary. We then will proceed to syllogize, and avail ourselves of the general proposition recorded in our memory, the proposition intimating that its subject is invariably concomitant with its predicate, e. g., «whatsoever is a product is not eternal». After that we can connect this general record with a particular case, «the sounds of speech are non-eternal». Between these (two premises, the major) contains the mnemic record, it represents the knowledge of the logical reason (and its concomitance). The syllogism (proper is contained in the next step when we in the minor premise), recollect that the causal origin which is inherent in the particular case of the sound is necessarily coexistent with the attribute of non-eternity. If that is so, then the cognition (or communication) of an unobserved thing is, as a matter of fact, nothing but a cognition of invariable concomitance. It is

---

1 NBT., transl., p. 129.

2 *bādhakena pramāṇena.*

therefore stated that analytical deductions (founded on the laws of Contradiction and Identity) can be resorted to when the deduced feature is already known necessarily to be present wherever the presence of the reason is ascertained, not in any other cases». The predicate is contained in the reason, the logical consequence therefore necessarily follows out of the mere fact of the presence of the reason.

But if that is so, if the deduced predicate of an analytical judgment is known to be contained in its subject and automatically flows out of the latter, its deduction is worthless.

«Why is it then, asks Dharmottara,[1] that something already quite certain, should be sought after?» «Why should we have recourse to logical reasoning for deducing from the reason what is already given in the reason?»

The answer is that, although the reason and the consequence of an analytical deduction (or the subject and the predicate of an analytical judgment) are connected through Identity, we nevertheless can start on such a deduction, or on such a judgment, albeit we already know that they are necessarily connected through Identity. Just as in the case of deducing the cause from an effect, we must beforehand know from experience that the phenomena are necessarily related as cause and effect, just so must we know from experience, or other sources, that two different features belonging to one and the same reality are connected through Identity. Their Identity is an identity of the common substratum, it is co-substrateness, or co-inherence.[2]

Although all our concepts are constructions of our understanding, their comprehension, their intention, their subalternation, their mutual exclusion are cognized from experience. It has been established above[3] that the laws of Identity, Causality and Contradiction are the original possession of our understanding, but their application is limited to the domain of sensuous experience. Dharmottara gives the following example.[4] Supposing a man having no experience about trees in general perceives a very high Ašoka tree and is informed that it is a tree. He might think that the height of the Ašoka is the reason why it is called a tree. Looking at a small Ašoka he might think that it is

---

1 NBT., p. 47. 17; transl., p. 131.

2 or Agreement, *Uebereinstimmung,* as Sigwart (Logik, I. 110), puts it.

3 Cp. p. 248 ff.

4 NBT., p. 24. 3 ff.; transl., p. 67.

not a tree. He will then be taught that the tree is the general term, and the Ašoka a special kind under it. If he then is informed that a certain country-place consists of bare rocks without a single tree on them, he will know that if there are no trees, there are also no Ašokas. The subalternation of all concepts is thus established by «perception and non-perception», i. e., by positive and negative experience, just as the relation of cause and effect between two phenomena, or the relation of their mutual incompatibility. An analytical relation between two concepts can be sometimes established by a very complicated train of argumentation. If the consequence is contained in the reason, this should not be understood psychologically, as a fact really always present to the mind. The analytical relation is logical and capable of infinite extension, it lies sometimes concealed at a great depth. Every case of an analytical relation must be established by corresponding proofs suitable to it, says Dharmakīrti.[1] The principle that all existence is instantaneous has been established by the Buddhists in a long effort of argumentation which is capable of further extension. The connection between these two concepts is analytical, it is protected under the law of Contradiction. If Existence would not be changing every instant, if it would be unchanging like the Cosmical Ether, or like Space, it would not be Existence. But this does not mean that every one who has the idea of Existence present in his mind, has at the same time present the idea of it being instantaneous. An analytical relation means a necessary relation which is not causal, since necessary relations are only two, Identity or non-Causality, and Causality or non-Identity. One and the same thing is called Existence and also a Point-instant. They are connected by Identity. With regard to the necessarily preceding point-instant it will be its effect. There is no third instantaneous relation possible, either Identity or Causality. Every separate instance of such relations, whether analytical relations of concepts or causal relations of point-instants, must be established by experience or, as Dharmakīrti puts it, «by its own proofs». A syllogism will add nothing to our cognition of them, except correct formulation.

§ 6. Historical sketch of syllogism viewed as inference for others.

Dharmottara testifies[2] that «the Master», i. e. Dignāga, was the first to draw a hard and fast line between inference and syllogism.

---

[1] *yathā-svam-pramāṇaih*, NBT., p. 47. 5 ff.

[2] NBT., p. 42. 3. Cp. Keith, Ind. Log., p. 106, and Randle, Ind. Log., p. 160.

He envisaged inference as a process of cognition, one of the two «sources» of our knowledge, and called it inference «for one self», or «in one self»; the second was regarded by him not as a source of knowledge at all, but as a method of correctly and convincingly expressing it in a series of propositions for the benefit of an audience. This doctrine, we have seen, is but a consequence of the theory of a difference in principle between the two sources of our knowledge. There are two, and only two, sources of knowledge, because there are two, and only two, kinds of cognized «essences». The senses apprehend the extreme concrete and particular only, inference apprehends the general alone.[1] Regarded as a source of knowledge which stands in a contradictory contrast with sensibility, inference and understanding are convertible terms.. Indeed our analysis has shown that inference is nothing but a variety of judgment and judgment is but another name for the procedure of the understanding; inference deals with the general, just as pure sensibility cognizes the absolute particular, or, the thing as it is strictly in itself. Such an inference must be separated from a series of propositions used for conveying a thesis to an audience. We thus not only have a direct testimony of an authoritative author to the effect that the theory of an inference «in one self» and an inference «in others» is due to Dignāga, but we can account for the *rationale* of such a separation, since it is a direct outflow of the fundamental principle of his philosophy.[2]

The statement of Dharmottara is supported by all what we at present know on the history of Indian Logic. We find in the works preceding the reform of Dignāga no mention of the inference «for one self» and «for others». Neither Gotama, nor Kaṇāda, nor Vātsyāyana, nor, for ought we know, Vasubandhu refer to it. But almost every post-Dignāgan work on logic contains it. Prašastapāda who most probably was a contemporary of Dignāga was the first to introduce it in the logic of the Vaišeṣika school.

Somewhat different was the fate of Dignāga's innovation in the school of the Naiyāyiks. It must be noticed that the original aphorisms of Gotama already contain a distinction between inference as one of the «sources» of cognition (*pramāṇa*) and the «five-membered syllogism» which is treated not under the head of the four «sources» of cognition, but under the head of one of the 16 Topics of Discourse

---

1 Cp. above, p. 71 ff.

2 Cp. my article Rapports etc. in the Muséon, V, p. 163 ff.

(*padārtha*). It seems as though the innovation of Dignāga were simply borrowed, or extracted, out of these rules of Gotama. However the five-membered syllogism is regarded in the Nyāya school not as an inference evoked in the head of the hearer, but as a faithful and adequate description of the gradual steps of our thought in a process of inference. These steps must be repeated when an inference is communicated to somebody else. The five-membered syllogism is itself already and abbreviation of another, ten-membered, syllogism which was in vogue in that school previously to the establishment of the five-membered one. It aimed at describing all the gradual steps of our inferential cognition, beginning with the first moment of inquisitiveness (*jijñāsā*) and ending in an inferred conclusion. The same psychological standpoint prevails in this school in regard of the five-membered syllogism.

According to the psychological views of the Nyāya-Vaišeṣika school every thought has a duration of three moments. In the third moment it becomes extinct and inoperative, it wants to be aroused anew in order to become efficient. The inferential process begins by a moment of inquisitiveness which gives rise to the thesis as a first member of a syllogism. The reason and the example follow in its track. The moment of the thesis is extinct and inoperative when the moment of the example appears. The concomitance as a thought contained in one moment would be extinct and inoperative for the conclusion from which it is separated by the moment of the minor premise, unless it would be repeated in that premise. This repetition is called «Reconsideration»,[1] or «Third evocation of the Mark».[2] The first consideration of the mark is, e. g., the perception of smoke in the kitchen, the second—its perception on the hill, and the third—its reconsideration at the time of the minor premise. To this «reconsideration», in the form «here is that very smoke which always is concomitant with fire», is assigned the office of being the proximate and immediate cause of the conclusion—«there must be some fire present on the hill».

It is clear that the Naiyāyiks did not regard at first their five-membered syllogism as consisting in mere propositions intended to communicate ready knowledge to some audience. Dignāga's view was however accepted by Uddyotakāra.[3] The Naiyāyiks followed

1 *parāmarṣa*, cp. NV., p. 46. 10 ff.

2 *trtīya-linga-parāmarṣa.*

3 NV., p. 18. 10—*vipratipanna-puruṣa-pratipādakatvam.*

the example of the Vaišeṣikas and incorporated the theory of an inference «for others» in their logical teaching. We meet with the distinction between an inference for one self and for others in the works of Gangeša and in all the works which followed.

The same remark must be *mutatis mutandis* applied to another characteristic feature of the Indian Logic, its doctrine of syllogistic figures. That there are two, and only two, real figures and that all particular judgments have no place in a syllogism was admitted by the schools long before Dignāga, but the discovery of the real meaning of this fact must be credited to him.

The positive and negative figure or, more precisely, the *modus ponens* and *modus tollens*, just as they are admitted by the Naiyāyiks probably have been admitted by the Sānkhyas before them. But for the realistic schools they are two independent forms of syllogism, whereas for the Buddhists every syllogism can be expressed either in the one or in the other form, since both forms are equipollent. As a proof of their independence the Naiyāyiks adduced the fact that there are deductions «purely positive»[1] which have no negative counterpart and there are also deductions «purely negative»[2] which have no positive counterpart. This the Buddhists denied and maintained that every deduction is positive and negative, just as all names and all judgments are necessarily in their essence, positive and negative.

The name «fire» and the judgment «this is fire» means that there is a real point which on the one side is similar with all fires and, on the other side, is dissimilar from all non-fires. The middle is excluded,[3] there is no third thing possible between being a fire and being a non-fire. Just the same applies to all inferences and syllogisms.

The Sānkhyas, it would seem, were the first to make an extensive use of the *modus tollens* for the establishment of their theory of Causality. They maintained the essential identity of cause and effect, i. e., the preexistence of the effect in its cause. Their aim was to support in this way their favorite idea of an Eternal Matter and the inclusion af all the universe of effects in this unique and universal Cause. They produced for its proof a canon of five syllogisms expressed *modo tollente.*[4] They are the following ones —

---

1 *kevala-anvayin.*

2 *kevala-vyatirekin.*

3 *tṛtīya-prakāra-abhāva.*

4 *avīta-pañcakam*, cp. NK., p. 30; the term *avīta* is rendered in Tibetan by *bsal-bas ḥoṅ-pa* «arrived in the way of exclusion» = negative, or *tollens*. On the

1. If the effect did not preexist, it never could be created out of nothing.
However it is created.
Therefore it does preexist (in its material cause).
2. If the effect did not preexist in its material cause, it would not be homogeneous with it.
But cloth is homogeneous with threads, and not with the weaver (who also is a cause).
Therefore the effect preexists in its material cause.
3. If the effect did not preexist in its material cause and if it did preexist elsewhere, then the cloth would not be produced out of thread, but could be produced out of straw etc.
However the cloth is produced out of threads and is not produced out of straw (like a matt).
Therefore it preexists in the threads.
4. The capacity to produce something requires an object upon which it is directed; if this object does not preexist, the force cannot be efficient.
However the forces are efficient.
Hence their objects preexist (in their material cause).
5. A cause is relative to an effect, if the effects did not preexist, there would be no causes altogether.
But the causes exist.
Hence the effects must preexist (in their causes).

These five Mixed Hypothetical Syllogisms expressed *modo tollente* are according to the Sānkhyas an independent way of proof. According to Dignāga[1] they are not independent, since every *modus tollens* presupposes the existence of a *modus ponens* with which it is virtually identical. Dharmakīrti proves convincingly that the syllogism of Agreement and the syllogism of Difference are but two figures of the same syllogism, the one establishing exactly the same thing as the other. Every syllogism and every inference are thus positive and negative at the same time.[2]

The «purely positive» and the «purely negative» syllogisms are an invention of Uddyotakāra.[3] Animated by his extreme hatred of

---

'avīta cp. NV., p. 123, Sānkhya—Kaum. 5; H. Jacobi in Aus Indiens Kultur, p. 8 ff.

[1] Cp. N. mukha, p. 22.

[2] Cp. *definitio est omnis negatio.*

[3] NV., p. 48. 10 ff.

Buddhism and all things Buddhistic he most vehemently assails Dignāga's definition of inference, his theory of the Three-Aspected Logical Reason, his doctrine of syllogistic figures, his system of logical fallacies, etc. He pours upon them a stream of quite artificial, falsely subtle criticisms in order rather to bewilder than to convince the reader. The greatest part of these inventions were dropped in the sequel, but the theory of the purely-positive and purely-negative reasons remained for ever as a part of the Naiyāyika syllogistic teaching. The favourite syllogism of the Buddhists, e. g., «everything having a cause is impermanent», will, according to the Naiyāyiks, be purely positive, or a logical fallacy. There are no uncaused things for the Buddhists, since every thing existing has necessarily a cause. Uncaused things do not exist. But the Buddhists maintain that there is a negative example, viz., the ubiquitous, unchanging, motionless Cosmical Ether, or the Space. A negative example need not be a reality. For logical purposes, serving as a contrast, such an example as eternal Space is quite sufficient.[1]

An inference like «the living body possesses a Soul, because it possesses animal functions» is an instance of «purely negative» inference. There are no positive examples to prove this concomitance of a living body with a Soul, but there are a lot of examples where these two attributes are both absent. According to the Realists these examples have the force to prove the invariable connexion of the living body with a Soul. According to the Buddhists they prove nothing, the deduction is a fallacy. The negative examples are a corollary from the positive ones. If there are no positive ones, neither can there be any real negative ones.

§ 7. European and Buddhist Syllogism.

In the present condition of our knowledge of the Indian Syllogism it may seem premature to attempt a full comparative statement and estimate of the Buddhist theory as against the European. Nevertheless some hints in that direction will not be amiss as a help for a better understanding of the Indian position, of that independent and original view which the Indian logicians took in dealing with Syllogism. The following points of the Aristotetelian theory deserve to be considered, 1) Aristotle's idea of the Syllogism in general, 2) his idea of a Syllogism from Example, 3) his idea of Induction, 4) the real members

[1] N. mukha, p. 27; NBT., p. 87. 3.

of a Syllogism, 5) its real Figures, 6) its Axiom and the import of the Mixed Hypothetical Syllogism.

a) Definitions by Aristotle and by the Buddhists.

According to Aristotle a Syllogism is «a speech in which, some positions having been laid down, something different from these positions follows as a necessary consequence from their having been laid down».[1] This definition implies that the syllogism consists of three propositions (at least), and one of them (the conclusion) follows necessarily from the two others (the premises). It is clear however that the syllogism is not only «a speech». Apart from the expression in «a speech» there is the thing to be expressed in that speech. The contents of a syllogism has been characterized by Aristotle in the *Dictum de omni et nullo,* meaning that «Whatever is affirmed or denied of a class, is affirmed or denied of any part of that class». According to this rule the Syllogism must always contain a deduction of the particular from the general. There is also another way of stating the contents, or, as it is called, the «axiom» of the Syllogism. It is the principle *nota notae est nota rei ipsius* with its correlative *repugnans notae repugnat rei ipsi.* According to this «Axiom», the syllogism contains the cognition of an object through an intermediate mark. It represents an indirect cognition as distinguished from the direct cognition through the senses. We have already mentioned that the Buddhist definition of Inference as cognition of an object through its mark coincides with the principle *nota notae.* Its expression in a sequence of propositions will therefore correspond to Aristotle's «speech». We thus find in the European theory something corresponding to the Buddhist distinction of the Inference «for one self» from the Syllogism «for others». But in this point lies also the great difference between the two theories.

In the Buddhist Inference-for-One-Self there are, properly speaking, no propositions at all, at least no such propositions as always are present in the Aristotelian Syllogism. The cognition of the form «sound is impermanent, because it is a product, like a jar» is laid down in a single proposition. The important part is not the proposition, but its three terms, or, if the Example is counted, its four terms. We thus are faced by two quite different definitions of Syllogism. The one says that it is a «speech» in which the concluding

---

[1] Grote's translation, op. cit., p. 143.

proposition necessarily follows from two premises; the other says that it is a «speech» which expresses the Three-Aspected Logical Mark,[1] i. e. the mutual relation of the three terms.

Thus it is that, notwithstanding the identity of the «axiom» of the Syllogism, there is a great difference between both theories in the importance given to the «speech» in which it is laid down. For Aristotle Syllogism is, first, a series of three propositions, next, a *Dictum de omni et nullo;* for Dignāga Syllogism (and Inference) is, first, three interrelated terms; next, a sequence of two propositions, expressing a general rule and its application.

b) Aristotle's Syllogism from Example.

Apart from this distinction between what a Syllogism is and the fact which it essentially expresses, there is in the Aristotelian theory another distinction which Aristotle himself characterizes as a difference between Syllogism for us *(pro nobis)* and Syllogism in its own nature *(notius natura).* The designation «for us» suggests some similarity with the Buddhist Inference «for one-self».

The antithesis between *notiora natura* and *notiora nobis* (or *quoad nos*) is recognized by Aristotle as a capital point in his philosophy. The first is nearer to perception, more within the apprehension of mankind generally and constitutes Experience. The second is nearer to final or perfect knowledge and constitutes Science.

Aristotle counts several varieties of Syllogism which he brings under the head of knowledge for one-self. The principle are the Syllogisms from Example and the Syllogism from Induction.

The nearest to the Indian Inference-for-One-Self is the Aristotelian Syllogism from Example. The Example is here, just as in India, considered as a fourth term, besides the three terms, the major, middle and minor.[2] The inference is from one particular case to the general and through the general to another particular.

Example includes not all, but only one or few particulars; inferring from them, first, to the entire class, next, to some new analogous particular belonging to the class. The ratiocinative process consists of two parts, an ascending one and a descending one. Inference proceeds from one particular instance to other similar instances through an intermediate general premise which is, if not expressly stated,

1 *trirūpa-linga.*

2 Grote, op. cit., p. 191.

always included in the Example. From this point of view one must admit that the five-membered Syllogism of the Naiyāyiks alone does full justice to this double march of the ratiocinative process. Indeed its three first members contain four terms. The order of the premises is inverted. The Syllogism starts at its conclusion which is also the thesis. It then mentions the minor premise. The third member is the Example. The major premise is not a separate member. We then have the following syllogistic form —

1. Thesis. Sound is impermanent.
2. Reason. Because it is produced by effort.
3. Example. Like a jar.

This represents the natural march of the intellect when it leaps from one particular to another. The major premise is not fully realized, but it lies burried somewhere in the depths of consciousness and emerges to the surface when the next step, or deduction, is taken. The Syllogism then receives the following shape:

1. Thesis. Sound is impermanent.
2. Reason. Because produced at will by an effort.
3. Example. Like a jar. Where an effort there impermanence.
4. Application. Sound is produced at will by an effort.
5. Conclusion. It is impermanent.

This seems to be exactly the Syllogism which Aristotle had in view in establishing his Syllogism from Example. He refers it to the class of inferences for one self, *notiora quoad nos.* For the Naiyāyiks however — only its three first members, with the suppressed major premise, represent inference for one-self. Its full five members they consider as inference for others or as a full Syllogism to be used in a public debate.

It seems that the celebrated modern theory of J. S. Mill who considers Syllogism as a process of inferring particulars from particulars with a suppressed collateral major premise, which is the result of passed experience, corresponds in its main points to the theory of the Naiyāyiks.

c) Inference and Induction.

That the universal or the major premise must be established by Induction from particulars is equally maintained by the Buddhists and by Aristotle. Syllogism presupposes and rests upon the process of

Induction. Aristotle declares unequivocally that universal propositions are obtained only from Induction.[1] The particular facts remembered and compared constitute Experience with its universal notions and conjunctions.[2] «Conjunctions, says Dharmakīrti, (or the major premise) must be established by corresponding (particular) facts».[3] If this really is so, it seems impossible or quite artificial to cut the natural inductive-deductive process of thinking into two different halves, Induction and Deduction. Both are complementary of one another and cannot be separated otherwise than in abstraction. This is, as we shall see, the substance of the Indian view. We shall see that the link between Induction and Deduction is so strong that the figures or moods of Deduction can be rightly established only when the principle methods of Induction are taken into account. There is between the two parts a natural antithesis, inasmuch as we in life sometimes concentrate our attention on the inductive process and supress, as it were, the deductive one. This is called inference for one self. Or we presuppose the process of Induction as already achieved and direct all our attention to the second part of the process, to deduction. This is called inference for others by the Indians, or the real, genuine Syllogism (*notius natura*) by Aristótle. But the name of Syllogism is applied by Aristotle to both Induction and Deduction. The Syllogism from Induction is in his treatment a very special kind of Syllogism in which there is no real middle term, because the supposed middle reciprocates with the major. The order of the premises is inverted just as in the Syllogism from Example. The conclusion in which it results is the first or major proposition. Aristotle adds that the genuine Syllogism, which demonstrates through a middle term, is *notius natura*, it is prior and more effective as to cognition; but that the Syllogism from Induction is to us (*pro nobis*) plainer and clearer.[4]

The Syllogism from Induction, as imagined by Aristotle, must have the following form —

Conclusion (= thesis). One man and all observable humanity are mortals.

Minor premise. They represent the totality of humanity.

Major premise (= conclusion). All men are mortal.

---

[1] Grote, op. cit., p. 187.

[2] Ibid., p. 193.

[3] *yathā-svam-pramāṇaiḥ*, NBT., p. 47.1 ff., on the meaning of *pramāna* in this context cp. NBT., p. 64.1, 81.1.

[4] Grote, op. cit., p. 191 and 196.

Such a syllogism is not only a process ascending from the particular to the universal, it contains moreover an unwarranted jump from the observed totality of a class to its absolute totality. However Aristotle conceives repeated and uncontradicted Induction as carrying with it the maximum of certainty and necessity.[1] The Universal (*notius natura*) is thus generated in the mind by a process of Induction out of particulars which are *notiora nobis.*

Both Dignāga and Aristotle, it is true, content themselves with barely recognizing the inductive part of ratiocination, while they both bestow elaborate care upon the analysis of the deductive part and of the canon of rules regulating it.

Some critics have impugned the procedure of Aristotle in his converting Induction into a peculiar form of Syllogism and thus effacing the great contrast between the ascending and descending process in ratiocination. For them the capital difference between both processes lies in the constraining force or necessity inhering in Syllogism, a necessity which Induction never can attain.[2] Every Induction, according to them, includes a jump, and an unwarranted, risky jump, from particular cases to the universal assertion. But there is no unwarranted jump, there is strict necessity in syllogistic deduction. The distinction between the totality of particulars and the meaning of the class-term, these critics maintain, is incorrectly employed by Aristotle to slur over the radical distinction between Induction and Syllogism. Aristotle says: «you must conceive the minor term in the Inductive Syllogism as composed of all the particulars; for Induction is through all of them».[3] According to these critics the unwarranted jump from particulars to the class can be admitted in Induction without spoiling it. But its admission into Syllogism must be refused, because it would degrade the dignity of that method. It seems that in this question as in many others the Indian view deserves to be considered. The difficulty is inherent in knowledge itself. It cannot be slurred over by dividing the full ratiocinative process in two halves and relegating it to one half only, thereby getting another half which becomes quite innocent of the flaw of the first half. The universality and necessity of judgments is the core of all logic, it must be explained in some way or other. As long as it is not explained, neither Induction nor Syllogism will appear innocent, an internal desease, a «cancer»,

---

1 Ibid., p. 192 ff.

2 Ibid., p. 197.

3 Ibid., p. 260.

as the Hindus say, will be lurking in them. The Buddhist solution is explained by us in the chapter on Inference and will be considered once more later on.

d) The Buddhist Syllogism contains two propositions.

It follows from the Aristotelian definition that the Syllogism must consist of three propositions, two of them exercising a similar function and united by the common characteristic of being «premises» to the Conclusion. From the Buddhist definition it follows that the Syllogism must consist of only two indispensable propositions, the one expressing the general rule of invariable concomitance between the reason and its consequence, and the other expressing the application of the rule to a given instance. Indeed the connection between the minor premise and the conclusion is much narrower than between the two so called premises. Lotze and Sigwart remark rightly that the «minor premise presupposes the conclusion».[1] The minor with the conclusion together constitute the Application or Qualification of the Locus.[2] It is easy to see that the two indispensable members of a Syllogism represent nothing else than Induction and Deduction. The real evidence whereby the conclusion of a Syllogism is proved, is the minor premise together with, not the major premise itself, but together with the assemblage of particular facts from which by Induction the major premise is drawn.[3] Example and Application are the two members of the Buddhist syllogism, as stated above.[4]

e) Contraposition.

The Indian theory deals with conversion and obversion of subject and predicate in propositions merely in connexion with inference and syllogism. Conversion is possible only in the major premise, or grounding proposition. In the applying proposition, which is a combination of the minor premise and the conclusion, the subject has a fixed position which cannot be changed. The grounding proposition expresses

---

[1] Lotze, Logik, p. 122; Sigwart, op. cit., I. 478,—«Socrates could not be a man, as stated in the minor premise, if we were not already sure that he is mortal».

[2] *pakṣa-dharmatā*.

[3] Grote, op. cit., p. 199.

[4] Cp. above, p. 279.

the fact that the reason, or middle term, is present in similar instances only and absent in dissimilar instances always. These are the two rules of the major premise which imply one another, because if the reason is present in similar instances only, it is *eo ipso* absent in dissimilar instances always. But in order to express the necessary dependence of the reason upon the predicate both must be stated, either expressedly or by implication. The presence of the reason in similar instances only is the Position.[1] Its absence in dissimilar instances always is the Contraposition.[2]

The position is established by the inductive method of Agreement. The Contraposition is established by its corollary, the method of Difference. Both express one and the same fact. They are two manners of expressing the same idea. The logical value and validity of contraposition is easy to understand. It is clear that if the middle term is necessarily dependent upon the major, it is included in the latter. The compass of its negation must therefore exceed the compass of the negation of the major in exactly the same proportion in which the compass of the major exceeds the compass of the middle. In circles this can be represented so —

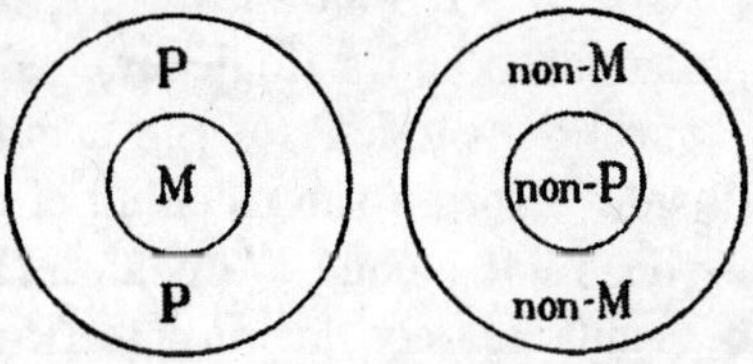

E. g., «whatsoever is a product (M) is non eternal (P)» and «whatsoever is eternal (non-P) is not a product (non-M)»; or «wheresoever there is smoke (M), there is fire (P)», and «without fire (non-P) there is no smoke (non-M)». The whole compass of M is included in the compass of P. The non-P remains outside the greater circle. And because non-P is outside, non-M is still more outside. Thus the whole of non-P is embraced by the non-M.

That the universal negative can be converted is equally clear. If there is no connection at all between subject and predicate, this disconnection is mutual.

But the universal affirmative cannot be converted. It expresses the necessary dependence of one term upon the other. This relation can-

1 *anvaya.*
2 *vyatireka*

not be reversed. The subject has a fixed position just as the subject of the conclusion. A great many fallacies owe their origin to the neglect of that rule. E. g., if we have the proposition «whatsoever is produced by an effort is non-eternal» and convert it simply, we shall have «whatsoever is non-eternal is produced by an effort». This will be a fallacy of Uncertain Reason, since the reason «non-eternal» will be equally present in similar instances like jars etc. and in dissimilar ones like lightning etc.

Aristotle's dealing with the problem of Conversion is formal and grammatical. He tries to change the mutual positions of subject and predicate. He then sees that the same operation is possible in some instances and, quite incomprehensively, impossible in other cases.

Among the European logicians Sigwart holds views which fall in line with the attitude of the Indians. He insists that the position of being a predicate must be «left to what really is the predicate».[1] «All the meaning of Contraposition, says he, becomes at once clear when we put the connection into the form of a hypothetical proposition, and instead of maintaining that „all A are B" express that „if something is A it is also B". It follows that „if something is not B, it neither is A». «A good sense and a (logically) valuable sense have only these two cases, pure Conversion (of the negative) and Contraposition. They from all sides express the meaning of the assertion that a predicate belongs, or does not belong, necessarily to its subject. All other cases which result merely in particular propositions, demonstrate therewith that no definite conclusion is possible».

That is the reason why the Indian theory excludes particular propositions from the domain of logic altogether. Logic is the province of universal and necessary propositions.

f) Figures.

The Aristotelian Logic distinguishes between the Categorical and Hypothetical Syllogism and divides the Categorical in 4 Figures and 19 Moods. On the division in Categorical and Hypothetical, on the question, namely, how far this division affects the grammatical form alone or belongs to the essence of inference, some remarks will be made later on. But the division into 4 figures and their 19 moods, just as the theory of Conversion, is founded on the grammatical principle of the position of the Middle term in both premises.

---

[1] Op. cit., I. 451.

Grammatically the middle term can be subject in the major and predicate in the minor, or *vice versa*, subject in the minor and predicate in the major, or subject in both, or predicate in both. One of the premises can be moreover either particular or negative. By combining each of the four positions of the middle term with the possibility of one of the premises being either particular or negative, a scheme of 19 valid moods is constituted. Only one of them, the first mood of the first figure (*Barbara*), is regarded by Aristotle as «final» or genuine. All others can be by a complicated process of reduction converted into it.

Of all this complicated doctrine which forms almost the entire edifice of mediaeval and modern Formal Logic we find on the Indian side not a whisper. Particular conclusions are, first of all, excluded altogether from the domain of logic in India. A particular conclusion means that the Reason is not present in the whole compass of the Subject. This is a violation of the first rule of the canon and produces a fallacy. Negative conclusions are relegated by the Buddhists to a special class and altogether separated from universal affirmative conclusions. The third and fourth syllogistic figures are thus excluded from the domain of syllogism. The complicated rules for their reduction and validity become therefore quite superfluous. Neither can the grammatical principle of converting the Middle Term into the predicate of the major premise and into the subject of the minor be rightly introduced into logic. Among the three terms of an inference one (the minor) is the Subject, it is the real Subject, the logical Subject. It cannot be converted into a predicate otherwise than in a confused and perverse expression. The subject of the minor premise and the subject of the conclusion are the same thing and must occupy in a correct expression the same position, it is the subject of the applying proposition. The subject of the grounding or major proposition is necessarily the Middle term, because this proposition expresses the necessary dependence of the middle on the major, and this fact is expressed linguistically by bringing it under the predication of the major. «Let the predicate be what predicate is», says Sigwart.[1] Every change in his position is superfluous and useless. We are thus left with one of the moods of the first figure (*Barbara*),

[1] Sigwart, op. cit., I. 451. In the first mood of the second figure (*Camestres*) the Middle term is supposed to be the predicate of the major premise. But the middle which is a predicate in the major premise is *contradictio in adjecto*. This is

and one of the moods of the second figure (*Cesare*), the last corresponds to the contraposition of the first. We have already explained that in a contraposition the middle can really exchange its place with the major, because both these forms are two different but equipollent ways of expressing one and the same fact. This double expression is not the result of arbitrarily changing the places of subject and predicate, but they represent the two universal procedures of knowledge, inductive as well as deductive.

The Buddhist theory divides Syllogism and Inference in three kinds according to its content. They are the Analytical, the Causal (= Synthetical) and Negative deduction. From the formal side each of them can be expressed either according to the method of Agreement or according to the method of Difference; the first will be a *modus ponens*, the second a *modus tollens*, of the Mixed Hypothetical Syllogism.

There are according to Dignāga these two, and only two, figures in Syllogism, accordingly as the major is expressed in the form of a Position or in the form of a Contraposition. Both forms are always possible, they are complementary of one another, they both express the same thing and when the one is expressed the other is implied, even if it is not expressed. They correspond to the second and third rule of the syllogistic canon, viz., the presence of the reason in similar instances only and its absence in dissimilar instances always. Dharmottara says,[1] «The meaning is the aim of the syllogism, the real fact which must be expressed by it, it is the fact concerning which both the syllogisms (of Agreement and of Difference) are drawn. There is no difference whatsoever in the fact which they aim at establishing. Indeed, the aim is to express a logical connection... Although they represent two different methods, they express just the same fact of one logical connection... The expressions differ so far the *prima facie* meaning is concerned, but regarding the aim for which they are used, there is no difference. Indeed, when the direct or positive concomitance has been expressed in the major premise, its contraposition follows by implication... And likewise, when the contraposed concomitance has been expressed, its positive form follows by implication».

---

only possible by transposing the premises. Bain says (op. cit., p. 140) — «A much greater variation from the standard negative (*Celarent*) is observable here (in *Camestres*). The grounding proposition which must be universal is the minor premise: so that there is an inversion of the normal order of the premises».

[1] NBT., p. 48. 2 ff.; transl., p., 115.

Now if the field of the Syllogism is divided in European formal logic in 19 moods and in the Indian system in only two moods, the questions naturally arise, 1) what is the correspondence, if any, between the 19 European moods and the 2 Indian ones, 2) what is the comparative logical value of both these divisions. As already stated, the third and fourth figure of the European Syllogism need not to be considered in this context, since they yield only particular conclusions, which by themselves without reduction are logically valueless. For the same reason are the third and fourth moods of the first and of the second figure to be excluded, since they also give only particular conclusions. The first mood of the second figure represents a perverse expression concealing a real fallacy.[1] From the moods of the second figure remains the second mood (*Cesare*) which is the contraposition of the first mood of the first figure (*Barbara*) and therefore corresponds to Dignāga's positive or direct figure. As to the second mood of the first figure (*Celarent*), its negation is nothing but linguistic. All really negative conclusions, we shall see, are reducible to the type-instance «there is here no jar, because we do not perceive any». But since all names, as will be shown later on, are positive and negative names, it is always possible to disguise a positive conclusion in a kind of negative judgment. E. g., we can say —

All men do not live eternally,
Socrates is a man,
He does not live eternally.

This conclusion differs from the conclusion «Socrates is mortal» only linguistically. Or take the Indian type-instance —

All products are not eternal,
Sounds are produced,
They are not eternal.

It has no sense at all to erect this linguistical difference into a separate mood. Since every judgment and every name can be expressed both ways, positively and negatively, it seems more convenient, as the Indians have done, to treat the problem of Negation separately as a feature of our thought which may appear everywhere instead of doubling all figures and moods, without ever considering the real nature of Negation.

The same critique applies to the distinction between the moods with a general and particular conclusion, since the second is included

[1] Since the Middle cannot be the predicate of the major premise.

in the first. Dharmottara[1] delivers himself on this subject in the following way—«The subject of an inference is a combination of a (singular) part perceived directly and a part not actually perceived... E. g., when it is being deduced that the sound represents an instantaneous Ens, only some particular sound can be directly pointed to, others are not actually perceived». That is to say, that in the above type-instance the term «sound» means «all sounds», «some sounds» and «one sound». But it has no sense to constitute these three possibilities into three different items in a classification, because the difference is unimportant and its distinction a useless subtlety.

Thus it is that the two moods of Dignāga correspond to the first mood of the first figure (*Barbara*) and to the second mood of the second figure (*Cesare*) of the Aristotelian syllogism.

We may now touch upon the question of the comparative value of the statement that there are only two figures of syllogism and the theory which conceals these two real figures in an artificial scheme of 19 moods.

Some writers have assumed that the comparative simplicity of Dignāga's table is a sign of inferiority. Others, on the contrary, have preferred the simple theory to the complicated one. Sigwart[2] says—«If we reduce the necessary rule according to which a deduction is made (in the first figure) to its corresponding formula, we shall have—if something is M it is P. If we then assume that S is M, the result will be that S is P».

«The same rules, he continues, must underlie the second figure, because there can be no other consequence from the simple relation of concepts. But we conclude here from the absence of the (necessary) consequent to the absence of its (necessary) antecedent». «Therefore, says the same Sigwart,[3] the first two figures of Aristotle coincide exactly with what we have stated in a former section», i. e., that the real moods of the syllogism are only two, the *modus ponens* and the *modus tollens*.[4] «The connection and the difference between the first and the second figure is elicited by the simple fact that in the first we conclude from the validity ot the antecedent ground to the validity of its necessary consequence (positive or negative), whereas in the second figure we conclude from the absence of the necessary

---

1 NBT., p 31. 21, transl., p. 89.
2 Op. cit., I. 485.
3 Op. cit., I. 466.
4 Cp. ibid., p. 465.

consequence to the absence of its necessary antecedent ground». These two figures coincide with the *modus ponens* and the *modus tollens* of the Mixed Hypothetical Syllogism.

This is also admitted by J. N. Keynes.[1] After having made a statement of the two moods of the Mixed Hypothetical Syllogism, he remarks — «These moods fall into line respectively with the first and the second figures of the categorical syllogism. For we have seen that in the figure 1 we pass from ground to consequence and in figure 2 — from denial of consequence to denial of ground».

According to Kant[2] the rule of the second figure is this, that «what contradicts the mark of a thing contradicts the thing itself», i. e., *repugnans notae repugnat rei ipsi*. He then shows that the second figure can always by contraposition be converted into the first. This again falls in line with the Buddhist theory according to which the two figures of the syllogism are nothing but the major premise and its contraposition, or the two rules requiring the presence of the reason in similar instances only and its absence in all dissimilar ones.

If we summarize the critique which has been bestowed upon the Aristotelian scheme of figures and moods, we find 1) that it was an unhappy idea of Aristotle to change the natural positions of Subject and Predicate in the premises, 2) that it was inconvenient to introduce in it other negative moods than the *modus tollens* or Contraposition, 3) that it was useless to introduce particular conclusions which could be valid only as far as reducible to the first figure. «It cannot be denied, says Kant,[3] that valid conclusions are possible in all the four figures. But it is the aim of logic to disentangle and not to entangle, to enunciate every thing openly and simply, and not in a concealed and perverse manner». «It is easy to discover the first inducement to the false subtlety (of the Aristotelian figures). The man who was the first to write down a Syllogism in three propositions, the one above the other in three lines, considered it as a chess-board and tried to change the positions of the middle term and to observe the consequences. When he saw that valid conclusions emerged, he was struck just as when an anagram is found in a name. It was as childish to rejoice about the one as about the other».[4] Kant therefore

---

1 Formal Logic, p. 352.

2 In his small tract „Von der falschen Spitzfindigkeit der vier syllogistischen Figuren".

3 Ibid.

4 Ibid.

calls the Aristotelian doctrine «false subtlety», and Sigwart falls in line by characterizing it as «superfluous specification». The two figures established by these two leaders of European science are exactly those that are established by Dignāga. «False subtlety» and «superfluous specification» are also found in India and even in a much higher degree than with Aristotle. We will see that Uddyotakāra, wishing to overdo Dignāga's computation of the nine positions of the Reason between instances Similar and Dissimilar, has adopted the method of superfluous and irrelevant specification and false subtlety. He then easily reached the total number of 2032 middle terms, right and wrong together!

g) The Causal and Hypothetical Syllogisms.

Our arguments, according to Dharmakīrti, are founded upon two great principles, the principle of Identity and the principle of Causation.[1] We speak only of positive arguments, leaving the negative ones for special consideration. The Identity, we have seen, is not the logical identity of two concepts. The Identity which Dharmakīrti has in view is the identity of that reality which underlies two different concepts. These concepts are united by the identity of their objective reference. A conception is not a fiction of pure imagination, but real knowledge only as far as it possesses an objective reference. Dharmakīrti's principle could also be expressed thus — all logical connection of two concepts is founded either upon Identity of their one and the same objective reference, or upon Interdependence of their two different references.

The objective reference of two interdependent concepts can be either the same or, if it is not the same, it must consist of two different, but necessarily interdependent, things. The judgment «*śiṃśapā* is a tree», or the inference «this is a tree, because it is a *śiṃśapā*», contains three terms of which the one is the point of reality underlying the two others. There is between the two concepts also a kind of identity, an indirect identity or, as some of the European logicians have preferred to call it, a «partial identity»,[2] in that sense that they are not contradictory, not incompatible. A single reality could not possess at once two incompatible concepts. They are identical in so far they are not incompatible and belong to the same identical thing. The *śiṃśapā* is necessarily a tree, it cannot be a non-tree, because

1 *tādātmya-tadutpatti.*

2 Sigwart, op. cit., I. 110 ff.

if it were not a tree, it would not be itself. We would have an object which would be at once a tree and a non-tree. If the qualities (or concepts) are incompatible, the reality of which they are, the qualities cannot be identical,[1] says the Buddhist law of Contradiction. It is a logical law between concepts, but it also is a law of reality.[2] Identity thus understood is as much a real relation[3] as Causality, it is the necessary corollary from Causality. In Identity the objective reference is one, in Causality it is double, but interdependent.

Now, what is the essence of the law of Causality? Its formula, we have seen, is «this being, that appears». It is a law of necessary dependence of every point-instant of reality upon its immediate antecedent point-instants; its expression is a Hypothetical Judgment. Since to every point-instant of reality corresponds some concept and the point-instant cannot be cognized otherwise than through a concept, there must be between the concepts corresponding to reality a logical relation similar to that real relation which obtains between the point-instants to which they correspond. Smoke is produced by fire, i. e., there is causal tie between a sequence of uninterrupted moments, a part of which is subsumed under the head of the concept of fire, and the following part of which is united under the concept of smoke. However the logical relation of these concepts is the reverse of the real relation between the corresponding points of reality. For logic means necessity and a cause is not necessarily followed by its result. Something can always appear which will prevent[4] the production of a given result. There is absolutely no causal judgment about the necessity of which one could be sure directly.[5] But the reverse relation is characterized by necessity. A result is necessarily the result of its cause, it could not exist if it were not a result and it could not be a result if it were not the necessary result of its cause. Therefore the logical law of Causation is really the law of the Effect. This is also the name which Dharmakīrti gives it.[6] He calls it inference «through the Effect».[7]

---

1 *virrudha-dharma-saṃsargād (dharmī) nānā.*

2 *vastuni avastuni ca*, cp. NBT., p. 70. 22.

3 Sigwart, op. cit., I. 442.

4 *geg-byed-pa srid-pai-phyir = pratibandha-sambhavāt.*

5 Sigwart, op. cit., I. 418.

6 *kārya-anumāna = kāryeṇa anumāna.*

7 Necessity between the very last moment of the cause and the first moment of the result is apparently also admitted, cp. NBT., p. 39. 72; transl., p. 88.

In this sense the logical law of Causation is the reverse of the real law of Causation. A cause is not a reason. The cause is not a sufficient reason for predicating (or predicting) the effect. But the effect is a sufficient reason for affirming apodictically the preceding existence of its cause. In this sense the law of Causation is also a law subaltern to the law of Contradiction in the same degree as the law of Identity. Every thing would not be a thing if it were not the result of some other thing.

It is therefore wrong to coordinate the law of Causation with the law of Contradiction. The latter is a universal law which equally governs all generalities or concepts and all realities or point-instants. But Causality governs the production of point-instants alone.

Sigwart thinks that it was a mistake on the part of Leibniz to coordinate the law of Contradiction and the law of Sufficient Reason as the only two great principles of all our arguments. For, according to him,[1] Leibnizens law of Sufficient Reason is nothing but the law of Causation and it was wrong to coordinate the logical law of Contradiction with the not logical, but real law of Causation.

Now, from Dharmakīrti's standpoint we have a law of Sufficient Reason which is the universal law of all our arguments and of which the two great principles of Identity and Causation are mere specifications. This law is called simply the Reason,[2] or the law of the Threefold Logical Mark.[3] Its formula, we have seen, is 1) in Subject presence wholly, 2) in Similars only, 3) in Dissimilars never. According to its two main figures the law is also called the Law of Position and Contraposition.[4] Its formula is this that the reason being posited its necessary consequence is likewise posited and in the absence of the necessary consequence the reason is likewise absent.

The Buddhist law of Causation, viewed as Dependent Origination, is expressed in a hypothetical judgment, «this being that appears». The Buddhist law of Sufficient Reason is likewise expressed in

---

1 Op. cit., I. 254 — „Wenn ich den realen Grund einer tatsächlichen Wahrheit (*vérité de fait*) angebe, nenne ich die Ursache... Ebendaraus erhellt wie wenig Recht man hatte nun daraus ein schlechthin allgemeines logisches Gesetz zu machen, das neben dem Gesetze des Widerspruchs, inbetreff derselben Sätze gälte, welche auch unter dem Gesetze des Widerspruchs stehen, und in dem Leibniz'schen Satze einen logischen Grund zu suchen, der von der realen Ursache verschieden wäre".

2 *hetu* = *gtan-thsigs.*

3 *trirūpa-linga* = *thsul-gsum-rtags.*

4 *anvaya-vyatireka.*

a hypothetical judgment or a hypothetical Syllogism. The Position and the Contraposition[1] of this law corresponds to the *modus ponens* and *modus tollens* of the Mixed Hypothetical Syllogism. Since the universal law of Sufficient Reason is equally realized in deductions founded on Identity, as in those founded on Causation, we can maintain that all our arguments are founded on these two great principles and the syllogism of Causation exists in equal rights with the analytical syllogism.

The European syllogistic theory has never admitted causal deductions as a special variety of syllogism. The modern theory assumes that Causality, or the principle of Uniformity in nature, the principle namely that the same causes produce the same effects, is the fundamental principle of Induction and Induction is the opposite of Deduction or Syllogism. The latter are based on the principle of analytic Identity. Induction can never attain strict universality and necessity in its conclusions, whereas syllogistic deduction is characterized by necessity.

This was not the opinion of Aristotle. For him Induction was also a Syllogism and Causation was also founded upon the principle of analytic Identity. His causal Syllogism is a deduction of the effect from its cause. The cause is brought in line and identified with the middle term,[2] the effect occupies the place of the major term in the conclusion. But this deduction founded on Causality is not, as with the Buddhists, a second variety[3] coordinated with the analytic deduction of the particular from the universal; it is subordinated to it, or, on the contrary, the analytic deduction is subordinated to the causal one, since the Universal is regarded as a kind of cause. For Aristotle the cause is always the Universal of which the effect is the particular. The research of a cause of something is the research of a middle term.[4] The universal connection of cause and effect becomes known to us through induction from particular cases. All the four varieties of cause assumed by Aristotle are so many middle terms from which

---

1 *anvaya-vyatireka.*

2 Aristotle, it is true, also admits that often the effect is more notorious, so that we employ it as a middle term (cp. Grote, p. 223), and conclude from it to its reciprocating cause. But in this case the syllogism is supposed to be not causal, it is knowledge of the Ens, not of the διότι.

3 However Aristotle also admits that the *quaesitum* is sometimes the Quiddity or essential nature of the thing itself and sometimes an extraneous fact (Analyt. Post., II, ii, a 31, cp. Grote, op. cit., p. 220). In this place Aristotle seems to admit that the two exclusive ultimate grounds for every inference are either Co-inherence (= Identity) or Causation (= dependence on an extraneous fact).

4 Grote, op. cit., p. 240.

the effect, or the major, is deduced.[1] The essence of the cause is to produce its effect, just as the essence of a triangle is the cause, or the ground, for having its three angles equal to two right angles.[2]

The conception of Causality as an analytic relation was inherited from Aristotle by the schoolmen and by modern philosophy. It culminated in Spinoza's identification of *causa sive ratio.* Its result has been that the causal syllogism was ignored as a separate variety and neglected as a subordinate species, it did not exist at all. When the analytic theory of causation was destroyed by Hume psychologically and by Kant transcendentally, the causal syllogism was nevertheless not acknowledged as a second variety having equal rights with the analytical. Hume denied the necessity and universality of all causal sequences, and Kant, although he established them upon a transcendental basis, identified them with the hypothetical judgment and left the categorical syllogistic form to analytic deductions exclusively.

In connection with Kant's deduction of the category of causation from the hypothetical judgment, it is interesting to note a theory for which Kant himself is not directly responsible, but which is a consequence of his deduction and which deserves to be mentioned in the light of its Indian parallel. According to this theory the relation of Coinherence is expressed in the categorical judgment, «all A is B»; but the relation of Causality is expressed in the hypothetical one «if there is A, there necessarily was B». This theory seems to admit that there are only two great principles upon which all our arguments are founded, the principle of Coinherence and the principle of Causality. It is then easily shown that the hypothetical form is equally applicable to both, it is not exclusively adapted to the causal relation.[3] The universal premise «*omne* A *est* B» really means that if something is A, it necessarily is B. The necessity of the relation is expressed by the hypothetical form[4] in this case, just as in the case of causation. The universal premise «A is always produced by B» means that «if there is A, there necessarily preceded some B». With these corrections and additions the theory would correspond to the Indian one. Indeed there is a general law controlling all our

---

1 Ibid., p. 246.

2 Ibid.

3 Cp. Sigwart, op. cit., p. 297, cp. also Bain, Logic, I. 117; cp. J. S. Mill, Logic I, 92, he seems to have been the first to express the opinion that the hypothetical judgment does not differ very substantially from the categorical one.

4 In sanscrit *yo yo dlūmavān sa so'gnimān.*

arguments. We can call it the law of the Reason or of the Sufficient Reason or, as the Buddhists call it, of the Threefold Logical Reason. It is expressed in the hypothetical judgment and means that, being given the reason the consequence necessarily follows, and if the necessary consequence is absent, the reason is also absent. Another name for this law is the law of Position and Contraposition.[1] It corresponds to the *modus ponens* and *modus tollens* of the Mixed Hypothetical Syllogism. Its canon of rules consists of these three—in subject presence wholly, in similars only, in dissimilars never. This corresponds to the principle *nota notae est nota rei ipsius* and to the *dictum de omni*.[2] It is equally applicable to both the «great principles» upon which all our arguments are founded, the principle of Identity and the principle of Causation. Indeed, take the Indian type-instance—

If something is a product, it is not eternal, as a jar etc.
If it is eternal, it never is a product, like Space etc.
The sounds are products.
They are not eternal.

Or take the corresponding European type-instance—

If some being is a man, he necessarily is mortal, as this one and that one,
If he is immortal, he cannot be a man, like God.
This one is a man,
He is mortal.

The mathematical deductions reduce to the same form, e. g.,

If something is a straight line, it necessarily is the shortest distance between two points, as this and that straight lines.
If it is not the shortest distance, it is not straight, as the curve etc.
This is a straight line,
It is the shortest distance.

These deductions do not differ in form from the causal one. Indeed, take the Indian type-instance[3]—

Wheresoever there is smoke, there is fire, as in the kitchen etc.

---

1 *anvaya-vyatireka.*

2 That these both formulas are the same, has been proved by Kant, cp. Von der falschen Spitzfindigkeit.

3 The hypothetical character of this judgment is expressed in Sanscrit by the words *yatra yatra dhūmaḥ* or *yo yo dhūmavān*, this corresponds to the latin *quis quis*, cp. Sigwart, I. 288.

Where there never is fire, there can be no smoke, as in water etc.
There is here smoke.
There is also (or there was) fire.

No formal difference exists between the two sets of instances. Both come under the head of the law of Position and Contraposition or of the threefold logical mark, or of the two moods of the Hypothetical Syllogism.[1] The difference consists only in this, that universality of the causal sequence is not the same as the universality and necessity of a connection founded on Identity. What the Indian solution of this problem is and how far it coincides with the Kantian one has been mentioned in the chapter on Inference.

h) Summary.

In summarizing our comparison of the European, chiefly Greek, and the Indian, chiefly Buddhist, system we find.

1. There is in the human intellect a fundamental procedure constituting its very essence, with the investigation of which both the Greek and the Indian science have busied themselves, with a view to a clear definition of its substance and forms. This procedure is Inference or Syllogism. Inference for Buddhists is the same as thought in general, since there are only two sources of knowledge, sensation and inference, the same as the senses and the understanding.

2. On both sides the investigation is conditioned by the general philosophic outlook. The Greek philosopher surveys the world as an ordered system of realized concepts whose total and partial connections and disconnections are laid down in Syllogisms. The Indian philosopher surveys the world as a running stream of point-instants out of which some points are illuminated by stabilized concepts and reached by the striving humanity in their purposive actions.

3. The Greek science defines syllogism as a series of three propositions containing together three terms and capable of yielding 19 different moods of valid judgments according to a change of the grammatical position of these terms in these propositions. The Indian science defines it as a method of cognizing and reaching reality, not directly as in sense-perception, but indirectly

---

[1] The importance given to of the Hypothetical Syllogism is also an outstanding feature of the logic of the Stoics, cp. Paul Barth, Die Stoa[3], p. 74.

through a superstructure of two necessarily interdependent concepts.

4. The fact that Syllogism contains an internal process of inferential cognition is not unknown in European science, but it is treated as an imperfect and incomplete form of what is fully expressed by the formulation in three propositions with an interchangeable position of their subjects and predicates. The Indian Syllogism, on the contrary, being subservient to internal Inference, is a method of formulating in propositions the mutual necessary interdependence of the three terms which therefore have a logically fixed position in corresponding propositions.

5. Although in Aristotle's intention Syllogism is the general form of all Deductions as well as Inductions, it became in the hands of his followers restricted to Deduction alone, and as soon as Induction raised its head in modern times, the position of the Syllogism, restricted to mere deductions, became endangered. By many philosophers it is declared to represent futile scholasticism worthless for the progress of knowledge. On the Indian side Deduction is inseparable from Induction, they mutually contain each the other, the one is the justification of the other. Deduction not preceded by Induction is impossible. Even purely deductive sciences have an inductive foundation like the rest. On the other hand Induction without an application to further particular instances would be quite worthless.

6. There is therefore in the Buddhist Syllogism only two members, an Inductive one and a Deductive one, which correspond to a grounding and an applying march of thought.

7. The Buddhist System contains a Causal Syllogism which in European logic was at first merged in the analytical one and later excluded from the domain of syllogism altogether.

8. The Buddhist System coordinates Causation and Identity (Coinherence) as the two great principles upon which all our arguments and their expression, the syllogisms, are founded.

9. The formal unity of these two great principles is expressed in a Universal law of Sufficient Reason or, as it is called, the Threefold Reason.

In European science the problems of a law of Sufficient Reason, of the analytic and causal relations and the allied problem of the analytic and synthetic judgments are mostly treated outside the theory of syllogism. In India they are its integral parts. The Intellect is but another name for Reason and the Reason is nothing but the Sufficient Reason or the principle representing the formal unity of the two great principles of Identity and Causality. There is no difference between Reason in general and the Syllogistic Reason with its canon of threerules.

10. The second and third of these rules correspond to the *modus ponens* and *modus tollens* of the Mixed Hypothetical Syllogism. There is therefore only two real syllogistic figures, the positive and the contraposed one. The fundamental principle of all Syllogism is the principle of the Mixed Hypothetical Syllogism, the principle namely that «the ground is followed by the necessary consequence and the denial of the necessary consequence is logically followed by the denial of the ground».

11. The law of Sufficient Reason, since it is expressed in the canon of the three syllogistic rules is also expressed in the equipollent principle of the Mixed Hypothetical Syllogism, or in Position and Contraposition. They express the law of logical necessity. The Mixed Hypothetical Syllogism, which in the majority of European logics is treated as an additional, secondary, not genuine syllogistic process, appears in Buddhist logic as its fundamental principle.

There is thus a great difference between the European and the Buddhist syllogistic theory. However both theories are groping after one and the same central problem, the problem, namely, of the principles of human knowledge. The solution proposed by Dignāga and Dharmakīrti is, in some respects, nearer to Kant and Sigwart, than to Aristotle.

The opinion of Kant upon the «False Subtlety» of the Aristotelian figures has already been mentioned. But this is not the only point of agreement between the Kantian and the Buddhist theory. The following Kantian ideas must in this connection attract our attention. «To compare a thing with its mark, says Kant, is to judge». «A judgment through an intermediate mark (i. e., through the mark of the mark) is our reason's inference (*Vernunft-schluss*)». He then calls attention to the principle of Contraposition and gives to those Syllogisms where the conclusion is arrived at through Position and Contraposition of the major the name of *ratrocinium hybridum.*[1] He then identifies the syllogism of Position with the first Aristotelian figure and the syllogism of Contraposition with its second figure, declaring the rest to be useless and false subtlety. By giving such importance to the fact of Position and Contraposition Kant has virtually (although he does not state it

---

[1] Cp. *anvaya-vyatireki anumānam.*

expressly) admitted that syllogism is founded upon the principle of the Mixed Hypothetical Syllogism with its two moods, the *modus ponens* and the *modus tollens*. Kant says that although the four figures are nothing but useless rubbish (*Plunder*), he has no hope to overthrow at once the colossus of Aristotelian syllogistic. Indeed Sigwart, for aught I know, was the only logician who has taken up Kant's suggestions and established his syllogistic theory on the principle of the Mixed Hypothetical Syllogism.

Indeed Sigwart maintains[1] that «the most general form of all and every inference is the so called Mixed Hypothetical Conclusion». «When a valid judgment A is given, it is clear that another judgment X can be founded on it only if the unconditional and universal proposition be admitted that „if A is valid, X is also valid".[2] «The order of the premises, he continues, depends on the movement of thought in every individual case».[3] This corresponds to Dignāga's view that in private thinking we usually begin with the minor premise and in a public debate we must begin by the universal proposition.

«All kinds of deduction of a simple statement, he then says, must be traceable to the two forms which usually are called the *modus ponens* and the *modus tollens* of the Mixed Hypothetical Conclusion». «The *modus tollens*, he adds in a note, is always reducible to a corresponding *modus ponens*». He thus maintains the equipollency of both these moods, thus siding, as it were, with Dignāga against the Sānkhyas.

He then makes a remark which receives a particular interest from the standpoint of a parallelism with Indian theories.[4] «A further development of the theory of Inference, says he, should touch on the problem, what is it then that makes the connection between two judgments A and X a necessary connection? Whether it is not possible to trace this necessity back to a limited small number of laws?» This question is only suggested, no definite answer is given, although the interesting remark is passed that «Identity is also a relation between thoughts». Now the other relation of necessary dependence, we have seen, is non-Identity between two interdependent facts, and *dependent non-identity* is nothing but another word for Causation. There is, according to the Indians, from this point of view, no other relation

[1] Op. cit., I. 434.
[2] Ibid.
[3] Ibid.
[4] Ibid., p. 442.

than Causality (between two facts of necessary consecution), and Identity (in the objective reference of two concepts).

The laws upon which all necessary connection reposes, we have seen, are those of Identity, Causality and Contradiction, in their Indian interpretation.

The views expressed by Sigwart in this connection on Conversion, Contraposition and the particular judgments are notorious by their parallelism with some Indian conceptions. They have already been quoted above.

CHAPTER V.

LOGICAL FALLACIES.

§ 1. Classification.

Dignāga clearly saw that having established a strict canon of the rules of syllogism, he at the same time has solved the problem of a strict canon of Logical Fallacies. For a fallacy is nothing but the infringement of a rule. If the rules are definite in number and are arranged in systematical order, their infringements must be likewise definite in number and capable of being arranged in systematical unity. The logical import of every proposition is double, it has a positive and an implied negative meaning. A rule always affirms something and at the same time excludes the opposite. Every syllogistic rule condemns a corresponding fallacy.[1]

The rules of a logical inference are, we have seen, three.

1. The presence of the Reason in the Subject of the conclusion, viz., its necessary presence in the whole compass of the Subject;

2. Its necessary presence in similar instances only, i. e., in instances similar by the presence in them of the deduced Predicate;

3. Its necessary absence in *all* dissimilar instances, i. e., in instances which are contrary to those in which the deduced property is present.

Now, a fallacious reason will run either against the first or the second or the third rule. But we must distinguish between the fallacies against the first rule and the fallacies against the combined second and third rules. It is indeed impossible to infringe the second rule without, at the same time, infringing the third one. The second and the third rules are only two aspects of one and the same rule.[2] If the reason is not present in similar instances only, it *eo ipso* is present, either wholly or partially, in dissimilar instances also. We thus will have two main classes of fallacies, the one against the first rule of the syllogistic canon and the other against its combined second and third rules. Reduced to the language of European logic this will mean a class of fallacies against the minor premise and another class

1 NBT., p. 61.18; transl., p. 171.

2 NBT., p. 20.5; transl., p. 57.

of fallacies against the major premise, or undistributed Middle in the minor premise and undistributed Middle in the major premise. For an inference, or a syllogism consists, we have seen, in 1) a fact of invariable concomitance or, more precisely, a fact of the necessary dependence between two terms, and 2) in the reference of these two interdependent terms to some point of reality. The first fact is expressed in the major premise, the second is expressed in the minor one.

Since the minor premise contains the reference of a logical construction to a point of reality, an infringement of this rule will represent a fallacy against reality. A reason, which fails in respect of reference to reality, may be called an «Unreal Reason».[1] The major premise, on the other hand, contains the expression of the necessary dependence of the reason upon its consequence. If the reason represents a fact which is necessarily dependent upon the consequence, its presence will always entail the presence of the consequence. A reason which fails in this respect will represent a fallacy, not of reality, but of consistency. The invariable concomitance between the two terms will be falsified. No definite conclusion will follow and the reason will be «uncertain».[2] Thus we shall have two main classes of logical fallacies, fallacies against reality and fallacies against consistency. The latter class are the logical fallacies in the strictest sense and, in order to establish their number and system, Dignāga has devised a systematical table, called by him «The Wheel of Logical Reasons».[3]

All the possible positions of the reason between similar and dissimilar instances are computed in this table, according to a mathematical principle. The result is that there are only nine positions of the Reason, neither more, nor less. Of them two only represent right reasons, the remaining seven are fallacies. Out of these seven, two represent the fallacy at its maximum, they are the contradictorily opposed part of right reason, and are called «contrary»[4] or «inverted» reasons.

The five remaining ones are «uncertain»,[5] because the position of the middle term between similar and dissimilar instances is not definite; it either overlaps from the similar into the forbidden province of

---

1 *asiddha-hetv-ābhāsa.*

2 *anaikāntika-hetv-ābhāsa.*

3 Hetu-cakra, sometimes called Hetu-cakra-ḍamaru and Hetu-cakra-samarthana.

4 *viruddha-hetv-ābhāsa.*

5 *anaikāntika = sandigdha.*

the dissimilar ones, or it embraces all the similar as well as the dissimilar ones, or finally it is strictly confined to the mere subject, and is not to be found neither in any similar nor in any dissimilar instance. In the latter case the reason is «exclusive» or «over-narrow»[1] and therefore leads to no consequence. If the reason, on the contrary, embraces all similar as well as all dissimilar instances, it becomes «over-wide» or «too general»[2] and therefore allows of no conclusion. These two reasons, the «over-wide» and the «over-over-narrow», are evidently of seldom occurrence in practice, but their theoretical importance should not be underestimated, since they clearly indicate the maximum and the minimum limits between which the right reason is to be found. Remain only three uncertain reasons, uncertain in the strictest sense, since the reason overlaps into the forbidden domain of the dissimilar instances, either partially or wholly.[3] Thus among all possible nine positions of the logical reason between instances similar and dissimilar two will be right, two inverted, i. e., contrary to right, two representing the maximum and the minimum limits of comprehension, and the three remaining ones will be overlapping into the forbidden domain and uncertain.

This is represented in Dignāga's table situated on the following page. We indicate in it the presence of the reason in similar instances by the sign S. Three cases are then possible — its presence in all S, its presence in no S (= absence), and its presence in some S. The presence of the reason in dissimilar instances we will indicate by the sign D. Three cases are then possible: its presence in all D, its presence in no D (= absence), and its presence in some D. By combining each of the first set of three positions alternately with each of the set of the second three positions, we shall have a total of nine combinations of the reason's position between instances similar and dissimilar, neither less nor more.

In	this	table	the	item	«in all S»	is	found	3	times	(in	1,4 and	7)
»	»	»	»	»	«in no S»	»	»	3	»	(»	2,5 »	8)
»	»	»	»	»	«in some S»	»	»	3	»	(»	3,6 »	9)
»	»	»	»	»	«in all D»	»	»	3	»	(»	1,2 »	3)
»	»	»	»	»	«in no D»	»	»	3	»	(»	4,5 »	6)
»	»	»	»	»	«in some D»	»	»	3	»	(»	7,8 »	9)

---

1 *asādhāraṇa-hetv-ābhāsa = avyāpaka-anaikāntika.*

2 *sādhāraṇa-anaikāntika = ati-vyāpaka.*

3 *asiddha-vyatirekin.*

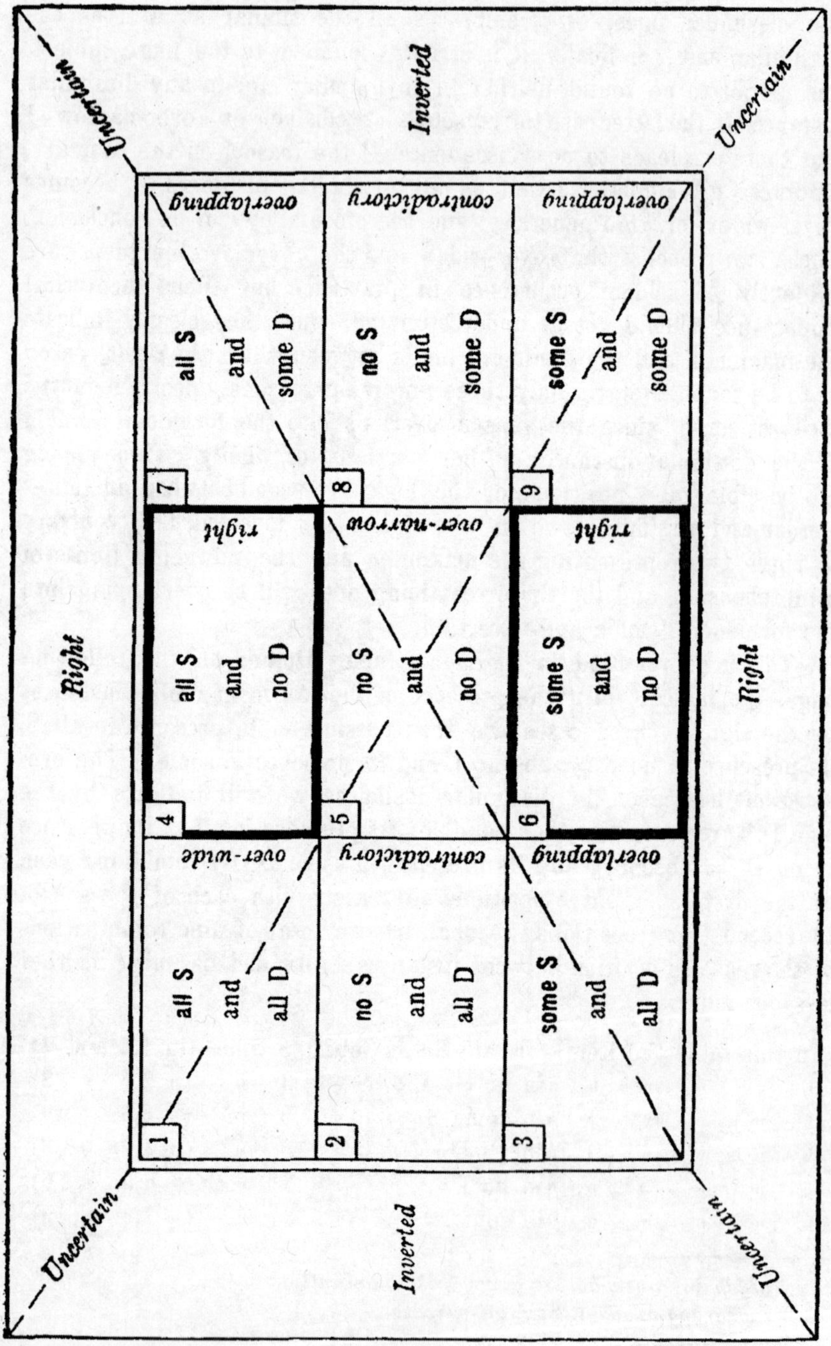
Uncertain
Inverted
Uncertain
Right
Right
Uncertain
Inverted
Uncertain
1 all S and all D over-wide
2 no S and all D contradictory
3 some S and all D overlapping
4 all S and no D right
5 no S and no D over-narrow
6 some S and no D right
7 all S and some D overlapping
8 no S and some D contradictory
9 some S and some D overlapping

Together, 18 items arranged in 9 combinations. Two combinations (No. 4 and 6) represent the reason and consequence situated firmly and travelling regularly on the right rails. All other combinations deviate from the right rails. Two (No. 2 and 8) contain the maximum of deviation, the deviation is catastrophic, it is the inverted reason. Two of them (No. 1 and 5) have a theoretical interest, showing the limits of the overlapping capacity of the reason and in the three remaining ones (No. 3, 7 and 9) the overlapping capacity is normal. In two cases only the concomitance is all right, in seven cases the concomitance is falsified, there is no invariable concomitance. In all these 7 cases the fallacy will be in the major premise. If the reason will be over-wide, over-narrow or overlapping, it will be inconclusive or «uncertain». If it is contrary, it is, although definite, but definite in the undesirable sense, representing the contradictorily opposed part of the right one.

Thus it is that every logical fallacy corresponds to some rule of the syllogistic canon, every fallacy is nothing but the infringement of that rule.[1]

It is evident that the same mathematical method could also be applied in respect of the first rule of the syllogistic canon. The reason can be present in the Subject wholly, partially or not at all. Combining each of these three possibilities of reality, resp. unreality, with the nine varieties of consistency, we will get 27 kinds of reason, out of which only four will be right reasons, i. e., real and consistent. By introducing further subtleties the table of reasons could be increased *ad infinitum.*[2] Some of Dignāga's imitators have indulged in that useless occupation, but he abstained from it. The most useful principle may be reduced *ad absurdum* by senseless exaggeration. Important and useful are only the fundamental distinctions established by Dignāga— a reason is either 1) right, i. e. real and consistent, or 2) it is unreal, or 3) it is inverted, or 4) uncertain, i. e., non-concomitant and inconsistent.

To summarize. An inference, of which the syllogism is but the verbal expression, is a complex relation between three terms. One of them is the substratum or Subject (S). It represents, or contains, a point of ultimate reality to which the superstructure of the two

---

1 Cp. NB. and NBT., p. 80. 9; transl., p. 220.

2 Cp. Stasiak, Fallacies and their classification according to the Early Indian Logicians, art. in Rocznik Orientalistyczny, t. VI, pp. 191—198.

other interdependent terms is referred. Of these two, one is the dependent part, and the other the part upon which it necessarily depends. The dependent part, because it is necessarily dependent, possesses the force to convey the presence of the part upon which it depends. The latter is therefore called the logical Consequence, or the logical Predicate or Major Term (P). The dependent part must moreover be present upon the substratum in order to connect the predicate with that substratum. It is therefore the reason or middle term (M) through which P is connected with S. There is thus a double relation between these three terms. M is dependent upon P, universally, necessarily, logically; and M is present upon S wholly and really, as a fact. The presence of M upon S carries as its consequence the presence of P upon S. The form of the Buddhist syllogism as practised in our days in Tibet and Mongolia is the following one —

My S is So and So
My P » » » »
My M » » » »

Is it right or is it wrong? That is to say, is the presence of M on S right or wrong? And is the dependence of M on P right or wrong? If both are right, the reason is conclusive and the syllogism unimpeachable.

If it is wrong, what is wrong? Is the presence of M on S wrong? Or is the necessary dependence of M on P wrong? In the first case the reason will lack Reality, in the second it will lack Consistency.

Thus three answers are only possible when the validity of a syllogism is tested. The examined pupil will answer either—

1. Reason all right. I accept it! (*ḥ dod = kāmam*).
2. Reason unreal! (*rtags-ma-hgrub = asiddho hetuḥ*).
3. No concomitance! (*khyab-pa-ma-hbyuñ = vyāptir na bhavati*).

The classification is exhaustive. No other answer than these three is possible. That the disputants understand what they say and that the terms used by them are not ambiguous is a self-evident condition.

The fallacy may be concealed under terms unsufficiently clear. It must be analysed and made clear beyond the possibility of doubt. In a crude form a fallacy will never, or very seldom, occur. The human mind, says Vācaspatimišra, has a natural bias for truth. It will not go astray, if the fallacy is clearly shown to him. For didactical purposes it is therefore useful to practice on propositions which are quite wrong, so strikingly wrong that they will never occur to any one. A fallacy is really produced only when its character is concealed by an obscure phrasing. When the phrasing is elucidated, the crude form of the fallacy appears. A fallacy in which there is absolutely no connection neither between M and S, nor between M and P, a *nec plus ultra* fallacy, is the following one — «all sheep are horses, because they are cows». Such a syllogism has never occurred to anybody, because, as stated by Vācaspati, the human mind has a bias for truth. But celebrated arguments in which there neither is reality nor concomitance, neither any whatsoever tie between M and S, nor any tie between M and P, have been produced in a concealed form.

The following examples will illustrate, in crude form, the instances where either 1) both relations are right, or 2) the reason lacks reality, or 3) there is no concomitance.

1. The subject of discourse (S) is a jar.[1] The logical predicate (P) «a non-eternal Ens». Reason (M) — «because it exists». We shall have the following syllogism.

Whatsoever exists is a non-eternal Ens.

The jar exists.

It is a non-eternal Ens.

Answer — all right!

2. The subject of discourse (S) is a jar. The logical predicate (P) is a «non-Ens». Reason (M) — «because it does not exist». We then shall have the syllogism —

Whatsoever does not exist is not an Ens.

The jar does not exist.

It is not an Ens.

Answer — reason unreal. The fault is in the minor premise, since the jar does exist.

3. The Subject of discourse (S) is a jar. The logical predicate (P) «an eternal Ens». The reason (M) — «because it exists». We then shall have the following syllogism —

Whatsoever exists, is an Eternal Ens.

The jar exists.

It is an Eternal Ens.

Answer — no concomitance! The major premise is wrong, since there are non-eternal things.

Reduced to a schematical form these relations between S, M and P can be represented thus —

---

[1] Dignāga's example is «sound».

1. When P is right in respect of S, the answer is: yes!

2. When P is not right in respect of S, it is asked: why?

3. When M (the reason) is not right in respect of P, albeit it is right in respect of S, the answer is: no concomitance!

4. When M (the reason) is not right in respect of S and right (or also unright) in respect of P, the answer is: reason unreal!

This is only the crude schema, examples will be given in the sequel. Every fallacy is reducible to one of these crude forms.

§ 2. Fallacy against Reality (asiddha-hetv-ābhāsa).

What a Fallacy against Reality is, has been stated. We have said that when the invariable connection of the Reason with the Consequence is established beyond any doubt, but the presence of the Reason in the Subject is either denied altogether or doubted; in other words, when the First Aspect of the Reason is not realized, or the first rule of the syllogistic canon is infringed, — we shall have a logical fallacy of an Unreal Reason.

We have also said that in the phrasing of the European theory this could be called a fallacy of the minor premise. When the presence of the Reason upon the Minor Term is either impossible or doubtfull, the conclusion will be a fallacy. The simplest example of such a fallacy will appear, when there is not the slightest doubt of the invariable connection between two facts, but the place to which it must be applied in a given instance is uncertain.

Supposing we hear the cry of a pea-cock.[1] There is no doubt that this cry is the mark of its presence. And there are several caves before us among which the pea-cock is hidden, but we cannot decide in which. The conclusion, which requires certainty, is impossible. Indeed we shall have —

Major premise. Whereever there is a pea-cock's cry, it is present.

Minor premise. The cry comes (probably) from that cave.

Conclusion. The pea-cock is present in that cave (probably).

The conclusion is only probable, it is not certain, and, in this sense, it is a fallacy. It is a fallacy of Unreality. It is not a fallacy of uncertainty. We shall see later on that the name of an Uncertain Reason is restricted to other kinds.

---

[1] NB. and NBT., p. 64.17; transl., p. 177.

Not only doubt regarding the reality underlying the inferential judgment makes the Reason Unreal, its established unreality will *a fortiori* convert every reason referred to it into a fallacy of Unreality. E. g., the Soul as a separate spiritual substance is denied by the Buddhists; it is an unreal object. Consequently whatever predicate be connected with it as a reason, will be an unreal reason.

The Vaišeṣikas, e. g., conceive the Soul of the individual as an ubiquitous substance, unconscious by itself and motionless; motionless because ubiquitous. The feelings, pleasant and unpleasant, although inherent properties of the Soul are not ubiquitous. They appear only in that part of it which coincides with the presence of the body and its internal organ. A special interaction between the internal organ and the Soul produces at a special moment in a definite part of the ubiquitous Soul the feeling of something pleasant or unpleasant. When the body displaces itself, the feelings are accordingly produced in other parts of the motionless Soul of the same individual.

These ideas may be thrown in the form of the following syllogism[1]—

Major premise. A substance whose properties can be apprehended anywhere is ubiquitous, like Space.

Minor premise. The Soul is a substance whose properties can be apprehended anywhere.

Conclusion. The Soul is ubiquitous.

The invariable concomitance of the Reason with its Consequence is established beyond any doubt. The major premise is all right. But not the minor. The reasoning lacks reality, because the point of application, the point of reality to which the logical superstructure of two interdependent concepts ought to have been referred is a fantom. The Soul as a separate ubiquitous substance does not exist, at least for the Buddhist. The reasoning therefore represents a fallacy of unreality, a fallacy against the first rule of the Buddhist syllogistic canon.

Although the Soul as a separate substance is, in the opinion of the Buddhist, a non-entity, and every predicate connected with the Soul will be equally unreal, nevertheless it will be «unreal» only when the Soul occupies the position of the minor term, the Subject of the conclusion, because here is the point of contact between logic and reality. If the point of reality, the Substratum or the reality underlying the whole reasoning is absent, the fallacy will be one of unreality. Other syllogisms, in which the Soul will not occupy the place of the

---

1 NB. and NBT., p. 63.13; transl., p. 178.

minor term, will be regarded from the standpoint of logical consistency without referring to the special theory of the Buddhist Soul-denial. E. g., the inference of the form «the living body possesses a Soul, because it possesses animal functions» will be analysed, as will be shown in the sequel, from the standpoint of pure logic, quite independently from the opinion of the contending parties on its reality or unreality. The fallacy of Unreality is a fallacy concerning the reality or uncertainty of the minor term and of the minor premise.

It is a matter of course that in all public debates, as well as in all ratiocination, the terms used by the contending parties must have a definite and identical meaning. If one party understands a term in one sense and the adversary understands it in another sense, there can be between them no regular *bona fide* debate.

But when one party *bona fide* uses a term in a meaning which is unacceptable for its opponent, it may happen that the deduction will be all right for that party, but unacceptable and unreal for its opponents. E. g., when the Jaina argues[1] —

Major premise. An organism which dies when its covering texture is stripped off is a sensient being.

Minor premise. The trees are such organisms.

Conclusion. They are sentient beings.

This argument can be considered as right by the Jaina from his point of view, since he has his own views on what death and a sentient being is. But for the Buddhist the reason will be unreal, because he has other definitions of what death and sentient beings are. According to his views the trees are not the real point where they can be found. The fallacy will be for him a fallacy of unreality, a fallacy of the minor premise. The Buddhist can also object against the major premise, viz. against the rule that «whatsoever dies when its covering texture is stripped off is a sentient being», but that is another question. In the present instance this rule is neither denied nor doubted. But supposing it is all right, its application to trees is impossible from the Buddhist point of view, because the term death has for him a different meaning. Death means for him — cessation of conscious life and this is not really found in trees.

A similar argument of the Jainas,[2] «the trees sleep because they close their leaves at night» will be denied as unreal, because not all

---

[1] NB. and NBT., p. 62.13; transl., p. 173.

[2] NB. and NBT., p. 19.7; transl., p. 54.

trees close their leaves at night, but only some special kind of them. It is again a fallacy of the minor premise. No particular judgment is admissible in a correct syllogism. The judgment «some trees close their leaves at night» does not lead to any definite conclusion.

But the contrary may also happen. It may happen that the minor premise will be unreal for that philosopher who himself quotes it. This may happen in those instances when he, albeit he does not accept the opinion of his adversary, nevertheless quotes it in order to extract out of it some advantage for his own theory. This method of taking advantage from a foreign and disbelieved theory is condemned by Dignāga.

The Sānkhya philosopher, e. g., holds that all feelings of pleasure and pain are unconscious by themselves, since conscious is only the Soul. But the Soul is changeless and can only illumine, it cannot contain any feelings. The feelings are, for the Sānkhya philosopher, evolutes of eternal Matter, and in this sense they are for him eternal,[1] because their stuff is eternal Matter. But in order to prove that they are unconscious, he wishes to take advantage from the Buddhist theory which denies the existence of any enduring substance. Feelings come and go without being inherent in some perduring substance. The Sānkhya then argues — if feelings are impermanent, they cannot be self-conscious, because conscious is the eternal substance of the Soul alone.

This method of taking advantage from the theory of an adversary is condemned by Dignāga. It is a fallacy of unreality, since the reason is unreal just for that philosopher himself who nevertheless seeks support from it.

A combined fallacy of unreality and inconsistency is, of course, possible, but in such cases it is usually referred to the Unreal class, because the reality of the reason, its presence in a real Subject, is the first condition to which it must satisfy.[2]

§ 3. Fallacy of a Contrary Reason.

This is a fallacy of consistency, or of concomitance. The reason, or middle term, is represented as invariably concomitant, not with its natural consequence, but with the inverted consequence, with the

---

1 *kāraṇa-avasthāyām nityam.*

2 Dignāga counts four *asiddhas: ubhaya, anyatara, sandigdha* and *āśraya- (dharmi-) asiddha.* By subdividing the second and the last Dharmakīrti apparently counts six. Cp. Nyāya-mukha, p. 14.

contradictorily opposed part to the natural consequence. In Dignāga's systematical table it occupies the 2-d and 8-th positions. Its importance is chiefly theoretical as showing the maximum of inconsistency which a logical reason may incur. In practice its occurence in an unconcealed, pure form is hardly possible. The natural «bias of the human mind» for truth and consistency will too strongly revolt against such a «reason». But when concealed behind an uncertain, unclear or unsufficiently digested terminology, it happens frequently that this fallacy is found at the bottom of some specious argumentation. The difference between the position No. 2 and the position No. 8 is that in the first the reason is present in all dissimilar cases and in the second it covers only one part of that forbidden domain. Their common feature is the total absence of the reason in all similar cases, where it ought to have been necessarily present. Such a concealed contrary reason is founded whenever a philosopher produces an argument which, on analysis, is found to run against the fundamental principles admitted by himself. The unconcealed form of the contrary argument is found in the two following examples.

1. The sounds (of the Veda) are eternal entities,
Because they are produced by causes.
Whatsoever is a product is an eternal entity, like Space.

The reverse of the expressed concomitance is true. Therefore the reason adduced is a reason to the contrary. It occupies the position No. 2 since it is absent in all similar, i. e., eternal objects, like Space etc.; and it is present in all dissimilar, i. e., non-eternal objects, like jars etc.

2. The sounds (of the Veda) are eternal entities,
Because they are produced at will.
Whatsoever is produced by human will is an eternal entity.

This reason is likewise absent in all similar, i. e., eternal objects. But it differs from the former one in that it is present not in the whole forbidden domain of the dissimilar instances; it is present only in some non-eternal things, like jars etc. It is absent in another part of the dissimilar objects, like lightning etc.

An example of a concealed contrary reason is the following one.[1] The Sānkhya philosopher wishes to establish that the sense-organs are the organs of somebody, viz., the organs of the Soul. The Soul is a simple substance, the sense-organs are composite physical bodies. He

---

[1] NB. and NBT., p. 63.13; transl., p. 175.

therefore establishes the general principle, that the composite exists for the sake of the simple, *ergo* the sense-organs exist for the sake of the Soul. The real character of this argument is concealed by the ambiguity of the term «to exist for the sake» of somebody. As a matter of fact, to exist for the sake of somebody means to affect him directly or indirectly. And to affect him means to produce a change in him. But a change can be produced only in a composite substance, a simple substance cannot change.

Thus it is that the argument of the Sānkhya that the sense-organs exist for the sake of the Soul runs against his fundamental principle that the Soul is a simple, uncomposite, unchanging substance.

This variety of a concealed contrary reason is of no unfrequent occurrence in philosophy. It is already established as a special fallacy in the Aphorisms of the Nyāya school. Dignāga admits it as a variety of his contrary reason, but Dharmakīrti refuses to consider it as a special variety.[1] He maintains that it is included in the two varieties of the contrary reason as established by Dignāga, and occupying the positions Nos. 2 and 8 of his Wheel.

§ 4. Fallacy of an Uncertain Reason.

In Dignāga's Wheel of Logical Reasons the centre is occupied by the reason which possesses the minimum of comprehension.[2] This reason is ascertained as being present neither in the similar nor in the dissimilar instances. It is conterminous with the subject, and therefore inconclusive. It is no reason at all. If we say that the sounds of the Veda are eternal substances because they are audible, the reason audibility will be present in the subject, sound, exclusively; it will be absent in all similar as well as in all dissimilar instances. It will be over-narrow and therefore inconclusive. Its establishment has evidently a merely theoretical importance, when it is stated in such crude unconcealed and pure manner. But it can receive considerable practical importance, just as the «contrary» reason, when it is concealed behind some not sufficiently analysed and unclear concepts or expressions, as will be seen later on. In any case it represents the minimum of conclusiveness, its conclusive force is equal to 0.

---

1 NB. and NBT., p. 73.8 ff.; transl., p. 203 ff.

2 *asādhāraṇa*.

Above and beneath this central fallacy are situated the two right reasons; at the right and at the left side of it the two contrary ones; and at the four corners are situated four «uncertain» reasons. «Certainty is one issue, says Dharmottara,[1] it is the aim of the syllogism which becomes then conclusive. Inconclusive is uncertain. It is a case when neither the conclusion nor its negation can be ascertained, but, on the contrary, the only result is doubt. We call uncertain a reason which makes us fluctuate between a conclusion and its denial».

The common feature of all these uncertain reasons is that the contraposition of the major premise is either wrong of doubtful.[2] It is an infringement of the third rule of the syllogistic canon. The total absence of the reason in dissimilar instances is either falsified or doubtful. Although the third rule of the syllogistic canon is but another aspect of the second rule, nevertheless it is this aspect of the rule which is directly attended to in all fallacies of uncertainty. It was therefore necessary for Vasubandhu and Dignāga to distinguish between these two rules, just as it was incumbent upon them to make a distinction between the syllogism of Agreement and the syllogism of Difference or between the *modus ponens* and the *modus tollens* of the mixed Hypothetical Syllogism.

The four varieties of the uncertain reason which contain a direct infringement of the third rule of the syllogistic canon are situated, we have said, in the four corners of Dignāga's table. Those two of them which are situated to the left side, in the upper left corner and in the under left corner, have that feature in common that the overlapping reason is present in the whole forbidden field of dissimilar instances. The other two, situated in the right upper and in the right under corners, have a reason which overlaps only a part of the forbidden domain.

If we shall draw across Dignāga's table two diagonal lines, they will cross in the centre occupied by the «over-narrow» reason, and will unite it with all four corners where the four «uncertain reasons» reside. At the same time these diagonal lines will separate the uncertain reasons from the certain ones. The four certain ones are, we have seen, either the two which are certain and right, situated in the upper and in the under centre; and the two which are certain invertedly, they are situated in the left and the right centre. It is indeed a «magical wheel».

---

1 NBT., p. 65. 18; transl., p. 180.

2 *asiddha-vyatirekin, sandigdha-vyatirekin vā.*

At the left upper corner of the table of reasons we find the overwide fallacy. This is a reason which is inconclusive because it is present in all similar as well as in all dissimilar instances. It is uncertain in the same degree as the over-narrow reason. If we say that «the sounds of the Veda are eternal entities, because they are cognizable»,[1] the reason cognizability is equally found in eternal entities, like Space, and in the impermanent ones, like jars etc. It is inconclusive because of being over-comprehensive. Its theoretical importance is considerable, as showing the maximum limit of an overlapping reason, just as the «over-narrow» one shows its minimum limit. In its crude form it could hardly be met with in practice. In a concealed form its occurence is not only possible, but European philosophy exhibits cases when far-reaching, important conclusions have been drawn from the logical mark of cognizability and a long effort of generations was needed to detect the crude fallacy of the argument.

The second uncertain variety, situated in the under left corner of the table, is produced by a reason which is present in some similar instances, but overlaps into the dissimilar domain and covers it entirely. Dharmakīrti gives the following example[2] — «The sounds of speech are not produced by a conscious effort, because they are impermanent». The reason impermanence is partially present in the similar cases, like lightening which is not a human production. It is absent in the other part of the similar cases, like Space which is also not a human product. On the other hand, this reason of impermanence is present. against the third syllogistic rule, in all dissimilar instances, like jars etc. which are human productions and impermanent. Wheresoever there is production by a human effort, the character of impermanence is also present. This fallacy comes very near to the contrary one and will hardly occur in its crude form. However the right mutual position of the three terms of 1) «sounds», 2) «eternity» or «unchanging existence» and 3) «causal production» or changing existence, with its subaltern notion of «voluntary production», will be clearly established only by excluding all those their mutual positions which are not right. Their right logical position can be clearly and definitely established only *per differentiam*. If the logical theory can clearly show what in this case is excluded, only then will it definitely show what is

---

1 NB. and NBT.

2 NB. and NBT., p. 66.8 ff.; transl., p. 182.

included. If we make the same transpositions with the three terms of the Aristotelian example, «Socrates is mortal, because he is a man», if we try every kind of position for the three terms Socrates, mortal and man, in order to exclude the fallacious positions, we will have a corresponding fallacy of the second uncertain reason in the following form «Socrates is not a man, because he is mortal». Such a reason is very near to the contrary one. The reason mortality covers the whole field of dissimilar cases, since all men are not immortal, but mortal. However it is not a contrary reason, because it is present in a part of the similar cases also. Mortality is present among non-human beings, just as it is present in mankind.

The third variety of the uncertain reason, the one situated in the table at the right upper corner, consists in its presence in the entire domain of the similar instances and its partial overlapping into the contrary domain of dissimilar instances. This fallacy is the nearest to the right reason. It is of the most frequent occurence. It is mostly a result of an illicite contraposition. If all things produced by an effort are impermanent, it does not follow that all impermanent things are produced by an effort. If smoke is always produced by fire, it does not follow that fire always produces smoke. If all men are mortal, it does not follow that all mortal beings are men. This fallacy has been taken notice of by Aristotle and christened as the fallacy of inverted order (*Fallacia Consequentis*), that is of an illicite conversion between the reason and its logical consequence. Its full importance and meaning, of course, becomes clearly elicited when its position among the nine other positions, i. e., in the whole system of all possible positions of the reason, is clearly shown in a table.

The fourth fallacy of an uncertain reason, the one occupying the under corner to the right in Dignāga's table, consists in its partial presence on both sides, in one part of the similar as well as in one part of the dissimilar instances. Dignāga gives the following example[1]— «the sounds of speech are eternal entities, because they are not bodies». A body is a physical entity of limited dimensions. In the similar field, among eternal entities, we find the eternal atoms of the Vaišeṣikas which are bodies and are eternal. But we also find Space which is eternal and not a body of limited dimensions. In the dissimilar field of non-eternal, changing entities we find jars etc. which are bodies; and we find motion which is not a body. On

[1] NB. and NBT., p.66. 12; transl., p. 183.

the analogy of atoms we would conclude that sounds are unchanging. On the analogy of motion we would conclude that they are changing. The position of the reason is quite uncertain, the uncertainty is here at its maximum.

The maximum of inconsistency is found in the contrary reason, the maximum of comprehension in the over-wide fallacy, the minimum of comprehension in the over-narrow one, and the maximum of uncertainty in its fourth variety. The easiest and most natural fallacy is found in the third variety.

§ 5. The Antinomical Fallacy.

Independently from the 9 positions of the middle term, in respect of instances similar and dissimilar, Dignāga mentions a special fallacy which he refers to the uncertain class, although it has no place in his table. The table is supposed to be exhaustive and its items exclusive of each another. That supplementary reason however, if it is to be inserted in the table, would simultaneously occupy two positions, the positions of the right reason (No. 4 or 6) and of the inverted or contrary one (No. 2 or 8). For it is right and inverted at the same time, it is counterbalanced. Every uncertain reason contains a fluctuation between two opposite possibilities. The characteristic of such uncertainty is the absence of any decision, the mental attitude is doubt. But when the two opposed solutions are asserted with equal strength, the mental attitude is not doubt, but certainty. There are at once two certainties; both stand, although, on consideration, they ought to exclude one another according to the law of contradiction. The Vaišeṣikas theory of the reality of Universals and the opposite theory of their unreality are quoted as an instance of antinomy. The problem of the infinity and finiteness of Time and Space, which are formulated already in the earliest records of Buddhism, could perhaps have afforded a better example. Dignāga states that such antinomies are possible predominantly in metaphysics and religion and adds the remark[1] that «in this world the force of direct perception and of authority of scripture is (sometimes) stronger than any argument». Notwithstanding this limitation, Dharmakīrti accuses his Master of having introduced into the domain of logic a translogical element. «The proper domain of inference, says he, is the threefold logical tie, (i. e., the necessary

1 Nyāya-mukha, p. 35 of Tucci's translation.

presence of the reason upon the subject, its necessary presence in similar and absolute absence in all dissimilar instances). This threefold logical connection, as far as it is established by positive facts... produces inference. Therefore we call it the domain of inference... Since real inference alone is our subject matter, we cannot deal with a reason which is at once right and wrong... A double reason which is right and contradictory is not something established on real facts».[1] Since inference is founded on the three laws of Identity, Causality and Negation only, he then continues — «therefore in order that there should be a real contradiction, the effect must exist altogether without its real cause, or a property must exist somewhere beyond the concept under which it is contained. Negation then should also be something different from what has been established by us». These three relations — and there are no others — afford no opportunity for contradiction or antinomy. «When the argument is founded on the properly observed real condition of real things... there is no room for antinomy».[2] In the dialectic syllogism which borrows its principles from dogmatic beliefs of some sort and does not deduce its conclusion from principles obtained by Induction, such fallacies are possible. Therefore the antinomical argument must be distinguished from the real or demonstrative syllogism.

§ 6. Dharmakīrti's additions.

The opposition of Dharmakīrti against the antinomical reason is remarkable. As a matter of fact Dignāga does not seem to insist upon this kind of fallacy and does not differ substantially from Dhamakīrti's estimate of it. But the latter seized this opportunity to insist on the strict correspondence between the canon of syllogistic rules and the varieties of fallacy. «There are only three kinds of fallacy, says he, the Unreal, the Contrary and the Uncertain. They are respectively produced when either one rule singly or a pair of them simultaneously are either wrong or uncertain». «Respectively, says Dharmottara, means that each fallacy is determined by the unreality or the doubt which is inherent in the unreality or the doubt concerning the corresponding rule».[3] The antinomic or counterbalanced fallacy being outside this scheme is repudiated.

---

1 NBT., p. 80. 21 ff.; transl., p. 221.

2 Ibid.; transl., p. 222.

3 NB., p. 80.6; transl., p. 220.

But logic evidently cannot remain absolutely desinterested before metaphysical and religious problems. Having emphatically closed the very modest entrance which was left for it by Dignāga, Dharmakīrti reintroduces it by a kind of back door in the shape of two additional fallacies which, he thought, could be forced into the accepted scheme. The religious problem of the Omniscient, the mahāyānistic divine Buddha and the counterproblem of the Soul receive each of them from Dharmakīrti an additional item in the final scheme of fallacies.

The problem of the Soul is formulated in the following Syllogism.[1] «The living body possesses a Soul, because it possesses breath and other animal functions». The reason is not unreal, since it is found in the subject. But its concomitance is uncertain. The Realists maintain that the concomitance is proved in a «purely negative» way. Animal functions being admittedly absent in things which possess no Soul, their presence becomes a valid reason for establishing *per differentiam* the presence of a Soul wherever they be present. The treatment of the problem by Dharmakīrti is purely logical. He does not appeal to the Buddhist dogma of Soul denial.[2] But in logic he does not admit any «purely positive» or «purely negative» reason. He, for the sake of argument, admits that there are similar and dissimilar instances, objects possessing a Soul and objects not possessing it, and that this feature is present somewhere among living and unliving things. But the necessary connection of one class with the presence of the Soul and of the other class with its absence is not established. Both the second and the third rule of the canon are infringed, because, even admitting that the Soul exists somewhere, the presence of the reason in similar instances *only* and its necessary absence in *all* dissimilar instances are uncertain. Therefore the reason is uncertain. «Neither can we affirm on such grounds, says he, the necessary connection of a Soul with a living body, nor can we deny it».[3]

In connection with the theory of an Omniscient Absolute Being Dharmakīrti has added another fallacy which is slightly distinguished from Dignāga's reason No. 7. It is present in similar instances, but

1 NB., p. 75.20; transl., p. 208 ff.

2 Śrīdhara quotes the argument of Dharmakīrti and rejects it, cp. N. kandalī, p. 204.5, thus introducing into the Vaiśeṣika system the *kevala-vyatireki-hetu* which Praśastapāda ignores, cp. p. 201.

3 NB. and NBT., p. 79.23; transl., p. 219.

its absence in dissimilar ones is uncertain.[1] In the preceding fallacy there was uncertainty regarding both the 2-d and the 3-d rule of the canon. In the present one the 2-d rule is not infringed, but the third contains a problem that cannot be solved. The formulation is the following one: «Some human being is non-omniscient, because he possesses the faculty of speech and other (attributes of a human being)». The presence of the faculty of speech in that human being is ascertained. The first rule is realized. The reason is not «unreal». Its presence in similar instances, i. e., in non-omniscient ordinary people, is also ascertained. The 2-d rule is thus realized. But its absence in the dissimilar instances, i. e., the absence of the faculty of speech in omniscient beings, remains for ever a problem, since an omniscient being is a metaphysical and translogical entity. We cannot with certainty maintain that he does not exist altogether, because a negative judgment depends on experience. It is no use to deny a thing that never has been experienced. The denial will be void of any sense, as will be shown in the section on the negative judgment. Since the 3-d rule of the canon is thus infringed, the reason is uncertain. The origin of the example is probably due to the consideration that Absolute Reality, being something unutterable, the Omniscient Being will not express it in human language which is fitted to express only the general and vague notions constructed by imagination.[2] It coincides with the idea expressed by Dharmakīrti in other works,[3] the idea namely that we can neither cognize nor express omniscience. The Omniscient Being just as the Absolute Truth or Ultimate Reality is unutterable because incognizable, and every predicate referred to it, whether positive or negative, will remain problematic and uncertain. The formulation of the example may be due to purely formal combinations of three notions in different arrangements. It is not impossible that this example, just as the foregoing one, contain a point against the Nayāyika theory of a purely negative reason. Since all ordinary people are non-omniscient, the non-ordinary being must be omniscient. This deduction is rejected on the score that omniscience and speech are not contradictorily opposed. The presence of one of these attributes does not justify the conclusion denying the presence of the other.[4]

---

1 NB. and NBT., p. 66.16 ff.; transl., p. 184 ff.

2 Cp. NK., p. 112. 24—*upadešo... buddhādīnām sarvajñatva-abhāva-sādhanam.*

3 Cp. the concluding passage of Santānāntara-siddhi, p. 49 of my Russian translation.

4 NB. and NBT., p. 71.1 ff.; transl., p. 198.

As stated above, these two new varieties of the «uncertain» fallacy introduced by Dharmakīrti in replacement of Dignāga's antinomical fallacy differ from the latter but very slightly. All such fallacies are concerned with metaphysical objects and are problematic for that very reason. They are not strictly logical, because they transfer us beyond the sphere of logic.

§ 7. History.

a) Manuals on Dialectics.

Logic, the science of truth, in its beginnings in India, is much more concerned about the classification of error than about an investigation of truth. «Manuals on the Respondent's Failures» [1] were apparently in vogue at a date when the theory of the methods of right cognition [2] was not yet elaborated. The Aphorisms of the Nyāya-school contain such a manual appended to them, which evidently was originally an independent treatise.

When the Buddhists in the age of Asanga and Vasubandhu took up the study of Logic, they also composed such manuals which did not differ substantially from the one appended to the Nyāya-aphorisms. This manual contains an enumeration of 22 instances where the respondent committing a mistake deserves to be rebuked by his opponent and the contest is then declared lost for him by the presiding judge. The regular debate required the presence of a respondent,[3] a questioner or opponent [4] and an impartial judge [5] who was also entitled to pass remarks and put questions. The Manual on the Respondent's Failures was evidently a manual for the judge, its composition the result of a long experience in the practice of the art of debating, which resulted in the establishment of a system of type-instances and laws regulating the debate. The shortcomings which can be really or intentionnally imputed to the respondent are the following ones—

1) annihilation of one's own thesis (by an unsuitable example),

2) shifting to another thesis (during the same debate),

3) a contradictory thesis,

---

1 *nigraha-sthāna-śāstra.*

2 *pramāṇa.*

3 *pūrva-pakṣin.*

4 *uttara-pakṣin = prati-pakṣin = pratidvandvin.*

5 *madhyastha = prāśnika = sabhya.*

4) abandoning one's own thesis,

5—6) changing the reason or the topic,

7—10) a meaningless, unintelligible, incoherent or inopportune argument,

11—12) insufficiency or redundancy in expression,

13) repetition,

14) silence,

15) confession of ignorance,

16) failing to understand (the question),

17) stopping the debate under the pretext of going to attend another business when seeing that the defeat is inevitable,

18) (indirect) admission of a charge,

19—20) neglecting to rebuke the questioner when it is necessary or doing so when it is not necessary,

21) not keeping faithfully to one's own principles,

22) fallacious logical reasons.

The position of the last item is remarkable. It does not seem to be the principle shortcoming, but its fate has been to oust and supersede all the others. Moreover it is repeated in another place of the same Nyāya-aphorisms where in connection with the theory of the syllogism five varieties of a fallacious logical reasons are established.[1] This is an indirect proof of the hybrid origin of the treatise known under the name of the Nyāya-aphorisms. Its composition evidently belongs to that period in the development of Indian logic when the importance of a clear theory of the syllogism begins to dawn. The earliest commentator Vātsyāyana already characterizes syllogism as true logic, the tip-top of logical science.[2] The right application of the *modus ponens* and *modus tollens,* he says, is the characteristic feature of a first class scholar.[3]

Nevertheless the part devoted to inference and syllogism in the Nyāya-aphorisms is meagre as compared with the chapters on dialectical failures which, in compliance with tradition, are treated in detail. Vasubandhu, it seems, composed a manual on the Respondent's Failures, but Dignāga resolved to drop the corresponding chapter altogether, on the score that it includes either such points which must be formulated in a refutative syllogism or quite irrelevant

---

[1] NS., I. 2. 4.

[2] *paramo nyāyaḥ,* NBh., p. 5. 5.

[3] *paṇḍita-rūpa,* ibid., p. 43. 7.

matter which does not belong to the province of logic at all.[1] The chapter disappears completely in post-Dignāgan logic.

Just as this chapter, or separate manual, on the Failures of the Respondent, the early litterature possessed manuals, or chapters, on the Failures of the Opponent called Wrong Refutations, or Refutations having the semblance of refutation without the reality. Such refutations are mostly counter-arguments founded on false analogy. E. g., when the respondent asserts that «sound is non-eternal, because it is the effect of some effort, like a jar», the opponent meets him by the counter-argument «sound is eternal, because it is not a body of limited dimensions, like illimited Space. Whatsoever is not a body of limited dimensions must be eternal, etc.» The Nyāya-aphorisms contain a separate chapter enumerating 24 varieties of such Sophistical Refutations. Vasubandhu likewise composed a manual on them in which he reduced their number. Dignāga has not dropped this chapter altogether, but he has made a further reduction of type-instances to 14 varieties. He nevertheless does not attach much importance to this subject and says that the varieties of such wrong refutations are infinite,[2] they cannot be digested in any classes. Post-Dignāgan logic likewise drops this chapter altogether. Wrong refutations are wrong syllogisms and are nothing but logical fallacies of which an exhaustive system has been established by Dignāga.

Ambiguous speech, this most prolific source of fallacies and sophisms, is not mentioned neither among the Failures of the Respondent, nor among the methods of wrong Refutation. It is relegated to another chapter where the different types of debate are considered. Three sources of ambiguity are here mentioned. Homonymia[3] or equivocal words, Amphibolia or equivocal propositions[4] and metaphors.[5] Ambiguous speech is used by a dishonest agressor who aims at being victorious at all cost.

The debate was in India, just as in Ancient Greece, either didactic and peirastic,[6] or dialectical and sophistic.[7] In a *bona fide* debate between two honest debators or between a teacher and a pupil, in

---

1 Cp. N. mukha, transl., p. 71.
2 N. mukha, transl., p. 71.
3 *vāk-chala.*
4 *sāmānya-chala.*
5 *upacāra-chala.*
6 *vāda.*
7 *jalpa-vitaṇḍe.*

the presence of impartial judges, a thesis and a contra-thesis must be defended only by honest means, by facts and hypotheses.[1] But in a dialectical or sophistic debate the opponent eager for victory at all cost does not care for truth at all and has recourse to ambiguous speech, false refutations and false accusations[2] with the only object of imposing upon the audience and attaining victory. Ambiguity, sophistical accusations and sophistical refutations were also allowed to the *bona fide* debators, but not as a principle method of proof. If he had succeeded in establishing his own thesis by facts and sound hypotheses, but was nevertheless assailed by dishonest agressors, he was allowed to answer in the same spirit; not indeed in order to prove what has already been established in a normal way, but to protect truth against agression and to exhibit the inanity of the latter. Just as seeds are protected from birds by a layer of thorny twigs, just so is the honest debator allowed to use the thorny arguments of sophistry in order to dispel the semblance of victory on the part of an unscrupulous sophist.

b) The refutative syllogism of the Mādhyamikas.

Thus the dialectic debate which Dignāga found current in India allowed the use of ambiguity, unreal accusations and unreal refutations, albeit not for the final and peremptory establishment of truth, but for its test and defense against sophistic agressors. The dialectic procedure is from its beginning intrinsically contentious. It is permissible to make use of sophistry against the Sophist. There are however two different kinds of sophistical debate. Their common feature is ultimate disregard for logic and eagerness to gain victory at all cost. But in doing so the one sophist proposes to defend a real thesis while defending a semblance of it by dishonest means. The other proposes openly not to defend any real thesis at all, he simply undertakes it to destroy whatever argument be advanced against him. He is honest in a way, because he does not believe in logic altogether. Sophistry then ceases to be sophistry, because its most characteristic feature, dishonesty of purpose and of expedients, is absent. The object of a dialectical discussion is to convict an opponent of inconsistency. The assailant has gained his point if he can reduse the defendant to the necessity of contradicting himself. This according to a class of philosophers

---

1 *pramāṇa-tarka.*

2 *chala-jāti-nigrahasthāna.*

can always be done. The human mind is always in contradiction with itself, it is intrinsically dialectical. If a realistic philosopher who believes in congruence of logic with objective reality resorts to this kind of negative procedure, he is untrue to himself, his method is dishonest cavil. But for Buddhists reality is something quite different from logic. For a certain class of Buddhists truth consists in the negation of logic. Truth according to the conviction of these men will emerge from the destruction of all logic. This truth is the world of the mystic. It is cognized by the logical Method of Residues,[1] as a residue from the destruction of logic, it is translogical. The school of the Mādhyamikas identified itself with this method. Candrakīrti delivers himself in the following way[2]—

«It is indeed a general rule that the opponent should be at length induced to agree with that very line of argument which the respondent himself has set forth in order to prove his thesis. But (the case of the Mādhyamika is quite different). He does not vindicate any assertion in order to convince his opponent. He has no *bona fide* reasons and examples (of which he himself is convinced). He sets forth a (contra)-thesis of his own, and undertakes to prove it only so far it runs parallel and destroys the argument of his opponent. He thus brings assertions that cannot be proved. He is in conflict even with himself. He certainly cannot convince his opponent (of this imagined thesis). But can there be a more eloquent refutation of an opponent than the proof that he is not capable of establishing his own thesis? Is there really any necessity to produce any further argument?»

Every syllogism according to this school[3] is a fallacy, because it entails a contradictory syllogism, called «entailed inference, or counter-syllogism»[4] of the same force. The school received from this feature its second name as a school of the counter-syllogism (*Prāsangika*).

Buddhist Monism was thus established in the school of the Extreme Relativists (Mādhyamika-Prāsangika) not on logical grounds, but on a wholesale destruction of all logic. However this utter disregard for logic soon gave way to another attitude in the same school. A new branch of it was founded by Bhavya, (Bhāva-viveka), who

1 *pāriśeṣyāt,* cp. Tātp., p. 226.

2 Cp. my Nirvāna, p. 95.

3 As mentioned above, p. 29, the later Vedāntins have made this method their own. Srīharṣa bluntly calls himself a vaitaṇḍika and says that the Mādhyamika method cannot be upset by logic.

4 *prasanga-anumāṇa.*

maintained that it was impossible to escape from logical methods altogether. Even if you intend to establish that all syllogisms are fallacies you must do it by a sound argument thrown into the form of a correct syllogism.[1] In distinction from the school of the Counter-syllogism the new school was called a school of the Independent Syllogism.[2] Asanga was the first to introduce dialectic and logic among the subjects studied by a Bodhisattva, without forsaking the principles of Monism,[3] and Vasubandhu followed by taking up the study of dialectic according to the Nyāya system. He thus initiated that reform which was brought to its full development by Dignāga and Dharmakīrti.

What the system of logical fallacies established by Vasubandhu has been, we do not know precisely. But since the canon of syllogistic rules has been established by him, and since Dignāga's system of fallacies is established in strict correspondence with this canon, and since we already find the main items of this system in the Vaišeṣika school, we may presume that Vasubandhu's system was probably either the same or slightly different from the one of Dignāga.

Dignāga's system influenced the teaching of the Vaišeṣika and the Nyāya schools and we will now proceed to examine that influence on their doctrine of logical fallacies.

c) The Vaišesika system influenced by the Buddhists.

The Aphorisms of Kaṇāda do not concern themselves about the rules of debate and dialectic. But they contain a definition of inference,[4] an enumeration of relations upon which inference is founded[5] and the statement that the connection of the Logical Reason (with the Subject and Logical Consequence) must be «well known», i. e. definitely established.[6] If it is not definitely established, it is a non-reason,[7] or a Logical Fallacy. Fallacious reasons, they then procede to state, are «either unreal or uncertain».[8] What the precise implications of these terms were at the time of Kaṇāda we are not able to

---

1 *svatantra-anumāṇa.*

2 *svātantrika.*

3 Cp. Obermiller's translation of the Uttaratantra of Maitreya-Asanga.

4 VS., IX. 1. 1.

5 Ibid.

6 Ibid., III. 1. 13.

7 Ibid., III. 1. 14.

8 Ibid., III. 1. 15.

tell, since there is no old commentary available, but we can guess with great probablility from their names that these fallacies corresponded to the two main classes of Dignāga, the Unreal and the Uncertain one. In this point, as well as in some others, the Vaiśeṣikas, notwithstanding their realism, seem to have been the precursors of the Buddhist reform.[1] Whether this or some other reasons encouraged Praśastapāda to read into the text of Kaṇāda the full blown syllogistic theory of Dignāga without, of course, its epistemological foundation it is difficult for us to decide.[2] He begins by enunciating the exact Buddhist canon of the three syllogistic rules and by stating that the violation of one of these rules, or of a pair of them, produces a «non-reason» which will be either unreal or uncertain or contrary. He bluntly asserts that this doctrine belongs to Kāśyapa, i. e., to Kaṇāda himself, although nothing but the double division of fallacies (in unreal and uncertain) can be detected in them as partly similar

---

1 The VS., II. 2. 22 contains moreover a definition of an uncertain reason which in its substance coincides with Dignāga's definition of uncertainty as presence both in the similar (*tulya-jātīya*) and dissimilar (*arthāntara-bhūta*) instances. Praśastapāda, p. 239. 14, mentions this sūtra in connection with the varieties of fallacies.

2 The dependence of Praśastapāda upon Dignāga has been established in my paper Rapports entre la théorie bouddhique de la connaissance et l'enseignement des autres écoles de philosophie de l'Inde (Muséon, V, p. 129. ff). He has borrowed from Dignāga 1) the division of *anumāna* in *svārtha* and *parārtha*, 2) the *trirūpa-linga*, 3) the 4 inadmissible theses, 4) the fallacious examples, 5) the three classes of fallacies which he rearranged in four classes by adding the hybrid class of *anadhyavasita*. — Prof. H N. Randle (Ind. Logic, p. 31) ascribes to me an opinion which I have never expressed, at least in the form in which he puts it, viz., «that Dignāga's logic is derived through Vasubandhu from Praśastapāda». Neither have I ever assumed that «there was no development in the Vaiśeṣika school between the Sūtra and Praśastapāda». We now know that the *trairūpya* theory was already contained in Vasubandhu's works. It is true, I have pointed to some suspicious similarities between Vasubandhu and Praśastapāda, as well as to some affinities between Budhhists, especially of the Vātsīputrīya school and the Vaiśeṣikas. We cannot here deny the possibility of mutual influencing and borrowing at an early date. But the developed *trairūpya* theory is esentially Buddhistic. Its aim is the establishment of necessary inseparable connection, which the Realists deny. The relation of logical necessity (*niścaya*) to transcendental reality (*paramārtha-sat*) is involved. This was perfectly understood by the Realists. Vācaspati, NVTT., p. 127, introduces the Buddhist theory by quoting Dignāga who says that «logic (*anumāna-anumeya-bhāva*) is apart from reality (*na sad-asad' apekṣate*)». That is also the reason why Uddyotakara attacks *trairūpya* so vehemently. He hardly would have displayed so much animosity against a Vaiśeṣika or a Sāṅkhya theory.

to the Buddhist scheme.[1] He then supplements this double division by two other classes which correspond to Dignāga's «contrary» and «antinomic» fallacies. In order to ascribe this innovation likewise to Kaṇāda he performs a surgical operation[2] in the text of the aphorisms and artificially constructs in them four classes instead of the two which are actually to be found. He thus adds to the unreal and uncertain reason the contrary one and the «null and void» reason. The «contrary» reason is an inverted reason, it proves the contradictorily opposed fact with respect to the fact it was intended to establish. It is a fallacy at its maximum, e. g., «this is a horse, because it has horns» instead of «this is not a horse, because it has horns». The «null and void» reason is of a hybrid descent. It includes, first of all, Dignāga's «over-narrow» fallacy, the fallacy of the type «sound is non-eternal (or eternal), because it is audible». This reason, we have seen, occupies in Dignāga's table the central position (No. 5) as the limit or the null point of deductive force.[3] With this poorest shape of all reasons Prašastapāda identifies the antinomical reason which Dignāga refers to the «uncertain» class.[4] «There are some philosophers, says Prašastapāda,[5] (and Dignāga is evidently aimed at), who maintain that when two reasons (of equal strength) contradict

---

1 It is striking that Prašasta after having perverted sūtras III. 1. 14—15 justifies himself in saying, p. 204, that thus the Sūtrakāra will have the same system of fallacies as Kāšyapa (*etad eva āha*). But he does not care at all to connect the *trairūpya* with some sūtra. The position is such that the *trairūpya* is derived entirely from Kāšyapa, but his system of fallacies can be found also in the sūtras, if an alteration is introduced. Who is this mysterious Kāšyapa? After all is it not Dignāga or Vasubandhu?

2 This operation which is very much in vogue among grammarians is technically called *yoga-vibhāga*; it consists in artificially either uniting two sūtras into one or dividing one into two and thus creating a new sense. By uniting VS., III. 1. 14 with the following sūtra the sense is created that the *anapadeša* (= *ahetu*) is either *aprasiddha* or *asan* or *sandigdha,* cp. Prašast., p. 204. 26. By interpreting *aprasiddha* as meaning *viruddha* we have Dignāga's threefold division. But p. 238. 9 ff. Prašasta adds a fourth class which includes Dignāga's *asādhāraṇa* and *viruddha-avyabhicāri* and is called by him *anadhyavasita.* This term we can translate as «null and void», since *adhyavasāya* means judgment, *anadhyavasita* is «non-judging». Cp. on this point Jacobi, Ind. Logik, p. 481, Keith; Ind. Logic, p. 133, 139; Faddegon, Vaišeṣ. syst., p. 302.

3 On the reasons which compelled Dignāga to include it cp. Nyāya-mukha, transl., p. 33.

4 Ibid., pp. 31, 35, 60.

5 p. 239.

one another, doubt arises and the reason is uncertain. But we will prove that such a reason is «null and void»,[1] just as the «over-narrow»[2] reason. Prašastapāda apparently thinks that when two reasons are mutually destructive, they may be reasons if considered singly,[3] but they are «non-reasons» if they combine in one subject, since their combination is found in the subject only. There are neither similar nor dissimilar instances where this combination could be met with.[4] This forcible and artificial interpretation Prašastapāda puts in an aphorism of Kaṇāda which has nothing to do with it. The domain assigned by Dignāga to antinomical reasoning are metaphysical and religious problems. They are translogical and always uncertain. Both contradictory reasons have equal strength, a decision is impossible. But for Prašastapāda contrary to religion means contrary to truth. He therefore divides Dignāga's antinomical reason in two halves. The one he refers to the «contrary» class and the other to the «null and void» class. In the domain of religion an argument contradicting an established dogma is a fallacy. It is repudiated and referred to the «contrary» class, the class containing fallacy at its maximum. But in profane metaphysics when two conflicting arguments have equal strength they nullify the reasoning and must be referred, together with the «over-narrow» class, to the «null and void» variety.[5]

---

1 *anadhyavasita.*

2 *asādhāraṇa.*

3 The real ground why these two disparate reasons are thrown into the same bag in order to form a class of hybrid descent may, however, be another one, cp. the second note below.

4 VS., III. 1. 14, cp. Prašastap., p. 239. 13.

5 It is clear from Nyāya-mukha, transl., pp. 31—34, that some opponents of Dignāga excluded the *asādhāraṇa* (which is in the Wheel) and the *viruddha-avyabhicārin* (which is not in the Wheel, or must occupy in it simultaneously the positions Nos. 2 and 4) from the number of six *anaikāntika*'s, thus reducing their number to four items situated at the four corners of the table (Nos. 1, 3, 7 and 9). They thus threw the *asādhāraṇa* and the *viruddha-avyabhicārin* into the same bag as «non-reasons», as not even inconclusive reasons. This is exactly what Prašastapāda is doing in referring them both to the «null and void» (*anadhy-avasita*) class. Does that mean that Dignāga in this passage combats Prašastapāda or some of his predecessors? In the first case the passage would be a confirmation of Faddegon's and my hypothesis that both these authors were contemporaries, cp. the Nachtrag to the German transl. of my Erkenntnisstheorie u. Logik (München, 1920). Tucci (Buddhist Logic before Dignāga, p. 483) thinks that Prašastapāda borrowed from some predecessor of Dignāga, but he seems to have changed his opinion, cp. Nyāya-mukha, transl., p. 31, 58.

Thus Prašastapāda, the second legislator of the Vaišeṣika system, has transformed its logic by trying to imbibe in it some principles of Dignāga's formal logic. As fallacies he borrowed 1) the four fallacious theses, and 2) the threefold scheme of fallacious reasons, which he however remodeled into a fourfold division. In the unified Nyāya-Vaišeṣika system, we shall see, the fallacious theses have been dropped, and the system of fallacious reasons changed into a five-fold division.

The following table illustrates the influence of Dignāga upon Prašastapāda and the influence of the latter upon Bhāsarvajña.

Table showing the influence of Dignāga on the Vaišeṣika system of Fallacies.

Vaiš. Sūtra	*Dignāga*	*Prašastapāda*	*Bhāsarvajña*
1. asat	1. asiddha	1. asiddha	1. asiddha
2. sandigdha	2. anaikāntika (*incl.* asādhāraṇa and viruddha-avyabhicārin)	2. sandigdha (*excl.* asādhāraṇa *and* viruddha-avyabhicārin)	2. anaikāntika (*excl.* asādhār. *and* vir.-avyabhic.)
	3. viruddha	3. viruddha	3. viruddha
		4. anadhyavasita (= asādhāraṇa + viruddha-avyabhicārin)	4. anadhyavasita (= asādhāraṇa)
			5. sat-pratipakṣa (= viruddha-avyabhicārin)
	4. pakṣābhāsa	5. pakṣābhāsa	6. bādhita (= pakṣābhāsa)

d) The Nyāya system influenced by Dignāga.

The attitude of the Nyāya school towards the Buddhists is quite different from the attitude of the Vaišeṣikas. In substance both

---

The union of such disparate items as the *asādhāraṇa* and the *viruddha-avyabhicārin* would hardly be comprehensible if it were not preceded by the polemics alluded to in Nyāya-mukha, p. 31 ff.

these realistic schools are doing the same thing, they borrow without acknowledging. But the Vaišeṣikas are reticent and polite, the Naiyāyikas, on the contrary, are clamorous and abusive. Uddyotakara rejects Dignāga's theory of the Three Aspects of the Logical Mark. He vehemently assails its phrasing as well as its substance. He says the theory looks as if it were formulated by a fool. According to him the logical mark is not at all bound to have always three aspects. Some valid conclusions can be drawn from positive examples alone, the negative being absent. Other conclusions need only negative examples, the positive being lacking. This means supplementing Dignāga's reason which always has examples positive and negative (it always has them because both sides mutually imply one another), by two other classes, the one with merely positive examples, the other with merely negative ones. Indeed Uddyotakara is the originator of the Nayāyika division of logical reasons in purely positive, purely negative and hybrid, positive-negative. His vehement assault thus results in a tacit acceptance of Dignāga's scheme with the addition of the purely-positive and purely-negative reasons.

However when the author of the Uddyota faces the problem of logical fallacies, he again makes a show of rejecting Dignāga's principle of classification, but in reality he surreptitiously and with additions introduces it into his own system.[1]

Vātsyāyana comments upon a fivefold division of fallacious reasons established in the aphorisms of Gotama — the uncertain,[2] the

---

[1] To the 9 positions of Dignāga among similars and dissimilars, Uddyotakara adds 1) five positions with no dissimilars at all, 2) three positions with no similars at all, 3) one position where both the similars and the dissimilars are absent, since the subject embraces the sum-total of existing things (as in the pattern *sarvam-anityam kṛtakatvāt*, the subject embraces everything existing, there neither are similars nor dissimilars). This makes together 16 varieties of concomitance. Multiplying it by three varieties of the minor premise (in subject wholly, in subject partly, in subject absence) we shall have 48 varieties. Now in every one of these 48 varieties the reason can be either true (*siddha*) or untrue (*asiddha*), either relevant (*samartha*) or irrelevant (*asamartha*). By taking from the 48 varieties the first two sets of 16 varieties and by multiplying them by 4 we shall arrive at the number of 64 + 64 = 128, and adding to them the 48 original varieties with unqualified reasons, we shall get the number 176. But that is only the beginning of the play. By introducing further differentiations we arrive at the final number of 2032 reasons.

[2] *savyabhicāra*, NS., I. 2. 5, is by the meaning of its name and by its substance the same as *anaikāntika*. It is a fallacy of concomitance (*vyāptir na bhavati*).

contrary,[1] the unproved,[2] the undecided[3] and the mis-timed.[4] From these five items the first two evidently correspond to the uncertain and contrary classes of Dignāga. But the three remaining ones, in the interpretation given them by Vātsyāyana, overlap the whole field of fallacies, since every fallacy is more or less unproved, undecided and mis-timed. Uddyotakara asks, whatfor is the fivefold division introduced, and answers that the aim is to give an exhaustive classification of logical fallacies. «But how many are the varieties of reasons false and right which are current (among human kind)?» he continues to ask, and gives the following answer, «The varieties which are conditioned by circumstances of time, individual character and (every kind of) object are infinite; but the varieties of right and wrong reasons in their connection with the deduced facts (i. e., the varieties of the purely logical connection of reason and consequence), when systematized, are generally speaking one hundred and seventy six». And even when the computation of new varieties produced by new qualifications be continued we will easily arrive at the number of 2032 varieties of possible reasons, says Uddyotakara.[5]

Now what is the aim of this ridiculous exaggeration? Uddyotakara well knows that every sound principle can be reduced *ad absurdum* by exaggeration. His aim is to overdo Dignāga and to bluff the

---

1 *viruddha*, NS., I. 2. 6, is the reason contradicting one's owu principles. It corresponds to the *iṣṭavighātakṛt* of Dignāga, it is a special case of the *viruddha* as stated by Dharmakīrti, cp. NB., p. 73, 10; transl., p. 203.

2 *sādhya-sama*, NS., I. 2. 8, is, according to Gotama and Vātsyāyana, *petitio principii*. But U. converts it into Dignāga's *asiddha*, since it includes according to him the *āśraya-asiddha*. According to Dignāga, Gotama's sūtra refers to an inference where the example does not differ from the *probandum* (Tātp., p. 238. 27), but U. objects and converts it into the threefold *asiddha-āśraya*, *prajñāpanīya* (= *sādhya*) *asiddha* and *anyathā-siddha*. In later Nyāya it roughly corresponds to Dignāga's *asiddha*.

3 *prakaraṇa-sama*, NS., I. 2. 7, is easily converted in the *sat-pratipakṣa*, «counterbalanced» or «antinomic» reason.

4 *kalātyaya-apadiṣṭa*, NS., I. 2. 9; its meaning was very differently understood at Vātsyāyana's time (cp. p. 54. 11). Vācaspatimiśra explained that «mistimed» means a reason which is not even worthly of being considered, since it is beyond «the moment when it could be affecting our inquisitiveness» (*saṃśaya-kālam atipatitaḥ*). It is thus identified with the inadmissible theses of Dignāga and includes the same varieties in later unified Nyāya-Vaiśeṣika.

5 Cp. upon the system of Uddyotakara the very interesting remarks of Prof. S. Stasiak in his article «Fallacies and their Classification according to the Early Hindu Logicians» in Rocznik Orientalistyczny, t. VI, p. 191 ff.

naive reader by an exhibition of extraordinary cleverness. Dignāga has established according to a mathematical principle 9 positions of the reason. «Well nigh, I will establish mathematically 2032 positions!» But he confesses that this number is unimportant, it is a mere modification of the fundamental number. Important is, on the contrary, the principle that the purely logical fallacies must exist in a fixed number and are capable of being arranged in a systematical table. This fundamental idea is borrowed by Uddyotakara from Dignaga and the figure of 176 or 2032 is nothing but an artificial derivative and amplified, bluffing form of Dignāga's 9 items. Uddyotakara admits 1) that a purely logical fallacy is produced by the overlapping of the middle term in the forbidden domain of dissimilar instances; when the overlapping is complete, the reason becomes contrary; 2) that the possible positions of the middle term regarding the instances similar and dissimilar can be mathematically computed, and 3) that the number of fallacies thus arrived at must agree with the number of syllogistic rules determining the position of the reason between these similar and dissimilar instances. In the Buddhist system the rules are three and the classes of fallacies also three. Uddyotakara was not free to change the number of five classes of fallacies, since this number was consecrated by the authority of Gotama and Vātsyāyana, but he changed completely their interpretation and constructed in accordance with this new interpretation the number of five rules instead of three. The proportion between the number of injunctions and the number of prohibitions was thus saved. The five rules are the following ones:

1) presence in the subject,
2) presence in similar instances,
3) absence from dissimilar instances,
4) being non-antinomic,
5) being not repudiated (from the start).

The first three rules coincide with the Buddhist canon, the fourth is constructed in accordance with Dignāga's «antinomical» reason and the fifth replaces his fallacious theses, which are dropped as theses, but introduced as reasons, according to the new principle that every fallacy is a fallacy of the reason. The corresponding five classes of fallacious reasons are 1) the uncertain, corresponding to Dignāga's uncertain, 2) the contrary corresponding to Dignāga's contrary, 3) the unreal corresponding to Dignāga's unreal, 4) the antinomical corresponding to the same of Dignāga, 5) the «repudiated» corresponding to the four impossible theses of Dignāga.

The following table illustrates the development of the system of Fallacies in the Nyāya school. It will be noticed that the borrowings of Bhāsarvajña presuppose the borrowings of Praśastapāda.

Table showing the influence of Dignāga on the Nyāya system of Fallacies.

Nyāya Sūtra and Bhāṣya	*Dignāga*	*Uddyotakara*	*Bhāsarvajña*	*Gangeśa*
1. savyabhicāra	1. anaikāntika	1. savyabhicāra	1. anaikāntika	1. savyabhicāra
2. viruddha	2. viruddha	2. viruddha	2. viruddha	2. viruddha
3. prakaraṇa-sama	—	—	—	—
4. sādhya-sama	—	—	—	—
5. kālātīta	—	—	—	—
	3. asiddha	3. sādhya-sama (= asiddha)	3. asiddha	3. sādhya-sama (= asiddha)
	4. asādhāraṇa (*included* in anaikāntika)		4. anadhyavasita (cp. Praśastapāda)	
	5. viruddha-avyabhicārin (*included* in anaikāntika)	4. prakaraṇa-sama	5. sat-pratipakṣa	4. sat-pratipakṣa
	6. pakṣābhāsa	5. kālātīta	6. bādhita	5. bādhita

§ 8. European Parallels.

There is perhaps no other chapter of European Logic in which such helpless confusion reigns as the chapter on Logical Fallacies. The opinion of the majority of modern authors seems to be that truth may have its norms, but not error. The sources and kinds of error, according to 'them, are infinite as life itself and cannot be digested into any coherent system. They therefore resolved to drop the chapter on Logical Fallacies altogether. Neither Sigwart, nor B. Erdmann, nor Schuppe, nor Wundt, nor Bradley, nor Bosanquet etc. devote any consideration to this capital problem. The Aristotelian classification survives in some modern works. Its principle has been pronounced illogical and new arrangements have been proposed, nevertheless his enumeration has not been materially increased.[1] Archbishop Whately who has done his best to improve it by an arrangement more logical, is led to confess that «it must be often a matter of doubt, or rather of arbitrary choice, not only to which genus each kind of fallacy should be referred, but even to which kind to refer any individual fallacy». Nay Aristotle himself, after having distinguished and classified Fallacies under thirteen distinct heads, proceeds to show that they are all reducible to one of them, the Ignoratio Elenchi — the misconception or neglect of the conditions of a good Elenchus. The Elenchus is nothing but a counter-syllogism advanced against some given proposition.[2] Every fallacy, whatever it be, transgresses or fails to satisfy the canons or conditions which go to constitute a valid Elenchus, or a valid Syllogism. The rules of a valid counter-syllogism are just the same as the rules of a valid syllogism. The natural consequence of that confession would have been to admit that there must be just as many kinds of fallacies as there are kinds of rules. This is, we have seen, the Indian view. Since the attention is here directed not to the propositions, but to the three terms and, most of all, to the middle term or Reason, a logical fallacy is defined as the violation either of one of the three rules of the Logical Reason singly, or of a pair of them together. All other fallacies which are not infringements of some rule of the syllogistic canon may be infinite, they are not logical fallacies in the strict sense of the word. Dharmottara indeed in dealing with each of the rules of the canon takes care to indicate the corresponding errors which are excluded by it.[3] In introducing the chapter on Logical Fallacies he says,[4] «If someone wishes to formulate in speech (a case under the canon of the rules of Syllogism, i. e.,) the Three Aspects of the Logical Reason, he should do it with precision, and precision is attained when the negative counterpart (of every rule) is likewise stated. When we know what is to be excluded, we then have a better knowledge of what is to be accepted». Syllogism is the verbal expression of a fact under the three rules of the Logical Reason. If one of the rules singly or two of them conjointly are violated, we shall have a logical fallacy.

---

1 Bain, op. cit., I. 278.

2 Grote, op. cit., p. 390.

3 NBT., p. 19.6, 19.8, 19.10 etc.; transl., p. 53, 54 etc.

4 NBT., p. 61. 18 ff.; transl., p. 171.

«A fallacy is what has the semblance of a syllogism», without having the reality. «It is a fault consisting in some of the three rules being infringed».

That Aristotle has failed to keep to this simple and evident view is easily explained by his aim. His treatise, which is sometimes represented as an investigation of logical fallacies, is really devoted to the detection and proper refutation of sophisms. A sophism is rarely founded on a fallacy of reasoning. Its sources are multifarious. They may be logical, but they also may be psychological or linguistic. Aristotle's treatise on Sophisms corresponds to the Indian treatises on the «Failures of the Opponent»[1] and on the «Failures of the Respondent» in which the logical fallacies, or the fallacies of the Reason, are mentioned only as a part, and a comparatively small part, of all possible failures.[2]

The title of Aristotle's treatise is Sophistical Refutations. The sophistical refutation is the counterpart of the Socratic Elenchus which consists in putting questions to a respondent for the sake of eliciting truth. A sophistical refutation, on the contrary, consists in questioning for the sake of producing confusion. It is «a delusive semblance of refutation which imposes on ordinary men and induces them to accept it as real».[3] This corresponds exactly to the sanscrit term jāti explained as *dūṣaṇa-ābhāsa*, semblance of refutation. We have seen that 24 varieties of such refutations are enumerated in the Aphorisms of Nyāya and 14 have been admitted by Dignāga. The exact coincidence, however, is only in the title. The Indian «apparent refutation» really represents an Elenchus, i. e., a counter-syllogism. A fallacious counter-syllogism is a syllogism founded on a false analogy, it corresponds to the *Ignoratio Elenchi* in its narrow sense. But Aristotle's linguistic fallacies, *Fallacia in Dictione*, correspond to the Indian category called *chala*, i. e., ambiguous speech. They are treated quite separately, as fallacies founded on ambiguity. That all the 6 kinds of such fallacies enumerated by Aristotle are not logical fallacies, is clearly seen from the fact that they disappear as fallacies, as soon as you attempt to translate them into a foreign language. They are in the opinion of Aristotle himself linguistic, founded *in Dictione*. The remaining 7 varieties are characterized by him as

---

1 *jāti-śāstra.*

2 *nigraha-shāna-sāstra.*

3 Grote, op. cit., p. 376.

non-linguistic, *extra Dictione*, but only three of them are logical in the strict sense of the term,[1] the rest are psychological or material.

Archbishop Whately divides Fallacies into Logical and Non-Logical. But, strangely enough, his logical class includes, under the title of semi-logical, all Aristotelian linguistic fallacies, such as Equivocation, Amphibolia, etc. As to his non-logical kinds it is clear from the title that they are not logical. Whately refers to it all cases of begging the conclusion (*petitio principii*) and of shirking the question (*ignoratio elenchi*). These are indeed not logical fallacies, i. e., they are not failures in the position of the middle term in regard of the major and in regard of the minor. They are failures to have three clearly determined terms. In the *petitio principii* there is no major term at all, since it reciprocates with the middle. In the *ignoratio elenchi* the middle term is not fixed.

There is however some seed of truth in Whately's division, if we understand it as meaning that the fallacies may be divided into two main classes, the uncertain and the unreal. The first alone will be strictly logical and refer to failures in the major premise. The second will be material or semi-logical, and will refer to the failures against the minor premise. It is nearly the same principle as appears in the Vaišeṣika sūtras[2] and is the foundation of Dignāga's system. It has the great merit of drawing a hard and fast line between the natural mistakes of the human mind and the purposeful cavil of the sophist. There was apparently some similarity in conditions which prevailed in ancient Greece and in ancient India in so far they engendered in both countries the prosperity of the professional debater. In both countries public debating was very much in vogue and this feature of public life has produced a class of professional debaters who for pecuniary profit[3] exploited the natural liability of the human mind to be bluffed by unscrupulous sophistry. The human mind, says Vācaspatimišra,[4] has a natural bias for truth. But, at the same time, error is rampant[5] in it. When sham learning[6] seeks to inculcate sophisms[7] for the sake

---

1 *Fallacia Accidentis, Fallacia Consequentis, Fallacia a dicto secundum quid ad dictum simpliciter.*

2 VS., III. 1.15—*asan sandigdhaš ca.*

3 NV., p. 15. 2 — *lābha-pūjā-khyāti-kāma.*

4 NK., p. 151.15 — *buddher bhūtārtha-pakṣapataḥ.*

5 NV., 21. 21 — *puruṣa-dharma eva bhrāntir iti* = *errare est humanum.*

6 *paṇḍita-vyañjana*, NVTT., p. 29. 7.

7 *tīrtha-pratirūpakaḥ pravādaḥ*, NV., p. 15. 2.

of profit, of honours or fame, logic is doomed, says Uddyotakara.[1] The honest debate should be didactic.[2] It must not be sophistic and contentious.[3] It must continue until the respondent be convinced.[4] A logical fallacy under these conditions is not an intentional sophism, it is the natural counterpart of logical truth.[5] We must therefore distinguish real logical fallacies which are incidental on the human intellect from mere traps laid down by Sophists and litigans. Aristotle's main object is to expose the Sophist. Therefore the true logical fallacies occupy a very small part in his enumeration.

Since the European logic has not succeeded to free itself in this respect from the Aristotelian ban, it has failed to establish a strictly logical system of Fallacies.

We have seen, that Dignāga, on the contrary, has established his system of Logical Fallacies in strict conformity with his canon of syllogistic rules and thus clearly distinguishes them from all sophisms founded on ambiguous speech and psychological shortcomings.

Dharmakīrti made a further step in the same direction. He objected, we have seen, to the Dignāgan Antinomical Fallacy, because in his opinion such a fallacy is impossible in the natural run of logical thought.[6] Thought may deviate from the right path regulated by the canon of rules, but it cannot do both, deviate and non deviate, so as to be right and wrong simultaneously. The argument of Dharmakīrti in this particular instance is highly instructive. It fully discloses his theory of syllogism or, which is the same, of the Reason. What indeed is a Reason? It is presence in subject wholly, presence in similars merely and absence in dissimilars always. These rules establish its necessary connections in two directions, towards the Subject and towards the Predicate. One rule singly or two of them conjointly can be unintentionally violated in the natural run of human thought, but not any of them can be at once violated and non-violated. What is syllogism according to its content? It is either an instance of Identity, or of Causation, or of Negation.[7] There is no other necessary and universal connection. The human intellect can by a mistake misrepresent

---

1 NV., p. 15. 2 — *nyāya-viplavo'sau.*

2 Ibid., p. 21. 18 — *vādasya śiṣyādi-viṣayatvāt.*

3 Ibid. — *na śiṣyādibhiḥ saha apratibhādi-deśanā kāryā.*

4 *yāvad asau bodhito bhavati*, ibid.

5 *pramāṇa-pratirūpakatvād dhetv-ābhāsānām avirodhaḥ*, ibid.

6 NB., III. 112—113; transl., p. 220 ff.

7 Ibid., transl., p. 222.

the real connection, but it cannot in the natural run do both, represent it rightly and wrongly together. Therefore there can be no actually antinomical Fallacy.

It remains for us to consider in detail the correspondence between the Aristotelian and the Indian classes of Fallacies. But at first we must consider those instances when a valid Aristotelian Syllogism would be viewed as a fallacy by Dignāga. E. g., the Syllogism «Socrates is poor, Socrates is wise, *ergo* some poor men are wise» would be a valid syllogism according to the third figure. There are three propositions, three terms, and the middle term is distributed in both premises. But for Dignāga the judgment «some poor men are wise» is not an inferential judgment at all. All that it could be is an perceptual judgment, a judgment of observation. For what is inference? It is a fact of necessary and universal dependence of one term upon the other and the necessary compresence of both these terms conjointly upon a place. Now, if the syllogism had the following form «Whosoever is wise is always poor, Socrates is wise, he necessarily must be poor»— this would be in its form a real, i. e., necessary deduction. But stated in that form its fallacy becomes evident. Although the minor premise is all right,— wisdom is present in Socrates, — but on this ground we cannot decide whether Socrates must necessarily be poor, because there is no invariable concomitance. The reason «wisdom» is in the position No. 9 of Dignāga's table. It is present both in some similar — poor men — and also present in some dissimilar instances — rich men. The reason is uncertain, no conclusion on its basis is possible. That poverty may sometimes be compresent with wisdom is a fact which has no importance at all, because «sometimes» poverty may be compresent with everything except its contradictorily opposed richness. Particular judgments have no place in a regular syllogism.

Professor A. Bain[1] also thinks — on grounds somewhat different — that on examining such cases as «Socrates is poor, Socrates is wise, *ergo* some poor men are wise», we may see good reason for banishing them from the syllogism. There is here «no march of reasoning», there are «Equivalent Propositional Forms or Immediate Inference». The same opinion is expressed by Dharmottara[2] regarding the standard Indian example[3] «The fat Devadatta does not eat at

---

1 Logic, I. 159; cp. Keynes, op. cit., p. 299.

2 NBT., p. 43. 12; transl., p. 115.

3 The Mīmāṃsakas regard it as a proof by implication (*arthāpatti*); Praśastapāda (p. 223) — as an inference, the Buddhists — as an equivalent proposition.

day-time, *ergo* he eats at night». Those are equivalent propositions, there is no change of meaning. If the meaning were to establish a universal and necessary connection between two terms and its application to a given instance, only then could it be brought under the head of syllogism.

On the other hand some of the fallacies counted by Aristotle as logical (*extra Dictione*) are dropped by Dignāga as not belonging to the domain of fallacious reasons, since they do not affect the right position of the middle term, neither in respect of the minor nor in respect of the major. Such is the fallacy of *petitio principii*. Reduced to its crude form and applied to the type-instance of the problem of eternal, resp. non-eternal, sounds, this fallacy will appear in the form «sounds are non-eternal, because they are non-eternal» or «eternal because eternal». According to the Buddhists there is here no reason at all.[1] The respondent accordingly must answer by a question: Why? Give me a reason! Sound is non-eternal because it is non-eternal is equivalent to saying «sound is non-eternal» simply. It may be a fallacy in practice, when it is concealed and difficult to detect. As such it is very often mentioned by Indian logicians[2], but theoretically, in a strictly logical system of all positions of a reason, it has no place, since there is in it no reason at all. Even the over-narrow reason «sound is non-eternal, because it is audible», representing the absolute minimum of a reason, is nevertheless a reason. It supposes the existence of a major premise «whatsoever is audible is non-eternal». But in a *petitio principii* fallacy, the major premise would be reducible to the form — «whatsoever is non-eternal is non-eternal», and that means total absence of a reason and the natural retort «give me a reason!»

Strictly logical are only three of Aristotle's fallacies: 1) *Fallacia Accidentis*, 2) *Fallacia a dicto secundum quid ad dictum simpliciter* and 3) *Fallacia consequentis.*

They have that feature in common that they are all due to an erroneous conversion of an universal affirmative. The contraposition is not established,[3] as the Buddhist would have said. They are fallacies of the major premise.[4] There is no universal and necessary

---

1 Such is the definition of Aristotle: the premise is identical with the conclusion. But the German manual Antibarbarus Logicus defines — *die Beweisgründe sind entweder falsch oder bedürfen eines Beweises.* Such a definition would permit us to regard every fallacy as *petitio principii.*

2 *sādhya-sama, siddha-sādhana.*

3 *asiddha-vyatireka.*

4 Or in other words they correspond to the Fallacy of Undistributed Middle, since «Distribution or Universal Quantity in the middle term is essential to its

dependence of the reason upon the predicate. It follows that the predicate is not deducible from such a reason. They are all reasons which Dignāga refers to the Uncertain and Contrary Classes.

The relation of these fallacies to the corresponding classes of Dignāga is the following one —

1. *Fallacia Accidentis.* Aristotle gives the example «Koriskus is not a man, because he is not Socrates who is a man», or «this one is not Koriskus, because he is a man, while a man is not Koriskus». Both these cases cannot be classified as «unreal» reasons, because the reason is present upon the subject. But the invariable concomitance of the reason with the predicate is not established. The respondent to whom these syllogisms are submitted must answer: «no concomitance!» The fallacy is in the major premise. In the first example Koriskus is the Subject, non-man is the Predicate, non-Socrates is the Reason. The concomitance «whosoever is a non-Socrates is a non-man» is uncertain. There are non-Socrates'es among non-men (similar) and also among men (dissimilar). The reason is in the position No. 9, it is present in some similars as well as in some dissimilars. No conclusion is possible. In the second example the Subject is «this one», the predicate is «non-man», the Reason is Koriskus. There also is no concomitance. The concomitance implied is that «whatsoever is Koriskus, (all events united under this name) is non-man». The contrary is true, the reason is incompatible with the predicate. It is an inverted reason and therefore must be referred to the «contrary» class; its position is in No. 8, Koriskus is never present in non-men (similar) and always present in some man (dissimilar).

Aristotle singles out these not quite similar fallacies and puts them in the first place evidently because the trick of arguing from and accident (Koriskus is not Socrates) to a general rule (Koriskus is not a man) was very much in vogue among Sophists.

2. The second fallacy, *extra Dictione*, is hardly distinguishable from the first. Aristotle's example is «the Ethiopian is white in his teeth and black in his skin, therefore he is simultaneously black and non-black». The reason «black in the skin and white in the teeth» is in the position No. 2, it belongs to the contrary class. It is never

---

total coincidence» (Bain, op. cit., I. 163). Stated in this form it represents the only or universal logical fallacy. It is curious that some European logicians have imputed to Aristotle the total omission of this, the only truly logical, fallacy, cp. Bain, ibid., p. 278.

found in similar instances (black and non-black wholly) and always present in all dissimilar (partly black and partly non-black) ones.

3. *Fallacia Consequentis* is the most natural fallacy, the reason overlaps a little bit into the dissimilar province. It is the nearest to a right reason, its sophistical value is not very great. The major premise represents a wrong conversion of an universal affirmative. The reason is either in the position No. 7, when it is present in the whole compass of the similar and moreover in some dissimilar instances; or in, the position No. 9, when it is present on both sides partly, in a part of the similar and a part of the dissimilar province. Example «this one is a thief, because he walks out by night». The position is No. 9; since people walking out by night are partially met on both sides, in the thievish as well as in the non-thievish department.

4. The fallacies of *Ignoratio Elenchi* or wrong answer, of *Non-Causa pro Causa*[1] or drawing a conclusion from something what is not really an essential premise thereof, and of *Plurium Interrogationum ut Unius* are not strictly logical fallacies, they repose on misunderstandings.

Although all fallacies repose on misunderstandings, all are, as Aristotle says, more or less *Ignoratio Elenchi*, nevertheless strictly logical are those which are produced 1) either by a wrong position of the Middle Term between instances similar and dissimilar, these are fallacies of the major premise, 2) or by a wrong position of the Middle Term regarding the Subject of the Conclusion, these are fallacies of the minor premise. Therefore in order to make an estimate of the strict logical value of a syllogism its three terms should be singled out and the relation of 1) M to S and 2) M to P should be tested. The fallacies of answering beside the point, of adducing an unessential premise and of a plurality of questions cannot occur when the three terms are presented in their unambiguous expressions. These fallacies very often occur in practical life, but they are psychological, not logical. It is therefore advisable to formulate a syllogism not in propositions which can easily mislead, but to single out the three terms S, M and P expressing them without a shade of ambiguity. This is the method adopted in the schools of Tibet and Mongolia. The relation of M to S and of M to P becomes apparent. The answer of the respondent can

[1] This would correspond to the *anyathā-siddha*, a very often occuring mistake, but more psychological than logical.

then only be either «yes!» or «reason unreal!» or «no concomitance!» The latter is then divided in two contrary or inverted reasons (position Nos. 2 and 8), four uncertain ones (positions Nos. 1, 3, 7 and 9) and one over-narrow (position No. 5). The antinomic reason which at once occupies two positions in the table (Nos. 2 or 8 combined with 4 or 6) may be added. No other position is possible. Dignāga's table is exhaustive, it brings order and systematical unity into the problem of fallacies. There never can be any doubt regarding the class to which a fallacy should be referred.

Aristotle comes very near Dignāga's solution when he states that a respondent to whom a false refutative Syllogism has been presented must examine «in which of the premises and in what way the false appearance of a syllogism has arisen».[1] Had Aristotle remained by this principle and had he set aside all linguistic and psychological causes, he would have probably arrived at a system like the one of Dignāga.

---

[1] Grote, op. cit., p. 406.

PART IV.

NEGATION.

CHAPTER I.

THE NEGATIVE JUDGMENT.

§ 1. The essence of Negation.

Since every cognition is regarded by the Buddhists as a direct or indirect cognition of some point of external reality, and the interest which they take in logic is not formal, but epistemological, the problem of Negation contains for them special difficulties. It is therefore treated with extraordinary thorougness. Indeed, what is Negation? Is it cognition? Is it cognition of reality? Is it direct or indirect cognition, i. e., is it to be treated under perception or under inference? At first glance it seems to be non-cognition, the cancellation of cognition; or, if it is cognition at all, it must be a cognition of a non-reality, that is to say, of nothing. It nevertheless exists and seems to be a kind of cognition and a cognition not of nothing, but of something. The solution proposed by the realistic schools has already been mentioned above, incidentally, when considering the Buddhist analysis of our notion of Existence. For them Negation is either a special mode of cognition or a mode of existence.

Quite different is the position of the Buddhists. Existence for them, we have seen, refers to the ultimate reality of a point-instant, and its cognition is the corresponding pure sensation. A non-existing or absent thing is imagination, it can produce no sensation directly; but the positive thing which has produced the sensation can be interpreted by the intellect as involving the absence of another thing whose presence is thus denied. Negation is therefore never a direct or original attitude of the mind, as pure sensation always is.[1] It is

[1] Pure sensation is *vidhi* = *bgrubs-byed*, pure affirmation.

always the work of the understanding which calling in mnemic representations interprets a given sensation on its negative side. If we have a cognition of the type «there is here no jar», or «the jar is absent», the direct cognition, the visual sensation is produced by the empty place, not by the absent jar. The absent jar is a representation called forth by memory and constructed by the intellect, it is not perceived by the senses. So far the Buddhist view seems unimpeachable and the Realists have the greatest difficulties in combating it. However the necessity of repudiating it is urged upon them by their extreme realism. They cannot admit the pure ideality of the absent. They therefore imagine that the absent thing is somehow really connected with the empty place.[1] The Buddhists having established a hard and fast line between reality and ideality, between sensation and imagination, had no necessity of fluctuating between reality and unreality in assuming the ideality of negation. They had no difficulty of repudiating the direct perception of the absent thing through the senses. But the question remained whether the negative judgment of the form «there is no jar» was to be classed as a perceptual judgment just as the judgment «this is a jar», or that it was to be referred to the inferential class of judgments, where an absent thing is cognized on the basis of its visible mark; for inference, we have seen, is essentially the cognition of something not present in the ken. However the line of demarcation between a perceptual judgment and inference is not so sharp, since every perception, as distinguished from pure sensation, contains a great amount of mnemic elements and a synthesis of the understanding. On the other hand every inference may be viewed as a single operation of the understanding, as a single conception[2] erected on the basis of a pure sensation. It will then contain a part visible and a part invisible, a non-constructed and a constructed part, a non-imagined and imagined part. The inference «there is fire on the hill, because I see smoke» may be viewed as one synthetically constructed image of smoke-fire whose basis is a sensation. There is no difference in principle, there is only a difference of degree; imagination is predominant in an inference. In the negative judgment «there is here no jar, because I do not perceive any», imagination is likewise predominant. Therefore negation must be referred to the class of inferential cognition, although it also can be viewed as a single conception, containing a part visible and a part invisible, a part imagined and a part non-imagined

---

[1] connected by *svarūpa-sambandha* = *viśeṣaṇa-viśeṣya-bhāva.*

[2] *ekam vijñānam anumānam,* cp. NK., p. 125.

Negation is thus predominantly imagination. In marked opposition to the realists, who maintain that negation is based on the positive perception of an absent thing, (the *absence* is present), the Buddhists assert that it is founded on the negative perception of a present thing (the *presence* is absent). The perception of an absent thing is impossible, it is a contradiction. If it is perception, the thing is present, it cannot be absent. But how is it present? It is present in imagination and that means that all the conditions necessary for its perception are fulfilled. It would be necessarily perceived if it were present; but it is absent and therefore it is only imagined, but not perceived, it is perceived in imagination. Sigwart[1] calls our attention to the fact that from the ordinary, realistic, point of view the proposition «there is here no fire» or «the fire does not burn» contains a contradiction. If it does not burn, how is it a fire? The person, asked to look in the stove and not finding there the fire which he expected to find, answers that there is no fire, meaning really that the expected fire is not there. The negation is thus directed on an imagined fire, its imagined visibility. Dharmottara[2] gives the following explanation. «How is it possible for an object, say a jar, to be perceptible, when it is absent? It is said to be perceptible, although it is absent, because its perceptibility is imagined! We imagine it in the following way: „If it were present on this spot, it certainly would have been perceived". In this case an object, although absent, is *ex hypothesi* visible. And what is the object which can so be imagined? It is the object whose empty place is perceived, since all conditions necessary for its perception are fulfilled. When can we decide that all necessary conditions are fulfilled? When we actually perceive another object included in the same act of cognition, (when we perceive the counterpart of our negation, the empty place on which the denied object is imagined as present). We call „included in the same act of cognition" two interconnected objects amenable to the same sense-faculty, an object upon which the eye or another organ can be simultaneously fixed with attention. Indeed when two such objects are before us, we cannot confine our perception to one of them, since there is no difference between them as regards possibility of perception. Therefore if we actually perceive only one of them, we naturally imagine that if the other were present, we should likewise perceive it, because the totality of the necessary conditions is fulfilled.

---

1 Logik³, I. 168.

2 NBT., p. 33. 8 ff.; transl., p. 62.

Thus a fancied perceptibility is imparted to the object. The non-cognition of such an object is called negation, but it is a negation of a hypothetical visibility. Therefore that very spot from which the jar is absent and that cognition which is intent upon it, are both understood as a negation of a possible visibility, since they are the real source of the negative judgment. Negation is the absent thing, as well as its cognition; or its bare substratum and the corresponding perception. Every cognition, *quà* cognition, is a cognition of reality, «consequently, continues Dharmottara,[1] negation *quà* cognition is not simple absence of knowledge, it is a positive reality and an assertory cognition of it. The simple, unqualified absence of cognition, since it itself contains no assertion at all, can convey no knowledge. But when we speak of negation whose essence is a negation of hypothetical perceptibility, these words may be regarded as neccesarily implying the presence of a bare place from which the object is absent and the cognition of that same place; in so far it is a place where the object would have been necessarily perceived, perceived just as well as its empty place is perceived, if it were present».

Negation is thus taken ontologically, as well as logically. It means the presence of a bare spot, as well as the fact of its cognition.

§ 2. Negation is an Inference.

It has been found so far that Negation is no exception to the general rule that all cognition is cognition of reality. The un-reality or non-existence, which at first glance seems to be cognized in negation, discloses itself as an imagined unreality. Reality, existence, thing, are synonyms, we must not forget; they are contradictorily opposed to ideality, non-existence, image or conception, which are all different names of unreality. But there is a wrong ideality, as, e. g., the «flower in the sky», which is an ideality out of touch with reality; and a consistent or trustworthy ideality which is in touch with reality, as e. g., a real flower which is in touch with some point-instant of ultimate reality, as revealed in a sensation. Negation is an unreality of the latter kind. It is an idea, it is imagination, but it is a trustworthy idea, it is productive imagination, it is a source of knowledge capable of guiding our purposive actions.

But if Negation is nothing but a cognition of a point of reality followed by a mental construction, it does not differ in principle from

[1] NBT., p. 22, 17 ff.; transl., p. 63.

perception, which is also a sensation immediately followed by an image of the thing perceived. It is not a cognition of a thing absent, whose mark alone is perceived. It is not a cognition through a mark, of «that which it is a mark of», that is to say, it is not an inference, it does not contain any movement of thought from the known to the unknown? And since there are no other sources of knowledge than these two, the direct one and the indirect one, it will not differ in principle from perception, it will be coordinated to perception. There will be a positive and negative perception, an affirmative and negative perceptual judgment, as maintained by the Realists? Indeed, if Negation has no other real meaning as the presence of an empty place and of its cognition, then the inference «there is here no jar, because I do not see any» has no other meaning than «there is here no jar, because there is none» or «I do not perceive here any jar, because I do not perceive it». Dharmottara[1] says, «an absent jar is called present, because it is imagined as present, as being cognized in all the normal conditions of perceptibility, on a place where it is expected to reside, a place which is the connterpart of the absent jar and which is connected with it in the same act of cognition, but which is empty... Therefore[2] what we call negation or cancellation of perception, is nothing but the positive existence of an object connected with it and the cognition of that object...» that is to say[3] «what is called non-existence of a present jar, (i. e. what is an absent jar), is nothing but a positive perception of a reality».[4] «If it would have been real, says Dharmakīrti,[5] negation would be impossible». That is to say, if absence, or non-existence, would have been a reality, as the realistic schools assume, then negative cognition could not be possible, it wonld then be an absence of cognition, an absolute blank. But it is imagined, imagined not as a «flower in the sky», but on the basis of a real perception of an existent object. This is why it is a variety of trustworthy knowledge and a reason for successful purposive action.

The mutual accusations of Buddhists and Realists regarding the problem of Non-existence have been already mentioned when considering the Buddhist views respecting reality. The Realists accuse the

---

[1] NBT., p. 28. 18 ff.; transl., p. 80.
[2] Ibid., p. 28. 20.
[3] Ibid., p. 28. 22.
[4] *artha-jñāna eva*, ibid.
[5] NB., p. 27. 17.

Buddhists Non-existence of being nothing and nil, since it is nothing by itself, nothing apart from its substratum, no different unity, it is included in its positive counterpart. The Buddhists, on the contrary, accuse the Realists of assuming a real non-Ens,[1] a hypostasized non-Ens, a bodily non-Ens,[2] a separately shaped non-Ens,[3] a, so to speak, Right Honourable non-Ens,[4] which, on being critically examined, reveals itself as mere imagination. However the unreal non-Ens imagined on a basis of a positive perception does not differ in principle from simple perception, which consists of a sensation followed by an image constructed through the understanding. It is not something to be deduced[5] out of another fact, it is an ultimate fact itself,[6] it is not an inference. The fact of not perceiving the hypothetically assumed object cannot be resorted to as a middle term, from which its absence could be deduced, because its absence is nothing over and above its imagined presence on a place which is empty. However, since Dignāga and Dharmakīrti define sense-perception as the purely sensuous element in the process of perception, and since negation *quà* negation is not sensation at all, they nevertheless refer negation to the domain of inference, as a source of knowledge in which the part of the constructive function of the understanding is predominant.

Moreover, if the absence of the object, say, of a jar, is something perceived, not something inferred, the practical consequences of such a perception of a bare place are so different from the direct sense-perception of the object, that this justifies our referring negation to the class of indirect cognition. «The absence of the jar, says Dharmottara,[7] is not really deduced, deduced are much more the practical consequences of that negation». What are these consequences? They are the negative propositions and the respective purposive activity, as well as its successful end, when they are all founded upon a negative perception of the described type.[8] There is however another negation, a negation which is not the negative cognition of an imagined presence, but a negative cognition of absence, of an unimagined or unimaginable

1 *vāstavo'bhāvaḥ.*

2 *vigravahān abhāvaḥ.*

3 *bhinna-mūrtir abhāvaḥ.*

4 *āyuṣmān abhāvaḥ.*

5 *sādhya.*

6 *siddha*, cp. NBT., p. 29. 9; transl., p. 84, n. 4; cp. TSP., 479. 22, and 481. 2.

7 NBT., p. 29. 10; transl., p. 83.

8 NBT., p. 29. 22; transl., p. 84.

presence. It is not a source of right knowledge, it does not lead to successful purposive action. Some interesting details on such a negative cognition of absence will be considered later on.

On the grounds which oblige us to refer negation to the domain of inference, Dharmottara[1] delivers himself in the following way. «Has it not been stated that the judgment „there is no jar" is produced by sense-perception, by the perception of a bare place? And now we include this judgment into the practical consequences deduced by inference from this perception. (Yes! We do not deny that!) Since the bare place is cognized by sense-perception, and since the negative judgment „there is here no jar" is a judgment produced by the direct function of perception, that function that makes the object present to our senses, therefore it is quite true that the negative judgment immediately following on the perception of the bare place is a perceptual judgment. Indeed the negative judgment, according to what has been precedently explained, is directly produced by sense-perception, because qualified perception (beyond pure sensation) has just the capacity of producing a judgment as to the existence before us of a bare place. However, the proper function of Negation consists in the next following step. Objects might be not perceived, but this only gives rise to doubt, (the question arises as to which of them might be present). So long as this doubt has not been removed, negation has no practical importance, it cannot guide our purposive actions. Imagination then steps in, and it is thus that negation, as a negative deduction, gives practical significance to the idea of a non-Ens.[2] Since an object, which I imagine as present on a given place, is not really perceived, just therefore do I judge that „it is not there". Consequently this negation of an imagined presence is an inference which gives life to the ready concept of a non-Ens, it does not newly create this concept itself. Thus it is that the negative judgment receives its practical significance through an inference from challenged imagination, although it is really produced by sense-perception and only applied in life through a deductive process of an inference, whose logical reason consists in the fact of a negative experience. A negative inference therefore guides our steps when we apply in life the idea of a non-Ens».

---

[1] Ibid., p. 30. 1; transl., p. 84.

[2] Cp. with this the theory of Windelband, that negation is a second judgment, a rejudgment; cp. below in the part on European Parallels.

§ 3. The figures of the Negative Syllogism. The figure of Simple Negation.

So far the essence and the function of Negation have been established. Its essence always reduces to some hypothetical perceptibility. There is no Negation in the external world; Negation is never a direct cognition of reality. However, indirectly there is an external reality corresponding to negation, it is the reality of its substratum. This substratum and its cognition may also be characterized as the essence of Negation. Owing to this its feature, Negation, although appertaining to the domain of imagination, has «meaning and validity». Its function is to guide our purposive actions in a special way. It is an indirect valid source of knowledge, a knowledge of the inferential type, the fact of hypothetical visibility taking the office of the middle term connecting the substratum with negation. The denial of hypothetical perceptibility is thus the essence or the general form of Negation, a form which is present in every particular instance of it. When thrown into a syllogistic form we, as in every inference, have the choice between the Method of Agreement, or the Method of Difference. We thus shall have Negation expressed through agreement with the denied fact and Negation expressed through disagreement with the denied fact; i. e. Negation expressed positively and Negation expressed negatively. The negative method of expressing Negation will result in deducing it from an Affirmation, since every double negation always results in an affirmation. They patterns of these syllogisms will be shown presently. They are only formal varieties, differences in formulation or in expression. We are as yet not told what are the objects upon which negation is intent.

Negation can be intent either upon a thing or upon a relation. The things are subdivided, we have seen, in five categories; the relations in only two, Existential Necessary Identity and Existential Necessary Sequence; the last also called Causality. The five categories of things, viz., the Individuals, Classes, Qualities, Motions and Substances, can be the content of simple negation. They afford no ground for a classification of Negation *quà* Negation. But the Relations, being relations of interdependence, can be differently viewed as a relation of the dependent part to that upon which it depends, and *vice versa*, as that of the independent to the dependent; as the cause to the effect and *vice versa* as the effect to the cause; as the inclusive to the included and of the included to the inclusive terms. They can moreover intercross, and we can have such instances as the relation of one thing with another when the latter is, say, the inclusive term in regard of the cause of the former. In denying the one or the other, our negation will be based on a double relation of Causation *plus* Identity.

Considering all the possible combinations we will have eleven figures of the Negative Syllogism. Only universal judgments are admitted as members of a syllogism. Particular judgments are regarded either as no logical conclusions at all or as logical fallacies.

The eleven negative figures are the following ones, first of all—

Simple Negation. This figure is contained in every negative perceptual judgment. Nevertheless it is not a perceptual judgment, since the object cognized is invisible. It is cognized through its mark which is non-perception. Since the deduced part does not differ much from that part out of which it is deduced, since non perception and non-presence (or absence) are practically the same thing, it is assumed that the deduced part consists in the special sort of behaviour which is consequent on a negative judgment. Every cognition in general is nothing but a preparation for an action. The figures of Negation are not being distinguished by themselves, their essence is always the same, it is cancellation of hypothetical visibility. But the consequences to which a denial leads are different; the formulae of negation are distinguished according to them. The consequence of simple negation is a corresponding sort of behaviour. The affirmative perceptual judgment can, of course, also be regarded as an inference of the presence of the perceived object from the fact of its perception, and the deduced consequence would then also be the corresponding sort of behaviour. But the difference consists in the immediate vividness of the concrete image, which is characteristic for perception and distinguishes it from the vague image of absent things with which inferences have to deal. It has a different essence, a different function and its figures must be treated separately from the figures of the affirmative syllogism.

As mentioned above, simple negation can be expressed in a formula according to the Method of Agreement, as well as in a formula according to the Method of Difference. The first will be as follows—

Major premise. The non-perception of a representable object is followed by respective negative behaviour.

Example. Just as the non-perception of a flower in the sky, (is *not* followed by the action of plucking it).

Minor premise. On this place we don't perceive a jar, which is representable.

Conclusion. On this place we will not find it.

The minor term is represented here by the conception «on this place». It is the substratum of reality underlying the whole ratiocination. The major terms is represented by the conception of the respective negative behaviour «we will not find it here». The middle term consists in the abolition of the hypothetical presence of the denied object. The major premise points to their concomitance. Indeed, as M. H. Bergson puts it, «from abolition to negation, which is the more general operation, there is but one step!» «This means, says Dharmottara, that a representable object not being perceived, this circumstance affords an opportunity for a negative purposive action in respect of it».[1] Non-perception is the included[2] part, the dependent part, the Reason. Negation or negative behaviour is the inclusive[3] part, the more general operation, the part on which the former depends,[4] the necessary Consequence.[5]

The statement that the logical reason is necessarily associated with its consequence is a statement of invariable concomitance. This is according to the canons of the rules of syllogism, viz., Invariable Concomitance between the Reason and its necessary Consequence (or between its subject and predicate) consists in 1) the necessary presence (never absence) of the predicate upon the subject and 2) in the presence of the subject exclusively in the sphere of the predicate, never beyond it.[6]

The example points to the individual instances, of which the general proposition expressing concomitance is a generalization by Induction. Every imagined object, an object existing as present only in imagination, is an instance of an object which does not exist in reality, i. e., in the objective world. By this reference to the facts proving the general law, concomitance is fully established.

After having established the general rule, the syllogistic process proceeds to indicate its application to a particular instance in the minor premise «on this place we do not perceive any representable jar». The manner in which a non existing jar is placed by representation or imagination, hypothetically, in all the necessary conditions

---

1 NBT., p. 44. 1; transl., p. 117.

2 *vyāpya.*

3 *vyāpaka.*

4 *pratibandha-viṣaya.*

5 *niścita-anubandha.*

6 NBT., p. 44. 4 ff.; transl., p. 118.

of perceptibility, consists in an hypothetical judgment of the form «if the jar would have been present on this spot, I would have necessarily perceived it, but I do not perceive any, therefore it is not present».

Thus it is that every negative experience may be regarded as a particular fact containing by implication the general rule; non-existing are only those objects, which we could have perceived under other circumstances. On the other hand, objects which we do not perceive and which we are not capable hypothetically to place in the conditions of perceptibility, objects that are unimaginable by their nature — cannot be denied, because negation is nothing but an abolition of imagination.

That same figure of Simple Negation can be expressed according to the Method of Difference. We then shall have a negative expression of negation, a denied negation, i. e., an affirmative general proposition, from which negation will follow. Its formula is the following one —

Major premise. A thing present in the ken is necessarily perceived, when all the other conditions of perceptibility are fulfilled.

Example. As a patch of blue etc.

Minor premise. Here no jar is perceived, all conditions of perceptibility being fulfilled.

Conclusion. Here there is no jar.

In order to investigate the problem of the essence of Negation we here resort to the Method of Difference. We compare two instances which have every circumstance in common save one. If an instance in which a phenomenon under investigation occurs, i. e., where Negation occurs, where we can pronounce «this is not here», and an instance in which it does not occur, i. e., where there is no Negation, where we cannot pronounce «this is not here», because it is here — if these two instances have every circumstance in common, i. e., all the conditions of perceptibility are fulfilled, save one,[1] viz. the non-perception

---

[1] *pratyayāntara* = other circumstances, *pratyayāntara-sākalyam* = all other circumstances save one, *sākalyam* = *sannidhiḥ* = common possession or presence, cp. NBT., p. 22.23—23.1. Non-perception can hardly be characterized as the cause of Negation, since non-existence and its cognition are likewise understood by this term, cp. NBT., p. 28. 22 — *artha-jñāna eva pratyakṣasya ghaṭasya abhāva ucyate.* Negation is contained in a denied perception. The relation between denied perception and denial in general is analytical, the first is a part of the second in intention, and contains it in comprehension. Therefore the inferential step from non-perception to non-existence is permissible, because the first is necessarily a part of the second. It is interesting to note that A. Bain in his formulation of the second Canon if Induction has dropped the words «or an indispensable part of the.

of the object, which is hypothetically visible, as situated in all the necessary conditions of perceptibility; that one condition which occurs only in the former instance and does not occur in the latter is the cause, or the indispensable part, of the phenomenon of Negation. It is thus proved that the essence of Negation consists in the abolition of a hypothetical visibility. The same result, we have seen, can be arrived at by the Method of Agreement. We then compare an instance where an imagined jar is pronounced to be absent from a given place, because if it were present it would have been perceived. We compare it with the other instances, where the objects must be surely pronounced to be absent, because they are merely imagined, as, e. g., a flower in the sky, the horns on the head of a hare, the son of a barren woman, etc. etc. The circumstance alone, in which these instances agree with the first, is the imagined presence of the absent thing. That circumstance is the cause or the indispensable part of Negation. Thus the essence of Negation consists in an abolition of a hypothetical presence. The Method of Difference states here that with the abolition of the consequence the reason is also abolished. It is a Mixed Hypothetical Syllogism, expressed *modo tollente.* Indeed the major premise states that —

If the object is present, it is perceived, supposing there is no other impediment for its perception. But on the given place it is not perceived. Consequently it is absent (not present).

The universal proposition expresses that the existence of something perceivable, the totality of the indispensable conditions being fulfilled, is invariably followed by perception. Existence is the negation of non-existence, and cognition — the negation of non-cognition. Hence we have here a contraposition of the universal premise expressed according to the Method of Agreement (where non-perception was represented as concomitant with non-existence). The negation of the subject is made the predicate, and the negation of the predicate is made the subject. Thus the universal proposition expresses that the negation of the consequence is invariably concomitant, with the negation of the reason, because

---

cause», which are contained in the formulation of J. St. Mill. If Mr. Mill would have said: «the circumstance in which alone the two instances differ is either the effect or the indispensable part of the phenomenon», his statement would have then fallen in line with the Buddhist view, according to which there are only two kinds of relation between objects, those founded on Identity (= law of Contradiction), and those founded on Causality; the contents of every single case is established in both cases by Induction from similar and dissimilar cases.

the former negation is dependent upon the latter. If non-existence is denied, i. e., if existence is affirmed, then perception (non non-perception) necessarily follows, whereever no other impediments are in the way. The absence of the consequence (i. e. of non-existence) necessarily involves the absence of the reason (i. e. of non-perception). But the reason is present. Hence its consequence must also be present. That is to say, that the object is not perceived, all necessary conditions having been fulfilled; therefore it is not present, it does not exist on the given place. The negation of the reason always represents the inclusive term[1] to which the negation of the consequence, being the included[2] term, is subordinate. When the Method of Difference is applied, it always must be shown that with the abolition of the deduced Consequence, which is here non-perception of the hypothetically visible, the abolition of the Reason is necessarily involved.

§ 4. The ten remaining figures.

The remaining ten figures of the negative syllogism «do not express directly a negation of imagined visibility, but they express either an affirmation or a negation of something else, and this necessarily reduces to a Simple Negation of the hypothetically visible».[3] Therefore they, although indirectly, are nothing but disguised formulas of Simple Negation.

The order of the eleven figures is apparently settled according to the progressing complication of the deduction. It begins with the figure of Simple Negation and ends with the figure of Affirmation of an Effect which is incompatible with the cause of the denied fact. The ten figures may be divided in two principal classes. One class comprises all formulas, which consist in deducing Negation from the Affirmation of something Incompatible. It contains the seven figures, IV—VIII and X—XI. The other class contains three figures, II, III and IX, which deduce Negation from another negation, from the negation of something either causally connected with the fact denied, or from the negation of an inclusive term from which the denial of the included term logically follows.

The second figure consists in the Negation of Effect, from wich the negation of its causes necessarily follows, e. g. —

---

1 *vyāpaka.*

2 *vyāpya.*

3 NBT., p. 37. 7; transl., p. 100.

Major premise. Wheresoever there is no smoke, there are no efficient causes of it.

Minor premise. There is here no smoke.

Conclusion. There are here no efficient causes of it.

The place pointed to by the word «there» corresponds to the minor term. The fact of the presence of efficient causes producing smoke corresponds to the major, and the fact «no smoke» — to the middle term. If we take the term «no-smoke» as a positive one, the syllogism will be Celarent. Otherwise it will consist of three negative propositions and there is no other escape to save the Aristotelian rule than to admit that the major premise as containing a double negation is affirmative, the figure will then be Camestres.

The inference from the presence of causes to the necessity of their effect is not supposed to be safe in Buddhist logic, since the causes do not always produce their effects. Up to the last moment some unexpected fact may always interfere and the predicted result will not happen. Therefore only the last moment, as we have seen when examining the Buddhist theory of causation, is the real cause, the real moment of efficiency, the ultimate reality. In an inference from an absent effect to the absent cause the cause refers therefore to the efficient cause, i. e. to the last moment preceeding the effect.

This figure of ratiocination is resorted to in cases when the causes are invisible. Their assumed hypothetical visibility is denied.

The next, third figure is also a case when the negation of one fact is deduced from the negation of another fact, but the connection between them is not founded on Causation. It is founded on the Identity of the substratum. It consists in a negation of the inclusive term from which the negation of the included term logically follows, e. g. —

Major premise. Wheresoever there are no trees at all, there naturally are no Ašoka-trees.

Minor premise. There are there no trees at all.

Conclusion. There also are no Ašoka-trees.

The minor term is expressed by the term «there», the major by the term «no Ašoka-trees», and the middle by «no trees». Just as in the preceding case the figure consists of three negative propositions and may be pressed either into Celarent or Camestres. The absence of the inclusive term is here ascertained by simple negation. The absence of the included one is founded on the law of Identity.

In this and the following figures the realistic schools are satisfied in establishing an invariable connection between two facts or conceptions, without inquiring into the character of the connection and without telling us what kind of connection exists between the two terms, and on what law it is founded. All the figures of the Buddhist negative syllogism will be brought under one and the same figure of Celarent, some of them perhaps under Camestres. But the Buddhist theory starts from the principle that there are only two kinds of connection between facts and concepts, the one is founded on the law of Contradiction, the other on the law of Causation and from this point of view the practice of syllogizing may offer eleven different combinations, which although all being Celarent in form are different types of the negative reasoning. This division cannot be accused of representing a «False Subtlety of the Syllogistic Figures», but they are a classification of figures founded upon their relation to the two fundamental laws of cognition.

The fourth figure consists in the Affirmation of an Incompatible fact, from which the negation of its counterpart follows, e. g.—

Major premise. Wheresoever there is an efficient fire, there is no cold.

Minor premise. There is there an efficient fire.

Conclusion. There is there no cold.

The figure is in Celarent and refers to facts connected by Identity according to the law of Contradiction. Heat, the contradictorily opposed part of cold, is not felt directly, and fire, excluding heat, is perceived, or else another figure would have been resorted to. This figure is applied in such cases where fire is directly perceived by vision, but heat cannot be felt, because of the distance separating the observer from the fire. An imagined sensation of cold is thus denied.

The next, fifth figure is a modification of the former one by introducing the relation of causality in addition to the relation of contradiction. It consists in an Affirmation of an Incompatible Effect, e. g.—

Major premise. Wheresoever there is smoke, there is no cold.

Minor premise. There is there no smoke.

Conclusion. There is there no cold.

Such smoke is of course meant, which suggests the presence of a sufficiently powerful fire. This figure is resorted to when both the fire and the sensation of cold are not experienced directly. When cold could be felt directly, its Simple Negation would have been used according to the First Negative Figure. Where fire is perceived directly, the Fourth Figure of Negation, the Affirmation of the Incompatible, must be used. But when both are beyond the reach of the senses, this figure, i. e., the figure of the Affirmation of Incompatible Effect is applied.

The next, sixth figure of Negation consists in an Affirmation of an Incompatible Subordinate. It introduces a further complication, but is, nevertheless, founded on an analytical connection of two facts, the one being the part of the other, e. g.—

Major premise. What depends on discontinuous causes is not constant.

Minor premise. The evanescence of empirical things depends on special causes.

Conclusion. It is not constant.

This is the argument of the Realists against the Buddhist theory of Instantaneous Existence or Constant Evanescence. The Buddhists maintain that the destruction of everything is certain *a priori*, because it is the very essence of existence. Existence and destruction are connected by Identity; whatsoever exists as real and has an origin, is *eo ipso* constantly evanescent. The realists appeal to the fact that every destruction has its cause, as for instance, the jar is destroyed not by time, but by the stroke of a hammer. This accidental causation is the contradictorily opposed part of non-causation and non-causation is subordinate to constancy or eternity. Eternity is thus denied by pointing to a subordinate feature which is incompatible with eternity. The connection of the notions of causality, non-causality and eternity is founded upon the laws of Contradiction and Identity.

Since we evidently have to deal in this instance with abstract notions, the question arises whether the principle of the negation of hypothetical perceptibility can here be maintained as being always the essence of every negation. «When denying the reality of the predicate or major term „constancy", says Dharmottara,[1] we indeed must argue in the following manner: if the fact before us were permanent, we would have some experience of its permanent essence; however no permanent essence is ever experienced, therefore it is not permanent». It follows that when we deny permanence (or eternity), this denial refers to something hypothetically placed in all conditions of perceptibility. Even in denying the presence of a ghost, which is supposed to be invisible, we can do it only after trying to imagine it for a moment as something perceptible. It is only thus that we can arrive at the judgments «this is a jar», «it is not a ghost». From the Bud-

1 NBT., p. 33. 16; transl., p. 94.

dhist theory of judgment and its identification with the couple sensation-conception, it follows directly that there are no totally abstract ideas, every abstract idea is a «flower in the sky», if it is not somehow attached to sensation.

The seventh figure of Negation is again an indirect negation and is founded on Causality, it is an Affirmation of Incompatibility with the Effect, e. g. —

Major premise. Wherever there is an efficient fire, there are no efficient causes of cold.

Minor premise. But there is here an efficient fire.

Conclusion. Therefore there are here no efficient causes producing cold.

There being no possibility of directly perceiving the presence of those factors which are known to produce cold, we imagine their presence and then repel that suggestion by pointing at a distance to the refulgence of a fire directly perceived. We must avail ourselves of this figure when neither the cold itself, nor its causes can be directly perceived. Where the cold could be felt, we would apply the second figure, the figure of denying the result, «there are here no causes producing cold, since there is no cold». And when its causes are amenable to sensation, we would avail ourselves of Simple Negation, the First Figure — «there are here no causes of cold, because we do not feel them». Here the deduction is partly founded on the law of Causation and partly on the law of Contradiction. The presence of fire is connected with the absence of cold by the law of Contradiction. The absence of the causes of cold is connected with the absence of fire by the law of Causation.

The next, eighth figure of negative syllogism, is again founded exclusively on the laws of Identity and Contradiction, it consists in the Affirmation of Incompatibility with an inclusive fact, e. g. —

Major premise. What is associated with a name, is not a simple reflex produced by a sensory stimulus.

Examples. Just as the ideas of God, of Matter, etc.

Minor premise. Anyone of our ideas is associated with a name.

Conclusion. It is not a simple reflex.[1]

What is here denied is the fact of being produced by a sensory stimulus coming from the object. This feature is subordinate to the fact of not being susceptible to receive a name, and this is contradictorily

---

[1] Tātp., p. 88. 17 ff.

opposed to the fact of being susceptible to receive a name. Therefore this latter fact being established, it excludes the possibility for utterable ideas to be simple reflexes.

In this case also, in order to deny that utterable ideas are simple reflexes, we must try to imagine a simple reflex producing such an idea and then bar the progress of imagination by a categorical denial. The interconnection and mutual dependence of the notions of an utterable idea, as a constructed conception, and an unutterable reflex, is founded on the laws of Identity and Contradiction. It is a negative deduction by Existential Identity. The hypothetical perceptibility of the denied fact must be understood as in the sixth figure.

The ninth figure of Negation is founded exclusively on the principle of Causation. It consists in a Negation of Causes, e. g.—

Major premise. Wheresoever there is no fire, there is also no smoke.

Minor premise. There is here no fire.

Conclusion. There is here no smoke.

This figure is resorted to when the effect of a cause cannot be directly perceived. When its presence can be imagined on a place lying in the ken, we will avail ourselves of the figure of Simple Negation.

This same major premise can be used for an Affirmative Syllogism expressed according to the Method of Difference. It will then represent the normal type of the Indian inductive-deductive syllogism, in which the Induction is founded on the Method of Difference and which represents the *modus tollens* of the Mixed Hypothetical Syllogism. Indeed, we will then have—

Major premise. Wheresoever no fire, there also no smoke.

Minor premise. But there is here smoke.

Conclusion. There is here fire.

The tenth figure of a negative syllogism is again based on a double connection, one founded on Causality, and another founded on the law of Contradiction. It consists in Affirmation of Incompatibility with the Cause of the denied fact, e. g.—

Major premise. Wheresoever there is an efficient fire, there can be no shivering from cold.

Minor premise. There is here such a fire.

Conclusion. There is here no shivering.

This figure is resorted to when cold, although existent, cannot be directly felt, neither can its symptoms like shivering etc. be directly perceived. They are then imagined and the suggestion baffled by pointing to the presence of a good fire. The connection of shivering with cold is founded on the law of Causation. The connection of cold with non-cold or fire is founded on the law of Contradiction.

The last, eleventh figure of the negative syllogism is still more complicated by a further causal relation. It consists in the Affirmation of Effect, produced by something Incompatible with the cause of the denied fact, e. g. —

Major premise. Wherever there is smoke, there is no shivering.

Minor premise. There is here smoke.

Conclusion. There is here no shivering, etc.

In cases where the shivering could have been observed directly, we would deny it by Simple Negation. In cases where its cause, the sensation of cold, could be felt directly, we would apply for its negation the ninth figure, the non-perception of the cause. In cases where the fire is perceptible, we apply the tenth figure of the negative syllogism, the Affirmation of Incompatibility with the Cause. But when all three cannot be directly perceived, we imagine the presence of the deduced fact and then repudiate it in a negative syllogism, where there is an Affirmation of an Effect, produced by something incompatible with its causes. This figure also is thus essentially nothing more than a repelled suggestion. The first figure thus virtually includes in itself the remaining ten figures. No other figure is possible. For instance, the figure of Affirmation of an Incompatible Included term will yield no valid figure, it would yield only a particular judgment, and all particular judgments, we have seen, are banned from the domain of valid ratiocination in Indian logic.

§ 5. Importance of Negation.

We have followed the Buddhist logicians in their minute analysis of Negation. Simple Negation, as well as every possible variety of deduced negation, have been examined. Everywhere it has been found to repose on the same principle, it is a baffled suggestion, it is not a direct way of cognizing reality. As such it has some importance in guiding our behaviour, it possess indirect «meaning» and validity, but nevertheless it seems to be something utterly superfluous and not indispensable. Why should our knowledge, which is by its essence cognition of reality, why should half of its whole province concern itself with nothing but baffled suggestions?[1] Since the relation between reality

[1] Cp. Sigwart, op. cit., I. 171: «es handelt sich nur darum, zu erkennen, warum wir dieser subjectiven Wege bedürfen um die Welt des Realen zu erkennen».

and its cognition is a causal one—positive knowledge is a product of reality—it would be natural to surmise that negative knowledge must be the product of absence of reality. Such is the view of many philosophic schools in India and in the West. But this is an error. Reality does not consist of existence and non-existence. Reality is always existence. The question remains why is a whole half of our knowledge busy in repudiating suggestions, when it could apparently be better employed in direct cognition of reality? The answer to this question is the following one. Although reality does not consist of reality and unreality, and knowledge does not consist of knowledge and non-knowledge, nevertheless every perception consists in a perception preceded by a non-perception of the same object, that is to say, by the absence of its own hypothetical visibility, not by non-perception simply, not by non-perception of something absolutely invisible. Perception which would never be interrupted by intervals of non-perception would not be perception. Perception is always interrupted perception, perception separated by intervals of non-perception of the same object. Therefore non-perception can never transgress the limits of sense-perception. Negation is nothing but non-perception, and non-perception always refers to a possible perception, it must keep our knowledge within the borders of sensuous experience.

Dharmottara delivers himself on this question in the following sentences.[1] «Since every variety of negation refers to such objects which can be placed in the conditions of perceptibility, which, therefore, are *sensibilia*,[2] for this reason every negation is virtually nothing else but a simple negation of hypothetical perceptibility». All other varieties of Negation are founded moreover either on the law of Contradiction, or on the law of Causation. But both these laws do not extend their sway beyond the sphere of possible experience. If something contradicts the established extension and comprehension of a concept, or if something contradicts the cause or the effect of a thing, we pronounce a judgment of negation. «Whensoever we cognize», says the same author,[3] «a contradiction with the (established) subalternation of facts, or a contradiction with their (established) causal relation, we must necessarily be aware that «we have had of them a perception, as well as a non-perception preceded by perception. Now those objects, which

---

[1] NBT., p. 38. 6; transl., p. 102.

[2] *dṛśya.*

[3] Ibid., p. 38. 11; transl., p. 103.

(alternately) have been perceived and non-perceived, are necessarily perceptible. Therefore, in all the figures founded on the law of Contradiction, as for instance, in the fourth figure, the figure of Affirmation of an Incompatible fact; and in all the figures founded on the law of Causation, as for instance, the ninth figure, the figure of Negation of Causes; in all these figures it must be understood that Negation of contradicting facts, (of causes or effects) refers to sensible experience only!»

§ 6. CONTRADICTION AND CAUSALITY ONLY IN THE EMPIRICAL SPHERE.

It has been thus established that all the possible varieties of Negation are possible only on the basis of sensible facts. On the other hand, it has also been established, that all these varieties are founded on the two fundamental laws, upon which all our knowledge of relations is founded, the laws of Identity and Causality. It follows that the domain, in which these two fundamental laws obtain, must be experience. Beyond that domain, in the sphere of the Absolute, there is no place neither for Negation, nor for Contradiction; for in that sphere there is no non-existence, there is only pure absolute non-relative Existence, and therefore there can neither be any Contradiction, nor any Causality. «The two fundamental laws therefore, says Dharmakīrti,[1] do not extend their sway over objects other than empirical». In explaining this sentence Dharmottara says:[2] «Objects, different from those that are alternately perceived and non-perceived, are metaphysical objects, which are never perceived. Their contradiction to something, their causal relation with something it is impossible to imagine. Therefore is it impossible to ascertain what is it they are contradictorily opposed to, and what are they causally related to. For this reason contradicting facts, (as well as causes or effects), are fit to be denied only after their positive and negative observation has been found to be recurrent». The impossibility of any other contradiction or any other causality thus being established, the incompatible facts can be denied only when they are *sensibilia*, i. e., open to both perception and non-perception. Indeed[3] Contradiction is realized when on the presence of one term we distinctly realize the absence of the other. Causal relation

---

[1] NB., p. 38. 19; transl., p. 104.
[2] NBT, p. 38.20; transl., p. 104.
[3] *Ibid.*, p. 39.2; transl., p. 105.

is established when on the absence of the result, another fact, its cause, is also absent. The Subalternation of concepts is deemed to be established when on the absence of the inclusive term, the included is necessarily absent. We must indeed be alive to the fact that the extension and comprehension of our concepts are founded on Negation. The comparative extension of the terms tree and Ašoka is fixed when we know that if on a certain place there are no trees, there certainly are no Ašokas. And the knowledge of the absence of something is always produced by repelling its imagined presence. Therefore if we remember some instances of Contradiction, of Causality, or of different Extension, we needs must have in our memory some negative experience. Negation of *sensibilia* is the foundation of our concepts of non-Existence, which is underlying our knowledge of the laws of Contradiction, Causation and Subalternation». «If we do not have in our memory some corresponding negative experience, we will not remember contradiction and other relations, and then, in that case, the non-existence of a fact would not follow from the presence of an incompatible fact, or from the negation of its cause, etc. Since the negative experience, which we have had at the time when we first became aware of the fact of incompatibility or of a causal relation, must necessarily be present in our memory, it is clear that a negative cognition is always founded on a present or former repudiation of imagined perceptibility».[1]

§ 7. Negation of supersensuous objects.

The Buddhist theory of Negation is a direct consequence of the Buddhist theory of Judgment. The fundamental form of the Judgment, we have seen, is the perceptual judgment, or — what is the same — the name-giving judgment, of the pattern «this is a jar». Such a judgment is contained in every conception referred to objective reality and in this sense conception and judgment become convertible terms.[2] Negation consists therefore in repelling an attempted perceptive judgment and for this reason every negation is a negation of *sensibilia*, of such objects which can be imagined as present. The negation of the presence of an invisible ghost, we have seen, is just only a negation of its presence, i. e., of its visible form. But the Realists and Rationalists, the Vaišeṣikas and the Sāṅkhyas, speak of super-

---

1 NBT., p. 39.9; transl., p. 106.
2 *vikalpa* = *adhyavasāya*.

sensuous[1] objects, objects which are invisible by their nature, objects which never can be present to the senses, which are *non-sensibilia.* The negation or non-perception of such objects is a «non-perception of the unperceivable». Non-perception of imagined *sensibilia* is a source of right knowledge,[2] because it leads on to successful action. But the non-perception, or negation, of objects whose presence to the senses cannot be imagined is not a source of knowledge, since it cannot lead on to successful purposeful action. Dharmakīrti[3] asks what is the essence and what the function of such Negation? And answers that its essence consists «in excluding both the direct and indirect way of knowledge», and its function is the same as the function of a problematic judgment, that is to say, it is a non-judgment. There is no knowledge, neither direct nor indirect, about metaphysical objects, there are only problems, i. e. questions. Metaphysical objects are non-objects, metaphysical concepts are non-concepts, and metaphysical judgments are non-judgments. The problematic judgment is a *contradictio in abjecto.* A problem is a question and a judgment, we have seen, is an answer, a verdict.

Dharmottara[4] explains. «An object can be inaccessible in three respects, in time, in space and in essence». This means that a metaphysical object is beyond time, beyond space and beyond sensible reality «Negation regarding such objects is a source of problematic reasoning. Now, what is the essence of such reasoning? It is repudiation of both direct and indirect knowledge. This means that it is not knowledge at all, because the essence of knowledge is to be an assertory relation between cognition and its object».

Knowledge is a relation between the cognizable and cognition, between the object and its cognition or between reality and logic. It is therefore asked[5] «if cognition proves the existence of the cognized, it would be only natural to expect that absence of cognition would be a proof of the absence of a cognized object?»

This question is answered by Dharmakīrti[6] in the following way: «When there are altogether no means of cognition, the non-existence of the object cannot be established». This means that when an object

[1] *adṛśya-anupalabdhi.*
[2] *pramāṇa.*
[3] NB., p. 39. 19; transl., p. 107.
[4] NBT., p. 39. 21; transl., p. 107.
[5] NBT., p. 40. 1; transl., p. 107.
[6] NB., p. 40. 2; transl., p. 107.

is incognizable in a positive way, neither is it cognizable in a negative way. A metaphysical entity can be neither affirmed, nor denied, it always remains a problem.

Dharmottara gives the following explanation.[1] «When a cause is absent, the result does not occur; and when a fact of greater extension is absent, its subordinate fact, the fact of lesser extension, comprehended under it, is likewise absent». There are only two relations of necessary interdependence, Causation and Coinherence. If knowledge is necessarily connected with reality, what kind of relation is it? Is it Causality or is it Identity of reference? If knowledge were the cause of reality or if it did contain reality as a subordinate part, then the absence of knowledge would establish the absence of the corresponding reality. But knowledge is neither the one, nor the other. Therefore its absence proves nothing. The relation between reality and cognition is indeed causal, reality produces cognition. The heterogeneity of the cause does not prove the impossibility of causation. According to the principle of Dependent Origination, it does not prevent causal interdependence. Since every thing real is a result of its causes, we can always legitimately infer the reality of a cause, when we have the result. Therefore the inference from knowledge to the reality of its object is legitimate. The existence of a suitable source of knowledge proves the existence of the corresponding object, but not *vice versa*. The absence of the knowledge of a thing does not prove its non-existence. Dharmottara[2] says: «The existence of right knowledge proves the existence of real objects, but absence of knowledge cannot prove the non-existence of the corresponding object».

It is true that the absence of the result can prove the absence of the cause according to Dharmakīrti's Second Figure of the negative Syllogism. The Negation of the Effect is possible when, for instance, on the ground of the absence of smoke we deny the existence of its cause, the fire. Dharmottara explains[3] that «since causes, indeed, do not necessarily produce their effects, therefore, when we observe the absence of the effect, we can infer only the absence of such causes, whose efficiency has not been interfered with, but not of other ones». And what are these causes? «Causes whose efficiency remains (necessarily) unopposed, are the causes which exist at the ultimate moment

---

[1] NBT., p. 40. 4 ff; transl., p. 107.

[2] NBT., p. 40. 8; transl., p. 108.

[3] NBR., p. 31. 10; transl., p. 88.

(of the preceding compact chain of moments), because the possibility of other preceding moments being checked in their efficiency can never be excluded». If we then maintain that the Negation as a mental phenomenon must in any case have a cause in external reality, this will be right only in the sense that even that Negation is a positive cognition of something, i. e., of an indefinite moment of reality.

These considerations are very important, they strike at the heart of Buddhism as a religion. The existence of the Omniscent, of the Buddha is at stake. He is decidedly a metaphysical entity and according to the principles just laid down nothing can be denied and nothing can be affirmed of him. If he be identified with existence itself, with ultimate existence, he then, of course, cannot be denied. Existence cannot be non-existence. But of this kind of existence nothing can be cognized neither in the way of negation, nor in the way of affirmation

§ 8. Indian developments.

The originality of the Buddhist theory of Negation and the arguments by which it was supported could not but produce a kind of revolution in the domain of Indian logic and oblige all schools to reconsider their own views on the subject, so as to adapt the new theory, as far as possible, to their fundamental principles, which, of course, could not be abandoned. Some of them adopted the Buddhist theory almost entirely, some adopted it partly, others again opposed it with stubborn resistance. The Buddhists, indeed, maintained 1) that reality is not split in existence and non-existence, it consists of existence only, 2) that nevertheless non-existence of a special kind has objective validity, as a method of cognition capable of guiding purposive actions, 3) that negation is not a direct way of cognizing reality, it is a roundabout way and therefore included in inference, 4) that the logical reason in this inference is «non-perception», that is to say, a repelled hypothetical sense-perception. From all these four points the Naiyāyiks admitted only the last one, but they interpreted it so as to deprive it of all its value. Vātsyāyana[1] admits that non-existence is cognized in the way of a hypothetical judgment. If the object is existent, it is cognized, if it is non-existent, it is not cognized, for if it were existent it would have been cognized. However, this does not interfere with his fundamental view that reality consists of existence

[1] NB., p. 2.5.

and non-existence, both are perceived by sense-perception. The hypothetical judgment, by which the absence of the object is cognized, is interpreted as a special kind of direct perception through the senses and non-existence as a kind of additional qualification of existence. Between the absent jar and the place from which it is absent there is a relation of the «qualifing to the qualified;»[1] this relation being neither conjunction, nor inherence, but a «simple relation»,[2] is nevertheless something objectively real, cognized through the senses. There is thus a real interaction[3] between the senses and the absent object; absence is a reality.

The Vaišeṣikas departed at considerable length from their matches in realism, the Naiyāyiks. They admitted that non-existence is not existence, that there is no such category of Being which is called non-existence.[4] It is therefore not cognized by the senses,[5] but it is cognized in inference;[6] e. g., when the non-production of a result is a sufficient reason to infer the absence of its cause. They admitted that this inference consists in the repudiation of a possible perception.[7] But they nevertheless continued to maintain the reality of the relation of a «qualifier to a qualified» as existing between the abseut object and its perceived empty place. The perception of the absent thing was for them not an independent, but a dependent cognition.[8] On this ground the Vaišeṣikas somehow made their peace with the Naiyāyiks and the views of the latter school were incorporated into the common stock when the schools amalgamated.

The Mīmāṃsaka school became divided on this problem of Negation, just as on many others, in two subschools. Prabhākara «the friend of the Buddhists»[9] accepted the Buddhist theory integrally. He maintained that non-Existence is no separate reality, and Negation is not a separate source of knowledge. The empty place is the external reality, the absent object is imagination. The empty place is perceived

---

1 *višeṣya-višeṣaṇa-bhāva.*

2 *svabhāva-sambandha.*

3 *sannikarṣa.*

4 Cp. N. Kandalī, p. 226. 21, where the Nyāya-vārtika-kāra is quoted with approval, but the direct perception of absence is rejected.

5 Ibid., p. 225. 16, 23.

6 Prašast., p. 225. 14.

7 They admit that *yogya-anupalambhaḥ pratipādakaḥ,* but they do not admit the *bhūtalasyaiva abhāvasya pratyakṣatā,* cp. N. Kandalī, p. 226.

8 Ibid., p. 226. 23.

9 *bauddha-bandhuḥ Prabhākaraḥ,* cp. my article in Jacobi's Festschrift.

by the senses, the absent object is denied in a negative judgment which repels its imagined presence.[1] But the main stock of the school, the followers of Kumārila-bhaṭṭa, remained faithful to the letter of their old authority Šabarasvāmin, who had declared that «the non-existence of a means of cognition is a proof of the non-existence (of the object»).[2] They rejected the Buddhist theory that the non-existent thing is an imagined thing. They not only admitted Non-existence as an external reality, but they admitted a double reality of non-existence, an objective one and a subjective one. Such a view, they thought, was urged upon them by the words of Šabara. The objective Non-existence is the real absence of the object, either before its production, or after its destruction, or mutual non-existence, alias «otherness» of one object in regard of the other, or absolute non-existence. All four kinds of non-existence are objective realities. The subjective Non-existence is the non-existence, or non-efficiency, of all means of cognition. When neither perception, nor inference, nor any other source of knowledge is available, this absence of a source of knowledge becomes itself a new source of cognition. Thus the real absence of the object becomes cognized by the real absence of all sources of knowledge.[3] Non-existence (*abhāva*) is both the non-existence of the object and the non-existence of the corresponding source of knowledge. The school opposed the view of the Buddhists and of Prabhākara by denying that the absent object is imagined. They opposed the Naiyāyikas by denying that non-existence could be perceived through the senses directly. They opposed the Vaišeṣikas by denying that it could be cognized by inference. They maintained that non-Existence itself was a special, primordial source of knowledge, coordinated to inference, but not subordinated to it.[4]

Thus we have here an example of the double influence of a logical theory, positive and negative. One party yields to the influence of a new idea, gives up its own theory and replaces it by the new and foreign one. The other party rejects the novelty, hardens in the old belief and develops it into its most remote, but logically deduced, consequences.

---

1 Šāst. Dīp., p. 326 ff.

2 *abhāvopi prāmāṇyābhavo nastīty asya arthasya asannikṛṣṭasya.*

3 Šlokavārt (abhāva), p. 473 ff.; Š. D., p. 322 ff.

4 The Bhāṭṭa-Mīmāṃsaka theory of Negation is criticized in N. Kandalī, p. 227. 5 ff.

Scholastic Vedānta has admitted Negation as a special source of knowledge coordinated to perception, inference and other sources. Its theory of Negation is borrowed from the Buddhists. To maintain that Negation is a source of right knowledge is the same as to maintain that it is assertive, it contains a necessary assertion and, in this sense, it is not negation, but affirmation, affirmation of the Ultimately Real. Indeed according to scholastic Vedānta all its sources of right knowledge are cognitions of brahma, of the only Reality, the One-without-a-Second. Just as sense-perception is a cognition of pure reality in the element «this» of the judgment «this is a jar», just so Negation is also a right cognition of the element «this» in the judgment «this is no jar» or «this is an empty place». The «this» of these judgments is the transcendental «Thisness». The Thing-in-Itself of Buddhist logic is identified in scholastic Vedānta with the Ultimate Reality of the Eternal Brahma.[1]

§ 9. European Parallels.

a) Sigwart's theory.

The problem of Negation has been solved in Europe by **Sigwart**, just as it has been solved in India by **Dharmakīrti** (and partly Dignāga). There is therefore a certain analogy between the respective position of these two logicians in their respective fields of action, of the one in the VII-th century AD in India and the other in the XIX-th century in Germany. Just as the history of the Indian views on Negation has to consider the conditions before Dharmakīrti, his reform and its repercussion among different schools, just so on the European side we have to consider the condition before Sigwart, his reform and its reaction in modern times.

Aristotle saw no difficulty in treating Negation on the same level as Affirmation. For him both were independent, equally primordial and coordinated modes of cognition. He however did not include neither Negation nor Non-existence among his Categories and thus avoided the necessity of assuming a non-existent Existence. However the fact that negation is not as primordial as affirmation is so obvious, that it could not have escaped his attention altogether. He remarks that «affirmation precedes negation, just as existence precedes non-existence».[2] This observation did not prevent him from putting negation side by side on the same level with affirmation in the definition of a proposi-

---

1 Cp. Vedānta-Paribhāṣā, Nyāyamakaranda, etc., passim.

2 Anal. Post., I. 25, 86 b 33, cp. B. Erdmann, Logik[3], p. 495, n. 4.

tion or judgment. This attitude was faithfully preserved in European logic through all the middle ages and in modern times up to the time of Sigwart. Kant did not depart in this case from traditional logic, although, as it appears from one of his very illuminating remarks,[1] the future theory was present to his mind. He however did not attach much importance to it and it received at his hand no development. For Aristotle Affirmation and Negation are the logical counterparts of Existence and Non-existence, for Kant the affirmative and negative judgments are the patterns from which the categories of Reality and Negation are deduced. They represent two coordinated aspects of the world of mere phenomena.

Sigwart begins by stating that Aristotle and all those logicians who followed him in characterizing judgment as either affirmation or negation and included the division in the definition, were right in so-far as all judgments are exhaustively so divided, and that judgment in general is only possible either by affirming or denying a predicate of a subject, but they were not right in coordinating these two modes of cognition as both equally primordial and independent from one another.[2] «Negation is always directed against an attempted synthesis, and presupposes a suggestion,[3] either internally arisen or brought in from without, to connect subject and predicate». Accordingly «a denial has a good meaning only when it is preceded by an attempt which is repelled in a negative judgment». The positive judgment does not require a preceding denial, whereas it is a necessary condition of every negation, that it shoud be preceded in thought by an attempted affirmation.[4]

---

[1] He says, CPR., p. 508 (2-nd ed., p. 709), «The proper object of negative judgments is to prevent error. Hence negative propositions intended to prevent erroneous knowledge in cases where error is never possible, may no doubt be very true, but they are empty, they do not answer any purpose and sound therefore often absurd; like the well known utterance of a schoolmaster that Alexander could not have conquered any countries without an army».

[2] Op. cit., I. 155.

[3] *Zumuthung* = *āropa*.

[4] A remarkable foreshadowing of Sigwart's theory is found in J. S. Mill's Logic[8], I, p. 44. Treating of *privative* names, he says that these names are «positive and negative together». Names like *blind* cannot be applied to sticks and stones, albeit they are *not seeing*. They connote the absence of a quality and the fact that its presence «might naturally have been expected». Therefore we never would say, except in poetry, that the stones are blind. The example of stones that are not seeing, or not speaking, is then repeated by Sigwart, I. 172, Bradley,[2] I. 119 and others.

That this is really so, «that the negation has a meaning only in the face of an attempted positive assertion, becomes at once clear, when we consider that only a restricted number of positive predicates can be ascribed to a subject, whereas the number of predicates which can be denied is infinite».[1] However actually denied are only those whose presence it is natural to expect. The judgments «there is no fire in the stove» or «it does not thunder»[2] are judgments about non-existing things. How is a judgment about a non-existing thing possible? Only in imagination!—in the way of the non-existing thing being imagined. A negative judgment is concerned about an absent thing which has been hypothetically imagined as present. Therefore the negation of things expected and easily imaginable is natural. But it becomes ridiculous, if the presence of the denied object never could be expected. If someone instead of saying «there is no fire in the stove» would have said «there is in it no elephant», although both the fire and the elephant are equally absent, the second judgment would seem strange, because unexpected.

If we compare with this statement of Sigwart the theory of Dharmakīrti, we cannot but find the similarity striking. The Buddhist philosopher begins, we have seen, by dividing all cognition in direct and indirect. Negation is referred to the indirect class, to what he calls inferential cognition.[3] Even the simplest case of negation, the judgment of the pattern «there is here no jar» is treated not as a variety of perception, but as an indirect cognition, as an inferential non-perception. The full meaning of such a judgment is the following one. «Since all conditions of normal perceptibility are intact, the jar, had it been present on this spot, would have been perceived; but it is not actually perceived, therefore we must conclude that it is absent».[4] The simple judgment of non-perception thus reduces to a full Mixed Hypothetical Syllogism. «How is an absent thing cognized on a given spot», asks Dharmottara,[5] and gives the very natural answer: «it is imagined»; imagined in the way of a hypothetical judgment of the following form: «if a jar would have been present on this spot, it would have been perceived, but since it is not perceived, we can deny its presence». The fact of non-perception is the middle term from which the

---

1 Ibid., I. 156.

2 Ibid., I. 168.

3 *anumāna* = *anumāna-vikalpa*.

4 NBT., p. 49.17; transl., p. 138.

5 NBT., p. 22.8; transl., p. 62.

absence of the jar is deduced. The negative judgment, even the most simple one, the judgment of non-perception, is an inference. The fact that Dharmakīrti calls it inference, while Sigwart speaks of negative judgments, has no importance, since inference means here indirect cognition. Negation is an indirect cognition and consists in repelling a hypothetical affirmation.

The discovery and the clear formulation of the meaning of Negation must thus be credited to Dharmakīrti in India and to Sigwart in Europe. This coincident solution of a capital logical problem must be regarded as an outstanding fact in the comparative history of philosophy.

Both philosophers seem to have been led to this discovery in a somewhat similar manner. Sigwart declares it to be impossible to save the independent rank of the negative judgment by defining it, in accord with an occasional utterance of Aristotle, as a separation of subject and object, contrasting with their synthesis in an affirmative proposition. «The predicate of a judgment», says he,[1] «is never an Ens, it never can be conceived as a separate Ens, to be posited as something really separate from the subject». «This separation does not exist in that reality, to which our judgment refers».[2] «The thing exists only with its quality and the quality only with the thing. Both constitute an inseparable unity». «If we remain by the simplest, the perceptual[3] judgment, the congruence of the sensation with the representation is an entirely internal relation and we cannot maintain that the connecting of the elements of a judgment corresponds to a union of analogous objective elements».[4] This, we know, is exactly the Indian view according to which the real judgment is the perceptual which unites a sensation with a representation, and reduces to a relation of synthesis between a subject which is always an Ens with a predicate which is never an Ens.

If the predicate is always a subjective construction, whether it be affirmed or denied, the difference between affirmation and negation reduces to a difference of a direct and an indirect characterization of the same Ens. Aristotle hints the right point when he posits the real

---

1 Ibid., I. 170.

2 Ibid., I. 104. As all European logicians, Sigwart has that judgment in view which the Indians call analytical *(svabhāva-anumāna)*, for in the inferential judgment founded on causation the subject and predicate refer to two different Ens'es.

3 Benennungsurtheil.

4 Ibid.

Ens, the *Hoc-Aliquid*, as the common subject of all predication and does not assume any category of Non-existence.

b) Denied Copula and Negative Predicate.

As a result of the coincidence in the general view of Negation there is a further coincidence in answering the question about the proper residence of the negative particle. Since the judgment consists of subject, predicate and copula, it is natural to enquire whether Negation resides with the copula or with the predicate. It evidently cannot reside in the subject. The subject in the epistemological form of the judgment is the real particular, the element «this» which is existence itself and cannot be non-existence. But the predicate is always a Universal which can be either affirmed or denied. In the type-instance «this is that», the copula can be denied, and we shall have the type «this is not that»; or the predicate can be denied and we then shall have «this is non-that». Sigwart maintains that negation affects always the copula. The copula is denied, not the predicate. He remarks that there can be no denying copula, for a denying copula is a *contradictio in adjecto*. There can be only a denied copula. According to this view the judgment with a negative predicate will be positive, because the copula will not be denied. Such is also the opinion of Aristotle[1] for whom the predicates *non-homo, non-justus* are positive, although indefinite, and the judgment *non est justus* is negative, but the judgment *est non-justus* affirmative. And such must also have been the opinion of Kant, who called these negative or infinite predicates «limiting» and the corresponding judgment indefinite. The view of Sigwart has been energetically opposed by Wundt,[2] for whom the judgment with a negative predicate is the predominant class of negative judgments, the judgment with a negative copula, which he calls «separation-judgment», being minor in importance. B. Erdmann,[3] after some fluctuation, decides, that the judgment with a negative predicate is «nevertheless» negative, and Bradley[4] does the same.

Now what is the position of the Buddhist Logic in the face of Sigwart's opinion and the controversy it has provoked?

---

1 Cp. Grote, op. cit., p. 122.

2 Logik[2] (Erkenntnisslehre, p. 223, n.).

3 Logik[3], p. 500.

4 Principles of Logic, p. 116. He thinks that the ground for a negation is always some open or latent opposition between subject and predicate, the negative predicate is the opposed predicate.

According to Dharmakīrti Negation is directed against an attempted affirmation of some presence, it is consequently directed against the copula, if the copula means existence and presence. A judgment with a negative predicate will «nevertheless» be affirmative. It may also be negative if the copula is also negative, as e. g., Aristotle's example *non est justus non homo,* or the Indian example *«all things are not im-permanent»*, but the judgments *est justus non-homo* and *all things are impermanent* will be affirmative. In this respect there is full agreement between Sigwart and Dharmakīrti.

There is a divergence in another respect. The Indian theory takes its stand on the perceptual judgment. The negative judgment is accordingly a judgment of non-perception, non-perception of a thing expected to be present on a given place. Dharmakīrti and Dharmottara compare all possible instances of negative judgments and reduce each of them to the non-perception of an imagined visibility. The ground for repudiating a suggested presence is, first of all, direct sense-perception, viz., the perception of the empty place where the denied object is expected to be present. This is simple or direct Negation.[1] But there is also an indirect or deduced Negation. We can through inference ascertain the absence of a thing in a place which is not accessible to direct perception. And that is possible in two ways, viz., we either fail to perceive on a given spot something which would necessarily have been present, if the object of our denial were also there present[2] or we perceive by positive sense-perception the presence of something incompatible with it.[3] But whether the ground be the absence of a necessarily connected thing or the presence of an incompatible thing, whether it be privation or opposition,[4] in any case negation will be reducible to an instance of non-perception of hypothetical visibility. Thus negation always affects the copula and its ground is either direct perception or the laws of necessary conjunction, which are the three laws of Contradiction, of Identity and Causality. What Figures of Negation are produced by the interaction of the positive laws of Identity and Causation with the negative law of Contradiction, has been indicated above[5] and need not be repeated here.

---

1 NBT., p. 38.5

2 *svabhāvānupalabdhi.*

3 Cp. Sigwart, op. cit., I. 172 — «entweder fehlt das Prädikat, oder... ist das Subject mit dem Prädicate unverträglich».

4 Cp. Bradley, Logic², p. 117.

5 Sigwart. op. cit., p. 179 ff. seems to be seeking for a law, or laws, explaining why some representations (or conceptions) are by their nature incompatible

But although it is true that negation in a negative judgment affects the copula, we must not forget that the verb substantive, which expresses the copula, has a double function: 1) to express existence and 2) to serve as a copula in predication. In full accord with this, the negative or negatived copula has also a double function: 1) to express non-existence and 2) to deny connection, that is, to express separation. It is true, as Sigwart remarks, that a separating copula is a *contradictio in adjecto*, however the copula will then be copula only by name, it will be a sign of separation in the sense of non-congruence. And since such separation can only be found between two concepts, such a judgment is always a judgment with two concepts, or an inferential judgment, a major premise. It will be no perceptual judgment any more. However, the substitute for the perceptual judgment will then be in the minor premise of the inference, e. g.—

Major premise. Wheresoever there are no trees at all, there can be no *šiṃšapās*.

Minor premise. There are here no trees at all (=Perception!).

Conclusion. There are here no *šiṃšapās*.

The conclusion must be taken with the *proviso* «if they would be present and nothing interfering with their perceptibility would bar us, we would see them». Thus in all cases negation must be reduced to non-perception of a hypothetically visible object. It cannot be objected that there are abstract concepts, which cannot be treated as visible or invisible, because, according to the Buddhist view, every concept must be at the same time a perceptual judgment; it must refer to reality, otherwise it will be outside the domain of knowledge.

It can be maintained, as it appears from what has been explained above, that there is in the negative judgment no copula at all, since the substantive verb in these judgments of non-perception has neither the meaning of a copula or conjuntion, nor of a negative copula or separation; it is here used in its other sense, the sense of existence. Its negative form means then absence of a given object on a given place, but not separation between two qualities or predication of a

---

and others not; he wants to have a basis for denial. He says that incompatibility is something «given» with the actual nature of the contents of our representations and their relation; and Bradley, who follows Sigwart in this research, finds an explanation, p. 119, in a subjective «mental repulsion of qualities», that is, a mental impenetrability which is but a metaphor from physical impenetrability. We shall see that, according to the Indians, incompatibility always reposes, directly or indirectly, on the law of Contradiction. No other explanation is needed.

negative quality. A negative quality is but a differentiating quality, and all qualities are differentiating, there is not a single one which would not be differentiating and negative in that sense. The Buddhist theory concerning Negative Predicates will be discussed later on, as well as some other important problems, inseparable from the problem of Negation. They will be treated, and their Indian shape compared with the European one, in connection with the Law of Contradiction.[1]

c) Judgment and Re-judgment.

Many philosophers, as e. g. Bergson in France, Bradley and Bosanquet in England, accepted Sigwart's theory fullheartedly, others, as e. g. Wundt, rejected it, others, as e. g. B. Erdmann, admitted it with important modifications. It is perhaps worth our while to mention here the attitude of Windelband, because its Indian parallels are apt to throw some light on the problem itself. According to this theory[2] every judgment is double; it consists of a judgment and a re-judgment (*Beurtheilung*). The second is a judgment about the first (*ein Urtheil über ein Urtheil*). Affirmation and Negation are coordinated and placed on the same footing. But they both belong to the re-judgment class. They are not judgments. The judgment contains initially no decision, it is neither affirmative nor negative. Thus the indirect and subjective character which Sigwart's theory ascribes to the negative judgment as its distinctive feature, is extended by Windelband to affirmation and both these fundamental varieties of cognition become again coordinated as being both secondary and indirect. Lotzé calls the second step, which contains a decision about the validity or unvalidity of the first, a secondary «by-thought» (*Nebengedanke*); B. Erdmann retains the term «re-judgment» (*Beurtheilung*),

---

[1] It is thus clear that the Indian philosophers were thoroughly aware of the double function of the substantive verb. It is curious that the Tibetan and Mongolian nations could never had confused the two functions, because their languages provide them with two quite different words for their expression. The verbs *yod* and *med* in Tibetan can never be confounded with the *yin* and *min*, the first pair meaning presence, resp. absence, the second pair meaning conjunction and separation. But in Europe the two meanings were always confounded. The first who has clearly and sharply described the distinction, is the French philosopher Laromiguière, and all the acumen of men like Hobbes, James Mill and J. S. Mill was needed fully to bring out and illustrate the confusion. Cp. Grote, op. cit., p. 387.

[2] W. Windelband, Beiträge zur Lehre vom negativem Urtheil. Tübingen, 1921.

but Brentano and Bergman prefer to call the first step simple presentation and reserve the term judgment for the second step. According to them the first step, when there as yet is neither affirmation nor negation, is no judgment at all. The real judgment is contained in the second step, which has been christened by Windelband as rejudgment,[1] but is, according to them, the real judgment. The latter opinion fully agrees with some views expressed by Dharmakīrti without in the least affecting his view of the negative judgment as an indirect cognition repelling an imagined affirmation.

We have quoted above[2] his very characteristic utterance about the difference between the two steps in cognition, which correspond to two different faculties of the human mind. «(Simple) sensation, says he, does not convince anybody; if it cognizes something, it does it in the way of a simple reflex, not as a judgment (*na niščayena, kiṃtarhi, tat-pratibhāsena*). Only inasmuch (*yatrāṃše*) as it is capable of producing a *subsequent judgment* (or decision), does it assume (the dignity of a real) source of cognition». The subsequent judgment is really a second step in cognition, but the first step then contains no judgment at all. This fundamental distinction has however nothing to do with the division of judgments into affirmative and negative. Every judgment is a second step with regard to a simple reflex, or a simple presentation; but every negative judgment is a secondary step with regard to an attempted affirmation, which is baffled by it. Windelband's theory clearly appears as untenable, when we apply it to the perceptual judgment, the only real judgment. Indeed on the strength of this theory the judgment «this is a jar» would not contain neither affirmation, nor negation in itself. But a re-judgment, or second judgment, comes, which tells us either that «it is true that there is here a jar», or that «it is false that there is here a jar». This clearly leads to an infinite regress, it at the same time becomes an eloquent proof of the rightness of Sigwart's and Dharmakīrti's theory. Windelband admits[3] that the question turns round a right definition of what a judgment is and that, if the opinion of Schuppe and others is taken in consideration, the re-judgment will already be contained in the judgment, since according to this view, — which, we have seen, is also the Indian view, — there is no difference at all between concep-

[1] Cp. the Indian theory about *jñānasya tat-prāmāṇyasya ca svatastvam paratastvam* mentioned above, p. 65.

[2] Cp. above, p. 241.

[3] Ibid., p. 181.

tion and judgment. «The Existence already contained in the affirmation of every conception is not only a justified form of judgment, it is the purest and simplest fundamental type of every judgment in general». Such is, we have seen, the Indian theory. «The traditional distinction between concept and judgment appears under these conditions as irrelevant for the task, which usually is assigned to logic,[1] viz., the task of establishing a normative system of the forms of thought. The division is grammatical, not logical... Nothing else remains than to interpret every judgment as an existential one for the complex representation which is thought through it». According to the Indians, the real judgment is, however, not the existential, but the perceptual. Existence, i. e. Affirmation, is then contained in every judgment, not as its predicate, but as its necessary subject. If the real judgment is found in the synthesis, identification, objectivization and decision contained in the simple pattern «this is a jar», we shall have the Indian theory.

Windelband likewise comes very near to the other chief point of the Indian theory of judgment, the point which concerns the inferential judgment and the categories of Relation expressed in it.[2] «The existence, which is understood in the judgment „the rose is a flower", says he, is quite different from the existence, which is contained in the judgment „lightning produces thunder"». If we change these both examples into Dharmakīrti's «the *śiṃśapā* is a tree» and «smoke is produced by fire», we will see that Windelband makes here an approach to the fundamental and exhaustive division of all relations into those founded on Identity and on Causation. Since in the proposition« the *śiṃśapā* is a tree» there are two concepts, there also are included in it two perceptual judgments «this is a *śiṃśapā*» and «this is a tree». A similar opinion is expressed by Sigwart[3] with regard to Kant's example «a learned man is not unlearned», in which he also distinguishes two perceptual judgments «x is learned» and «x is unlearned».[4]

---

1 Ibid., p. 182.

2 Cp. Ibid., p. 183—184.

3 Op. cit., I. 196.

4 In this connection we may perhaps venture an explanation of what lies at the bottom of Windelband's somewhat strange theory of «re-judgment». The judgment with two concepts, which is usually regarded as the pattern of all judgments, does not indeed contain any element asserting the reality of the synthesis. E. g., the judgment «the rose is a flower» is a judgment of concomitance or major premise, which only affirms consistency or congruence of two concepts. Their reality

CHAPTER II.

THE LAW OF CONTRADICTION.

§ 1. The Origin of Contradiction.

The origin of every judgment and of every conception, as they are understood in Buddhist logic, lies, we have seen,[1] in an act of running through[2] a manifold of undetermined intuition and in fastening[3] upon one point of that manifold, a point with regard to which the rest will be divided in two, usually unequal parts. On the one side we shall have the comparatively limited number of similar things, on the other the illimited, or less limited, number of the dissimilar ones. The similar will be «other» than the dissimilar and the dissimilar will be «other» than the similar; both parts mutually represent the absence of each the other, without any intermediate member.[4] Every conscious thought or cognition thus represents a dichotomy. The active part of consciousness, its spontaneity in cognition begins with an act of dichotomy. As soon as our intellectual eye begins to glimmer, our thought is already beset with contradiction. The moment our thought has stopped running and has fixed upon an external point, so as to be able internally to produce the judgment «this is blue», at that moment we have separated the universe of discourse into two unequal halves, the limited part of the blue and the less limited part of the non-blue. The definite thougt of the blue is nothing more than the definite exclusion of the non-blue; it is the fixation of a point of demarcation, which has nothing blue in itself, but with

---

is indeed affirmed in a second step, in the minor premise, «this is a rose» and, consequently, a flower. This minor premise appears as a kind of re-judgment concerning the reality, or truth, of the synthesis suggested in the major premise. The confusion between inference and judgment regarding the major premise has led to a confusion regarding the re-judgment contained in the minor premise. At the bottom of the re-judgment we find a function analogous to a minor premise. That is why Windelband's theory appears so strange when it is applied to the perceptual or real judgment. After having said «this is a jar» there is no need to repeat it in the re-judgment «it is true that this is a jar».

1 Cp. above, p. 209 ff.

2 *vitarka*.

3 *vicāra*.

4 *tṛtīya-prakāra-abhāva*.

regard to which we shall have on one side the blue and on the other side the non-blue. Just so in cognizing something as the object «fire», we at the same time think «this here is fire» and «that there is not fire», there is nothing intermediate. That the two parts are merely relative is clearly seen from the fact that a double negation is equal to affirmation; the not non-fire is the fire, because the fire is not the non-fire. When the two parts more or less hold the balance under the same determinable, it becomes indifferent what part will be expressed positively and what negatively, as, e. g., hot and cold, light and dark, permanent and impermanent, or non-impermanent and impermanent. But in the majority of cases the similar part is that part of the couple, to which we attend more than to the other and which we express positively, the correlative part is then expressed negatively. Thus to think actively, to think constructively, means to think dichotomizingly. The terms «construction»[1] and «dichotomy»,[2] in their application to thought, are synonymous and embrace every act of consciousness, except its purely passive part, the pure sensation. Conception, image, representation, presentation, judgment and inference will be comprised under dichotomy, as thought-construction or productive imagination. It will be opposed to pure sensation.

Now the law of Contradiction is nothing but the expression of the fact that all cognition is dichotomizing and relative. We can actively cognize or determine a thing only by opposing it to what it is not.

The negative part of the couple consists of the negation, or non-existence, of the positive part, and this negation in its turn consists either of something merely «other», or of something opposed to it. Non-existence is thus the general conception: otherness and contradiction are subordinated to it. «The different and the contrary, says Dharmottara,[3] cannot be conceived so long as the non-existence of the similar is not realized. Therefore otherness and opposition are realized as representing the negation of the similar, because such is the import of these otherness and opposition. Negation is conceived as the absence of the similar directly, otherness and opposition are conceived as the absence of the similar indirectly». The dissimilar class in regard of fire will embrace 1) the simple absence of fire, 2) the presence of something else instead of fire, and 3) the presence of

[1] *kalpanā=ekīkaraṇa.*

[2] *vikalpa=dvaidhīkaraṇa.*

[3] NBT., p. 21. 6; transl., p. 59.

something incompatible with fire and actively opposed to it. The different and incompatible presuppose the idea of simple absence.

The incompatibility or opposition is of a double kind. It is either efficient, agressive repugnancy of two things that cannot coexist without collision, as the hot and the cold; or it is the simple logical opposition of two things, of which the one is the «complete» negation of the other, as the blue and the non-blue. This is contradiction, it is logical, it is Antiphasis.[1]

§ 2. Logical Contradiction.

All and every thing in the Universe, whether real or only imagined, is subject to the law of «otherness», owing to which it is what it is, viz. it is different, or separate from all other things of the universe. This law could also be called the law of Identity, since it determines that the object is what it is, it is identical with itself. But according to the Buddhists there are altogether no identical real things. A thing is not the same at different moments or in different places. Every variation of time and place makes the thing «another» thing. «If the blue, says Šāntirakṣita, were a pervasive reality», i. e. a reality everywhere identical with itself, «there would be no limit assignable for identification, since similarity is found everywhere, the „all" would become the „whole", the universe would become the One-without-the-Second».[2] Therefore every thing in the universe is separate,[3] every thing is strictly real by itself, every ultimate reality is a Thing-in-Itself. Identity means Identity of Indiscernibles, things are identical or similar only as far as we do not discern their differences.[4] The law, according to which two things «are forbidden to be one thing»,[5] is the law of Contradiction. Ultimate reality is, in Buddhist philosophy, the reality of a point-instant; real or ultimate causality is the efficiency of a point-instant; just so ultimate diversity is the diversity of the Things-in-Themselves.

However, this ideal law of Contradiction is of no avail for the practical requirements of our life, it cannot serve us in forming con-

---

[1] *lākṣaṇiko virodhaḥ.*

[2] TS., p. 493. 3—4, cp. TSP., p. 493. 19 ff.

[3] *sarvam pṛthak.*

[4] *bhedāgrahāt.*

[5] *niṣiddha-ekatva.*, cp. NBT., p. 70. 19; transl., p. 197.

cepts and and in guiding our purposive actions. «Any pair of objects, says Dharmottara,[1] unavoidably include mutually the one the negation of the other», and he continues: «But what is it that we can conceive as non-existent in something else? Something distinct. Not something illimited, as, e. g., the fact of being a point-instant (of ultimate reality). Since the very essence of all existent objects, of patches of blue and other (coloured surfaces) consists of point-instants (of ultimate, pure reality, to which they are referred), therefore this fact has no limit. By a contrast with (mere) point-instants, nothing (definite) can be apprehended». Here the Buddhist is saved from the indefiniteness of the infinite judgment, or the illimited conception, by his theory of Negation. «Why indeed, asks Dharmottara, should this non-existence be illimited?» In so far as it has the definite shape of the repudiated object, whose presence has been imagined, it is not illimited. It is an imagined, concrete case of non-existence and therefore when we in a negative judgment distinctly cognize the absence of a definite thing on some definite place, we cognize it not in the shape of an illimited non-existence, but in a definite form, whether this form has been actually experienced as only imagined.

Dharmakīrti defines the law of Contradiction as that feature of each thing, whether real or imagined, owing to which everything presents itself in couples of two parts, of which the one is the complete negation of the other. «There is contradiction,[2] says he, in a couple whose essence is posited in a complete mutual exclusion, as, e. g., existence and non-existence». Complete[3] mutual exclusion means mutual exclusion without anything intermediate. From the ontological point of view the mutual opposition will be called existence and non-existence, from the logical standpoint it will be affirmation and negation of one and the same thing. Viewed dynamically, it can be characterized as mutual repulsion, viewed statically it will be position and opposition; as a relation it is a symmetrical relation or correlation, a relation in which the one fact is related to the other just in the same way as *vice versa* the latter to the former. It is not only a mutual reciprocated relation, it is complete reciprocation. There is, says Sāntisakṣita, on the one part not the slightest bit of what there is on the other.[4] Therefore this law may also be called the law

[1] Ibid.

[2] NB., p. 69.20; transl. 192 («complete» must be added).

[3] *pari-hāra* = *pari-tyāga* = *atyanta-tyāga* = *tṛtīya-prakāra-abhāva*.

[4] TSP., p. 1. 6, cp. 486. 20.

of Excluded Middle or of an Excluded Third Part,[1] since there are only two parts between which the respective whole is divided. It may also be called the law of Double Negation, since the one part is the negation of the other just in the same degree in which the latter is the negation of the former. If A is related to a non-A just in the same way in which a non-A is related to A, it is clear that the negation of a non-A will be equal to A. If there is in the blue nothing more than its opposition to the non-blue, it is clear that the opposition to the non-blue will be nothing else than the blue itself. Since all things are relative, every thing, except the ultimate reality of the point-instant, is nothing but the counterpart of its own negation. The Indian Realists are perhaps in the right when they maintain that every thing consists of existence and non-existence, but they are wrong in hypostasizing both existence and non-existence and forgetting that these are only mental superstructures upon an element of genuine reality, which alone is absolute and non relative. The superstructures are erected by our productive imagination operating upon the dichotomizing principle. Right are also partly the Mādhyamikas and Vedāntins which represent the opposite view, viz., that every thing is relative and therefore unreal, «just as the short and the long», the short being nothing over and above the negation of the long and *vice versa*. But they again are wrong in denying the reality of the point-instant underlying every relative thought-construction. The critical theory of the Sautrāntika-Yogācāra school alone escapes to the defects of both extremities in maintaining an imagined phenomenal world constructed by our productive imagination upon a foundation of transcendental reality.

§ 3. Dynamical Opposition.

The character of complete mutual exclusion or mutual repulsion can be ascribed to the contradictory parts of a couple only metaphorically. They can peacefully exist in close contiguity without interferring with the existence of one another, without the one encroaching upon the territory occupied by the other. It is a logical, but not a real mutual repulsion.

There is, however, a variety of contradiction which, in addition to being logical, is moreover real or dynamical. The diametrically opposed parts are not only the one the negation of the other logically,

1 *tṛtya-prakāra-abhāva*, TSP., p. 390.

they are moreover the one the militant adversary of the other. Properly speaking it is not at all a case of logical contradiction as Antiphasis; it can be called Contrapugnating Causality. In such cases both the opposed parts are mutually endeavouring to oust one another out of their mutual positions. Light and darkness are the one the complete negation of the other, and *vice versa.* In this respect there is between them a logical relation of contradiction. Light is the complete negation of darkness and darkness is nothing but the complete negation of light. However, they cannot peacefully coexist in close contiguity, as the blue and the non-blue. There is a constant warfare between them, the one will be constantly striving to occupy the territory of the other. Dharmakīrti gives the following definition of this kind of contradiction.[1] «If a phenomenon is produced by the totality of its causes (and therefore) endures, but (suddenly) disappears on the approach of another phenomenon, there is between both these phenomena a (real) opposition, as, for instance, between cold and hot». In this definition what calls our attention, first of all, is the mention of the «totality of causes of the opposed phenomenon». Is the cold, which in some junctures invariably precedes heat, the cause or one of the causes of that heat? Is the light, which in some junctures invariably follows on darkness, the effect of that darkness? Is the invariably preceding night the cause or one of the causes producing the invariably following day? These are the questions which always perplexed philosophers. The Buddhist answer is to the affirmative. We have examined the Buddhist theory of causation. According to this theory, every point of genuine reality, is arising in functional dependence on a sum-total of preceding factors, which all are its causes. In this totality not only positive magnitudes are arrayed, but negative magnitudes are also included, those that do not prevent the following phenomenon to appear.[2] If a break in the totality of the causes of a phenomenon supervenes and one of the factors that did not prevent its appearance is curtailed, that phenomenon vanishes and the break in the totality of its causes becomes the cause, or one of the causes, of the following phenomenon. In this sense the following light is produced by the preceding darkness, it is produced by the deficiency in the causes sustaining the existence of the preceding darkness. In these cases the preceding part is the cause, or one of the causes, producing

---

1 NBT., p. 68. 3; transl., p. 187.

2 Cp. above, p. 129.

the following part. If one part is opposed to the other, it is at the same time «doing something»[1], it indirectly partakes in its production.

Nor is the contradiction in all the cases of efficient repugnancy complete. Light is the complete contradiction of non-light. There is nothing intermediate between light and non-light. The law of the Excluded Middle fully applies. But between light and darkness considered as real phenomena there is always something in the middle. Even if the change is quite abrupt, even if light appears all of a sudden, on the very place[2] where the moment before there reigned absolute darkness, nevertheless there is at least one intermediate moment of twilight. The change, if it is produced as quickly as possible, requires nevertheless at least three moments: the ultimate moment of darkness, the initial moment of light and at least one moment between them, for the change to take place.

If the opposition is not complete as regards time, neither is it complete as regards space. When a light is produced in a large room darkness is completely annihilated only in that part of it, which is nearest to the lamp.[3] In the remaining part there is either twilight or darkness. Light is produced only as far as the efficient forces producing it are capable of doing it.

This is quite different in the cáse of a logical opposition between light and non-light. This opposition is complete, there is no twilight between light and non-light, twilight is included in the non-light. Neither is this opposition affected by the conditions of space. Light is the repudiation of non-light everywhere and always. The relation of opposition between light and non-light is characterized by logical necessity, which is not the case as regards the relation between light and darkness as real phenomena.

Such is also the meaning of the quarrel relating to the indifferent feeling. The Hīnayāna maintained that between pleasure and pain there is the indifferent feeling in the middle. But the logicians answered that the indifferent feeling, since it is not pleasure, must be reckoned as belonging to the category of pain,[4] since there are only two mutually

---

1 *kimcit-kara,* cp. NBT., p. 68. 9; cp. TSP., p. 157. 7—*akimcit-karo virodhī* the meaning is that the given point-instant is efficient as a cause, but not as opposition or contradiction, since the contradiction is constructed by the intellect.

2 NBT., p. 68. 19 ff.; transl., p. 189.

3 Ibid., p. 68. 16; transl., p. 189.

4 Tātp., p. 65.1 ff,

exclusive parts, pleasure and displeasure, the desired and the undesired. The Realists objected that if the indifferent feeling must be referred to pain, because it is not pleasure, it could be as well referred to pleasure because it is not pain. The quarrel is solved by pointing to the fact that there are two oppositions between pleasure and pain, the one logical without a middle term, the other real with a transition part.

But if the relation of this kind of contradiction reduces thus to a case of causality, is it not a misnomer to call it contradiction, is it not causality simple? This seems to have been the opinion of the early Vaišeṣikas, who characterized the relation of contradiction understood as efficient opposition as a relation of the «killer to the killed»,[1] a natural aversion between two things, as e. g. the natural irreconcilable enmity of the ichneumon and the snake. The Buddhists did not object to the characteristic of the relation of efficient opposition as a relation between «something stopping and something stopped»,[2] but with the reservation that the stopping and the stopped were «durations».[3] Hence the definition of that variety of contradiction, which consists in efficient opposition, includes the characteristic that the disappearing phenomenon must possess **duration**. This equally applies to the superseding phenomenon, it also must have duration. The causal relation in the sense of Dependent Origination obtains between the disappearing phenomenon, which had some duration and the superseding or the opposed phenomenon, which likewise endures for some time. It is metaphorical causation, not real causation, since, as we have seen, real causation is only that, which exists between efficient point-instants. The last moment of the series called darkness is the cause, in the sense of dependent origination, of the first moment of the series called light. But light and darkness are not mere moments, they become what they are, the phenomena of light and darkness, only when they have endured for some moments. This is consequently the difference between efficient opposition and real causation: real causation, just as real existence, belongs to sing e moments only, whereas efficient opposition is between one assemblage of moments and another assemblage; it is constructed just as the assemblages themselves are constructed by our intellect. In other words, the relation of efficient opposition is not an ultimate fact, it does not belong to the Things-in-Themselves,

[1] *ghātya-ghātaka-bhāva*, cp. VS., III. 1. 11.

[2] *nivartya-nivartaka-bhāva*.

[3] *bhavataḥ = prabandhena vartamānasya*. NBT., 69.9.

but only to constructed phenomena. That the logical law of contradiction does not apply to the Things-in-Themselves, has already been pointed out, it is moreover evident from its characteristic as logical, for logic is thought and thought is imagination, not ultimate reality.

It appears from the words of Dharmottara,[1] that there was a quarrel among Buddhist logicians on the problem as to whether the relation of efficient opposition was real or merely logical, whether it was transcendentally real or only phenomenal. The problem is solved by Dharmottara in that sense, that just as there are two kinds of causality, the one transcendental and real, obtaining between point-instants, the other, being a category, metaphorical, obtaining between phenomena; just so there are two kinds of efficient opposition. But the one obtaining between point-instants is causation simply, and causation is not contradiction. Kamalaŝīla explains[2] the point in the following manner: «Somer entities there are which are causes of curtailment in regard of other entities. They achieve it that the run of those point-instants (which constitute those entities) gradually becomes lower and feebler. E. g., fire in respect of cold. But other entities are not so, they are not causes of shrinkage, as, for instance, the same fire in regard of the smoke (produced by it). Now, although there is a relation of (mere) causality between the just mentioned counter-parts, between entities producing shrinkage and this shrinking; but common humanity, their faculty of vision being obscured by the darkness of ignorance, wrongly assume here a relation of contradiction. (It is opposition). This opposition appears in various forms, e. g., the cold is opposed by fire, the flame of a lamp is opposed by the wind, darkness is opposed by light, etc. In Ultimate Reality there is however no relation of opposition between entities (as Things-in Themselves)... That is the reason why the Master (Dharmakīrti) has delivered himself in the following way:[3] «When one fact has duration as long as the sum-total of its causes remains unimpaired, and it then shrinks as soon as another fact (being opposed to it) appears; it follows that both are (dynamically) opposed, (just as the sensations of heat and of cold). (The Master says) „their opposition follows", that means it is constructed (by our intellect) it is not ultimately real».

---

1 NBT., p. 69. 11 ff. transl., p. 192.

2 TPS., p. 156. 27 ff.

3 Cp. NBT., p. 68. 3; transl., p. 187.

§ 4. Law of Otherness.

The law of Otherness is a dependent law, dependent on the law of Contradiction. Indeed the blue and the non-blue are contradictory, because they mutually represent the one the complete negation of the other. But the blue and the yellow are also contradictory, because the yellow is a part of the non-blue. Therefore they are only partially contradictory, i. e., they are merely «other» with regard to one another. Thus the blue and the non-blue are contradictory directly, the blue and the yellow are contradictory indirectly, because the yellow is necessarily non-blue, «it cannot escape from being non-blue».[1] Just as we arrive at the negative judgment «there is no jar on this place», after having hypothetically imagined its presence on this place and after having repudiated that suggestion, just so do we decide that the blue is not the yellow, after having hypothetically assumed the presence of the blue on the yellow patch and having repelled that imagined presence. This is especially clearly elicited when two hardly discernible shades of colour are compared. They must be confronted and the one imagined on the place of the other and then declared to be either different, if their difference is discernible, or identical, if their difference is undiscernible. A difference there will always be, it may be infinitesimal. Identity is only the limit of difference, it is an «identity of indiscernibles». If an object is invisible by its essence, if its essence is such never to be visible, nevertheless it can be declared to be «other», i. e. its presence can be denied, only after having imputed to it a visible presence on a given place. When in darkness seeing standing before us an upright and long object we cannot decide whether it is a post or a man, we arrive at a decision only after having for a moment imagined the presence of the denied object. We then pronounce internally the judgment: «it is a post, it is not a man». We have already quoted Dharmottara on this point. He maintains that «Affirmation and Negation (or presence and absence) are in direct contradiction, but two members of a couple of objects are contradictory (or exclusive of one another) as far as they mutually necessarily include the one the negation of the other. Now what is the object whose negation is necessarily included in the other part (of the couple)? It is an object having a definite (representable) shape, not something indefinite (or illimited), as for instance Instantaneousness.

---

[1] NBT., p. 70. 3.

For Instantaneouness (we have seen) is the very essence of every (real thing, of every ultimate reality, underlying) a patch of blue or any other (real object). Therefore by the exclusion (of such an illimited thing as existence in general) nothing representable can be cognized». Dharmottara intends to say that by contrasting a thing with such an all-embracing character as Existence in general nothing definite can be cognized. Cognition is contrasting of a definite thing with an other definite thing, not with something illimited. «But then, continues Dharmottara,[1] is it not that negation (or non-existence) is something by itself (quite) indefinite?» (i. e. the non-A is illimited)? and answers: «why should it be necessarily indefinite? (why should non-A be shapeless?) Inasmuch as Negation (as we understand it) is the negation of an imagined presence, it is an imagined absence which has a definite shape as far as it is limited by the definite form of a (definite) real object». Thus Dharmottara maintains that by illimited negation, just as by illimited existence, nothing really can be cognized. The essence of knowledge is limitation, the law of contradiction is a fundamental law of thought, which says that our thought cannot operate otherwise than by dichotomizing, in every case of existence, in two imagined parts, which represent mutually the complete negation of one another. The law «of Efficient Opposition» and the law of «Otherness« are dependent laws, direct consequences of the law of Contradiction.

§ 5. Different formulations of the Laws of Contradiction and Otherness.

The great importance of the manner in which the Buddhists viewed the laws of Contradiction and Otherness for their ontology has already been indicated.[1] It is one of their chief arguments in establishing the theory of Instantaneous Being. In their endless controversies with their adversaries, the brahmanic schools, the Buddhists appeal to their law of Contradiction almost on every step. It is generally designated as the law of Contradictory Predication,[2] under which name all its different aspects, such as Efficient Opposition,[3] Logical Anti-

---

1 Cp. above, p. 103 and 403.

2 *viruddha-dharma-saṃsarga* (or *adhyāsa*) = *lākṣaṇika-virodha*.

3 *saha-anavasthāna-virodha* = *nivartya-nivartaka-bhāva*.

phasis,[1] laws of Otherness,[2] of Identity[3] and of Excluded Middle,[4] are commonly understood. It is usually expressed in the conditional proposition. «What is beset with contradictory qualities is manifold, as cold and heat».[5] The real meaning of this proposition, which seems at first to be a truism, is not that two things are different things, but if one thing, or what is supposed to represent a unity, possesses two contradictory qualities, it is really not one thing, but two things. This brings us to the formulation that one thing cannot possess two contradictory qualities at once. If we substitute for «two contradictory qualities» the presence and the absence of the same quality, we shall have the Aristotelian formula «it is impossible that the same at once appertains and does not appertain[6] to the same and in the same respect». However this meaning is quite different from the meaning which the Buddhists put into their formula. According to Aristotle, the same can appertain and not appertain to the same at different times and in different respects, or the same thing can possess two contradictory qualities at different times; the thing may be cold at one moment and become hot in another.[7] According to the Buddhists a thing can never possess two contradictory qualities. If it seems to possess them, it is not really the same thing, but there are two altogether different things, the cold thing and the hot thing. The position of the Buddhists could not be anything else. When a thing is composed of a permanent stuff and its changing qualities, the qualities can change and the thing will remain identical. But if the stuff is altogether absent and the thing consists of mere passing qualities, every change of the quality will be a change of the thing. We have seen from the analysis of the law of Contradiction that mere «otherness» is included in contradiction. If the yellow is merely different from the blue and not contradictory to it, it nevertheless is contradictory, because the yellow is included in the non-blue and every non-blue is contradictory to the blue. Therefore to possess contradictory qualities means simply to be different.

---

1 *paraspara-parihāra.*

2 *anyatva* (= *niṣiddha-ekatva*)-*virodha.*

3 *ekātmakatva-virodha.*

4 *tṛtīya-prakāra-abhāva.*

5 Cp. SDS., p. 24.

6 ὑπάρχει.

7 We find the same example in the fragments of Heracleitus, but there it means (or is supposed to have meant) that the hot and the cold coexist or are coimplied in the same thing. It is adduced as an instance against the law of contradiction.

A thing possessing two different qualities not included the one in the other, is therefore not one thing, but represents two separate things.

Another slightly different formulation says: «from union with a contradictory quality the thing becomes other».[1] That is, a thing looses its identity or becomes another thing, if it combines with incompatible qualities. And what are incompatible qualities? They are time, space and essence (sensible qualities etc.). If a thing exists at one time, it is contradictory to assume that it exists at another time or moment. If it exists in one place, it is contradictory to assume its existence in another place or another point. If the thing has one content or essence, it is contradictory to assume that it is the same as an «other» object with a different content. What is blue itself can never be made un-blue, a thousand of skilled men cannot change the blue itself into the non-blue. This, of course, does not mean that the colour of a thing cannot be changed in common life, but it means that the blue itself cannot be the non-blue. The identity of the blue is not something existing by itself, it is constructed on the basis of its contradiction to the non-blue. The law of contradiction destroys the reality of the blue and at the same time it constructs its ideality on the basis of its opposition to the non-blue.

Still another formulation, or proof, of the law of Contradiction comes from the following argument.[2] Whatsoever «is cleared off»[3] must be also «cleared up»[4] and it is cleared up exactly in the measure in which it is cleared off. E. g., a ruby is cleared up, i. e. definitely represented, as soon as it is cleared off, i. e. opposed to the non-rubies, topazes etc., and it is cleared up exactly in the measure in which it is cleared off. The contents of the representation, or of the concept, of the ruby will be definite exactly to the extent as it will be opposed to the non-rubies; and exactly in dependence on the properties included in the non-rubies. However this rule refers also to the time and space conditions of the ruby. For the ruby consists merely of certain time, space and sense-data conditions. The time of the ruby will be settled by the exclusion of all other times, i. e. all other moments except the given one. And so also its space condition. It will thus be reduced to a point instant of ultimate reality, to the *Hoc Aliquid*, which will have no duration and will disappear as soon as it appears.

---

1 NBT., p. 4. 2; transl., p. 8.

2 NBT., p. 69. 22 ff. and Tātp., p. 92. 15 ff.

3 *paricchinna* = *rnam-par-chad-pa.*

4 *vyavacchinna* = *yons-su-chad-pa.*

Thus the Buddhist law of Contradiction safeguards, to a certain extent, the identity of the ruby, it safeguards its ideal identity as a phenomenon, but only at the cost of destroying its real identity, as a Thing-in-Itself.

There are however qualifications and concepts which, although being mutually «other», are not contradictory, as, e. g., the blue and the lotus, or, more exactly, the «blueness» and the «lotusness» of a given point. They are not incompatible, their compresence in the same thing is not contradictory. They are, according to Buddhist terminology, identical. This part of the Buddhist doctrine will be examined in the sequel.

§ 6. Other Indian schools on Contradiction.

The law of Contradiction in India is, under the name of a Law of Contradictory Predication,[1] a specifically Buddhistic law. Not that the other schools denied or neglected this «best known and most forcible» among all the fundamental laws of thought, but they seem to have regarded it as something self-evident and not calling for explanations, until the problem was tackled by the Buddhists.

The Aphorisms of the Vaišeṣika system contain a doctrine of contradiction as a real relation between real facts, which are connected with one another by the tie of opposition.[2] It is real or dynamical opposition, considered apparently as a variety of Causation. There is no mention of logical contradiction even in the genuine logical part of that system. The contradictory logical reason, we have seen, is introduced in that system as a special logical fallacy under Buddhist influence.[3] The Aphorisms of the Nyāya system, on the contrary, neglect contradiction as a relation between real facts, but contain a doctrine of a logical fallacy called the contradicting reason.[4] Such a reason is a reason which destroys the thesis of the respondent. It is a contradiction of two judgments, the one denying what the other affirms.

The Sānkhya system also contained the relation of contradiction, or opposition, among the varieties of relation between real facts,[5] it

---

1 *viruddha-dharma-saṃsarga*.

2 V. S., III. 1. 10—12.

3 Cp. above, p. 349.

4 NS., 1. 2. 6.

5 Cp. Tātp., p. 131. 27.

was in this respect on the same level with the Vaišeṣika system. We would have expected that the Sānkhyas, since they were the allies of the Buddhists in their fight against the Category of Inherence,[1] could have, to a certain extent, shared in their theory of Contradictory Qualification, but we find in their survived records no traces of such a logical theory.

For the Buddhists, we have seen,[2] the law of Contradiction affords one of their prinicipal arguments in favour of their theory of Instantaneous Being. If a reality cannot include incompatible, mutually exclusive moments of time and mutually exclusive points of space, it is then reduced to a single point-instant. As an answer to this argument the Naiyāyikas produced their own definition of the law of Contradiction.[3] It is the following one: «That is the meaning of contradiction that two things cannot coexist together at the same place and at the same time». It is not different in principle from the formulation that «one and the same feature cannot both appertain and not appertain to the same thing at the same time», or the formula that «in the same place the thing cannot at the same time exist and non-exist». Since existence and non-existence are for the Realist both equally real as objects, their simultaneous presence in the same place and at the same time is impossible. This formulation is based on the principle that it is in general impossible for two different physical things to occupy at once the same place. The logical principle of contradiction is thus founded on the physical principle of the impenetrability of Matter. Dharmottara remarks[4] that this would not be the right formulation even for that law of dynamical repugnancy, which is but a dependent part of the law of Contradiction, a part which has only a comparatively restricted scope of application. All atoms, he says,[5] possess that common feature that they cannot occupy the same place, i. e. that the one cannot occupy the place where the other simultaneously resides. But this is not enough. Efficient opposition consists in this, that the «duration» of one thing on a definite place is counteracted, or efficiently opposed by the duration of another thing, which endeavours to disloge the former out of its position and to occupy its place.

---

1 Tātp., p. 131. 15.
2 Cp. above, p. 103 ff.
3 Cp *Jayanta*, p. 60
4 NBT., p. 69. 5 ff.
5 Ibid.

A separate position in regard of the law of Contradiction has been taken by the Jainas apparently at a very early date. They flatly deny the law of Contradiction. At the time when the battle raged between the founders of Buddhism and the Sānkhyas, when the latter maintained that «everything is eternal», because Matter is eternal, and the former rejoined that «everything is non-eternal», because Matter is a fiction, the Jainas opposed both parties by maintaining that «everything is eternal and non-eternal simultaneously». According to this theory you could neither wholly affirm, nor wholly deny any attribute of its subject. Both affirmation and denial were untrue. The real relation was something half way between affirmation and denial. Like the doctrine of Anaxagoras in Greece, this denial seems directed much more against the law of Excluded Middle, than against the law of Contradiction. However in the problem of Universals and Particulars the Jainas adopted an attitude of a direct challenge to the law of Contradiction.[1] They maintained that the concrete object was a particularized universal, a universal and a particular at the same time. Such is also the attitude of one of the earliest Buddhists sects, the sect of the Vātsīputrīyas. They were averse to the Hīnayāna priuciple, which, denying the Soul, maintained the existence of only detached separate Elements of a Personality, the Elements holding together exclusively by the causal laws of their concerted appearance. They maintained that the Personality, which consist of those Elements, was something half way real, it was, they maintained, something existing and non-existing at the same time.[2]

On the neglect of the law of Contradiction by the monistic Mādhyamikas and Vedāntins some remarks will be made in the sequel. From what has been expounded in this chapter it is already plain that the law of Contradiction does not extend its sway beyond the field of Experience, over the realm of the Things-in-Themselves. Although Dharmottara says that all objects, whether real or unreal, are subjected to the law of Contradiction,[3] but he in this context alludes to the conditioned reality of dynamical opposition. The cold and the hot are both real, because they refer to two point-instants, they are not two point-instants themselves. This kind of opposition, since it affects only objects having «duration», cannot be extended to the Things-in-

---

[1] TS. and TSP., p. 555. 5 ff; cp. *Ślokav.*, Śūnyav., 219.

[2] Cp. AK., IX and my Soul Theory of the Buddhists.

[3] NBT., p. 70. 22.

Themselves, which are objects without any duration. In absolute Reality there can be no Contradiction since here the contradictory parts coalesce.

§ 7. Some European Parallels.

Sigwart gives vent to his despair of the terms Identity, Opposition and Contradiction. «These terms», says he,[1] «have become unserviceable in philosophy, since quite a Babylonian confusion of language reigns in their application». The practical Englishman J. N. Keynes, we have seen, advises us not to touch on the subject of Negation, since «any attempt to explain it is apt to obscure rather than to illumine».[2] However, this hopeless condition does not deter us, but rather encourages us, in the attempt of a comparison with Indian views, in the expectation that the contrast may possibly contribute to some illumination rather than to an obscuration of the subject.

a) The Law of Excluded Middle.

To the three fundamental Laws of Thought of our modern European logic, the laws of Identity, Contradiction and Excluded Middle, we find corresponding on the Indian side only the single law of Contradiction, called the Principle of «Uniting Contradictory Predicates».[3] This condition falls in line with the view of Aristotle who singled out the law of Contradiction alone as the Principle (ἀρχή), «the most forcible and best known» principle, of all human thought.[4] The two other laws are for him nothing more than its consequences or aspects. The law of Contradiction is indeed nothing but a law of Excluded Middle, because ἀντίφασις is characterized and distinguished from mere opposition just by the fact of the absence of anything between two contradictory opposites. «Contradiction, says Dharmakīrti,[5] is complete mutual exclusion».[6] «Complete» exclusion is just exclusion of everything in the middle. Aristotle says the same: «there is nothing in the middle of the opposite parts of a contradiction».[7] Every cognition, we have

---

1 Logik[3], I, p. 167—168; cp. I, p. 108.

2 Formal Logic[4], p. 120.

3 *viruddha-dharma-saṃsarga* = *virodha.*

4 Cp. Sigwart, op. cit., I. 191.

5 NBT., p. 69. 21; transl., p. 193.

6 *paraspara-pari-hāra* = *pari-tyāga*, ibid.; *pari* = complete.

7 Metaph. I,7, 1057 a 33— τῶν δ'ἀντικειμένων ἀντιφάσεως μεν οὐκ ἔστι μεταξύ.

seen, is the cognition of a point of reality lying among things similar and distinguished from things dissimilar. The similars are united by the principle of Identity, they are distinguished from the dissimilars by the principle of Contradiction and they are «completely» distinguished by the law of Excluded Middle.[1] But these are not three different principles. It is one fundamental principle in its three applications. When we cognize a patch of blue in the judgment «this is blue», we then, owing to a Primordial Function of Productive Imagination,[2] construct out of the Universe of Discourse two parts, the blue and the non-blue. Everything that is not referred to the blue will be necessarily in the non-blue. There can be no third possibility, nothing in the middle. Such is the essence of contradictory opposition.[3]

b) The Law of Double Negation.

Another very important consequence flows out of Dharmakīrti's definition. Contradiction is not only «complete» exclusion, it also is «mutual» exclusion. That is to say, A and non-A exclude each the other mutually. There is among them nothing positive by itself, just as there is nothing negative by itself, their negation is mutual. A excludes non-A just in the same degree as non-A excludes A. A excludes non-A means, in other words, that A excludes the exclusion of A, since non-A is nothing but the exclusion of A. A excludes non-A means that A itself represents the exclusion of the exclusion of A, i. e., $A = -(-A)$. And *vice versa*, non-A represents the exclusion of A just in the same degree in which A represents the exclusion of non-A, that is $(-A) = -A$ just as $A = -(-A)$. This is the celebrated principle of Double Negation which more properly must be called the principle of Mutual Negation and mutual negation is nothing else than the principle of Contradiction expressed according to the Leibniz-Kantian formula.

Just as the law of Excluded Middle is not a separate principle, but it is the law of Contradiction itself, just so is the principle of

1 *tṛtīya-prakāra-abhāva = sapakṣa-vipakṣābhyām tṛtīya-abhāva.*

2 *prāgbhavīya-vikalpa-vāsanā.*

3 The name given to it by Aristotle, Antiphasis, points to its logical rather than ontological, character. It is «counter-speaking» and not «counter-existence». But Grote (op. cit., p. 579) thinks that both the Maxim of Contradiction and the Maxim of Excluded Middle have a logical as well as an ontological bearing with Aristotle.

Double Negation nothing else than again this very law of Contradiction itself. Dharmakīrti's definition of the law as 1) «complete» and 2) «mutual» negation simply says that the law of Contradiction is 1) a law of Excluded Middle and 2) a law of Double Negation.

The law of Mutual Negation can also be stated in the following form. Just as A = —(—A), just so (—A), taken as a real co-unit of A, will be = —(—(—A)). It will then be a law of Treble Negation. Šāntirakṣita says[1], when it is said «he desists of not cooking», this means that he cooks. By a third negation (i. e., he does not not-not-cook) desistence again is implied. By a fourth negation (i. e., he does not not-not-not cook) this desistence is cancelled and the meaning «he cooks» is again reestablished. Thus a negation is implied in every affirmative proposition. The law of Double Negation could indeed also be called the law of Treble, of Quadruple Negation and so on. The important fact is that every proposition is at the same time negative in itself. The Soul of the world is Negativity, says Hegel, and his dictum finds some partial support in the Buddhist theory.

Sigwart however has rightly seen that «just because the cancellation of a negation is affirmation itself, just for this reason is there nothing in the middle between affirmation and negation».[2] He thus establishes the identity of the law of Double Negation with the law of Excluded Middle. He also rightly remarks that both the principles of Excluded Middle and of Double Negation together with the law of Contradiction only serve to elicite the essence and the meaning of Negation.[3] There is only one most general law of thought, that is the law of Negation. Aristotle rightly calls it the «Law of all Laws».[4] According to Buddhist logicians, this means that human thought is dialectical. Since one of our next chapters will be devoted to an exposition and consideration of the Buddhist Dialectical Method, we may at present limit our exposition to this short indication which was indispensable in connection with the statement of the law of Contradiction and its European parallels.

---

1 TS., p. 354. 6.

2 Ibid., I. 200.

3 Ibid., I. 202.

4 The law of Negation is the same as the law of Contradiction. It is the first axiom. Unfortunately there are as many methods to understand its ultimate value as there are systems of philosophy. Cp. Metaph. Γ, 3. 1005 b. — ἀρχὴ τῶν ἄλλων ἀξιωμάτων.

c) The law of Identity.

This law is usually stated as «A is A» or «what is is», and is given as the principle of all logical affirmation, just as its corollary, the law of contradiction, in the form of «A is not non-A», is supposed to be the principle of all negation. The adequateness of such formulas has been questioned.

The law is sometimes interpreted so as to mean identity of sense in spite of difference in statement. The Buddhists would then reject it, because for them linguistic differences are not the domain of logic. Dharmottara says [1] that if the two propositions «the fat Devadatta eats nothing at day time» and «he eats at night» are used to express the same fact, they contain no inference, they contain the same fact in different language. They ought not to be considered in logic, since logic is concerned about the necessary connection of two different facts through Causality or of two different concepts through Identical Reference, but not about the meaning of different words.

The law of Identity is then represented as the law of the constancy of our cognitions to which a certain duration of things must correspond. Vācaspati calls it the Consecrated Recognition,[2] it means that I can maintain «this is the same crystal-gem which I have seen before», or «this is that same Devadatta whom I have seen in another place». Without such constancy neither cognition nor intelligible speech nor purposive action are at all possible. The Buddhists themselves define cognition as uncontradicted experience [3] which means consistent or constant experience and is impossible without recognition. However of Constancy and Identity there is no trace in the ever moving, ever changing reality. Constancy and Identity are logical, they are in our head, not in the objective world. So it is that instead of a law of Identity we have in Buddhism a law of Identical Construction [4] or Identical Objectivization. The identical things are projected images. [5]

But if the Buddhists insist that there is in Ultimate Reality no real Identity at all, they with equal emphasis insist that in logic

---

1 NBT., p. 43. 12; cp. above, p. 357 note.

2 *pratyabhijñā bhagavatī*, cp. NK., p. 125. 8.

3 *avisaṃvādakam samyag-jñānam*, cp. NBT., p. 3.

4 *ekatva-adhyavasāya* = *kalpanā*, cp. vol. II, p. 406, 409.

5 *alīka-bāhyatva*, cp. vol. II, p. 411.

there is absolutely no change. The Forms, the nature of the general essences superimposed upon reality, are immutable and eternal. There is no power in the world which could change an Ens and convert it into a non-Ens. The allmighty god Indra himself cannot alter the essence of things,[1] their real nature. The whole drama of cognition consists in Buddhist philosophy, just as in the system of Plato, of that contradiction between absolutely changeless forms and always changing reality.

A somewhat different law of Identity is suggested by Sigwart. It is directly connected with his theory of judgment and must be considered here, since it exhibits some interesting traits of coincidence, as well as an interesting contrast, with the theory of judgment of the Buddhist logicians and their law of Identity.

According to Sigwart there must be a law of Identity which is the principle of a union between subject and predicate in a judgment and of imparting to this union objective reality and constancy.[2] It is a law of Agreement and Objectivization. The realistic theory, he says, which maintains that the connection between the elements of the judgment is the same as between the corresponding objective elements of reality, must decidedly be rejected. Reality is never «congruent», i. e. equal and similar, to logic. In objective reality the subject and the predicate are a united organic whole.[3] The understanding separates them in order to reunite them in a judgment. There is no *distinctio realis* corresponding to the *distinctio rationis.*[4]

The so constructed predicate is always a Universal, whereas the subject is always something unique. «The Universal exists only in my head, whereas in objective reality the Unique only exists».[5] Moreover, whether the external objects exist at all or whether they do not exist, is a metaphysical problem with which logic is not directly concerned.[6] The judgment «this is snow» implies not only the unity of subject and predicate, but their objective reality in the sense of a constance of

---

1 Cp. NK., p. 124. 13.

2 Sigwart, Logik[3], I. 105 ff.; cp. J. N. Keynes, op. cit., p. 451 ff.; Bradley, op. cit., p. 142.

3 Ibid. I. 104 — *ungeschiedene Einheit*; cp. TPS., p. 157. 5 — *sarvātmanā utpadyate.*

4 Ibid., I. 105.

5 Ibid., I. 107, note.

6 Ibid., I. 105; cp. Dignāga's words *anumāna-anymeya-bhāvo na sad-asad apekṣate,* Tātp., p. 127.

the object «snow» at different times, for different people and from different points of view. The constructive function of the judgment remains absolutely the same whether we assume with the Realists that an independent reality lies behind our presentations or whether we, with the Idealists, maintain that this reality reduces to the mere fact of the constancy of these our presentations. This is, we have seen, exactly the view of the Buddhist logicians. They admit that the judgment remains a mental construction in both cases, whether we admit an external world or not.[1] The law of constancy could then be called a law of Identity. This law would be the necessary condition of all cognition, all speech and all purposive action. But Sigwart objects to the name of Identity for such a law, since the identity of subject and predicate (except in meaningless tautology) is never complete. The term «partial identity», suggested by some logicians, is contradictory, since partial identity means non identity. He therefore prefers to call it the law of Agreement[2] or the law of «Unipositing».[3]

In connection with this view of the judgment as an objectivizing function which, we have seen, is also the Buddhist view, two remarks of Sigwart must be noticed, since they are important parallels to Indian views. He says that the predicate, being general, is always vague, as compared with the vividness of the particular in intuition.[4] It refers only to a part of the concrete unity of the subject. He also remarks that identity is never produced by a mere repetition of observation, «it is produced by a negation of the difference of content between two or more temporarily separated representations».[5] This idea, the idea namely that identity reduces to a negation of difference and does not reach any further, that it is no real affirmation,[6] we shall later see, is the foundation of the Buddhist theory of general names. The law of Identity or Agreement is thus supposed, if not to explain, at least to fix the fact of a union between the concrete vivid reality of the subject and the vague and general ideality of the predicate.

---

1 Cp. above, p. 63.

2 *Übereinstimmung.*

3 *In-eins-setzung.*

4 Sigwart, op cit., I. 111; cp. NK., p. 263. 12 — *na vikalpānubandhasya spaṣṭārtha-pratibhāsatā*; cp. TSP., p. 553. 9.

5 Ibid., I. 42; this is the Indian principle of *bheda-agraha* contrasted with the realistic principles of *abheda-graha*, cp. Tātp., p. 56.

6 Real affirmation is only sensuous, reality *vastu* = *vidhi* = *pratyakṣa* = *vidhi-svarūpa*, cp. above, p. 192.

We have seen that the Buddhists call this fact by the name of a law of Conformity [1] and that the whole Buddhist theory of judgment reposes upon that law.

What the Buddhists call the law of Identity is something essentially different. The law of Conformity refers to all perceptual judgments, i. e. to judgments with one predicate. The law of Identity refers only to a definite variety of judgments with two concepts, viz., the analytical judgments. The great importance of the distinction between a judgment with one concept and a judgment with two concepts, or judgment of consistency, must be here taken in account. In such a judgment both subject and predicate are general and vague. The concrete vividness of the subject is absent. They can be called judgments with two predicates. However Sigwart brings under the same head of his law of Agreement both the connections of subject and predicate in a perceptual judgment, e. g. «this is snow», and their connection in a judgment uniting two concepts, e. g. «the snow is white». From the Indian point of view these are quite different forms of judgment and quite different principles are lying at the bottom. The judgment uniting two concepts is one of consistency between them, not of their objective reality. The objective reality lies in another judgment, in the following one, in the judgment «this is snow, it is white», or «this is the white snow». The real subject is contained in the element «this». The consistency, the possibility of connecting «the snow» with «the white», reposes indeed on the Identity of the objective reference of both these concepts. This is a real law of Identity, but it is concerned about only one part of our judgments, namely the Analytical Judgments; which, according to their Indian interpretation, should be more properly called Judgments of Identical Reference.

Sigwart streches out his law of Agreement-Identity so as to include the other half of all our judgments. He says [2] — «This real Identity does not ecxlude the difference of the objects at different times». «The same tree which was covered with leaves before is now barren» «the same man whom I have known as a youth is now old». This in Buddhist philosophy is quite different. These judgments are not judgments of Identity, they are not analytical.[3] They are synthetical, or causal. Their logical meaning is «wheresoever there is a baren tree

---

[1] *sārūpya*, cp. above, p.220.

[2] Op. cit., p. I. 109.

[3] *tādātmya-vat.*

there was a green tree before», «if this tree is baren, it was a green tree before», «wheresoever there is an old man, there was before a young man from which the old one is produced». If an object can be the same at different times, where is the limit? If the dried up old tree is the same as the former young one, the young one is the same as the sprout, and the sprout the same as the seed, the seed the same as its elements and so on. We will be directly landed in the Sānkhya theory of the Identity between (material) cause and effect.[1] This is a law against which the Buddhists from the start declared the most uncompromising war. The Sānkhya law of Identity the Buddhists opposed by their law of Contradiction, the law namely that «mutually exclusive attributes belong to different things».[2] Every object at every moment of its existence is a different object. The unity here is logical, it is a neglect of difference, it is a construction of our productive imagination, not a real unity. The term «agreement», if it is used so as to include both the identical reference of two concepts in an analytical major premise and the non indentical objective reference of cause and effect, is misleading. The agreement in an analytical major premise is founded on Identity, in a synthetical premise it is founded on Causation.

Thus we must distinguish between 1) the Sānkhya law of Identity, which is an identity between cause and effect, 2) the Buddhist law of Identity, which is an identity between concepts referred to one and the same point of reality, 3) the Buddhist law of Conformity, which connects the unique subject with the general predicate, and 4) Sigwart's law of Agreement, which apparently confounds all these relations owing to an insufficient discrimination between the perceptual judgment and the judgment of concomitance.

A somewhat similar interpretation of the law of Identity is found in Sir W. Hamilton's Logic. Although deferring to the traditional version of the law as «A is A», he represents it to mean an assertion of identity between a whole concept and its parts in comprehension. This reminds us of the identity of the *śimśapā* with the tree, since the concept tree is an attribute, or a part, of the concept *śiṃśapā*. Sir W. Hamilton represents this principle of Identity to be «the principle of all logical affirmation». But J. S. Mill rightly remarks[3]

---

1 *sat-kārya-vāda.*

2 *yad viruddha-dharma-saṃsṛṣṭam tan nānā.*

3 An Examination of Sir. W. Hamilton's philosophy (6th ed.), p. 484.

that it can be admitted as a correct account of the nature of affirmation only in the case of Analytical Judgments. He then proceeds to say that we then would be obliged to have «as many fundamental principles as there are kinds of relation».[1]

This last remark is made ironically. Mr. Mill evidently thinks that the varieties of relations are infinite and cannot be digested into a system. But the Buddhist will repeat Mill's suggestion with perfect good faith. He understands relation as necessary dependence and admits only two fundamental varieties of such relation. He cannot be deterred by the necessity of having «as many fundamental principles as there are kinds of relation», because the relations are not infinite, but only two. These two varieties of relation are founded either on the principle of Identity or of non-Identity. The second is nothing else than the principle of Causality.[2]

d) Two European Logics.

Turning to the Law of Contradiction proper, we must remark that there is in Europe two logics, the one founded on the law of Contradiction, the other founded on the neglect of the law of Contradiction. The first is a logic of non-contradiction, a logic of escaping and garding against contradiction. It has been founded by Aristotle and has been inherited from him by modern Europe. It has received a mighty extension into Epistemology from Kant and continues to reign at the present moment.

The other logic is a logic of contradiction, a logic according to which Reality consists of mere contraries, because all things proceed from contraries and the corresponding thought is nothing but mere contradiction. Viewed from the standpoint of the first, or real, logic, this second logic must be termed non-logic. It existed in ancient Greece previously to Aristotle, from whom it received a deadly blow. It however recovered in the European Middle Ages at the hands of N. Cusano and arrived at full eclosion in the system of Hegel, in the first half of the last century. After having been condemned and forsaken in

---

1 Ibid., p. 482.

2 It must be noted that the domain of Mill's analytical judgment is much narrower than of the Buddhist one. He says (ibid., p. 484), «in a synthetical judgment the attribute predicated is thought not as a part, but as existing in a common subject along with the group of attributes composing the concept». But to exist «in a subject» is just to be a part of it, to have a common objective reference!

the second half of that century, it now shows a tendency at revival, at least in some philosophic circles. Hegel in his «Science of Logic» expressly refers to the Indians [1] and quotes Indian theories in support of his logic of contradiction. He quotes the Buddhist doctrine of the so-called «Void». Although his knowledge was, of course, very indirect and scanty, he rightly guessed that this Void is not a mere negation, it is a positive principle of Pure Ultimate Reality, that reality where existence becomes identical with non-existence. Hegel was apparently guided by the natural inclination of many philosophers to antedate their own cherished ideas. But his guess is justified by our present knowledge of the Mādhyamika system. We have devoted to that system a special work [2] and need not repeat here its results.

e) Heracleitus.

The striking similarity between the Buddhist theory of Constant Change and the ontology of Heracleitus, the Ephesian, has already been pointed out. Still more striking is the fact that this similar ontology has led to opposite results, in regard of the law of Contradiction. Heracleitus bluntly denied that law, whereas the Buddhists, as we have seen,[3] appealed to it, as a strong argument establishing their theory of Instantaneous Reality.

Indeed, like the Buddhists, Heracleitus maintained that ultimate reality is a running reality. There is in it no stability at all. It is comparable to a streaming river which is never the same at a given spot, or to a flashing fire «metrically» appearing and «metrically» disappearing.[4] Its flashings are appearing «metrically», because there is a «harmony», a reason, a Logos, a general law controlling the running flashes of reality. So far this theory is not different from the Buddhistic one. The conception of Reality as constant change under a general law of Harmony corresponds very closely to the Hīnayāna conception of instantaneous elements (*dharmas*), appearing according to a strict Norm (*dharmatā*) of Dependent Origination. There is however the great difference that Heracleitus, being a physical philosopher, believed in a pervasive primordial Matter (ὕλη) in which the changing flashes of reality are merged. His theory of constant change is thus

[1] Wissenschaft der Logik, I, p. 68 (ed. G. Lasson).

[2] The Conception of Buddhist Nirvāṇa, (Leningrad 1928), cp. p. 53.

[3] Cp. above, p. 103 ff.

[4] ἁπτόμενον μέτρα καὶ ἀποσβεννύμενον μέτρα (Diels, 30).

much more akin to its Sānkhya variety than to the Buddhistic one. There is in his fragments neither any trace of denying substance, nor any clear trace of the theory of an absolute point-instant of reality.[1] His «metrical» flashings are probably small bits of reality having some duration. This is clear from his theory of Causality. He maintained that the «running» reality is constantly «running into the opposite» (ἐναντιοδρομία), that the result is always the opposite of the cause. It is clear that in order to be opposite cause and effect must possess some amount of definiteness and duration. They cannot be bare point-instants as with the Buddhists. They are momentary flashes having definite character. The wet becomes dry, the hot becomes cold, light changes into darkness, the new becomes old, life becomes death, etc. etc. Heracleitus maintained that these «opposites» (ἐνάντια) were nevertheless identical. Although the majority of examples of change adduced by him can be explained, and have been sometimes explained, as simple causation, it seems certain that he insisted upon the oppositeness, if not contradiction, of cause and effect and upon their real identity at the same time. This again is a trait of striking similarity between the Greek philosopher and Sānkhya ideas, since one of the fundamental Sānkhya principles is the «Identity» of cause and effect, the pre-existence of the effect in the cause, their simultaneous existence.[2] Thus the idea of constant change upon a hylozoistic substratum led Heracleitus to maintain the identity of opposites, in neglect of the law of contradiction. The ever-renewed junction of contraries and the perpetual transition of one contrary into the other he interpreted as their coexistence and identity. Aristotle disclosed the logical mistake inherent in the Heracleitan equations. The cause and the result, though being manifestations of the same matter, or of the same material cause, are not simultaneous. The identity of cause and effect can be established only by neglecting the element of time. The blunt denial of the law of contradiction by Heracleitus is, first of all, founded upon the neglect of what for the Buddhist is the

---

1 Although this theory is involved in the Heracleitan denial of duration, according to which «is» and «is not» are both alike and conjointly true, while neither is true separately to the exclusion of the other. Each successive moment of existence involves thus generation and destruction implicated with each other and this is exactly the theory that «everything represents its own destruction» as expressed by Kamalaśīla. However there is no evidence that Heracleitus denied Matter (ὕλη); he only denied duration, cp. G. Grote, Aristotle, p. 429.

2 *sat-kārya-vāda* = *tādātmya-vāda*.

essential part of Reality, the point-instant, the moment of time. The effect never appertains to the same moment as the cause. Every real thing is real only inasmuch as it is a cause, and the cause is always the moment preceding the effect. We have seen that the logical consequence of this Buddhist view is an absolute denial of real duration and the reduction of all reality to point-instants.

Thus it is that the same idea of a running reality has led in the hands of Heracleitus to a denial of the law of contradiction and in the hands of the Buddhists to its establishment.

The opposition which Heracleitus finds between cause and effect is the same as the first variety of opposition established by Dharmakīrti.[1] It is a dynamical or real opposition, as between hot and cold. It is to be distinguished from the logical opposition or contradiction (*antiphasis*). The example of Dharmakīrti, the opposition between the cold and the hot, is found among the examples of Heracleitus. This kind of opposition exists not between all real things, but only between some of them. We have seen how Dharmottara explains the change of darkness into light as a case of causation. Kamalašīla[2] insists that it is quite misleading to apply the designation of opposition, or even contradiction (*virodha*), to these instances. «There are some things», he says, «that become the cause of a gradual curtailment in some other things, as for example fire is the cause of diminishing cold. Such a relation does not exist between other couples of things, as for example, between that same fire and smoke. Although there is nothing but causality in the first mentioned cases, the causes which produce the curtailement of a phenomenon, nevertheless common humanity, whose faculty of understanding is obscured by the gloom of ignorance, wrongly assumes it to be a contradiction. Thus they assume that fire is the contradictory of cold, wind the contradictory of a lamp, light the contradictory of darkness. But in ultimate reality, among things ultimately real, there can be no relation of mutual elimination. What exists (ultimately) appears finally at once and in its essence can by no means be changed into another Ens. If we establish the dilemma whether the change of a thing is something different from the thing itself or whether it does not differ from it, in both cases an Ens cannot be changed into another Ens (still less can it be changed into a non-Ens). Something

---

[1] NB., p. 68; transl., p. 187.

[2] Partly quoted above, p. 408; here the passage is translated in full.

non-existent, indeed, since it is not real, can in no way be converted into something else. Thus in both cases (whether the counterpart be an Ens or non-Ens), the (supposed) contradiction cannot be real. This is the reason why the Master (Dharmakīrti) when discussing the opposition between contrary realities, has expressed himself in the following way — «When one fact has duration as long as the sum-total of its causes remains unimpaired, and it then vanishes as soon as another fact appears; it follows that both are incompatible, (or efficiently opposed), just as the sensations of heat and cold». The Master says that imcompatibility (or efficient opposition) «follows»; follows means that it is constructed by our understanding; it does not mean that there is a real opposition (between the Things-in-Themselves as point-instants).

When heat and cold are imagined as changing attributes of one and the same enduring substance, they can be constructed as causally inter-connected and even, to a certain extent, by neglecting the condition of time, declared to be identical, but if reality is envisaged as instantaneous there can be no real opposition in it. The opposition is then logical and refers to the concepts constructed by the understanding in accordance with the law of Contradiction.[1]

f) Causation and Identity in the fragments of Heracleitus.

The great majority of the instances envisaged by Heracleitus as opposition (ἐνάντια) of things which he deems really identical, are instances of causation. The new and the old, life and death, heat and cold, are instances of a change in the same stuff. The cause is correlative to' its effect, a cause cannot exist without its effect. They are interdependent. Owing to the vagueness of the notion of identity, interdependence can easily be interpreted as a kind of unity and identity. The effect stands «by» its cause; since it cannot exist without some cause it is said to exist, or preexist, «in» its cause. The historian of philosophy sees absolutely the same jump from «by» to «in» executed by the Sānkhya philosopher many centuries before our era and by Hegel in the XIXth century in Europe.[2] This jump has been

---

1 Cp. NBT., p. 70. 13; transl. p. 196.

2 Cp. the celebrated passage in the introduction of his Phenomenology (Lasson's ed., p. 10), where he maintains that the bud is removed and contradicted by the flower and the fruit declares the flower to be a falsified Ens of the plant.

disclosed in Greece by Aristotle and has obliged him to introduce the condition of time into his formulation of the law of Identity.

But by no means are all Heracleitan coincidences of opposites cases of causation. He quotes a number of identical opposition which cannot be interpreted as causation. Identical are good and evil, the clean and the dirty, the whole and the parts, the one and the many, etc. All these are instances not of causation, i. e. of two things necessarily following one another in time, but instances of identical objective reference, of the same thing differently regarded from a different point of view. A thing which is a unity as an aggregate is a plurality when considered as composed of parts. The same thing will be good from one stand-point and bad from another: clean or dirty, agreable or disagreable, moving or at rest, etc. These are cases which must be characterized as identical also from the Buddhist point of view. The identity, we have seen, means here identity of objective reference. The objective reality,the thing, is one and the same, it is identical. Its superimposed characteristics are different, or may be even contrary, in accordance with the point of view. Among the very numerous historians, philosophers and philologists who have attempted different interpretations of the fragments of Heracleitus[1] I find one who has called attention to this radical difference between the two groups of his examples.

«These forms», says he, «are not only different, but they dislodge one another and are incompatible with one another». However they are indispensable members of an organic whole, and in this sense identical, as contained in the one identical concept of a plant. From the Indian point of view Hegel confounds here four things, viz. 1) the relation of simple causation, as of fire and smoke, 2) the relation of efficient repugnancy, as of fire and cold, 3) contradiction, as of cold and not cold at the same moment and in the same respect, and 4) that identity of transition in which the thing, as Kamalašila puts it, represents «its own annihilation», i. e. existence and non-existence coalesce. This leads to a non-discrimination between opposites as they stand «by» one another and as they stand «in» one another.

[1] That the interpretation is very widely fluctuating is no wonder, considering that Heracleitus was even in his own time reputed an «obscure» philosopher and that only a few fragments of his work have reached us. Nevertheless it seems, — to quote J. S. Mill, — «that no extent and accuracy of knowledge concerning the opinion of predecessors can preserve a thinker from giving an erroneous interpretation of their meaning by antedating a confusion of ideas which exists in his own mind». The celebrated F. Lassalle has read into these fragments a full blown Hegel and in our days, in a work otherwise exceedingly painstaking and thorough, M. A. Dynnik (Диалектика Гераклита Ефесского, Moscow, 1929) reads into them a full blown Karl Marx. What Marx himself held about such exaggerations he expressed in his letter to F. Engels, datet 1st Febr. 1858(Briefwechsel, v. II, p. 242).

«There are in these fragments, says G. T. W. Patrick,[1] two distinct classes of oppositions which, though confused in Heracleitus mind, led historically into different paths of development. The first is that unity of opposites which results from the fact that they are endlessly passing into one another... they are the same because they are reciprocal transmutations of each other. But now we have another class of opposites to which this reasoning will not apply. «Good and evil, he says, are the same». This is simply that identity of opposites which developed into the Protogorean doctrine of relativity». It is to guard against this second class of identity of opposites that Aristotle introduced in his law the proviso «in the same respect» (κατὰ τὸ αυτό). The most eloquent example of this class of identical opposition is the identity of the One and the Many, this identity which puzzled the mind of Plato and to which he has devoted some of his most eloquent pages. Both classes are united as being always reducible to an identity of existence and non-existence. «In entering the same rivers», says Heracleitus, «we at the same time enter them and do not enter them, we exist and do not exist (in them)»[2]. The identity of opposites is the identity of existence and non-existence, the cardinal tenet of Hegel. Aristotle, as well as the modern logicians, protest against it by maintaining that the same thing cannot exist and not exist «1) at the same time and 2) in the same respect».

What is here interesting from the Indian point of view is the fact that we can clearly discern in the double character of the facts upon which the Heracleitan denial of the law of Contradiction is founded, as well as in its formulation by Aristotle, the difference between the two fundamental relations on which all ratiocination, nay all thinking, is based. They are Causation and Identical Reference, these two necessary and general relations of Interdependence, which are also the foundation of the Indian table of Categories, as well as of the Indian theory of Inference.

g) The Eleatic Law of Contradiction.

In the passage from Kamalašīla quoted above[3] we come across an argument not unfrequently recurring in Indian philosophy, an argu-

---

1 G. T. W. Patrick, The fragments of twe work of Heracleitus on Nature, Baltimore, 1889, p. 63.

2 Fragment 49[a] by Diels.

3 Cp. pp. 408 and 427.

ment which, at the face of it, seems to be quite the same as the one that was reigning in Greek philosophy previously to Aristotle. The argument states that «the essence of a thing can never be changed». If something is an Ens in its essence, it can never be changed into a non-Ens. A non-Ens is Nothing,[1] it is neither causally efficient, nor cogitable, nor teachable. The essence of a thing is just its essence because it is not subject to the conditions of time and relativity. If something is a unity, if it is one, it must be so «wholly»,[2] i. e. essentially, for ever and unconditionally, it cannot be «many», a plurality. No hundred of artizans in the world can change the essence of blue into yellow[3] or a unity into a non-unity. This tacitly admitted principle is the reason why Heracleitus felt it as a contradiction that the same thing can be hot and non-hot, a whole and its parts, a unity and a plurality etc. And it is why Aristotle, fighting against this principle, felt the necessity of limiting the identity of a thing by the conditions of time and relation; a thing cannot be Ens and non-Ens at the same time and in the same respect. Previously to Aristotle the problem seemed insoluble. Parmenides maintained that the «non-Ens does not exist» and since all things relative and changing implied non-existence in some respect, he mantained that only the motionless Whole really existed. Plato was puzzled to find a solution for the contradictory tetralemma *Est unum, Non est unum, Est Multa, Non est Multa*,[4] because *Unum* and *Multa* were for him absolute Forms which could not be relative and changing. For the same reason he was also puzzled to explain the transition from Motion to Rest. Since Motion and Rest were for him absolute Forms and «no artizans in the world» can change the Essence, or Form, of motion into non-motion; the transition becomes as inconceivable as the transition from Ens to non-Ens.

We thus have in Greek philosophy previously to Aristotle a law of contradiction quite different from the Aristotelian. Mr. Svend Ranulf who recently has submitted this problem to a detailed and deep investigation thus states the two conflicting laws. The pre-Aristotelian law says that «non-Ens is never an Ens; in no respect, in no way, at no time, under no condition and from no point of view is it an Ens». Aristotle also could have said that «the non-

1 Cp. TSP., p. 157. 7 — *asato avastutvān na kiṃcit kriyate.*

2 *sarvātmanā*, ibid.

3 Tātp., p. 339. 11.

4 Cp. G. Grote, Plato, II, p. 302 ff.

Ens does not exist[1]», but this would mean with him that «what in a certain respect, at a certain time, under certain conditions, etc, is a non-Ens, cannot in the same respect, at the same time and under the same conditions be also an Ens», or, as he puts it, it is impossible that one and the same thing should exist and non exist in the same time, at once and in the same respect». Mr. Svend Ranulf gives vent[2] to a supposition that «the Logic of Absolute Concepts»[3] is not limited to Europe. He thinks that «in all probability we will find this logic reigning in Indian philosophy on a larger scale and with less limitation than in Europe». Now, as far as the Buddhists are concerned, it is in the highest degree remarkable that the same argument which is used by Parmenides to establish his Monism and by Plato to support his eternal Forms, is used by the Buddhists for exactly the contrary purpose. The passage from Kamalašīla quoted above intends by its argument to support the theory of Instantaneous Being. We have seen the manner in which the Buddhist argument proceeds. If reality is changing, it is always and necessarily changing, it is change itself, to exist means to change. If it is not changing even during a moment, it will never change. Therefore the same thing cannot be hot and then become cold. What is hot has the essence of hot, it is hot «wholly», i. e. for ever. The result is for the Buddhist that the hot and the cold are two different things. The different cannot be the same. The «combination with a different quality makes the thing itself different»[4] — such is the Buddhist law of Contradiction.

h) Plato.

In comparing the Buddhist system with the system of Plato the following points must call our attention.

1) Both systems are concerned about the connection between the running reality of the sensible world and the immutable stability of its Forms or concepts.

2) Every cognition reduces therefore to the type-instance of the judgment x = A,[5] where A is something eternally immutable, — it is

---

1 Svend Ranulf, Der eleatische Satz vom Widerspruch (Kopenhagen, 1924), p. 160.

2 Ibid., p. 207.

3 *Die Logik der absoluten Vieldeutigkeit*, as he calls it.

4 *viruddha-dharma-saṃsargād anyad vastu*, cp. NBT., p. 4. 2.

5 Cp. Natorp, Platon's Ideenlehre, p. 151, 152, 390, 403, 408.

always A and can never be changed into non-A[1] — whereas x is something eternally changing, it never is the same x, it is always passing from x into non-x.

3) The relation between the two worlds is however in Buddhism exactly the reverse of what it is with Plato. The world or Forms is for Plato the fundamental one and the ever changing sensible reality is its pale reflex. For the Buddhist Logicians, on the contrary, the bright vividness of concrete change[2] is the fundamental world, whereas the stable concepts are its vague and general reflex.

4) Therefore the ultimately real world is for Plato the intelligible world of Forms, the sensible world of change is for him ultimately unreal. For the Buddhist, on the contrary, the ultimate reality is the unit underlying its constant change, it is the sensible point-instant. The world of durable concepts, on the other hand, exists for him only in imagination.

5) Both systems start from different conceptions of reality. For Plato reality is truth, what is cognized as true.[3] Ideality if it is true is also reality.[4] For the Buddhist reality is efficiency.[5] Ultimately real is only the extreme concrete and particular object which exists in the external world.[6] The ideas exist only in our head. Reality is the same as non-Ideality,[7] and Ideality the same as non-Reality. Truth, i. e. cognizability as truth,[8] far from being the mark of reality, is the mark of ultimate unreality, because ultimate reality is unutterable and incognizable.[9]

5) For Plato likewise the sensible particular is incognizable, and this for him is only a reason to condemn its ultimate reality.[10]

6) The law of Contradiction tacitly admitted in the majority of Platonic dialogues is the Eleatic one.[11] An Ens is never a non-Ens.

---

1 Ibid., p. 155.

2 *spaṣṭārthatā.*

3 Natorp, op. cit., p. 391.

4 This standpoint is shared in India by the Naiyāyiks (*yat prameyam tat sat*). Under the veil of it a wealth of metaphysical entities and, first of all, a real Time and a real Space are surreptitiously introduced into the world of realities.

5 *yad artha-kriyā-kāri tat sat; yā bhūtiḥ saiva kriyā.*

6 *bāhya = artha-kriyā-kāri = svalakṣaṇa = paramārtha-sat.*

7 *paramārtha-sat = kalpanāpoḍha = pratyakṣa.*

8 *niścaya-ārūḍha = buddhy-ārūḍha = vikalpita.*

9 *anabhilāpya = jñānena aprāpya.*

10 Cp. S. Ranulf, op. cit., p. 150, 151, 152.

11 Ibid., p. 147 ff.

An idea «in itself» always remains what it is, «itself», «by itself», «uniform with itself», «eternally existent».[1] It is in itself beyond every relativity. But in relation to the sensible world Plato occasionally quotes a form of the law which in fact is the same as the Aristotelian one. An Ens, according to this formulation, cannot be a non-Ens only under the two conditions of «at the same time» and «in the same respect».[2]

7) The Buddhist law of Contradiction is the opposite corollary from the Eleatic law. Just as for the Eleatics uncontradicted is only the eternal Ens, just so for the Buddhists uncontradicted is only the sensational point-instant. Every duration, every extension, every definiteness, every concept necessarily involves contradiction since it involves «otherness», i. e., difference, or Ens and non-Ens together.

Thus it is that both Plato and the Buddhists agree that contradiction is produced whenever logic is applied to reality.[3] This application, says the Buddhist, is only possible by constructing an artificial «similarity between things absolutely dissimilar».[4] In sensible reality there is a constant mixing up of contradictory qualifications, contradiction is rampant. The same thing appears as a unity and as a plurality, as greater and smaller, as good and as evil, etc. etc. But in the pure concepts, in the concepts «themselves», according to Plato, there is no contradiction.[5] According to the Buddhists, there is no contradiction in the things «themselves», i. e., in pure sensation and in the point-instant which ontologically corresponds to it.[6]

---

1 Ibid., p. 150.

2 Natorp, op. cit., p. 151; cp. S. Ranulf, op. cit., p. 156.

3 S. Ranulf, op. cit., p. 153.

4 *atyanta-vilakṣaṇānām sālakṣaṇyam* = *sārūpyam*. Thus the Platonic term παρουσία corresponds to a certain extent to the sanscrit *sārūpya*, cp. S. Ranulf, op. cit., p. 180.

5 Natorp, op. cit., p. 197; S. Ranulf, op. cit., p. 153.

6 Bradley, op. cit., p. 148, in this point apparently shares in the Kantian view, which contains some analogy with the Buddhist one, as against the Hegelian. He represents an imaginary Hegelian reproaching him thus — « And then, for the sake of saving from contradiction this wretched ghost of a Thing-in-Itself, you are ready to plunge the whole world of phenomena, everything you know or can know, into utter confusion ». I wonder what would have been Bradley's opinion had he known the Buddhist conception of the Thing-in-Itself. The whole world is not at all plunged in confusion, but a distinction is made between the ultimate reality of a point-instant which is not dialectical and all superimposed, dialectical, mutually contradictory superstructures. It is just this everywhere present ultimate reality which saves the world from confusion.

In this connection a suggestion of Plato must be considered, which by itself is difficult of comprehension, but becomes more or less explainable when confronted with its Indian solution. Just as the Buddhists Plato thinks that an object, while in motion, cannot change to rest, nor, while at rest, change to motion.[1] But at each time, whether present or past, it must be either in motion or at rest: at no time, neither present nor past nor future, can it be neither in motion nor at rest. «It follows that no time can be assigned for the change: neither the present, nor the past nor the future. Hence change is timeless (ἐν χρόνῳ οὐδενὶ οὖσα)». That which changes, changes at once and suddenly: at an instant when it is neither in motion nor at rest. «This suddenly (ἐξάιφνης) — is a halt, or break, in the flow of time, an extra-temporal condition, in which the subject has no existence, no attributes, though it revives again forthwith clothed with its new attributes: a point of total negation or annihilation, during which the subject with all its attributes disappears. At this interval all predicates may be truly denied of it, but none can be truly affirmed. The one thing is neither at rest, nor in motion; neither like nor unlike; neither the same with itself nor different from itself; neither *Unum*, nor *Multa*. Both predicate and subject vanish». «The thing, as Kamalašīla states, is its own annihilation». Is it not clear that Plato comes here very near to the Buddhist idea of Instantaneous Being as a support for the universal and eternal Forms? His moment of a sudden change lies out of, or apart from, time. This means that it has no duration, it is the absolute moment. As such it has no qualities, it is pure qualityless existence. And it is at the same time non-existence, since it disappears at that very instant in which it appears, to be followed by another moment. Plato's moment of sudden change is what the Buddhist call «production of a dissimilar moment»,[2] but it is «dissimilar» only in connection with the united series of previous moments, not by itself. Plato admits the objective reality of Time as a special Form. This time does not exist for the Buddhist. Each moment is a moment of change, change thus becomes the perpetual Form of Existence. What Plato was led to admit as a moment explaining conspicuous or gross change, is going on perpetually, it is pure existence, the subtle change underlying the world of stabilized images. This absolute moment of change is a challenge to

---

1 In his Parmenides, cp. G. Grote, Plato, II, 309 ff.

2 *vijātīya-kṣaṇa-utpāda.*

the Aristotelian law of contradiction, since it at once contains creation and annihilation, existence and non-existence. Grote rightly remarks that «this appears to be an illustration of the doctrine which Lassale ascribes to Heracleitus; perpetual implication of negativity and positivity, — *des Nichtseins mit dem Sein*; perpetual absorbtion of each particular into the universal; and perpetual reappearance as an opposite particular».[1] In this interpretation of Heracleitus Lassale, as is well known, only followed in the steps of Hegel, his master who identified his own denial of the law of contradiction with the ἐνατιοδρομία of Heracleitus.

We thus have in Indian philosophy both the principles of Identity and non-Identity, of the absolute identity of the changeless essences and the absolute non-identity of changing sensuous reality. Both are exploited in the service of the theory of Instantaneous Being. The first is similar to the Eleatic law of contradiction. The second is supported by the Buddhist law of contradiction.

i) Kant and Sigwart.

The clear distinction between real opposition «without contradiction» and logical opposition «through contradiction», this distinction so emphatically insisted upon by Dharmakīrti, is stated, partly with the same arguments and the same examples, by Kant in his youthful tract on the «Application of Negative Magnitudes in life».[2] He says that, e. g., dark and not dark is impossible in the same sense, at the same time and in the same subject. The first predicate is positive, the second is negative logically, although both may be «metaphysically» negative. They are related as existence and non-existence through contradiction. In real repugnancy both predicates, dark and light, are positive. The one cannot be contradictorily opposed to the other, «because then the opposition would be logical», not real. Contradictory opposition is existence and non-existence at the same time and in the same respect.

It is clear that it was quite indispensable for Aristotle to take into his formulation of the law of Contradiction the conditions of simultaneous time and identical relation. The law could not be saved without them. The same person, e. g., can be unlearned and learned

---

1 G. Grote, Plato, II, p. 309 note.

2 Versuch den Begriff der negativen Grössen in die Weltweisheit einzuführen (1763), cp. p. 25—26 (Kirchmann).

at different times of his life and in respect of different[1] subjects. But he cannot be learned and unlearned at the same time and in respect of the same subject. For the Buddhists these conditions are something self-evident, because the subject of a judgment is always a point instant, the element «this». «This is learned», «this is not learned» are incompatible when referred to the same point instant. But «this is a *śiṃśapā*» and «this is a tree» can be referred to one and the same point-instant of reality; there is between these predicates no incompatibility, because there is identity of substratum or Coinherence.

The necessity of such a conditional formulation has however been challenged by no smaller an authority than Kant. He went even all the length of maintaining that the time-condition has been introduced by Aristotle «out of mere carelessness and without any real necessity»; «because», says he, «the principle of contradiction as a purely logical must not be limited in its application by time». A principle which is «purely logical» means apparently the same as what Mr. Svend Ranulf intends by the logic of absolute concepts.[2]

It is a return to the Eleatic formulation of the law. «A is not non-A» conduces logically to the Parmenidean «οὐκ ἔστι μὴ εἶναι». «If I want to say», Kant explains, «that a man who is unlearned is not learned, I must add the condition «at the same time», for a man who is unlearned at one time may very well be learned at another. But if I say «no unlearned man is learned», then the proposition is analytical, because the characteristic «unlearnedness» forms part now of the concept of the subject, so that the negative proposition becomes evident directly from the principle of contradiction and without the necessity of adding the condition «at the same time».

What is important in this problem from the standpoint of Indian logic is not alone the law of contradiction itself, but also the light it throws on the theory of judgment and of inference as understood by the Buddhists. Sigwart impugns the formulation of Kant and rejects the strictures addressed by him to the Aristotelian formula. He contends that the Kantian formula it something quite different from the Aristotelian. Kant's critique is therefore «a stroke in the air». Kant remarks quite rightly that the Aristotelian formula refers to two predicates which are contradictory. They cannot be applied to one and the same subject simultaneously, but may be applied in succession.

---

1 CPR., p. 125.

2 Logik der absoluten Vieldeutigkeit (= Eindeutigkeit) der Begriffe.

He therefore converts one of the predicates into a subject and thus constructs a judgment with two concepts, «A is not non-A». The judgment is then analytical, purely logical, it is not affected by time and refers to concepts in their absolute condition. What Aristotle has in view is something quite different. He has in his mind two judgments, of which the one is annulled by the other. Now from the Indian standpoint a judgment with two concepts is a judgment of concomitance, it is therefore an inferential judgment or an inference, a major premise. It is indeed an analytical conjunction of two absolute concepts. Such conjunction does not depend on time-conditions. But the time condition will reappear as soon as the concepts are referred to reality, which is always done in the minor premise and in the conclusion. Indeed we will then have the following formulation:

Major premise. Who is learned is not unlearned (A is not non-A).

Minor premise. This one here is learned (in a special subject).

Conclusion. He is not unlearned (at the same time, respecting the same subject).

The judgment proper according to the Indian view, is always a judgment with one concept which is the predicate. Every concept is in this sense a predicate. The subject is always represented by the element «this», which contains the time condition. The law of contradiction refers to two such judgments which are contradictory, «this» (here, now) is learned», «this (here, now) is not learned».[1]

The standpoint of Sigwart[2] coincides exactly with the Indian one. He asks: «Why does Kant's example «an unlearned man is learned» contain a contradiction? Because the predicate «learned» is applied to a subject which implicitly contains in itself another judgment, «he is not learned». Kant's example reduces to two judgments «x is learned» and «x is not learned». It contains in itself an affirmation of both these judgments and, only therefore does it contain a contradiction».

Up to the designation of the subject by the sign x[3] the coincidence of Sigwart's argument with the Indian is complete. This agrees also with his general view that «all real and genuine judgments» have an

---

1 Kant here incidentally calls the judgment with two concepts, i. e. a judgment uniting two concepts, a judgment of two predicates. He says: «the misunderstanding arises... only on condition that the first and second predicate have both been applied at the same time» (cp. CPR., p. 125).

2 Logik,[3] I. 196.

3 *kiṃcid idam.*

indefinite subject. The judgment «this rose is yellow», for instance, reduces to the perceptual, or real, judgment «this is yellow».[1] The real logical subject is always expressed by the demonstrative «this» and it follows that every concept referred to objective reality is a predicate. From the Indian point of view Kant is quite right in maintaining that the Aristotelian formula refers to two predicates, but he is not right in converting one of these predicates into a subject.[2]

j) The Aristotelian formula of Contradiction and Dharmakīrti's theory of Relations.

There is an intrinsic natural connection between all these Indian theories of Judgment, of Inference (Concomitance), of Relations, and of Contradiction; and if we attentively look into the Aristotelian formulation of Contradiction we will see the ghost of the Indian theory appearing behind the veil of it. Indeed Sigwart was right, more right perhaps than he himself suspected, when he maintained that the proposition «a learned man is not unlearned» contains two judgments, «x is learned» and «x is unlearned». For a judgment, as Kant clearly saw, consists in bringing the manifold of intuition under one general concept. It therefore always reduces to the form «x is A». It is a judgment with one concept. A judgment uniting two concepts, either according to the analytical or according to the synthetical principle, is something, Sigwart rightly maintains, essentially

---

[1] Logik,[3] I. 142.

[2] It is curious that the polemic between such leaders of European science as Kant and Sigwart on so capital a problem as the formulation of the law of Contradiction by Aristotle has had no echo. None of the subsequent writers on logic, for aught I know, cared to interfere into the quarrel and to side either with Sigwart and Aristotle or with Kant. B. Erdmann (Logik, pp. 511 and 513), without loosing a word of argument and without even mentioning the initiators of the two formulas, inserts them both and represents the matter so as if Kant's formula were the fundamental one and Aristotle's its consequence. The reverse of this seems to be the opinion of J. N. Keynes, op. cit., p. 455. Bradley's remarks, op. cit., p. 146 (I. V. § 13), are perhaps intended as a reply to Sigwart. J. St. Mill comes very near to the Indian solution when he states (Exam. of Hamilton's phil, ch. XXI) that «valid reasoning... is a negative conception». But in his Logic, II, 7, § 5, he thinks that the law of Contradiction is a generalisation from experience! A. Pfänder, Logic p. 343, seems to accept Sigwarts formula; we would have expected him to prefer the Kantian one as purely logical (analytical). He repudiates Sigwarts theory of Negation (p. 228) as being psychological and gives of Negation no explanation at all.

different. It is a major premise, a judgment of concomitance. That the minor premise represents in its essence a perceptual judgment — has been clear to the Indian logicians beginning with Vātsyāyana.[1] It would be perhaps better, in order to avoid confusion, to save the name of judgment[2] for the perceptual judgment, which is also an existential judgment, or a judgment of reality, and to give to the other judgment the name of concomitance or inference,[3] as the Hindus have done. For it is a judgment, not of reality, but of consistency. The great difference between the major and the minor premises in this respect is clearly elicited in the fact, that fallacies against the major premise are fallacies of inconsistency or of uncertainty, whereas fallacies against the minor premise are fallacies of the unreality of the logical reason, as has been explained in the chapter on Logical Fallacies. The judgment «snow is white» asserts the concomitance of two concepts. The judgment «this is snow» asserts the objective reality of the concept snow. It is a judgment of Conformity between one concept and the corresponding reality. It is also an existential judgment. Not in the grammatical sense of «the snow exists». Existence, i. e., real concrete existence is never a logical predicate,[4] it is the common subject of all predications. But such a judgment is an existential one because it asserts the objective reality of the object snow, not a mere concomitance of two concepts.

The double formulation of the law of Contradiction exactly corresponds to the double character of judgments. In perceptual or existential judgments it is a contradiction between two judgments which mutually annihilate one the other. In judgments of concomitance it is the principle of all analytical inferences and an analytical judgment

---

[1] NBh., p. 5. 4 — *udāharaṇam pratyakṣam, upanaya upamānam.* And NV. explains — *yathā pratyakṣe na vipratipadyate, evam udāharaṇe'pīti (upanayaḥ),* i. e. the minor premise (*upanaya*) contains a reference to sense-perception.

[2] *adhyavasāya = vikalpa.*

[3] *vyāpti.*

[4] In order to avoid confusion we must not forget that Existence or Reality which is the common subject of all predication (τὸ ὄν = *Hoc Aliquid*) is the Thing-in-Itself, the point-instant corresponding to a moment of concrete and vivid, although unutterable, sensation. There is another Existence which is a perfectly utterable, general concept. It can very well appear in the rôle of a predicate; e. g., «a tree «exists» (or more precisely — this treeness includes existence), «this is a tree, it exists». Such an abstract concept of existence is quoted in Pram. Samuccaya, V. This must be kept in mind in order to protect Dignāga from accusations to which Kant fell a victim, the accusation namely that he invented a non-existing Thing-in-Itself, a thing which on his own principles did not and could not exist (!).

itself, as Kant wanted it to be. The Aristotelian and Kantian formulas are different, because they refer to different things.

The double character of judgments falls also in line with the double meaning of the verb substantial. We have already mentioned the fact of this double meaning, viz., to serve as a copula in predication and to express existence. Now it is evident that the meaning of existence belongs to this verb in existential or perceptual judgments only. It serves as a copula, on the other hand, in propositions expressing the concomitance of two concepts

We therefore must take exception to the rule that a judgment, or proposition, consists of subject, predicate and copula. This is a correct account of the nature of analytical concomitances only. In those founded on causation there is no copula at all, otherwise than linguistic. We of course can say «smoke is a product of fire», but the meaning is not that the smoke is something, but that it is produced by something. Thus there must be a word expressing existence or reality in a perceptual judgment, in a judgment proper. It has the form of «this is» or «there is» or «is» simply in the meaning of existence. It is also present in a negative judgment in the form of «there is not». There must be a word expressing Identity in an analytical concomitance and that is the verb substantive in the meaning of a copula. Finally there must be a word expressing production in a concomitance founded on Causation.

The judgment therefore consists of subject, predicate and a word meaning either 1) existence or 2) identity (copula) or 3) causation. It is exceedingly curious that the Aristotelian formulation of the law of Contradiction — this the law of all laws — virtually presupposes the Threefold Logical Reason — this fundamental tenet of Buddhist logicians. Aristotle indeed was right, more right than he suspected, in introducing into his formulation of the law of Contradiction the two, and only two, relations of Necessary Dependence (*niyata-pratibandha*) which Dharmakīrti has established as underlying all logical thought. Indeed what are the sources of the denial of the law of Contradiction at different times by philosophers of different countries? It is always want of discrimination between the necessary interdependence of two different facts, or concepts, and their identity. The effect cannot exist without a cause, they are necessarily interdependent. In careless language, in a semi-poetical flight of imagination, we may call them united and identical. We shall then have existence and non-existence at the same time, the cardinal tenet of Hegel.

But the Buddhist law of Contradiction comes to interfere with this result and says that «everything is apart», there is no real identity at all. An Ens *quatenus* Ens is certainly a cause, it «has» an effect, but it «is» not its own effect. On the other hand two different concepts may be superimposed on the same point of objective reality describing it from two different points of view. The concepts are then united by a common reference to the same reality. They are so far identical. Here the Buddhist law of Identity does not interfere, but supports this kind of identity. However identical is only the common substratum, the constructed concepts are different.

The quarrel between the two logics in European, as well as in Indian, philosophy is founded really on a different interpretation of these two necessary relations. The one logic — from Heracleitus to Hegel in Europe, from Upanishad up to Mādhyamikas and Vedāntins in India — maintains that things necessarily interdependent cannot exist the one without the other, they are therefore not only opposed to one another, but they are also identical as included the one in the other. The other logic — from Aristotle to Sigwart in Europe and the Buddhists and Naiyāyiks in India — answers, «what is opposed is not the same».[1]

All empirical right cognition is uncontradicted cognition and there are only two great principles upon which this uncontradicted knowledge is founded. They are Causality and Identity of Reference. Uncontradicted cognition must be uncontradicted in regard of Causality, that is of different time; and uncontradicted in regard of its objective reference, that is of the different aspects of the same reality. Hence the proper formulation of the law of Contradiction must necessarily take into account those two general relations whose neglect vitiates empirical cognition and makes it contradictory. Thus it is that Aristotle, although unconsciously, in his formulation of the law of Contradiction affords an indirect, but very eloquent support to the rightness of Dharmakīrti's theory of relations. His law indeed contains an indirect, concealed reference to what, according to Dharmakīrti, are the three principles constituting together our Intellect[2] or our logical thought: Contradiction, Causation and Identity. Through this our Threefold Intellect we cognize Reality indirectly, i. e. inferentially. Without this

---

1 Cp. the formulation of Herbart «*Entgegensetztes ist nicht einerlei*» and of the Buddhists «*yad viruddham* (= *viruddha-dharma-saṃsṛṣṭam*) *tan nānā*, c. g. in SDS., p. 24.

2 *trirūpasya lingasya trīṇi rūpāṇi*.

threefold apparatus we can cognize Reality directly, through the senses; but pure sense-cognition is mere indefinite sensation.

We have in the different logics of Europe and India several laws of Contradiction: 1) the Eleatic law in its two varieties, the one of Parmenides and the one of Heracleitus, 2) the Platonic law which converts change into illusion, 3) the Buddhist law which converts stability into illusion, 4) Aristotle's law, which is also the law of the Indian Realists, according to which everything is alternately stabilized and changing, and finally, 5) Hegel's law introducing moving reality into the heart of his concepts and thus effacing all difference between reality and logic.

CHAPTER III.

UNIVERSALS.

§ 1. The static Universality of Things replaced by Similarity of Action.

The Indian theories of Universals can be divided into two main groups, the realistic one and the idealistic one.[1] The Realists assume that every Universal exists in the external world as a separate unit invariably connected with all the individuals in which it is present. The Idealists, who also can be characterized as Conceptualists and as Nominalists, maintain that only Individuals are real Ens-es, the Universals are mere images, mere concepts or mere names.[2]

The Realists again are divided in those who assume the additional reality of Inherence[3] as a separate Ens, and those who deny the reality, or necessity, of such an Ens. The maintainers of Inherence are further divided in those who assume that its reality is perceived by the senses directly, and those who assume that its reality is not perceived, but inferred. The Vaišeṣikas assume an inferred Inherence, the Naiyāyikas — a perceived one; the Jainas, Mīmāṃsakas and Sānkhyas do not assume any Inherence at all[4], and the Buddhists deny the reality of Universals altogether. The theory of the Buddhist logicians is characterized as an Idealism,[5] as a Nominalism,[6] as a Conceptualism,[7] as a theory of Conformity,[8] as a dynamical theory[9] and as a dialectical

---

1 There is scarcely an Indian work on philosophy in which the problem of Universals would not be touched. The best expositions of the Buddhist theory is found in the *ākṛtivāda* chapter of Kumārila's Šlokavārtika, in the chapters on *sāmānya-vāda* and the *syād-vāda* of TS. and TSP. and in all the works on *apoha-vāda*, cp. vol. II, p. 404.

2 *saṃjñā-mātra* = *vastu-šūnya-vikalpa.*

3 *samavāya.*

4 Cp. TSP., p. 262. 22.

5 *vijñāna-vāda.*

6 *vastu-šūnya-prajñapti-vāda.*

7 *vikalpa-vāsanā-vāda.*

8 *sārūpya-vāda.*

9 *šakti-vāda.*

theory.[1] It is Idealism since it maintains that Universals are mere subjective ideas. It is Nominalism and Conceptualism since these ideas are the same as images and concepts and are capable of being associated with names. It is a theory of Conformity, since it maintains the correspondence of an image with some efficient point-instant of external reality. It is a dynamical theory since it maintains that reality consists of Forces capable of evoking images. It is a dialectical theory because it maintains that all concepts are relative and dialectical.

The theory of Conformity has been examined as a theory of judgment. The dynamical and dialectical theories will be now examined.

All these theories can be illustrated by the different interpretations of the existence and cognition of a piece of cloth. For the Naiyāyika it consists of three units: the threads, the «cloth-ness» and the Inherence of the clothness in the threads, all three being real external separate units, and all three perceptible to the sense of vision. For the Vaišeṣikas Inherence is inferred, not perceived. But the threads and in them the presence of «cloth-ness» are perceived. For the Jainas, Sānkhyas and Mīmāṃsakas there is no Inherence at all, there are only two units — the threads and the clothness. They are directly united without the go-between of an Inherence. For the Buddhist logicians there is here only a point of pure reality which stimulates our Productive Imagination to produce the image of a cloth. This last theory is a theory of Conformity or Correspondence between two quite heterogeneous things. It is a dynamic theory. The real individual things are not substances, but Forces, capable of evoking images in our consciousness.

«The things, i. e. the causally originating things, says Šāntirakṣita, (are Things-in-Themselves), there is «not the slightest bit of another thing mixed up in (each of them»).[2] Reality consists of absolute particulars. Every vestige of generality is absent in it. Generality, similarity, relation or a Universal is always something imagined or constructed. What is then the connection between the real particular and its utterly heterogeneous cognition, since cognition is always a Universal? The answer is the following one.

There is in the things themselves not a bit of common substance. How could there be in them any similarity of substance, since, as we have seen, there is in them no substance at all? Forces they are, not

---

1 *apoha-vāda.*

2 TSP., p. 1. 9; cp. p. 486. 20.

substances! But nothing prevents us to assume that things, or forces, absolutely dissimilar produce similar results.[1] E. g., the plant *gūḍūcī* is known in medicine to produce a febrifuge effect. It has not the slightest similarity, in shape and stuff, with other plants which are known in medicine to have the same — or stronger, or feebler — febrifuge effect. Their similarity is not a similarity of substance, but a similarity of producing a similar, or nearly similar, effect. If the Universal would be an external real thing, a thing in itself, just as the real particular is, we would have necessarily a direct reflex of that Universal in our head. The function of the intellect would then be passive receptivity. But that is not so!

The Buddhist logicians attach great importance to what we have christened as the Experiment of Dharmakīrti;[2] the fact, namely, that when the mind of the observer is absent,[3] when his attention is otherwise engaged, the incoming stimulus may be fully exercised by the object, the photographic function of the senses may be fully discharged, but no recognition will follow, because «the mind is absent». The observer will «understand» nothing. His attention must be directed to the object and to the photographic process; past experience must be remembered; the name and its connotation must be recalled; only then will the observer begin to «understand» and recognition will follow.[4] What does that mean? It means that the understanding is a separate faculty, different from the senses. The understanding is the mind's spontaneous activity subsequent to the function of the sensuous passive apparatus. If the connotation of the name were an external reality; if it were an eternal form, residing in the object, a form in which the object would «partake»; recognition would have been produced straight off, as soon as the stimulus would have reached the senses. The processes of attention, recollection of passed experience and of the name, may go on with great rapidity, if the action is habitual.[5] But if it is not habitual, it will be gradual and revealed by introspection. If the febrifuge capacity belonging to some medicinal plants would represent an eternal Form residing in them, it would be always the same, never changing. But we know that it is changing

---

1 TSP., p. 497. 16; cp. ibid., p. 239. 27 ff.

2 Cp. above, p. 150.

3 *anyatra-gata-citta,* cp. TS., p. 241. 12.

4 *sanketa-manaskārāt sad-ādi-pratyayā ime jayamānās tu lakṣyante, na akṣa-vyāpṛty-anantaram,* TS., p. 240. 17.

5 TSP., p. 240. 25.

in every individual case. It depends on the quality of the plant, and this quality again depends on the quality of the field on which it is raised, its cultivation, manure, etc.[1] It belongs consequently to every individual case separately. There is in one case «not the slightest bit» of what is found in the other. The Universal is an illusion, it is a mere name without any pervasive reality corresponding to it. «It has been proved by us, says Kamalaśīla, that the particular real thing-in-itself,[2] which represents the substratum of what is designated by a name, is not touched by the dialectic of the understanding. But the empirical (non-ultimate) reality, whose form is constructed by the artist called Productive Imagination,[3] is internal,[4] not external. People not knowing the difference between *per*ception and *con*ception,[5] noticing that the form of the object seems to be external, run after it as if it were just external. But this does not prove that it really is external. Our behaviour towards external objects, such as e. g. a goad, is founded upon their projection into the empirical world in our perceptual judgments,[6] but they really represent a subjective construction of our mind». «Besides», says the same Kamalaśīla[7] to the Realist, «what you intend to prove is that the general ideas[8] refer to something different from those bodies (which are actually perceived).[9] But this is wrong, because (these general entities do not exist), they are not (separately) reflected».[10] Indeed what you describe as «cowness» is bereft of those colour, particular shape and (proper) name (which the actual cow possesses). The image which I experience (in my head) possesses these colour and other (particulars) reflected. How is it then possible that its pattern should be deprived of colour and (all these particular features). It is impossible to admit that the image should have one form and its external pattern a (general) form quite different, since in that case the super-absurdity[11] would arise (that every image would correspond to any object).

---

1 TSP., p. 240. 5.

2 *svalakṣaṇa.*

3 *kalpanā-śilpin.*

4 *antarmātrā-ārūdha.*

5 *dṛśya-vikalpayor viveka-anabhijñātayā.*

6 *bahī-rūpatayā adhyavasita.*

7 Ibid., p. 243. 17 ff.

8 *anugāmi-pratyayānām.*

9 namely because you consider the Universal to be a separate unity.

10 *tasya apratibhāsanāt.*

11 *ati-prasanga = sarvatra pravṛtti.*

We see that the argument of **Berkeley** against Conceptualism and in favour of Nominalism is here repeated by **Šāntirakṣita** and **Kamalašīla** in favour of the same Nominalism, but against Realism.[1] However the enormous difference between Berkeley and the Buddhists consists in the evident fact which has apparently escaped the attention of the great Englishman, namely the fact that what he calls «particular colour and shape» is also general, general in respect of the particulars under it. The non-general is only the thing as it is strictly in itself. If it is, e. g., blue in colour, this means already that it is not non-blue, and then it is general, it is no more «in itself», it is «in the other», relative, constructed, dialectical. The absolute particular blue is unutterable. It represents «the very first moment» of sensation, the sensation of the «pure» object, the object bereft of all its characteristic features,[2] the object not yet touched by the dialectic of the understanding.[3] This «pure» object is the foundation and cause of all our knowledge. It is efficient and consequently real. It is subsequently «understood», or «telescoped», by the understanding in an image which is universal and therefore unreal. It represents the object in a general picture. The knowledge of the first moment is **affirmative** knowledge, it cognizes pure reality. Is the knowledge of the image also affirmative? No, it is only **distinctive**, as we shall see in the sequel.

§ 2. History of the problem of Universals.

The problem of Universals apparently attracted the attention of Indian thinkers at a very early date. Names of philosophers are quoted who belong to the semi-mythical ages of philosophic pre-history and who were concerned about Universals, Particulars and their relation to names.[4]

---

1 **Berkeley's** words «whatever hand or eye I imagine, it must have some particular shape or colour» cannot be translated into sanscrit otherwise than thus: *yad eva cakṣuḥ-pāṇy-ādi-vijñānam mayā vikalpyate, višiṣṭa-varṇa-ākṛti-anugatam anubhūyate*. Cp. this with **Kamalašīla's** words, p. 243. 20, — *vijñānam ca varṇa-ādi-pratibhāsa-anugatam anubhūyate.*

2 *prathamataram sarva-upādhi-vivikta-vastumātra-daršanam pravartate*, cp. TSP., p. 241. 17.

3 *na tad vikalpaiḥ spṛšyate.*

4 TSP., p. 282. 24 — *jātiḥ padārtha iti Vājapyāyanaḥ*; probably to read *Vajapyāyana-Kātyāyanau*), *dravyam iti Vyādih, ubhayam Pāṇiniḥ*. Cp. **Ruben**. Die Nyāya-Sūtras, p. 195 ff. and Otto **Strauss**, ZDMG, 1927, p. 135 ff.

To the first historical period, the period of the rise of the Sānkhya, must probably be assigned the origin of the two principle doctrines between which the schools were divided in later times. With the doctrine of unity between cause and effect, hand in hand, must probably have developed the doctrine of a certain unity of Universal and Particular. With the doctrine of a divorce between Cause and Effect, and the splitting of all existence in separate minute elements, evidently, ran hand in hand the Buddhist doctrine denying the reality of Universals.

To a later period belongs the rise of the doctrine of Inherence in the two allied schools of Nyāya and Vaišeṣika in which realism, assailed by its adversaries, hardened to an extent which is unique in the history of philosophy.

In the third period of Indian speculation when the mutual position of the chief actors on the stage of philosophy was laid down in systematic works we find the following distribution of roles in the play of Universals.

On the extreme right we find the extreme Realists of Nyāya and Vaišeṣika. They make their appearance later than the others.

In the middle stand the moderate Realists of the Jaina, Mīmāṃsā and Sānkhya schools which probably represent the earliest doctrine.

On the extreme left stand the Buddhists which at a later date found adherence from the Vedāntins.

The Buddhists were probably the indirect cause of the exaggerated realism of some orthodox schools.

One of the aphorisms of the Vaišeṣika system contains the statement that «the General and the Special are relative to cognition».[1] This aphorism cannot be interpreted in the sense of Relativism as meaning unreality, because the general tendency of the system is very realistic. According to that system things can be relative and real at the same time.[2] The aphorism simply means that the generality of Universals has different degrees, and these degrees are relative to each other. The system not only admits the Inherence, i. e., so to speak, personal residence of a Universal in the Particular,[3] it moreover admits the presence in every particular thing of a second resident, called Difference.[4]

---

[1] V. S., I. 2 3.

[2] *apekṣiko vāstavaš ca kartṛ-karaṇādi-vyavahāraḥ,* cp. Šrīdhara, 197. 26.

[3] *sāmānyāni...*. *sva-viṣaya-sarva-gatāni,* Prašast., p. 314. 19.

[4] Prašast., p. 321. 2 ff., the question is asked that the Yogi could perhaps see the difference between atoms by his exceptional vision alone, without the

Since all things are, on the one hand, similar to other things and, on the other hand, different from other things, therefore consequent Realism admits the presence in every single thing of these two inmates, Similarity and Dissimilarity. Every atom, e. g., shelters a special reality called the Difference. All ultimate ubiquitous realities, such as Time, Space, Ether, Soul, etc., include such ultimate Differences which prevent them from being mixed up together. These real Differentiae are separate units perceived by the senses. In atoms and in ubiquitous substances they cannot be perceived by the eyes of ordinary people, but the Yogi who has a special gift of vision perceives them directly by his eyes. Realism could not proceed any further!

There was hardly any subsequent change or development of the realistic idea inside the Nyāya-Vaiśeṣika school, except their divergence on the problem of the perceptibility of Inherence, mentioned above. The Vaiśeṣikas quarrelled on the question of the omnipresence of the eternal Universals. A part of them maintained that they were present only in the places where the respective particulars resided. Another part maintained that they were present not only in these places, but also in the intervals between them,[1] although unmanifested. Praśastapāda rallied to the first of these views[2] and it became incorporated in the official doctrine of the school.

The Buddhist denial of Universals is divided in two periods. In the first period, in Hīnayāna, abstraction, synthesis, universality and name-giving were regarded as special Forces (*saṃskāra*), either mental[3] or general.[4] In the second period, in the school of the logicians, Universals were regarded as concepts (*vikalpa*) and contrasted with the objective reality of the particulars.

There is no other doctrine which would equal Hīnayāna Buddhism in its anti-universalist tendencies. What here corresponds to a Universal parades under the name of abstraction.[5] The term indicating it is

---

additional residence in every atom of a special reality, called Differentiae. The question is answered in the negative. According to VS., I. 2. 5—6, Generality and Differentiae are resident in all substances, qualities and motions, but in the ultimate substances Differentiae alone are resident. These ultimate Differentiae have alone survived in Praśastapāda's Bhāṣya.

1 Cp. NB and NBT., p. 82. 18 ff; transl., p. 225.

2 Praśastap., p. 311. 14; cp. Śrīdhara, p. 312. 21.

3 *citta-saṃprayukta.*

4 *rūpa-citta-viprayukta.*

5 *saṃjñā* = *udgrahaṇa*, cp. my CC., p. 17—18.

the same which in grammar is used to designate a name substantive, but it is here characterized as a mental energy[1] *sui generis.* The school of the Sarvāstivādins converts it into a non-mental, i. e. general, energy.[2]

It is clear that what is called generality or a Universal is here converted into a faculty of distinction, just as the genus[3] is here also converted into a separate force uniting some units which themselves are supposed to possess nothing in common.

This fundamental idea finds its clear expression in Dignāga's classification of the genus as a name-giving construction of our thought.[4] It is a Nominalism, but of the sort which cannot be distinguished from Conceptualism, since a concept and a name cover the same ground.

§ 3. Some European Parallels.

The Indian mediaeval logic is filled up with a struggle between Realism and Nominalism, just as the Middle Ages in Europe. The respective positions of both parties were fixed during the creative period of Buddhist logic, in the V—VIII centuries AD. From that time both doctrines became petrified and retained their mutual positions without any substantial change. Schools seldom change their fundamental principles in India. If they survive they remain in a changeless condition. Let us imagine for a moment that the school of Plato would have survived in the land of its origin to all political cataclysms and would continue to profess the same doctrine with but insignificant changes of style and literary form up to our days, — this would represent exactly the position of Indian Realism. Nominalism became extinct in India with the extinction of the school of Buddhist logicians. But in Tibet it continues exactly the same teaching during more than a millennium up to our own days.

The Indian Realists maintained that a Universal is an actual Ens residing in the objects of the external world. It possesses 1) unity, 2) eternity and 3) inherence;[5] that is to say, in every particular indi-

---

1 *caitta* = *citta-samprayukta-saṃskāra.*

2 *nāma-saṃskāra* contained among the *citta-viprayukkta-saṃskāra.*

3 *nikāya-sabhāgatā* = *jāti*; it is classified by the Sarvāstivādins as *citta-viprayukta-saṃskāra.*, cp. my CC., p. 105.

4 *jāti-nāma-kalpanā*, cp. above p. 217.

5 *ekatva-nityatva-anekasamavetatva.*

vidual it somehow resides in its completeness and eternity. The Buddhists retorted that the Universal is 1) a mere name,[1] 2) it is also a mere concept without an adequate external reality[2] and 3) that the concept is dialectical,[3] i. e. negative. Only in assuming that the concept is negative can we understand the otherwise absolute absurdity of the unity, eternity and complete inherence of the general in each particular.

There is an unmistakeable parallelism between the European struggle and the Indian controversy. Its general lines are similar, but not its details.

The first distinction is this, that in India the problem was closely linked together with two different theories of sense-perception. The Realists assumed an imageless[4] consciousness and a direct perception by the senses of both the external particular and of the universal residing in it. The Nominalists transferred these universals out of the external into the internal world and assumed an external world of mere particulars faced by an internal world of mere images; that is to say, of mere universals. Sensations became related to images as particulars to universals. Thus Nominalism became founded on the doctrine that the senses and the understanding are two utterly heterogeneous mental faculties, although united by a special causal relation, inasmuch as images always arise in functional dependence on sensations..

Another capital distinction is but a consequence of the first. The Buddhist conception of the particular is quite different from the European one. The particular apprehended in sensation is the bare particular, containing nothing of otherness or universality. All European Nominalism and Conceptualism is founded on the idea of a particular which is but a concrete universal.[5] The line of demarcation lies in India, as indicated above, between the absolute particular and the absolute universal, not between the concrete universal and the abstract

---

1 *saṃjnā-mātram.*

2 *vastu-šūnyo vikalpaḥ.*

3 *anya-vyāvṛtta = apoha.*

4 *nirākāra.*

5 Duns Scotus has insisted upon the primal character of individuality (*haeccitas*), but had still regarded it as the generic substantialized. Guillaume d'Occam asserted that the particular is the real and that the universals are gatherd from our intuitive knowledge of the individualities. This is very near to the Indian view, but the conception of a pure and absolute particular is nevertheless absent.

one; for these are both universals and both abstract. The difference is only in the degree of abstraction.

With these very important distinctions we may assume that the contest in India corresponded to the contest in the European Middle Ages.[1]

Turning to modern European philosophy, it becomes easy to imagine how Dignāga would have answered Berkeley and Locke, supposing they were all seated together at a round table discussing the problem of Universals. That the «general and universal» are mental «ideas», that they are «inventions and creatures of the understanding»,[2] Dignāga would have conceded at once. But that «simple ideas» can be concrete and particular he would have emphatically denied. If the universals are necessarilly intelligible, it follows that everything intelligible is necessarily a universal. The straight line which the geometer draws on the table is particular, but the straight line which is in my head is universal. It is infinite, it represents all straight lines of all times and places. It is of no use to say that while being particular it «represents» other particulars too. It is impossible to be one thing and to represent the opposite thing: to be particular and to represent the universal.

That the «simple idea» is nothing but the effect of certain «powers»,[3] is again quite an Indian idea. But this power is only the power of stimulating the understanding to product «its own creature». This equally refers to the power of constructing the simple idea of blue and to the power of constructing the «ideas» of cow, horse, tree, justice, infinity, eternity, and the «primary» qualities of extension, bulk, etc. etc. It is true that all ideas must be in touch with some particular, they must be «*cum fundamento in re*». But they never are particular, or adequate to particulars. They are, as Locke says, in respect of the general ideas, «only signs».[4]

Berkeley's contention that there are no general ideas, but only general names for particulars, «anyone of which the name indifferently

---

1 It can be mentioned that Abelard in his attempt at mediation between extreme Nominalism and extreme Realism expressed views which are partially found in India. He held that the Universal is more than a name, it is a predicate (*sermo*), even a natural predicate. We have seen that the universal as a general concept is always the prediate of a perceptual judgment, hence all universals are nothing but predicates.

2 Locke's Essay, book III, ch. III, § 11.

3 Ibid., book II, ch. XXI, § 2.

4 Ibid., book II, ch. VIII, § 7, VIII, § 10 & § 17.

suggests to the mind»—would have probably been answered by Dignāga in the following way. Names are just as general as ideas. The capacity to receive a name is the distinguishing sign of an image, when distinguished from a sensation. All namable things are ideas just as general as the names by which they are designated. There is no difference in respect of reality between an abstract idea and a name.

Supposing Dharmakīrti would have been present at the same symposion, he would have probably delivered himself in his peculiar style, addressing himself to Locke, in the following way. «You maintain that some ideas are adequate, others are not; some are simple and individual, others are creatures of the understanding, added to the things from without. But why? Who is the Universal Monarch by whose decree one set of ideas is declared to be adequate and another not? Ideas are ideas, they are not reality. Either all are inadequate or none!» But when Locke maintains that the objects are nothing but «powers» to produce various sensations and that the corresponding ideas being in the mind are no more the likeness of external object than their names «are the likeness of our ideas»,—this Dharmakīrti would have readily admitted in extending this feature to all «ideas» in general.

The battle between Realism and Nominalism in European logic has remained undecisive. The contending armies have forsaken the battlefield. The majority of modern logicians have dropped this subject as irrelevant and insoluble. There are, however, the schools of Marburg and of Husserl which contain attempts at a new interpretation of Platonic ideas. Nay, even the school of Experience is not disinclined under the pressure of necessity to have recourse to the same solution. It is easy to imagine how Dharmakīrti would have answered these quite modern doctrines. To Husserl he would have spoken thus: «You maintain that the ideal objects really exist,[1] that they are not mere *façon de parler*,[2] that there is no such interpreter's skill in the world which could repudiate ideal objects altogether».[3] On the other hand you maintain that there is a difference between the ideal existence of the Universal and the real existence of the particular.[4] We do not object! The real fire is the fire which burns

---

1 Log. Unt.,[2] II, 124.

2 Ibid., p. 125.

3 Ibid., p. 126.

4 Ibid., p. 125. «Wir leugnen es nicht... dass ein fundamentaler, kategorischer Unterschied bestehe, zwischen dem idealen Sein and realem Sein, zwischen Sein als Spezies and Sein als Individuelles».

and cooks. The ideal fire is the one I have in my head. I never have denied the existence of the universal fire in my head.[1] But the particular fire is in the external world, it represents the «ultimate reality»,[2] the efficient point-instant!»

In answer to Natorp's defense of Platonic ideas Dharmakīrti would have in all probability answered thus: «You maintain that Plato's theory reduces to the judgment x = A, where x represents the concrete and particular and A the universal.[3] Both «exist», because existence means for Plato «complete determination of the element x». We do not object! We only will add the proviso that «ultimately real» is the concrete particular, not the universal as assumed by Plato». In changing the application of Husserl's words, Dharmakīrti would have said that «no interpreter's skill in the world can do away the obvious fact that the real fire is the fire that burns and cooks, and the ideal fire which I have in my head can of course «completely determine» the particular fire, but it cannot burn and cook».[5] We necessarily must distinguish between ultimate reality and imagination. The latter is a mental reality which is real only as a *façon de parler*.

That there are two quite different concepts of reality, is the most commonly known fact in Buddhism. The old definition is that existence means cognizability.[6] Existence is divided in 12 categories[7] of which the last category (№ 12) contains all mental items.[8] But Mahāyāna has changed the definition into «real is the efficient»[9] and such is only the external ultimate concrete and particular, the point-instant. The internal objects are sensations and images. Images are always universals. They are divided into pure imagination (or flowers in the sky)[10] and imaginations which have an indirect or «general» bearing

---

1 This kind of reality is called *svarūpa-sattā*, cp. SDS, p. 26.

2 *paramārtha-sat.*

3 Natorp, Plato's Ideenlehre, p. 390.

4 Ibid., p. 391, «Existenz sagt vollständige Determination des «Diesen».

5 In this point the Budhists fall in line with the empirical schoolt, cp. W. James, Essays in radicall empiricism, pp. 32—33, and B. Russell, Analysis of the Mind, p. 137 ff; — with the very important difference that ultimately real is only the point-instant.

6 *yat prameyam tat sat* It is is also sometimes the definition of the Naiyāiks, who distinguish between *sattā-sāmānyam* and *svarūpa-sattā*, cp. the *prāmāṇya-vāda* section in the NK., p. 162. ff.

7 *dvādasa-āyatanāni* = *sarvam jñeyam.*

8 *dharma-āyatana* = *dharmāḥ.*

9 *yad artha-kriyā-kāri tat sat* = *paramārtha-sat.*

10 *anupākhya*

to the reality of a point-instant. These last are necessarily universals.[1]

According to Bertrand Russel[2] the relation between the external particular and the mental Universal is causal. This would correspond to that part of the Buddhist theory which replaces the reality of an universal by the similarity between different stimuli exercised by discrete particulars. Moreover causality is not sufficient, there is besides between the particular and the corresponding universal a «Conformity». What this conformity means will be explained in the next chapter.

---

1 This is also proved by the Buddhist theory of the Syllogism; for the major premise means consistency which is but the indirect reality of concepts and their laws, and the minor premise (incl. conclusion) means reference of these concepts to the ultimate reality of a sensuous element; the latter is the only ultimate reality.

2 Analysis of Mind, p. 227. — «The facts open to external observation are primarily habits having the peculiarity that very similar reactions are produced by stimuli which are in many respects very different from each other», cp. «Outline of Philosophy», p. 172 f.

CHAPTER IV.

DIALECTIC.

§ 1. Dignāga's Theory of Names.

We have arrived at the closing act of Dignāga's Drama of Cognition. This drama is characterized by classical unity of action and unity of place. There are only two *dramatis personae* evolving all the while on the stage of cognition. They are Reality and Ideality. The first is running, the second is stable. The first is called Point-instant, the second is called Concept or, some-times, simply Logic. Reality we have witnessed as appearing in the first act in its genuine purity, unintelligible and unutterable, but vivid, and directly reflected. «A prodigy!» exclaims Dharmottara,[1] the more it is vivid, the less it is comprehensible. In the second act we have watched the indirect, or conditioned, reflex of Reality in a Concept. The Judgment disclosed itself as a function bringing together the seemingly irreconcilable Reality and Ideality. Inference appeared as an extension of the Judgment, its function is to link together Reality with extended or inferred concepts. The Sufficient Reason of this linking is represented by two exceedingly important, though subordinate characters, Identity and Causality; which disclose themselves as reference to an identical point-instant and reference to two different, but interdependent, point-instants. This second act of the drama, establishing the Categories of relation between concepts and their relation to ultimate Reality, can be called the act of Transcendental Analytics, following the first act of Transcendental Aesthetics. In the last act the relation between Reality and Speech is represented. The unutterable reality can neverthelless be designated, of course indirectly, by names, and it becomes incumbent upon the author of the drama to represent the behaviour of Names towards Reality, to establish the part of reality they indirectly can touch. Since, as will be seen, the names can touch reality only dialectically, the concluding act of the drama may be called the act of Buddhist Nominalism, which is also the act of the Buddhist Dialectical Method. We thus will have, following a celebrated example, a transcendental Aesthetic, a transcendental Analytic and a transcendental Dialectic; transcendental because Logic becomes here related to ultimate Reality.

[1] In Apoha-prakaraṇa.

What is indeed the part of language in our cognition? Is it a real source of knowledge? Is it a separate source, different from the senses and the intellect, or is it a secondary source included in one of the two main sources? At the first glance the dignity of a source of real knowledge cannot be refused to verbal testimony. For what is a source of real knowledge, according to the system here analysed? It is, we have seen, uncontradicted experience. Real knowledge is successful knowledge. It precedes every successful purposive action. External reality produces a stimulus upon our cognitive apparatus, which constructs, when stimulated by reality, an image of the thing from which the incoming stimulus proceeds. Guided by this image we take action and, if the image is right, the action becomes successful, the object is reached. Supposing I am informed that there is a tree on the river and five apples on that tree. I then proceed to the river, find the tree and reach the apples. The action is successful, because the verbal testimony was right. But does that mean, as some philosophers have supposed, that the word is the adequate expression of external reality; that the connection between the object and its name is primordial and eternal; that reality is «interwoven» with names, that there is no reality without a name; that consequently the names precede reality, that language is a kind of Biotic Force, which shapes our concepts and even shapes reality itself in accordance with those concepts? We will see in the sequel that all these shades of opinion were represented in philosophic India. To all them the Buddhists opposed an emphatic denial. Language is not a separate source of knowledge and names are not the adequate or direct expressions of reality. Names correspond to images or concepts, they express only Universals. As such they are in no way the direct reflex of Reality, since reality consists of particulars, not of universals. The universals cannot be reached in purposive actions. Just as concepts and names they are the indirect, or conditional[1] reflex of reality; they are the «echo»[2] of reality, they are logical, not real. Being an indirect cognition of reality, language does not differ from inference, which has also been

---

[1] That the Indians clearly distinguisted the direct from the indirect reflects is seen from the following passage of Pārthasārathi (ad Šlokav, p. 559) — *jñānākāram... svalakṣaṇam vā bhāsamānām anubhāsate, śabdam iva prati-śabdaḥ*. Indeed the mental image (*jñānakara*) indirectly reflects (*anu-bhāsate*) the directly reflected reality (*bhāsamānam svalakṣanam*). *bhāsanam* = *pratibhhāsa* is a reflex as in a mirror (*ādarśavat*), and *anubhāsa* is an indirect or conditioned reflex.

[2] Cp. the passage quoted in the preceding note.

defined as an indirect mode of cognition. The name is a middle term through which its object is cognized. The connection between the middle and the major terms is here founded on Identity of objective reference, the deduction is analytical and the three aspects of the reason are realized; e. g.: 1) this object is called a jar, 2) wherever such objects are found they are called jars, 3) this name is never applied to a non-jar. However, this theory — the theory, namely, that names are, like logical reasons, the indirect mark of reality — is not the main feature of Dignāga's theory. He goes on to state that all names are negative or, as we may put it, dialectical.

The natural Dialectic of the human Intellect is thus considered in India, by the Buddhist Logicians, under the head of a Theory of Names. It is a kind of Nominalism. It is well understood that concepts and names cover the same ground, since conceptual thought is defined as namable thought, a thought capable of coalescing with a name. «Names originate in concepts», says Dignāga, and *vice vera* «concepts can originate in names». Hence to determine the import of names is the same as to determine the fundamental character of concepts. That the Theory of Concepts is brought under a Theory of Names is explainable by the special historical conditions out of which the Buddhist theory emerged. Language was for some schools a special source of our knowledge, fundamental and ultimate, coordinated to the senses and the intellect. In answer to these theories Dignāga makes the following statement:[1]

Knowledge derived from words does not differ (in principle) from Inference. Indeed the name can express its own meaning only by repudiating the opposite meaning, as for instance the words «to have an origin» (designate their own meaning only through a contrast with things having no origin or eternal).

That knowledge derived from words does not differ (in principle) from inference means that it is indirect knowledge. Knowledge indeed can be either direct or indirect, either originating in the senses or in the intellect, either perception (sensation) or inference (conception). Knowledge derived from words is not direct, it is not sensation, it is indirect, it is like knowledge through inference. It is moreover negative or dialectical. Thus a new feature in the contrast of direct and indirect knowledge, of the senses and the intellect, is given. The senses are

---

[1] Pram.-Samucc., V. 1.

affirmation, «pure» affirmation.[1] The intellect is dialectical, i. e. it is always negative. Its affirmation is never direct, never pure, it is affirmation of its own meaning necessarily through a repudiation of some other meaning. The word «white» does not communicate the cognition of all white objects. They are infinite and no one knows them all. Neither does it communicate cognition of a Universal Form of «whiteness» as an external Ens cognized by the senses. But it refers to a line of demarcation between the white and the non-white, which is cognized in every individual case of the white. The white is cognized through the non-white, and the non-white through the white. Just so is the cow, or cowness. It is cognized through a contrast with the non-cow. The concept of «having an origin» does contain absolutely nothing over and above its contrast with eternity. The negation is mutual. To have an origin means negation of eternity and eternity means negation of origin. Since the same refers to every concept and every name, we can in this sense say with Hegel that «Negativity is the soul of the Universe». But Hegel has left in the world nothing but logic; therefore there is in his world nothing but Negation. In the Buddhist view there is beside logic a genuine reality which is neither negative nor is it dialectical. Concepts, or logic, are all of them negative and dialectical. Reality, or the Things-in-Themselves, are affirmation, pure affirmation, they are non-dialectical. Negation at last discloses its real face. We at last can answer the puzzling question: «why on earth is Negation needed? Affirmation alone will do!». Cognition is an assertory cognition of reality. If Negation is also cognition of reality, why are the two needed? We now have the answer. The direct knowledge is Affirmation, the indirect is Negation. But pure affirmation is only sensation whereas Pure Reason is always dialectical, i. e. negative. The doctrine that there are only two sources of knowledge, the senses and the intellect, receives a new and deep foundation. The senses and the intellect are not only related as the direct and the indirect source of knowledge, they are related as affirmation and negation, as a non-dialectical and a dialectical source.

In the chapter of his great work dealing with the knowledge conveyed by words Dignāga begins by making the statement that verbal knowledge is not direct, it is inferential, relative and dialectical. He then examines the divergent theories of other schools. The theory that names express Universals he rejects, because of «infinity and

---

[1] Cp. above, p. 192.

discrepancy».[1] His critique is directed against the opinion that the Universal is a real Ens residing in a particular and cognized directly, by the senses. The Universal embraces an infinity of particulars, which cannot be cognized directly. He then rejects the Vaišeṣika theory, according to which names express the «differences». This theory seems to be closely allied to his own theory of negative names, but he rejects it, because of its realism. The Vaišeṣika's we have seen, indeed assumed that in every particular Ens there was residing a real Differentia, a real «otherness», by virtue of which every individual thing, and even every atom, could be distinguished from other things. He further rejects the Naiyāvika theory,[2] that names express three categories of things, abstract Universals, concrete Universals and Particulars. Absolute particulars are absolutely unutterable, and concrete Universals are not to be distinguished from the abstract ones. Both are Universals and both are abstract. Names of course express Universals, but what kind of Universals? These Universals exist in our head, they are constructed by the force of Productive Imagination and are essentially negative, relative and dialectical. After having rejected divergent opinions, Dignāga repeats that knowledge produced by words cognizes reality by the method of «Repudiating the Contrary», i. e. negatively or dialectically.

Jinendrabuddhi interrupts his commentary at this place[3] of Dignāga's text and gives the following summary of his theory, which I here translate in full.

§ 2. Jinendrabuddhi on the Theory of the Negative Meaning of Names.[6]

a) All names are negative.

(*Pram.-samucc.-vṛtti* ad V. 11). «Therefore the meaning of a word consists in a repudiation of the discrepant meaning». «This means» (as is clearly seen in such names) as «possessing origination», etc, that they contain in their own meaning a repudiation of the discrepant. (This theory has been mentioned at the beginning and now it is) established «by a rejection of all conflicting opinions».

---

[1] *ānantyād vyabhicārāc ca*, ibid., V. 2. Cp. TSP., p. 277. 27 — ***na jātiśabdo bhedānām vācaka ānantyāt.***

[2] NS., II, 1. 65.

[3] Cp. Višāla-amalavatī, Tanjur, Mdo., vol. 115 (Peking), pp. 285 ff.

(Jinendrabuddhi, f. 285 a. l.). These words mean that in summarizing the rejection (of all realistic opinions which maintain that words) express (real) Universals etc. (Dignāga) merely establishes his own theory (mentioned by him in the beginning). One could have objected that by a repudiation of foreign opinions one's own theory cannot be established, according to what has been explained when examining and rejecting the ***modus tollens*** of the Mixed Hypothetical Syllogism (which the Sānkhya school admits as an independent proof). But this stricture cannot be made, since the own theory (of Dignāga) has been mentioned at the very beginning, where he says that, just as in the word «having origination», the own meaning of the word is always expressed through the repudiation of the contrary. Thus it is proved that verbal testimony does not differ (in principle) from Inference. (385 a. 3). By rejecting the theory of those who maintain that language is a separate source of knowledge and that it expresses Universals and (Differences) through direct affirmation, (by rejecting them), the same theory (of the author, the theory, namely, that language expresses Universals not through affirmation, but through negation) becomes established.[1] (285. a. 4). These words are (an introductory remark). (Dignāga) intends to expound and prove his own theory.

(285. a. 4). Now, (does the word «repudiation) here refer to simple negation or does it refer to a special kind of it? And what is the consequence involved? If it be a simple negation of the discrepant, we will be in contradiction with the text, where it is stated that words express «their own meaning» by rejecting the contrary; because (usually), the simple rejection of something else is made independently from (the statement) of one's own (direct) meaning (285 a. 6). A part of the meaning will be then suggested by negation. The word will express a special (entailed) meaning in the way of an (implied) negation. The maintainers of this theory of a double meaning are contradicted by the text (of Dignaga).[2]

(285. a. 7). But if the (term «repudiation» here) refers to a special kind of negation,[3] then the view of equally[4] repudiating the contrary (i. e. of equally doing two different things, rejecting the contrary and

---

1 J. here comments on the word «established» (*gnas-pa* = *vyavasthita*) used by D. in connection with his own theory after rejecting divergent views. A rather superfluous comment.

2 The first part of line 285 a. 7. is a repetition through misprinting.

3 This special negation is also called *paryudāsa*.

4 Correct *mnan-par* into *mñam-par*.

asserting one's own meaning), this view is rejected. Indeed the meaning is then that just as the particle of negation has no other function than denial, (just so every word) can have no other function than the repudiation of the discrepant.

(285. b. 1). But is the view of a double meaning really a different view? The mistake found in this view, (i. e. the mistake that it contradicts the text of Dignāga), will it not also extend to this (other view, because Dignāga speaks of the word's «own» meaning)? No, it will not! because the repudiation of the contrary is the exclusive meaning (of every word). And there is no contradiction (with the statement of Dignāga), because the «own» meaning of the word is just repudiation of the contrary (and nothing else). It is here expressed by the term «Contrary Repudiation». Indeed the aim of the text of Dignāga is that the word «expresses *per differentiam*» its own meaning.

(285. b. 2). Another consideration! (We use Position and Contraposition as two different figures in Syllogism, the one is affirmation, the other negation). If we enjoin something special, we understand that it is different from something else. The practice of enjoining something is understood as a position and contraposition. The words are thus expressive of affirmation and repudiation. There is thus only one part of this relation which must be understood as a repudiation of the contrary (285. b. 4). But here it is maintained that words signify exclusively special meanings, (such meanings namely which consist in a negation of the discrepant). (There is only one meaning, there is between affirmation and negation of the contrary) no such relation that the one would characterize the other.

(285. b. 4). However, do we not in common life understand the words of speech either as having a sense of affirmation alone, or of negation alone?

No, that is not so! (The words express only negations, only differences!), because a pure affirmation without any (implied) negation is senseless (it conveys no definite) result. (285. b. 6). We likewise never can take our stand on any pure negation. There is no contraposition without a (corresponding) position, neither is there any position without contraposition.[1] A position (or positive concomitance)[2] is under-

[1] Cp. NBT., p. 78.22—*ekasya, anvayasya vyatirekasya vā, yo(a)bhāva-niścayaḥ sa eva aparasya dvitīyasya bhāva-niścaya-anantarīyakaḥ.*

[2] *anvaya-vyatireka* are the same as *bhāva-abhāva*. Cp. NBT., p. 79.7— *anvaya-vyatirekau bhāvābhāvau.*

stood as the direct meaning, but it is impossible without at the same being a negation (or contraposition). Contraposition consists in a repudiation of a foreign meaning from one's own meaning. It is unthinkable that a contraposition should exist without an implied position.

(285. b. 7). Just for this reason the word does not accomplish two different jobs, viz. the repudiation of the discrepant meaning and the positive statement of one's own meaning. Since the essence of one's own meaning of a word consists in its being different from other meanings. As soon as it is expressed, we straight off feel that the contrary is rejected.

(285. b. 8). Just as when we say «a twin-brother»! Since a couple is needed to constitute twinship, we necessarily understand that there is another twin when one is mentioned,—just so in any class which consists of two separate items; since they are only two, when the one is indicated, it is distinguished from the other.

(286. a. 2). (The objection has been made)[1] that if the word will have exhausted its function by repelling the contrary, we will be obliged to find another word in order to express its positive import. But this is a mistake, since the word *eo ipso* repells the contrary. Indeed a word by merely suggesting its own meaning, suggests also the repudiation of everything discrepant, because this suggested (negative) meaning is inseparable (from the positive one).

(286. a. 4). Thus there is not the slightest contradiction in maintaining that the «own» meaning of a word consists in Negation.

b) The origin of Universals.

(286. a. 4). Now further, (let it be negative!) What does this (negative meaning) represent? It represents a Universal Form which the speaker intends to designate. It is indeed invariably connected with a word. Therefore the word is the evidence of what the speaker wants to express.

(286. a. 5). However, if a (real) Universal is meant by a word, how is it that a (concrete) mental image is supposed to be the object corresponding to a word? (Yes, indeed!). It is just this mental image that constitutes the (whole) Universal. (286. a. 6). How is that? (This mental image is a Universal, because it represents a combined result of many causes). Indeed (take for instance) a visual sensation. It is the joint product of the organ of vision, of a reflex and of attention

[1] By Bhāmaha, cp. TS. and TSP., p. 291.

(according to one system),[1] or else (according to the Realists) it is produced by the Soul and its interaction with an inner sense, an outer sense and an external object. All these factors are separate units, there is in them no pervading Universal unity, (but they produce together one combined result). Just so a *śiṃśapā* and other single objects, without having in themselves any mutually pervasive real unity at all, being experienced (by every observer) in his own mind separately, nevertheless produce a single united presentation. They stimulate our faculty of Productive Imagination and the (several acts of this imagination) create a united reflex[2] which becomes a single concept.[3]

(286. a. 8). And this (single representation contrives) in some way to represent us (a series of things) having different forms, as though they were non-different. It represents a unity between the characterized (particular) and the characterizing (general). By imputation it superimposes its own undifferentiated reflex upon this (plurality of individual things). The nature of this faculty of Concepts consists in this that it effaces the difference of individual forms (and replaces them by one general form).

(286. b. 1). Now this (purely internal) general reflex is believed by mistaken humanity to be an external thing. It is extended so as to cover many different individuals, to represent them as projected in the external world and to endow them with causal efficacy.

(286. b. 2). Thus a purely mental thing is converted into an external object. It is projected and dispersed[4] in the external world as though (it were so many real objects). And such are the habits of thought of common humanity that they believe this projection to represent a real Universal.[5] (286. b. 3). How is it then that we maintain that the meaning of a word is such a Universal and that it consists merely in a repudiation of the contrary? (Yes, indeed!) Just this very Universal is nothing but a repudiation of the contrary. (286. b. 3). How is it then that what makes the difference of every external object from other objects is (nothing but the mental opera-

---

1 Cp. my CC., p. 54 ff.

2 *tha-mi-dad-par snañ-ba* = *abheda-pratibhāsa.*

3 *rnam-par-rtog-pai šes-pa* = *vikalpa-vijñāna.*

4 *kun-tu-hphro-ba-ñid* = *prapañcita.*

5 Lit. 286. b. 2—3. «This projection-dispersion of things entirely residing in the intellect, as if they were external, is settled by the cognizer, according to his manner of thinking, as a Universal».

tion) of repudiating the contrary? Indeed «difference», «repudiation of the contrary», «clearing out of what is different» are so many manners of expressing the same thing, since we do not admit that difference is something over and above the thing endowed with it.

(286. b. 5). Therefore (the following question arises). (If our cognition and our speech contain truth and refer us to reality, and if reality consists of mere particulars, whereas speech expresses mere universals and mere negations), how is it then that this self-same essence of an external particular, the Thing-in-Itself, is being converted in something whose essence is mental and negative? (286. b. 5). This question is out of place. The (Transcendental Philosophers) who are engaged in an investigation of Ultimate Reality will always know the distinction (between Reality and Ideality), but not so the others. (Ordinary mankind will always confound them), because they think that this very image which they have in their heads can be efficient and real. They believe that at the time when we first see a thing and give it a name, as well as at the moment of our practical behaviour towards this thing, it remains just the same thing as which it is constructed by our imagination, (they believe that reality is congruent with thought). (286. b. 7). Therefore it will be just in accord with their habits of thought, if they will impute to us their opinion that Repudiation-of-the-Contrary is an external reality. But the learned men, trained as they are in the investigation of ultimate truth, will never believe in the unity (and reality of the Universal), because each reflex and (each thing) are separate (in themselves).

(286. b. 8). Moreover, the only foundation for the production of general ideas by our intellect is that very Repudiation-of-the-Contrary. We have said that the meaning of words consists in a repudiation of the discrepant in order to prove that (the Universals are negative in their essence). (286. b. 8). (Indeed this kind of negative universality is the only one) that is contained in Reality itself and can be admitted without contradiction.

(287. a. 1). Therefore it is by no means contradictory to assume that the reality which represents the foundation of similar presentations consists in nothing but a repudiation of the contrary. (Different individual things produce really similar stimuli), a unity of result is thus produced, which allows to set aside those individuals, which do not produce the same result. (The things producing the same stimulus) become then the causes of a (transcendental) illusion and create a pervasive presentation, which has the form of a Universal. Thus it

is proved (that the Universal is the internal product which illusively appears as an external reality).[1]

c) Controversy with the Realist.

(287. a. 2). To this (the Realist) who maintains (the external reality) of Universals makes the following objection. If a «tree» were nothing over and above the negation of a «non-tree», we never could explain the first cognition of a tree. Indeed at the time of the first cognition of a tree, we do not yet know what a non-tree is. If to the question «what is a non-tree», we then answer «it is not a tree», and to the question «what is a tree?» we answer «it is not a non-tree», this would mean arguing in a circle. Therefore it is impossible by a mere repudiation of the contrary to fix a name upon a merely relative object, which has no (independent) stand in our intellect.

(287. a. 5). (The Transcendentalist). However, if you by convention fix the name upon the (real) Universal «tree», do you then rescind the non-trees or not? Supposing you are (willing) to rescind them, but without previously knowing what a tree is, you will not know how to do it. At that time indeed the cognizing (human mind) does not yet know what a tree is. He approaches the problem just with the desire to know what a tree and what a non-tree are. And not knowing it, how will he know how to rescind the non-trees from (the connotation) of the word?

Without knowing it, with a word formed without repudiating the contrary, it will be impossible for him, in his practical behaviour in life, to distinguish (the non-trees from the trees), just as it will be impossible for him to distinguisch the variety called *šiṃšapā* (if he does not previously know what a non-*šiṃšapā* is). (287. a. 7). If we give a name to a thing without having previously distinguished it (from other things), we in our practical behaviour will not be able to make a distinction (so as to reach what we want) and to avoid (what we do not want). (287. a. 8). Indeed if we attach the name «tree» to trees in general without having distinguished (the general meaning of the term)

---

[1] Lit. 287. a. 1—287. a. 2. «Thus indeed, owing to a unity of the result these individuals are set aside from the non-possession of that result; through the medium of an inner experience in one's own mind, they become the causes of a force (producing) an illusive result and create a connected idea of the form of a Universal; this has been shown».

from its varieties such as *śiṃśapā* and others, we will never know how to behave supposing we intend to avoid *śiṃśapās* (and get some other kind of wood). (287. b. 1). Besides it would mean running into a contradiction, if we were to apply the term «tree» to trees in general without having previously distinguished them from non-trees. (287. b. 1). But let this be (as the case may be)! The Realist who maintains that Universals are real things (has another argument). You may repudiate whatever you like (says he), you will achieve (by mere negation) nothing at all! But in pointing distinctly to an object situated before us, we establish its name by convention and say «this is a tree». Thus either the Universal which is itself perceived at the time of convention or the Universal which is connected (with the thing perceived) will be recognized by us in our behaviour, at the time (when we will want either to reach it or to avoid it).

(287. b. 3). Thus it is that (on this theory) the consequences for the behaviour will not be the same (for the Realist as for the Transcendentalist. He will recognize the tree and know how to behave)!

(287. b. 3). (The Transcendentalist). No! the consequences will not be «not the same!» (They will be just the same!) (Indeed consider the following dilemma). When you point to a single object and state «this is a tree», do you use this term with restriction or do you use it without restriction? In the first case the meaning will be «this alone is a tree, there are no others». If you never have seen any tree before and if you do not know at all what a non-tree is, how can this name convey any definite meaning? (287. b. 5). But if you speak without restriction, meaning «this is a tree, but there are other objects which also are trees», how will then the person so informed behave, supposing he wants at that time to avoid (coming in contact with trees)? The difficulty (for the Realist) is absolutely the same! (He must know what the non-trees are).

(287. b. 5). (The Realist). I maintain that when you have perceived a thing by the senses, it becomes easy to know what it is opposed to (and to distinguish it from what it is not). In this sense (the realistic theory) avoids the difficulty. (287. b. 6). Being endowed with a direct sense-perception of such a (definite) object, whatsoever it may be, when I internally feel that in the case of another object another image, having another form (is present in my head), (when I feel) that this form is different from the one that has been seen at the time when the name of the thing (was first suggested), — then I can distinguish (the trees) from the heterogeneous (non-trees). Just then will I well

know that «these alone are trees» and it will follow by itself that «all objects in which (this form) is not reflected are non-trees». (287. b. 8). This (theory which takes its stand on the fact of a direct perception of the same thing) becomes impossible on the Mutual Negation theory,[1] because on that theory the form perceived is one thing and the thing which was standing before us at the time of first name-giving is subsequently never apprehended any more. And even if it were cognized, that concrete particular tree which was seen at the time of the first name-giving is never recognized in another tree. We never can say «this is that very tree (which we have seen before)». Therefore a *palāša* or any other variety of trees will be different from that particular perceived tree just in the same degree in which it is different from a jar or any other object, because no pervasive form (equally existing in all varieties of trees and uniting them into one real species) is being admitted.

(288. a. 2). (The Transcendentalist). But look, see! This your theory is similar to the Negation theory! (You assume pervasive realities, really existing in the things belonging to the same class; we admit similar stimuli produced by separate objects which do not contain any pervasive unity in themselves). (288. a. 2). Indeed, these objects (the trees) are every one of them a separate thing (a monad). But nevertheless they, every one of them, by their own nature produce one and the same effect of recognition, which the other objects (the non-trees) do not produce. Having produced a discriminating judgment of the form «these things are the cause of my recognition, others are not», the human intellect thus divides (the Universe of Discourse) into these two groups. Thus it is that this my recognition apprehends, (although) indirectly, an identical object, only because it is produced by a thing which has an identical result, (not because there is an identical external thing in existence). (288. a. 4). Thus the dichotomizing (operations of our mind), which are the outcome of (different objects) producing one and the same result consists in a recognition which receives the form of a Universal projected into the external world in an objectivizing perceptual judgment. These dichotomies appear as separate individual images, seemingly endowed with externality, seemingly endowed with causal efficiency and seemingly endowed with some kind of invariable connection.

---

[1] *rnam-par-gcad-pai-smra-ba = pariccheda-vāda = paraspara-parihāra-vāda.*

d) The experience of Individuals becomes the agreed experience of the Human Mind.

(288. a. 6). A perceptual judgment establishes (one's own mental image) as having the character of an external object. It is thus constructed (in imagination). Every observer experiences in his own innermost his own images. Nevertheless the imaginative operations of (different) Individuals agree with one another. It is just as the visual experience of two persons suffering from the same eye disease. They both see the moon double; although every one of them in his innermost experiences only his own image, they are persuaded that they see the same (double moon).

(288. a. 7). Therefore, owing to an illusion, we seemingly perceive a single universal form pervading different objects. Comparing with those remote trees, these (here) are also trees. Thus (in fixing the general meaning) those objects are excluded, which are not the cause of producing (such an illusively exteriorized) image. We then naturally realize that all objects having a discrepant form are non-trees.

e) Conclusion.

(288. a. 8). A thing perceived as a separate thing which nevertheless at the same time would be perceived and not perceived, which would thus produce a difference between a tree and a non-tree, which would be a unity capable of being perceived by the senses, such a thing (i. e. a Universal thing) does not exist, because these (tree and non-tree) are not perceived separately, as a stick and the bearer of a stick. (288. b. 1). They cannot be so apprehended because the one is not the indirect mark of the other. (They are united dialectically, the one being simultaneously the affirmation of trees and the negation of non-trees).

(288. b. 2). The same form which is perceived in one (individual thing) is also perceived in another. If there were something in existence which at the same time would possess this definite form and not possess it, if it would at the same time be a tree and a non-tree, only then could we have a real individual which would be a tree in itself.

(288. b. 2). Our opponents are ignorant of the real essence of the theory of the Negative Meaning of words. They impute us (a theory

which we never professed). They maintain that this theory means a blunt denial of every reality and thereupon they are always ready to insult us. By this sober expounding alone of what the essence of Negation is, we have repudiated all their objections and thus (we deem) that our enemy is crushed.

In order to repudiate him a great deed must have been achieved (by Dignāga) and now it is enough dwelling upon this vast subject!».

§ 3. Šāntirakšita and Kamalašīla on the negative meaning of words.

The following is a statement of just the same theory of Dignāga concerning the Negative Meaning of words (*apoha*), but in a somewhat different phrasing. It belongs to Šāntirakṣita and his commentator Kamalašīla.[1] It lays more stress on the fact that the words of our speech, although directly meaning a concept or a universal, indirectly refer to the particular real thing. They call the Thing also Negation; since it is something unique in itself, it is a «negation of all the three worlds».[2] It is «ontological» (*arthātmaka*) negation, that is, the positive substratum of a negative concept. The main idea is just the same as the one emphasized by Jinendrabuddhi, namely, that the words express their own meaning through negation. They are therefore negative. Without negation they express nothing, they can express something only dialectically, i. e. in couples of mutual negation. Lotze[3] comes very near to this theory when he says—«the affirmative positing of a contents and the negative exclusion of everything other are so intimately connected, that we, in order to express the simple meaning of affirmation, can avail ourselves of expressions which mean... only negation (?!)». This is exactly the thesis of Dignāga, although expressed with some astonishment. Lotze nevertheless thinks that there is an affirmation in names, and that negation is here (in names and concepts) something quite different from affirmation. Where the real affirmation lies, according to the Buddhists, will appear in the sequel. We now pro ceed to quote Šāntirakšita.

---

1 Cp. T. S. pp. 274—366 (šabdārtha-parīkṣā).

2 *trailokya-vyāvṛtta.*

3 Logik², § 11.

(316. 25). «Negation is double, says he, it is either special[1] or simple.[2] The special contains an affirmation of the contrary. In its turn it also is double, it either is logical[3] or ontological.[4]

(317. 2). The logical variety of qualified Negation is the mental image[5] which we cognize in our perceptual judgments[6] (as an Universal) which has one and the same form pervasive (through many objects).[7]

The ontological variety of qualified Negation represents pure reality, when every thing unreal (i. e. every ideality) has been brushed away from it. (It is the Thing-in-Itself).[8]

(317. 5). The essence of the logically Negative Meaning will now be defined.

It has been stated before[9] that just as the *Harītakī* and other medicinal plants have one and the same febrifuge influence, without the presence in all of them of one pervasive universal form, just so such things as the brindled and the black cow etc., although they by their nature are separate things, nevertheless become the causes of the same repeated uniform image, without any reality of a universal in them. This is simply a similarity of action.[10] On the basis of these similar efficiencies, by an immediate experience of them, a conceptive knowledge is produced. In this conceptual cognition appears the form of the object, its image, its reflex.[11] (Reflex and object) become identified,[12] (but this reflex proves to be a dialectical concept) and the name of Negation (or Contrary-Repudiation) is applied to it. It is a concept,[13] it is mental,[14] it contains nothing external, (it resides in the head of

---

1 *paryudāsa.*

2 *prasajya-pratiṣedha.*

3 *buddhy-ātmaka.*

4 *artha-ātmaka.*

5 *buddhi-pratibhāsa.*

6 *adhyavasita.*

7 That is to say that what is Universal in a thing is merely a negation of the contrary.

8 Lit. «(Negation) whose essence is the Thing (*arthātmā*) is the own essence (*svalakṣaṇa*) of the Thing purified (*vyāvṛtta*) from the heterogeneous (ideality), the real essence (*svabhāva*) of the Thing (*artha*)».

9 TS., p. 239. 19; cp. TSP., p. 329. 7 and 497. 15.

10 *ekārtha-kāritayā sāmyam.*

11 *artha-ākāra, artha-pratibimbaka, artha-ābhāsa,* (convertible terms).

12 *tādātmyena.*

13 *savikalpaka.*

14 *jñāne samānādhikaraṇyam.*

the observer). It is merely (imagined as something external) in a perceptual judgment.[1]

(317. 25). But why then the name of Negation is given (to this image which does not seem to be negation at all)? There are four reasons, (a principal one and three derivative ones). The principal is the following one. The image itself appears only owing to its being distinguished from other images. (If it is not distinguished from others, it reflects nothing). It is called Negation, because it is distinguished from others, it is a negation of them.[2]

But although having in itself nothing of the external particular object, the general image is nevertheless connected with it in three different respects;

1) The image is the cause guiding our purposeful actions, and making us reach the particular external object. The image is thus regarded as the cause, although really it is the effect, of the particular thing;

2) Or, on the contrary, the object reached in a purposeful action, is regarded as its cause, (although italso is its effect); since the general image is the result of a direct sense-perception of the particular object. It is the expedient by which the image is produced.[3]

3) It is a natural illusion of the human mind to identify with the particular thing its (general) image which is nothing but a construction of productive imagination.

(318. 9) We go over to the ontological Negation.[4]

The name of Negation can also be applied (indirectly) to the Thing-in-Itself, because it contains a difference from, or a negation of, all other things. The (feature of a) repudiation of the discrepant is also present. This is meant. It is thus intimated that the meaning of negation is indirectly[5] applied also to the Thing-in-Itself.[6]

(318. 15). What is the essence of the simple Negation?

---

1 *adhyavasita.*

2 *aślișța-vastu = anya-asambaddha-vastu.*

3 Lit. (318. 1). «Either by imputing to the cause the quality of the effect, viz., by being the cause of reaching a (real particular) thing, it is distinguished from others; or by imputing to the effect the quality of the cause. He shows it. Because it goes through the door of the unconnected thing. Unconnected means unbound to the other. This is just the door of the thing, the expedient. Owing to its direct perception such an image (concept) arises».

4 *arthātmaka-apoha.*

5 Read *na mukhyataḥ.*

6 It follows that the direct meaning of a Thing-in-Itself (*svalakṣaṇa*) is pure affirmation (*vidhi-svarūpa*).

Simple Negation means, e. g., that a cow is not a non-cow. In this case the meaning of repudiating the contrary is very clear.

(318. 18). Having thus enunciated three forms of Negativity, the author connects them with the subject matter, i. e., the meaning of words.

The words intimate the first kind of Negation, since the word evokes an image identified with an external object (this image is negative).

(318. 21). That indeed is the meaning of a word what is reflected (in our consciousness) when a cognition is being communicated through a word. Neither pure (or simple) negation is ascertained when a word is cognized, nor have we then (affirmation, i. e.) a direct reflex of the object, as in sense perception. What have we then? We have a knowledge merely verbal which refers to an external object. Therefore the right meaning of a word consists in the image of the thing and in nothing else, since in verbal knowledge this image appears as identified with (the external) object. (318. 26). The connection between an object and its verbal designation is a causal one... The meaning of a word consists in the image which is evoked through it. (319. 7). Therefore the (objection made against our theory, the objection, namely), that «pure negation is not what presents itself to consciousness when a word is pronounced» — this objection is groundless. We never have admitted that the meaning of a word is pure negation.

(319. 9). Thus it is that the negative (or distinctive) meaning which is suggested by a word is nothing else than the (distinct) image of the object. It is directly evoked by its name. It is therefore the main meaning of the word. The two other meanings (the thing itself and simple negation) are subordinate to it and there is therefore no contradiction in admitting them. (319. 12). When this meaning, i. e. the meaning of an image, has been directly communicated by a word, the meaning of negation, or a simple negation, is suggested as implied in it. How is it? The essence of a reflected image of a cow, e. g., consists in this, that it is not the essence of another image, e. g., of the image of a horse. Thus simple negation is a subordinate meaning inseparable (from every distinct image).

(319. 21). The (ontological) meaning of the particular, of a Thing-in-Itself, (is also a consequence of the principal meaning). The connection between the real thing and the name is indirect and causal.[1]

---

1 Cp. B. Russel, Analysis of Mind. p. 227. — «According to this view (of Brentano regarding real Universals as real objects of cognition), a particular «cat» can.

(319. 23). At first we experience internally the thing as it exists (present to our senses). Then the desire to express it in language arises. Then the organs of speech are set in motion and a word is pronounced. When the word is connected in this indirect way with the external thing, such as fire etc., we implicitly cognize the particular object as distinguished from all dissimilar things.

(319. 25). Therefore the second and third meaning of Negation, i. e. its meaning as simple negation and its meaning referring to the thing itself as distinguished from all others, these two meanings are the metaphorical (secondary) meanings of Negation. (The principal is the meaning of the image, or concept, which is distinguished from all other concepts and represents thus a negation of them).

(320. 7). (The objection[1] that according to this theory the words represent mere negation and that therefore something else must be found to represent affirmation, is not founded), because we maintain that the particular (real) thing is also suggested by a name. And this meaning is affirmation, not negation. It is the indirect meaning of the word. When we say that a word «denotes», this means that it produces a Negation which is included in the definiteness of its concept (or image); it produces an image which is distinguished from among all other images and which (also) distinguishes its own object, the particular thing, from all other things.

Thus it is that the theory of our Master (Dignāga) contains no contradiction, (it does not assume in the meaning of words mere negations without leaving any room for affirmation)...»

(315. 15). «The counter-theory of the Realist Uddyotokara assumes real Universals representing each of them a real Unity, an Eternal Ens and an Ens wholly inherent in every attaining particular. It is the presence of this real Universal that imparts definiteness and constancy to knowledge according to his theory. But our Master Dignāga answers, that his Negative (or Distinctive) Meanings (possess all the advantages which are supposed to belong to real Universals

---

be *per*-ceived, while the universal «cat» is *con*-ceived. But this whole manner of viewing our dealings with Universals has to be abandoned when the relation of a mental occurence to its «object» is regarded as merely indirect and causal... (=*pāramparyeṇa kārya-kāraṇa-lakṣaṇaḥ pratibandhaḥ*, TSP., p. 319. 22). The mental content is, of course, always particular (?), and the question as to what it «means»... cannot be settled... but only by knowing its causal connections».

[1] By Bhāmaha, cp. TSP., p. 291. 7.

alone). They have Unity, since they are the same in each (particular); they are eternal (logically), since their (negative) substratum is never destroyed, (it remains the same in every changing individual); they inhere in every individual in their full completeness. They possess Unity, Eternity and Inherence[1] (although they are purely negative or relative). Thus the meaning of words is Negation (i. e. distinction from) other meanings. This theory is preferable, since (as compared with the realistic one) it has many advantages!».[2]

Such is the essence of the Buddhist Dialectical Method. It maintains that all concepts and the names expressing them are negative, because they express their own meaning through a negation of the contrary. Since, according to some interpreters, this is also the fundamental meaning of Hegel's dialectical method, we may, for want of another term, call it the Buddhist Dialectical Method. But we must carefully note that there is, according to the Buddhists, no contradiction between cause and effect (there is simple otherness), nor is there any self-development of the concept. Development and movement belongs to reality, not to logic.[3]

But, on the other hand, the Buddhist Dialectical Method contains the solution of the quarrel between Nominalism and Realism. Since Concepts are purely negative, their universality, their stability and their inherence are explained as being mental, logical and dialectical. There is no contradiction for a Universal to be at once completely and continually present in a multitude of things if it is only a negative mark of distinction from other things. Since all concepts

---

1 *ekatva-nityatva-anekasamavetatva.*

2 To these comments on Dignāga's Dialectic by Jinendrabuddhi, Šāntirakṣita and Kamalašīla we originally intended to add a translation of Dharmottara's tract on the same subject (Apoha-nāma-prakaraṇa, Tanjur, Mdo, vol. 112, ff. 252—264). It is perhaps the best exposition of the subject. But it prooved too bulky to be inserted in the present volume, and besides Vācaspatimišra's summary translated in vol. II, pp. 403 ff. is mainly founded on this work. Although the core of the theory is the same, every exposition follows its own method. It will be seen from Vācaspati's exposition that Dharmottara lays particular stress upon the *apoha*-theory as a theory of Neglected Difference (*bheda-agraha*) which contains an explanation of the identification of external reality with our subjective images of it and of the illusion of a belief in the objective reality of these images.

3 Those who make a sharp distinction between Contradictory Dialectic and Contrary Dialectik (like e. g., Benedetto Croce) will notice that the Buddhists admit only the first, and cancel the second.

and names are negative, the Buddhists would probably have said that Hegel was right in proclaming that Negativity is the Soul of the world. However the world also consists not only of a Soul, but also of a Body. What the body of the world, according to the Buddhists, is, we shall see later on.

§ 4. Historical Sketch of the Development of the Buddhist Dialectical Method.

The Dialectical Method of the Buddhists developed gradually from insignificant, but characteristic germs affecting some problems only, into a general theory of the Understanding whose essence, as a special source of cognition, has been found to be dialectical. Three periods are to be distinguished, 1) the early period (Hīnayāna), 2) early Mahāyāna, 3) the critical school of Logicians.

The earliest records contain the statement that the founder of Buddhism has refused to give an answer on some metaphysical questions. These questions are, 1) four questions regarding the beginning of the world, viz., there is a beginning, there is not, or both, or neither, 2) four similar questions regarding its end, 3) four questions on the identity between the body and the Ego, and 4) two questions regarding the survival or not of the Saint after death. It will be noticed that the characteristic quadrilemmic formulation is similar to the one used by Plato in his Parmenides for similar problems.[1]

Leaving alone their scholastic formulation, the 14 questions reduce to two fundamental problems, the problem of Infinity and the problem of the Absolute. The similarity with Kant's antinomies in the state-

---

[1] In his celebrated book on Buddha, which at present impresses one as being a rather naive account of Buddhist ideas, the late Prof. H. Oldenberg has nevertheless not overlooked the dialectical character of Buddhism from its beginning. «The sophists», says he, «cannot be absent in a place where a Socrates is to come» (Buddha[10], p. 80). But not only in the sense of sophistry does the dialectical character belong to early Buddhism, it contains also the natural dialectic of the human mind when it begins to deal with the ultimate problems of Infinity and the Absolute (ibid., pp. 81, 232, 315 ff.). Prof. H. Oldenberg calls this dialectic «moderately clever» (*wenig gewandt*), but this appreciation cannot carry much weight, since it belongs to a time when the right understanding and translation of the fundamental technical terms of *duḥkha*, *dharma*, *saṃskāra* and *pratītya-samutpāda*, without which Buddhism is unthinkable, was yet in its infancy.

ment of some of the problems, as well as in their solution, is unmistakable and has attracted the attention of scholars.[1]

These are problems to which neither yes, not no, not both, nor neither, can be given as an answer. They are absolutely unanswerable, but the human mind necessarily encounters them. Our Reason in dealing with them becomes «dialectical», i. e. self-contradictory.

The school of the Mādhyamikas has extended this verdict to the human understanding in general and to all concepts without exception. They all on analysis appear to contain contradictions. The human mind contains a logic of illusion, since no objects, congruent with its concepts, are given at all. They consist of parts which sublate each the other.

Candrakīrti summarizes the central conception of the Mādhyamika method in the following words.[2]

«Simple humanity[3] imagines (i. e. constructs dialectically) and dichotomizes[4] Matter and (Mind[5], etc.), without going to the bottom[6] (of the dichotomy). ... But all such (imagined dialectical) concepts[7] form an inveterated Habit of Thought,[8] coeval with the beginningless world-process.[9] They arise in a process of Dispersion-into-Manifold.[10] (of the original Unity of the Universe). Thus are created (in couples the dialectical) concepts[11] of cognition and cognized; the object (expressed) and the subject (expressing it); agent and action; cause and effect; a jar and a cloth; a diadem and a vehicle; woman and man; profit and loss; pleasure and pain; fame and infamy; blame and praise, etc. etc.[12] All this worldly

---

1 Cp. O. Franke, Kant u. die alt indische Philosophie in «Zur Erinnerung an Emanuel Kant» (Halle, 1904), p. 137—138; cp. my Nirvāṇa, p 21 and 205. On the antinomy of infinite divisilility cp. below in the section on the Reality of the External World, under Idealism, and S. Schayer, Prasannapadā, p. XXIX.

2 Mādhy, vṛtti, p. 350.

3 *bāla-pṛthag-jana.*

4 *vikalpayantaḥ.*

5 *rūpādi.*

6 *ayoniśaḥ.*

7 *vikalpāḥ.*

8 *abhyāsa.*

9 *anādi-saṃsāra.*

10 *vicitrāt prapañcāt.*

11 *vikalpa* meaning concept and logical dichotomy, = *dvaidhī-karaṇa.*

12 Cp. with these examples of dichotomy those quoted by Lasson in his explanation of Hegel's Dialectical Method, Introd. to Wissenschaft der Logik, vol. I, p. LVII.

Manifold disappears without leaving any trace in the Void (of Relativity), as soon as the essence of all separate existence is perceived to be relative (and ultimately unreal)».

Candrakīrti in his examples here throws into the same bag contradictory and contrary opposition. A jar and a cloth are opposed indirectly, inasmuch as a cloth enters into the category of non-jars. The opposition of man and woman is an exhaustive dichotomy. The opposition of blame and praise, or, more precisely, of blame and not-blame, is «complete and mutual» exclusion, or contradiction. Everything created by the understanding is created in couples or, as Jinendrabuddhi puts it, there are only «twin-brothers» born in the realm of the Understanding. The parts of such couples sublate each the other by their relativity, or the mutual negativity of their definitions. The result is, as Kant expresses it, ***nihil negativum irrepraesentabile*** or, in the language of the Mādhyamikas, «the Void of all separate objects»[1] and the unique reality of the Undispersed, non-manifold Whole.[2]

The school ot the Buddhist Logicians, although fully admitting the dialectical character of all the concepts of the Understanding, objects to the wholesale unreality of knowledge and admits the pure reality of a non-dialectical Thing-in-Itself behind every couple of dialectical concepts.

The theory of Dignāga may perhaps have been partly influenced, in its logical aspect, by some views entertained in the school of the Vaišeṣikas. This school has probably received its name from the Category of Difference which it assumed as an objective reality residing in every individual thing, in atoms as well as in ubiquitous substances. Every object, according to this view, contains both Similarity and Dissimilarity as residing in it.[3] If we reduce both these residents to the single one of Difference and brush aside its realistic character, we shall have just the essence of Dignāga's theory, i. e. purely negative and purely mental Universals. In this point, as in some others, there seems to

---

[1] *sarva-bhāva-svabhāva-šūnyatā = sarva-dharma-šūnyatā.*

[2] *nisprapañca.*

[3] Cp. above, p. 449—450. The wording of VS. I. 2. 6 suggests the theory that on the one end of the scale, in *sattā*, there is *sāmānya* only and no *višesa*, while on the other end, in atoms and ubiquitous substances, there is *višesa* and no *sāmānya*. But already Prašastpāda assumes *antya-višeṣas* only. The later definition *atyantavyāvṛtti-hetuḥ* and *svato-vyāvartakatvam* suggest some similarity with the Buddhist *vyāvṛtti = apoha.*

exist some common ground between the Vaiśeṣikas and the Buddhist logicians, with all that radical difference which ensues from the realistic principles of the first and idealistic views of the latter.

The fate of Dignāga's theory of Negative Names was the same as the fate of Buddhist logic in general. It did not survive the extinction of Buddhism in the land of its birth. Together with Buddhism the theory migrated to Tibet where it exists up to our own time. Its appearance in India was met by a unanimous protest of all other schools. Even Prabhākara, the «friend of the Buddhists», who followed them in their theory of Negation, could not follow them all the length of accepting their theory of Negative Names. He evidently could not remain a Mīmāṃsaka, if he followed them so far. The Mīmāṃsakas became the leaders in the fight against the theory of Dignāga. A school whose valuation of Speech and of Names had all the character of religious veneration, — for whom the Word was an eternal positive Ens existing in an eternal union with the things denoted by it, — for whom the Word was first of all the word of the holy Scripture; this school could evidently only be shocked in the highest degree by a theory which reduces the names to mere conventional negative signs of differentiation. Nor could the Naiyāyiks who believed that the positive meaning of words was established by God, look favourably upon it. The argument of the Realists of all shades is always the same. There are positive things and there are negative things. Reality consists in existence and non-existence. The positive things are denoted by positive names, the negative ones by the addition of the negative particle «non».

Bhāmaha,[1] the rhetorician, rejected Dignāga's theory on the score that if the words were really all negative, there should be other words, or means of expression, for positive things. If the meaning of the word «cow» were really the negation of the non-cow, then some other word would be needed to express the different fact of a positive perception of the domestic animal possessing horns, a dewlap, and other characteristic signs. A word cannot have two different and even opposite meanigs. Since according to the theory of Negation the negative meaning is the principal one and the positive follows in its trail, we accordingly in contemplating a cow must in the first place have the idea of «non-cow» and after that the secondary idea of the cow.

---

[1] TSP., p. 291. 7. ff.

This objection is disposed of by the consideration that the Buddhists do not at all maintain that the negative meaning suggests itself at first and is followed by the positive one. They, on the contrary, admit that the positive is direct, but it is nothing without the negative one, both are the same.

Kumārila's[1] chief objection consists in the following argument. When the Buddhist maintains that the meaning of «cow» is negative, that it is «not non-cow», he only in other words expresses the same opinion as is maintained by the realists, namely, that there is a real objective reality in the positive genus «cow». If «not non-cow» is a negation implying an affirmation of the contrary, then the negation of non-cow is the same as the affirmation of cow. Indeed what kind of object is suggested by the term «not non-cow» according to the Buddhists? Is it the individual thing, as it is strictly in itself, shorn of all extension? This is impossible, since such a thing is unutterable. It must therefore be admitted that there is an utterable essence of a cow present in every individual of that class. This general essence is the Universal of the Realists.

But if the Buddhist means by «non-cow» simple negation, without the affirmation of the contrary, this is pure idealism, a denial of the reality of the external world. The Mīmāṃsakas have opposed it as an ontological theory, now it reappears again in the garb of a theory concerning the import of Names.

The arguments of the Realists are numerous and of great variety and subtlety. It is superfluous to quote them here. They all reduce to this fundamental one: there are positive names, they correspond to Universals; the Universals are real external things, perceived by the senses; there are also negative things which also are realities perceived by the senses.

But although the theory of Dignāga is emphatically rejected by the Realists of all shades, an indirect influence of it seems to have survived in the method of negative definitions adopted by the later Naiyāyiks. They make almost all their definitions from the negative side, by stating the fact through a repudiation of the contrary. It is a well known and natural feature of speech that, in order to give more clearness to an expression, we must mention what it is opposed to. But the Naiyāyiks use the method of opposite definition even in such cases where it is absolutely useless for the sake of logical distinct-

1 Ślokav. Apoha-vāda, kār. 1 ff.; cp. TS. and TSP., pp. 292 ff.

ness. E. g., instead of defining Concomitance as a necessary connection of the effect with its cause, it is defined as the connection of the cause «with the counterpart of the absolute non-existence of the result». Instead of telling that smoke is the logical reason, it is mentioned in the guise of «the counterpart of the absolute non-existence of the smoke».[1] Such twisted negative definitions are exceedingly in vogue in later Nyāya and form its characteristic feature.

§ 5. European Parallels.

a) Kant and Hegel.

In the preceding pages we have made a statement of Dignāga's theory concerning the negative essence of all names and all concepts. We have made it as much as possible in the own words of Dignāga and of his Indian interpreters. We have called it a theory of Dialectics. We also could have called it a theory of Negativity or Relativity. There are good reasons in favour of each of these names, which, if not directly convertible, stand very near to one another. According to the method followed in this work we now will proceed to quote some parallels from the history of European philosophy, which, by way of similarity and contrast, are likely to throw some reflection on the Indian standpoint, and at the same time will justify our choice of the term Dialectics as the most appropriate for the designation of Dignāga's theory. Leaving alone the parallels found in ancient Greece and in mediaeval Europe, some of which have been mentioned when examining the law of Contradiction, we can turn our attention to modern philosophy.

According to Kant the Dialectic is a logic of illusion,[2] but not of every illusion. There are two[3] kinds of illusion, the one is empirical or simple, the other is the natural illusion of the human reason when dealing with the four problems of 1) Infinity, 2) Infinite Divisibility, 3) Free Will and 4) a Necessary Ultimate Being. These are the four antinomies, i. e. problems that cannot be logically answered neither

---

1 *hetu-samānādhikaraṇa-atyanta-abhāva-pratiyogi-sādhya-samānādhikaraṇyam*, where *hetu* is *dhūma* and *sādhya* is *agni*. Cp. Tarkasangraha (Athalye), p. 247, cp. p. 289 and *passim*.

2 Kant ascribes this use of the term dialectic to the ancients, CPR., p. 49. Cp. however Grote, Arist., p. 379.

3 Ibid., p. 242.

by yes nor by no, and therefore represent a natural illusion of the Human Reason. This corresponds more or less to the Hīnayāna standpoint, according to which the questions regarding the origin of the world, the questions regarding its end, the problem of infinite divisibility, and the problem of the existence of the absolute eternal Being are insoluble, neither in the positive nor in the negative sense. Mahāyāna Buddhism likewise assumes two kinds of illusion, an original or natural one;[1] and a simple mistake. The first is also called «an internal calamity»[2] of the human mind. The list of natural illusions is however very much increased, since every Universal and every concept is declared to be the result of a natural illusion of the human mind.

This would correspond to Hegel's standpoint, when he declares,[3] in answer to the Kantian theory of the limited number of four antinomies, that «there are as many antinomies as there are concepts». Every concept, inasmuch as it is a concept, is dialectical. According to Kant all empirical objects, as well as the corresponding images and concepts, will not be dialectical. These objects are «given» us. Although as containing a manifold of intuition, they are also constructed by Productive Imagination, they nevertheless are «given». They are given to the senses, but once more reconstructed by the understanding.[4] Some interpreters of Kant[5] are puzzled by this double origin of things which are «given» and then once more constructed. They are inclined to find a fluctuation and want of decision in Kant, regarding this point. According to the Indians only the extreme concrete and particular, the point-instant, is «given». All the rest is interpretation constructed by Productive Imagination and by the natural Dialectic of the human Understanding. If we interpret Kant so that «given» is only the Thing-in-Itself—and some support for such an interpretation is not altogether missing in his text[6]—then there will in this point be an agreement between him

---

1 *mukhyā bhrāntiḥ*.

2 *antar-upaplavaḥ*, cp. TSP., p. 322. 7.

3 Wiss. der Logik, I. 184 (Lasson)—«(es können) so viele Antinomien aufgestellt werden, als sich Begriffe ergeben».

4 CPR., p. 40. According to the Buddhists only the very first moment (*pratamatara-kṣaṇa*) is «given» (*nirvikalpaka*).

5 as e. g., Fr. Paulsen Kant[2], p. 171.

6 Cp. especially in his tract against Eberhard the passage p. 35 (Kirchmann). Eberhard asks: «wer giebt der Sinnlichkeit ihren Stoff?.. wir mögen wählen, welches wir wollen, so kommen wir auf Dinge an sich». Kant answers: «nun ist ja

and the Indians. Empirical objects will then be entirely constructed on a foundation of transcendental reality. But they will not be constructed dialectically, whereas according to Dignāga they also will be constructed dialectically, just as the notions of Infinity etc.[1] This falls in line with Hegelian views. «The Universality of a concept, says Hegel, is posited through its Negativity: the concept is identical with itself only inasmuch as it is a negation of its own negation».[2] This sounds exactly as the Indian theory that all universals are negative[3], e. g., a cow is nothing over and above the negation of its own negation, it is «not a non-cow». «The Dialectic, says Hegel,[4] is an eternal contemplation of one's own self in the other», i. e. in the non-self. «The Negative», says he, «is also positive. The Contradictory does not result in an absolute Nought, in a Null, but essentially in a negation of its own special contents».[5] The step which was taken by Kant when he established his antinomies was «infinitely important», according to Hegel,[6] since the Dialectic became then «again asserted as a necessity for the Reason». «The definitness of a concept is its Negativity posited as affirmation». This is the proposition of Spinoza *omnis determinatio est negatio*, it has «infinite importance».[7]

So far there is apparently complete coincidence between this aspect of Hegel's Dialectic and Dignāga's theory. What a concept means is nothing but the Negation of the contrary. Negativity is mutual. Affirmation is relative, it is not an affirmation in itself, it is also a negation. Hegel therefore maintains[8] «that light is negative and darkness positive; wirtue is negative and vice positive».

---

das eben die beständige Behauptung der Kritik; nur dass sie... enthalten den Grund, das Vorstellungsvermögen, seiner Sinnlichkeit gemäss, zu bestimmen, aber sie sind nicht der Stoff derselben». If this is interpreted as the capacity (Grund = Kraft) to evoke the corresponding image by stimulating productive imagination, the coincidence will be nearly complete.

1 Cp. above p. 459. Even such a general notion as «cognizability» must be interpreted as the counterpart of an imagined «incognizability», cp. the quotation from Dignāga's Hetu-mukha in TSP., p. 312. 21.

2 Wiss. der Logik, II. 240.

3 *anya-vyāvṛtti-rūpa.*

4 Encyclop., p. 192.

5 W. d. Logik, I. 36.

6 Ibid., II. 491.

7 Ibid., I. 100.

8 Ibid., II. 55.

However he takes a further step. According to Kant both opposed parts of a contradiction sublate one another and the result is Null (*nihil negativum irrepraesentabile*).[1] According to Hegel they do not sublate one another, the result is not Null, but only the «negation of one's own special contents».[2] This probably means that having declared all concepts to be negative Hegel feels it incumbent upon him to find out some kind of real affirmation. He then declares that «the Positive and the Negative are just the same».[3] The non-existence of an object is a moment contained in its existence.[4] «Existence, says he, is one with its other, with its non-existence». From the thesis that «everything is such as it is only insofar there is another; it exists through the other; through its own non-existence it is what it is», — from this thesis he goes over to the thesis that «existence is the same as non-existence» or «Position and Negation are just the same».[5] Dignāga, as a logician, on the contrary thinks that «whatever is other is not the same».[6] It is true that from another point of view, from a translogical point of view, Dignāga, as a monist, will admit the ultimate identity and confluence of all opposition within the unique substance of the world. He will admit this «voidnes»[7] of the whole. But this metaphysical and religious point of view is carefully distinguished from the logical.

The duality of the standpoint (which we also find in Dignāga) survives in Hegel through his distinction of Understanding and Reason, a distinction inherited from Kant. «The Understanding, says he,[8] is definite and firmly holds to the differences of the objects, but Reason is negative and dialectical». For the Reason there is no difference between affirmation and negation, but for the Understanding this difference is all-important. The Reason annihilates all the definitions of the Understanding and merges all differences in an undifferentiated Whole.

There is still another and very important difference between Hegel and Dignāga. Hegel denies the Thing-in-Itself[9] perceived in pure

---

1 «Versuch (über) den Begriff der negativen Grössen», p. 25 (Kirchmann).

2 W. d. Logik, I. 36.

3 Ibid., II. 54.

4 Ibid., II. 42 — beide sind negativ gegeneinander.

5 Ibid., II. 55.

6 *yad viruddha-dharma-saṃsṛṣṭam tan nānā.*

7 *prajñā-pāramitā = śūnyatā = jñānam advayam.*

8 W. d. Logik, I. 6.

9 Cp. Phaenomenologie, p. 427; W. d. Logik, II p. 440 ff.

sensation just as he denies the difference between the senses and the understanding as two heterogeneous sourses of our knowledge. The senses are for him a modification of the spirit.[1]

In summarizing roughly the mutual position of Kant, Hegel and Dignāga regarding the three cognitive faculties of the Senses, the Understanding and the Reason we can establish the following points.

1) Kant assumes three cognitive faculties: the Senses, the Understanding and Reason. Of them the Reason alone is dialectical.

2) Hegel abolishes the difference between the Senses and the Understanding and changes the relation between the Understanding and the Reason. All objects, or concepts, are viewed by the Understanding non-dialectically and by the Reason dialectically.

3) Dignāga abolishes the difference between Understanding and Reason, but retains the radical difference between the Senses and the Understanding. The senses are then the non-dialectical source of knowledge and the Understanding is all the while dialectical.

4) Kant and Dignāga, just as they agree in maintaining a radical difference between the Senses and the Understanding, likewise share in a common recognition of the Thing-in-Itself as the ultimate, non-dialectical, source of all real knowledge. Hegel, on the other hand, follows Fichte and Shelling in their dialectical destruction of the Thing-in-Itself.

5) In Kant's system Reality (the Thing-in-Itself) is divorced from Logic. In Hegel's system they become confounded.[2] In Dignāga's system they are kept asunder on the plane of Logic, but merged in a monistic whole on the plane of metaphysics.

b) J. S. Mill and A. Bain.

We now at last know that there is absolutely no definite thought which would not be negation. A thought which would deny nothing, would also affirm nothing. Every word, says Dignāga, expresses its own meaning through negation. It is false to suppose that negation is an implied consequence. The word itself is negative. Nega-

---

1 Encycopädie, § 418. However the consideration that pure sensibility is «das reichste an Inhalt, aber das ärmste an Gedanken» could also be applied to Dignāga's idea of the moment of pure sensation (*nirvikalpaka*).

2 However Hegel's conception of pure existence which is the same as non-existence remembers to a certain extent the Indian Instantaneous Being which represents «its own annihilation».

tivity is the Soul of the World. The Dialectic, or Mutual Negation, is the negativity of all the determinations made by the Understanding. As soon as our mental eyes begin to glimmer and we begin to seek an expression for our feeling in a verbal sign, our object is already beset with contradiction and our thought has become dialectical.[1]

As soon as the Intellect begins to «understand», that is to operate dialectically on the material presented it by the senses, it already denies something. Therefore the real name for the understanding is dichotomy,[2] or dilemma, partition in two parts, of which the one is the «complete and mutual negation» of the other.

We are now going to quote the opinions of some modern European philosophers on Negation in order to show that they are all the while groping after a solution which is more or less given in the Indian theory.

J. S. Mill[3] thinks that there are positive names and there are negative names. But it is not easy to determine which are positive and which are negative, because the negative ones are often expressed positively and the positive ones are expressed negatively. E. g., the world «unpleasant »is positive, really meaning «painful», the word «idle» is negative, really meaning «not working». If we then ask which names are really positive and which are really negative, no answer will apparently be given. They are negative and this is all. Mill then passes the remark that the word «civil» in the language of jurisprudence stands for the opposite (i. e. for a negation) of criminal, of ecclesiastical, of military and of political. This would mean that the word «civil» is negative. If it contains no negation, it has no meaning at all. But if civil is negative why not declare that all are negative, since he says, «that to every positive name a corresponding negative one might be framed» and we never can know whether a given word has been framed in the negative or in the positive intention. This remark contains in it the germ of Dignāga's theory of Negative Names.

Another remark of J. S. Mill[4] becomes also very interesting when confronted with Indian ideas. He says, «there is a class of names cal-

---

[1] Palagyi, Neue Theorie d. Raum u. Zeit, p. VII f.

[2] *vikalpa*=*dvaidhī-karana*; it is also the name for a concept, i. e.=*ekī-karaṇa*.

[3] Logic. I, 43 ff.

[4] Suggested perhaps by Locke's (Essay, book II, ch. VIII, § 1—2) «positive ideas from privative causes», which are «real positive ideas», though perhaps their cause «be but a privation in the subject».

led «privative»; they are equivalent in their signification to a positive and negative name taken together, being a name of something which might have been expected to have a certain attribute, but which has it not; e. g., the word «blind» which is not equivalent to «not seeing», since it is applicable only to things that can see, or did see, which are expected to see». This remark contains the germ of Dharmakīrti's and Sigwart's theory of negation and should not be restricted to names called privative, but extended to all negation in general. The conclusion would apparently be that all names are «positive and negative taken together», since all are privative in some respect.

This conclusion has been resolutely asserted by A. Bain with the rather unexpected by him result that he has been accused of having fallen into the Hegelian heresy and of having betrayed the faith of Empiricism.[1]

He indeed has maintained that all names are positive and negative together, that there is no affirmation which would not be negation at the same time, neither is there a negation which would not be an affirmation at the same time. It follows that there is no affirmation in itself, nor is there a real negation in itself, but every name just at the same time when it affirms also denies. This is nearly the substance of Dignāga's view and Prof. A. Bain maintains the same without feeling the abyss in which he is falling. He evidently did not think that Negativity is the Soul of the Universe. He thought that there are positive things and negative things and that the same word expresses both (!). But if the same name is a designation of the positive as well as of the negative thing, it becomes quite impossible to determine which things are positive and which are negative. «In fact, says Bain,[2] positive and negative must always be ready to change

---

[1] Bradley, Logic[2], p. 158. «It would be entertaining and an irony of fate, if the school of Experience fell into the cardinal mistake of Hegel. Prof. Bain's «Law of Relativity», approved by J. S. Mill, has at least shown a tendency to drift in that direction. Our cognition as it stands, is explained as a mutual negation of the two properties. Each has a positive existence, because of the presence of the other as its negative» (Emotions, p. 571). I do not suggest that Prof. A. Bain in this ominous utterance really means what he says, but he says quite enough to be on the edge of a precipice. If the school of «Experience» had any knowledge of the facts, they would know that the sin of Hegel consists not at all in the defect, but in the excess of «Relativity». Once say with Prof. Bain that «we know only relations», once mean (what he says) that those relations hold between positives and negatives, and you have accepted the main principle of orthodox Hegelianism».

[2] Logic, I. 58.

places». Then the only conclusion possible is that all are negative since they are negative of each other.

Kant, we have seen, makes an important distinction between a logical and a real opposition.[1] «In a logical repugnancy», says he, (i. e. in contradiction) only that relation is taken in account, through which the predicates of a thing mutually sublate each the other, and their consequences, through contradiction». Which among the two is really positive (*realitas*) and which really negative (*negatio*), is not attended to. But the opposition between light and dark, cold and hot, etc. is dynamical. Both parts of the opposition are real. This opposition is not logical contradiction, but real otherness and dynamical repugnancy.

The same theory is expressed, we have seen, by Dharmakīrti.[2] Logical Contradiction,[3] says he, embraces all objects whether real or non-real. Dynamical repugnancy, on the other hand, is present only in some real couples. The opposition between blue and non-blue is logical, the first is as much a negation of the second as the second is the negation of the first. The opposition between blue and yellow, between a jar and a cloth is simple otherness. «All atoms, says Dharmottara, do not occupy the same place, but their duration does not interfere with one another», they exist peacefully in close vicinity.

Now these two kinds of opposition so clearly distinguished by Kant and by Dharmakīrti, have been confounded by Bain on one side and by Hegel on the other. Bain says[4] «one might suppose that a chair is an absolute and unconnected fact, not involving any opposite, contrary or correlative fact. The case is quite otherwise». It involves the non-chair whose meaning is very wide. A chair is thus, according to Bain, merely the negation of a non-chair and a non-chair merely the negation of a chair. Both parts are negative of one another.

c) Sigwart.

Sigwart takes up the problem which puzzled J. S. Mill, A. Bain and F. H. Bradley,[5] and which appears to be the same as has been

---

1 Cp. Essay on Negative Magnitudes, p. 26 (Kirchmann's ed.). Cp. CPR.

2 NBT., p. 70. 22.

3 *paraspara-parihāra.*

4 Logik, I. 61.

5 Sigwart does not mention in this connection the names of Mill, Bain and Bradley, but it is clear that in part 12—13 of § 22 of his Logic he expresses his view on the problem discussed by them and answers them. It comes clearly to the surface in the attempt to explain the word «blind» on p. 187.

thoroughly investigated by Dignāga in the V-th chapter of his great work. «All names are always negative», says Dignāga. «Some names, the so-called „privative" ones, are negative and positive at the same time», says Mill. «All names are always negative and positive at the same time», says Bain. «Take care!» says Bradley.[1] «Do you really mean what you say? You are falling into the precipice of Hegelian dialectics!» And Sigwart, it seems, listened to Bradley's warning. He took every precaution in order not to fall in the precipice of Hegelianism; with what success we shall presently see.

«The theory, says he,[2] that all things consist of yes and no, of existence and non-existence, has been first definitely expressed by Thomas Campanella, as pointed out by Trendelenburg. According to this view, «a definite thing exists only inasmuch as it is not something other. «The man is» — that is positive, but he is a man, only because he is neither a stone, nor a lion, nor an ass, etc.». Sigwart rejects this view as a dangerous heresy preparing the way to full Hegelianism, with its confusion of logic and reality. But he confesses that then he is quite at a loss to explain negation! «The question, says he,[3] is to know why are we in need of those subjective circuits in order to cognize the world of Reality in which no counterpart of our negative thought can be detected?» To this question no answer is given. Sigwart apparently escapes to Hegelianism at the price of sacrificing negation! All names should be positive, because no counterpart of the negative ones can be detected!

He then proceeds to ask, can incompatibility be explained by negation? «Man» is incompatible with every «non-man». The same thing cannot be a man and a non-man together. But the «non-man», the οὐκ ἄνθρωπος of Aristotle, is not something real.[4] It means

---

[1] Logic,[2] p. 158.

[2] Logik, I. 171.

[3] Ibid.

[4] Sigwart bestows taunts upon Kant's Infinite Judgment and tries to make it ridiculous (ibid., p. 182—185). Lotze angrily attacks it (Logik[2], p. 62). But H. Cohen defends it (Logik, d. r. Erk., p. 74). From the Buddhist point of view all diatribes against the infinite judgment are discarded by pointing to the fact that non-A is real just in the same measure as A, for there is absolutely no A without its implied difference from non-A. Both are dialectical constructions. Besides the A is just as infinite as the non-A. The judgment «this is white», e. g., refers to a point of demarcation between two infinities. This Sigwart seems indirectly to admit when he says that «white» must be restricted, otherwise it also will be infinite, cp. ibid., p. 182 — «aber wo bedeutet das Wort «weiss» ohne weiteres alle weissen Dinge!»

everything in the Universe of discourse except man. It means that the image of man is absent. «The absence of the image of man, says Sigwart, is itself not another image». Thus non-A being not real, Sigwart concludes that there is no opposition at all between all those objects which are included under A and non-A. They can peacefully coexist close by one another without quarrelling. That they cannot be predicated together of the same subject, is a matter of fact, known from experience, it cannot be «explained by negation». In this manner Sigwart disposes of negation and escapes to the dangers of Hegelianism. The name «man» is purely positive and contains no negation at all and the name non-man is altogether nothing.[1]

There is, however, one case, according to Sigwart,[2] where «it seems impossible to deny the origin of opposition through negation». Such are the «privative» names.[3] «Is it indeed possible to express the relation between seeing and blind otherwise than that blind means not-seeing?» Blind would then be the simple privation of vision and we would have «an opposition produced by negation». «It would then be absolutely the same whether I deny one part or assert the counterpart, whether I say «he sees not» or «he is blind». Thus seeing would mean not blind and blind would mean not seeing. Some names at least would be negative in themselves and the danger of Hegelianism would become imminent again! «No proof is needed», says Sigwart,[4] «to establish that it is not so! If the man does not see, the reason is not stated why he does not see. But if it is said that he is blind, it is thereby intimated that the apparatus is destroyed which enabled him to see». The man can evidently fail to see through want of attention or through distance, without having lost his faculty of vision. He will be «not-seeing», but he will not be blind!

One is really astonished to see a logician of so extraordinary perspicacity as Professor Sigwart producing so poor an argument! He seems to have forgotten that a man cannot be blind and not blind

---

[1] Ibid., p. 178 — «Die Vorstellungen von Mensch und Löwe sind an sich so wenig im Streit, wie die von schwarz und roth oder schwarz und weiss». Sigwart apparently thinks that there will be mutual opposition in the concepts of man and lion only when the lion will attack the man and devour him!

[2] Ibid., p. 185.

[3] Here evidently Sigwart takes up the discussion initiated by J. S. Mill and Locke.

[4] Ibid., p. 186.

at the same time and in the same sense, but he can very well be blind and not blind at different times and in different senses. Then indeed seeing and blind will not sublate one another. Otherwise they do sublate one another and are both «sublating», i. e. both negative, not both positive.

Having thus established that the privative names are really positive, Sigwart is obliged to make a further step and to assert that there are no negative names at all, all are positive! Indeed, he says[1], «all negation has a meaning only in the domain of judgment»... The formula non-A has no meaning at all. The members of a logical division, the items that are brought under the head of a general notion, are exclusive of each the other, hence it would be natural to surmise that each includes in itself the negation of the other. But this, according to Sigwart,[2] is an illusion. «It is an illusion to think that black and white, oblique and straight, etc., have a special hostility against one another, as if they were the sons of the same father».[3] Sigwart admits that there is a contrary and a contradictory opposition — the last when we have an exhaustive division in two, the former when the division is in three and more items[4] — but only in judgments. The names are not opposed. There is the straight and the oblique. But there is no straight and non-straight, because «the formula non-A has no meaning at all!» Persevering in the same direction Sigwart would have been obliged to maintain that there is presence, but there is no absence, no non-existence; everything is existence! Thus, without

---

[1] Ibid., p. 181.

[2] Ibid., p. 180.

[3] It is curious that Dignāga (Pr. samucc., V. 27) appeals to the same example for an illustration of his opinion which is exactly the opposite of the opinion of Sigwart. He means that the varieties of a general notion are opposed to one another «just as the sons of a *rāja*». After the death of the *rāja* a quarrel begins between his sons regarding the regal power, which is their common property. The one says «it is mine», and the other says the same, the result is a civil war. Just so the *śimśapā* and the *palāśa* and other trees quarrel regarding the common property of the universal treehood. This quarrel is, of course, only logical or imagined, it is not real. It may seem real in such cases as heat and cold, or light and darknes, but these are, as proved by Dharmakīrti, cases of causality, not of logical contradiction.

[4] Ibid., p. 368, «der Unterschied des sog. contradictorischen und conträren Gegensatzes fällt richtig verstanden mit dem Unterschied einer zweigliederigen oder mehrgliederigen Eintheilung zusammen». Not quite so however: man and woman, right and left are real couples besides being contradictories, but man and non-man is only contradiction, purely logical.

noticing it, he would have fallen into Hegelianism from the other end, οὐκ ἔστι μὴ εἶναι. The result of the theory that there is no negation in objective reality is just the same as the result of the theory that there is in it nothing but negation.[1]

What the Indian attitude is in this question, is quite clear, viz. —

1) All definite things are negative. Definite means negative.

2) They are negative a) of the contradictory directly, and b) of the contrary indirectly.

3) They can be affirmative only as negations of their own negations.

4) Pure affirmation is only the Thing-in-Itself.

5) All other things are «things-in-the-other», i. e., negative of some other, without which negation they are nothing.

6) Direct contradiction (Negation) is only between existence and non-existence of the same thing.[2]

7) Indirect contradiction is lurking between any pair of definite objects inasmuch as the one is necessarily included under the non-existence of the other.[3]

8) Every object first of all excludes the varieties contained under the same universal.[4]

9) All other objects are excluded through the mutual exclusion of the universals under which they are contained.[5]

---

[1] Wishing to establish that there is no real negation in nature and that the incompatibility of objects is an ultimate fact «not to be explained by Negation», but simply to be gathered from experience, Sigwart rushes into quite impossible assertions. «We could imagine», says he (Logik, I, 179), «an organization of our faculty of vision, which would make it possible for us to see the same surface coloured in different colours». If Sigwart means what he says, if he means that the same thing can be at the same time blue and yellow, i. e. blue and non-blue — and what else can he mean? — the price paid by him for his escape from Hegelianism is not only the sacrifice of negation, it is the sacrifice of logic itself. There is no opposition between the blue and the non-blue, he thinks, because the non-blue is infinite and unreal. There is neither any opposition between the blue and the yellow, because they can peacefully coexist by one another!

[2] NBV.. p. 70. 5 — *bhāva-abhāvayoḥ sākṣād virodhaḥ.*

[3] Ibid. — *vastunos tu anyonya-abhāva-avyabhicāritayā virodhaḥ.*

[4] Pram. samucc., ad V. 27 — they are «like the sons of a *rāja* in a civil war».

[5] Ibid., ad V. 28 — «the word *śimśapā* does not exclude the jar directly why? Because there is no homogeneousness». But the jar is under the universal earthen-ware and the *śimśapā* under plants, these both again under the universal hard stuff (*pārthivatva*). Thus the *śimśapā* excludes the jar as «the enemy of a friend», not directly.

10) This direct and indirect contradiction (or otherness) is logical.[1] It prevents identity, but does not prevent peaceful coexistence.[2]

11) There is also a dynamical opposition, as between heat and cold.[3] It is really causation[4] and it does not interfere with logical contradiction of hot and non-hot. The logical opposition excludes their identity, the dynamical — their duration in close vicinity.[5]

12) Two properties of the same substratum are different only through the more or the less of exclusion. They are partly identical.[6]

13) Contradiction can exist only between definite concepts. The wholly indefinite Thing-in-Itself as well as the moment of pure sensation are beyond the reach of the law of contradiction, they are non-dialectical.[7] They exclude all difference, i. e., all contradiction.

There is indeed a logical contradiction between two opposites without anything intermediate and representing mutually the one the complete negation of the other; and there is, on the other hand, either simple otherness or dynamical opposition, which admits intermediate members and where the opposite parts do not represent directly the one the negation of the other. J. S. Mill and Sigwart both maintain that «unpleasant» is positive, it is not simply the negation of pleasant, and so is «blind». But they forget that the same fact cannot be pleasant and not pleasant at the same time and in the same sense. If unpleasant is something more than not-pleasant, it is only because not-pleasant is further divided into not-pleasant simply and unpleasant or painful, which is more than not-pleasant simply. Contradiction is always an absolute dichotomy, and it becomes quite the same whether we affirm the one part of the couple or deny the other. The position changes when the division is not an absolute dichotomy, but a division in three or more parts. Blue and non-blue are contradictories, the blue is not the non-blue and the non-blue is not the blue. But blue and yellow are contradictories indirectly. To deny blue does not mean to assert yellow and *vice versa*. Yellow is included under the non-

1 NBT., p. 70. 73 — *lākṣaṇiko'yam virodhaḥ.*

2 Ibid., p. 70. 20 — *saty api ca asmin virodhe sahāvasthānam syād' api.*

3 Ibid., p. 70. 22 — *vastuny eva katipaye.*

4 Ibid., p. 68. 9 — *yo yasya viruddaḥ sa tasya kimcitkara eva ... viruddho janaka eva.*

5 Ibid., p. 70. 20 — *ekena viorodhena śītoṣṇayor ekatvam vāryate; anyena sahāvasthānam.*

6 Pram. samucc., V. 28 — *rten-gyis ḥyal-ba med-pa-ñid.*

7 NBT., p. 70. 7. — *na tu aniyata-ākāro'rthaḥ kṣaṇikatvādivat, (kṣaṇa = svalakṣaṇa = vidhi-svarūpa = pratyakṣa = paramārtha sat).*

blue and only for this reason is it incompatible with blue. Thus blue is not non-blue, and blind is not non-blind and a cow is not a non-cow, and a tree is not non-tree, etc., etc. All names are negative in this sense.

Incompatible are therefore blue and yellow because, as just mentioned, the yellow is contained under non-blue, and blue is contained under non-yellow. But a tree and a *šiṃšapā* are not incompatible, because *šiṃšapā* is not contained under non-tree. They are therefore «identical» in the sense of the Buddhist law of Identity. Incompatibility or «uncompredicability» is fully explained by Negation and the law of Contradiction.[1] All definite things consist of yes and no. But does that mean that the Buddhists have fallen in the Hegelian heresy? The Mādhyamikas certainly have, but not the Logicians. Their salvation will be described presently.

d) Affirmation what.

Now if all names and concepts are negative, if without the negation contained in them they mean absolutely nothing; and if, on the other hand, every concept is a predicate in an implied perceptual judgment, does that mean that all judgments are likewise negative? Was Aristotle quite mistaken when he introduced the division of affirmation and negation into the definition of a judgment? Is it possible that Hegel is right and there is in the world only negation and no affirmation at

---

[1] According to Sigwart (ibid., p. 179) no rules can be given why some qualities are incompatible. They cannot be predicated at once of the same subject, but this cannot be explained by negation. It is an ultimate fact. According to the Buddhists it necessarily always comes under the law of Contradiction. Since the time of Aristotle two grounds of negation are distinguished in logic, privation and incompatibility (στέρησις, ἐναντιότης). The first is evidently the real negative judgment, the judgment of «non-perception» corresponding to the perceptual judgment; the judgment of the pattern «there is here no jar (because I do not perceive any)». The second is the negative concomitance, or contraposition, which contains two concepts (or two predicates) and a negatived copula between them. The latter is founded on the law of contradiction and should, therefore, be regarded as an incompatibility between two judgments, according to Sigwart's own statement. Just as in the case of the affirmative judgment we have established a difference between the judgment proper (with one concept) and the judgment of concomitance (between two concepts), and just as the verb «is» means existence in the first case and a copula in the second, just so can we establish the same difference on the negative side. Privation means non-existence. Incompatibility means disconnection The first is called in Tibetan *med-dgag (= abbāva-pratiṣedha)*, the second —*min-dgag (= sam-bandha-pratiṣedha)*.

all? Was Sigwart on the wrong path when he was puzzled to find some justification for the existence of negation? The Indian answer to these questions is the following one. All the difference between an isolated concept and the corresponding perceptual judgment consists in the fact that the latter contains two heterogeneous elements, a non-dialectical subject and a dialectical predicate. The affirmation is contained in the subject, in the element «this». E. g., the concept of «having an origin» contains nothing over and above the negation of eternity and the concept of eternity nothing above the negation of an origin. By themselves these concepts contain no reality, no affirmation. By themselves they sublate one anothor, the result would be *nihil negativum*. But the judgment «the jar has an origin» or, more properly, «*this* is something having an origin» contains in its element «this» a real affirmation. Thus it is that a concept having «meaning and validity» is positive only in the measure in which it is referred to some element «this». It can be positive indirectly, but in itself it is necessarily negative, or dialectical. The same refers to a concrete concept, like a jar or «jarness». If the concept would have been positive in itself, then the judgment «the jar is» would contain a superfluous repetition, and the judgment «the jar is not» a contradiction.[1] A concept and a name become affirmative or positive only in a judgment. Sigwart thought that negation has a meaning only in a judgment[2] and that all names by themselves are positive. The contrary is true! Affirmation manifests itself only in a perceptual judgment (or in a minor premise of the syllogism). By themselves all predicates, i. e. all concepts and names, are negative. That the concept is nothing positive by itself, that it does not contain in itself any element of existence, has also been established by Kant on the occasion of his critique of the ontological argument.

It follows that Aristotle was right indirectly. His definition must be changed in that sense, that there is in every perceptual judgment an element of affirmation and an element of negation.[3] A judgment is

[1] Cp. vol. II, p. 306 and 415.

[2] Logik, I. 181—2. «Die Verneinung hat nur einen Sinn im Gebiete des Urtheils... «Nein» und «nicht» haben ihre Stelle nur gegenüber einem Satze oder im Satze».

[3] The judgment «this is a jar» and «this is no jar» are both, from this point of view affirmative in the element «this» and both negative in the element «jar» and «non-jar», for jar is as negative of non-jar, as the non-jar is negative of the jar; they are mutually negative and can become positive only through the annexed element «this». This becomes evident in such cases as «this is impermanent», resp. «this is non-impermanent».

a union between two quite heterogeneous things, it consists in the reference of an ideal content to a point of reality. Hegel was mistaken when cancelling the difference between the two sources of our knowledge, and Sigwart was mistaken in not sufficiently appreciating the power of negation. But Sigwart was right in maintaining that reality contains negation only when it is brought in from without. He should have added that a concept, or a name, contains affirmation, also only when it is brought in from without. Such is the answer which Dignāga probably would have given to the three representatives of European logic.

Pure or real affirmation is contained only in the very first moment of every sense-cognition. Supposing I have received an immediate impression. I am struck. The impression is vivid and bright. I am baffled. In the very first moment I «understand» nothing. But this condition of absolute indefiniteness lasts only a single moment. In the very next moment it begins to clear up, gradually it becomes definite. *Definitio est negatio.* The process of understanding is capable of progressive development. We understand in the measure in which we deny. Sigwart asks, why on earth are we in need of the subjective circuit of negation in order to cognize reality, when we apparently could just as well cognize it directly? The only possible answer to this question is that we have two combined sources of knowledge and only one of them is direct. To the senses the objects are «given»,[1] but they are not understood. They are understood gradually in a process of continually progressing negation. The judgment containing non-A as its predicate is infinite in that sense, but it begins at once after the very first moment of pure sensation. We would never cognize the blue, if we did not contrast it with the non-blue. Those who maintain that they perceive, e. g., a tree exclusively by their senses directly, should, as Jinendrabuddhi says,[2] at once see in one and the same object the tree and the non-tree, see them simultaneously. But negation is the function of the understanding, not of sensation. Of the two sources of knowledge one is affirmation, the other negation.

From among all European philosophers Herbart appears to be the only one who,[3] just as the Buddhists, has identified pure sensation

---

[1] In sense-perception the objects are *sva-sattayā pramāṇam*, for the understanding (*anumāna*) they are *jñātatvena* (= *apohena*) *pramāṇam*, cp. Tātp., p. 9. 8.

[2] Cp. above, p. 470.

[3] Cp. however Kant's remarks CPR., p. 141 — «total absence of reality in a sensuous intuition can itself never be perceived», and ibid. p. 117 — «that which in phenomena (in perceptual judgments?) corresponds to sensation constitutes

with affirmation.[1] «In sensation, says he,[2] is contained Absolute Position, without our noticing it. In the Understanding we must begin by creating it a new, through a negation of its contrary».

This is also an answer to those critics who have deemed it possible to destroy the concept of the Thing-in-Itself dialectically. Of course the concepts of pure existence, pure causality, the pure object and the Thing-in-Itself are dialectically «constructed a new», through the repudiation of the contrary by the understanding. But the particular fact of this or that sensation, the particular efficiency of this or that point-instant, that Thing-in-Itself «which does not contain the slightest bit of „otherness“», such is the ultimate reality, and the sensation corresponding to it is Pure Affirmation.

It is highly instructive to follow the leading logician of post-Kantian Germany in his efforts to avoid the Hegelian Negativism. His efforts will hardly be found successful, and this is the more remarkable because the solution lies very near, and is half expressed by his own words. Being perplexed by the fact that Negation seems quite superfluous for the cognition of Reality and nevertheless is quite unavoidable, he says,[3] «In these opinions (of Spinoza, Hegel and others) is always contained a confusion between Negation itself and its assumed objective foundation, the enclosed in itself Individuality and Uniqueness of every one among the manifold of things. What they are not, never appertains to their existence and essence. It is imported into them from outwards by comparative thought». Negation is comparative, or distinguishing, thought. Negation and distinguishing thought are convertible terms. Hegel was quite right when he said that Negativity is the Soul of the world. But the Body of the world is not Negation. It is Affirmation and even «the essence of affirmation.»[4] In the words of Sigwart, it is the «enclosed in itself Individuality and Uniqueness of every single thing». It is a thing into which nothing at all has yet been «brought in from without». As Šāntirakṣita puts it, it is the thing «which has not (yet) become identical with

---

the things by themselves (reality, *Sachheit*)». Consequently pure sensation (*kalpanā-poḍha-pratyakṣa*) corresponds to the Thing-in-Itself and contains pure affirmation or absolute position.

1 *svalakṣaṇam=paramārtha-sat=vidhi-svarūpam=nirvikalpaka-pratyakṣam.*

2 Metaphysik, II, § 202; cp. above p. 192.

3 Logik. I, 171.

4 *vidhi-svarūpam*

the other by the admixture of whatsoever the slightest bit of otherness».[1]

We now see that if every concept contains in itself a «yes» and a «no», two parts sublating each the other; if it, in this sense, contains existence and non-existence; if a «cow» is nothing but a negation of a «non-cow», and a «non-cow» nothing but the negation of «cow»; that does not yet mean that there is nothing positive at the bottom of such dialectical concepts. It does not mean, as Kant puts it, that the result of such mutual negativity is the Nought, *nihil negativum irrepraesentabile*. Both Dignāga, as well as Hegel, will emphatically protest against the accusation that their philosophy leads to an absolute Null. Jinendrabuddhi[2] says — «our opponents are ignorant of the real essence of the theory of the Negative Meaning of words. They impute to us a theory (which we never professed). They maintain that this theory means a blunt denial of every reality and thereupon they always are ready to insult us». Hegel says[3] — «The contradictory does not result in an absolute Nought, in a Null, but essentially in a negation of its own special content». Kant perhaps would have answered that the «negation of one's own special content» is just the Nought. However, for the Buddhist Logicians there is a Pure Reality, just as there is a Pure Thing, and that is the thing as it is «locked up in itself», the thing cognized in pure sensation. It is the first moment of that bright vividness which is characteristic for a fresh impression. The Thing is then cognized in its full concreteness, but quite indefinitely, it is, as Sigwart says, «locked up». But as soon as it is «set free» and enters into the domain controlled by the Intellect, its vividness fades away and it *pari passu* becomes definite. It gains in definiteness what it looses in vivacity. Vividness and definitness stand in an inverse ratio to one another. The highly abstract notions, such as Existence, Cognizability, Causation, seem to be totally dead, divorced from concrete reality. Such notions as a jar or a cow (that is, jarness, cowness) etc. seem very near to the concreteness of a sensuous impression. Nevertheless they are also constructions of conceptual thought on the dichotomizing principle, just as the highly abstract ones. As soon as the Intellect is aroused, as soon as it begins to «understand», it compares and becomes dialectical. By its essence it is not a capacity of direct cognition. Is it not

---

1 TS., p. 1. 6—*aṇiyasāpi nāṃśena miśrībhūtāparātmakam*, (*i. e. pratītya-samutpannam artham svalakṣaṇam jagāda*).

2 Cp. above, p. 470.

3 Wiss. d. Logik, I. 36. Cp. Encyclop., § 82.

amazing in the highest degree! says Dharmottara. «Is it not, says he,[1] a very great miracle, that our concepts, although very well cognizing the (conceptually) definite essence of reality, are not capable to make definite Reality in itself?» (They cognize the Universal only, and are absolutely incapable of cognizing definitely the particular). «No, he continues, there is here not the slightest shade of a miracle! Concepts are by their nature imagination. They endow our knowledge with Consistency, but not with Reality.[2] Therefore whatsoever is definite is necessarily the object of conceptual thought. The immediately apprehended form of the object possesses no definiteness!»

It has been objected[3] that the notion of a Thing is also a Universal, it is repeated in every individual thing and embraces in its comprehension the totality of all things. Indeed Existence, Reality, Thingness, Substantiality are general notions, this is not denied by the Buddhists, If these general notions did not exist, we could not name them. Every name refers to a Universal. But the concrete Thing-in-Itself, the *Hoc Aliquid*, is not a general notion, it is the contradictorily opposed part of a general notion. The general notion, being something ideal, requires genuine reality as its counterpart. The Thing as it is locked up in itself is *the Reality*; it is the Particular, a Unity, *the* Real. Pure Affirmation is something pre-logical, logic is always negative or dialectical.[4]

It must clearly appear from what has been stated precedently that the position of Dignāga is such as though he had taken the Dialectic from Hegel and the Thing-in-Itself from Kant. But at the same time it looks as if he had divested both the Kantian Thing-in-Itself as well as the Hegelian Dialectic of a great deal of their mystery and thus disarmed the enemies of both these theories. Indeed cognition is judgment and the epistemological pattern of a judg-

---

[1] In his Apoha-nāma-prakaraṇa, Tanjur, Mdo, vol. 112, fol. 253. b. 8—254. a. 2.

[2] *rnam-par-rtog-pa-rnams-ni .... dnōs-po ñes-pa-ñid-du skyes-pa-rtogs-pa yin-gyi, de-gag dnōs-po yod-pa-ñid ñes-pa-ni ma-yin-no,* ibid.

[3] By the Jains, cp. TSP., p. 487.22 (kār. 1713).

[4] This pre-logical element in our cognition is perhaps just the same as the one noticed and described as present in the cognitions of primitive humanity. The understanding is here at its lowest capacity, it is not altogether absent, but very near to the absolutely undifferentiated «Complex-quality», which by itself is incognizable, because not intelligible; however it is the source of all future operations of the Intellect. Cp. Lévy-Bruhl, Les fonctions mentales dans les sociétés inférieures (Paris, 1910), and S. Ranulf, op. cit., p. 206 ff.

ment reduces to the form «this is a jar» or, more precisely, «the image of jar-ness is referred to this instantaneous event». It is a perceptual or real judgmeut. It is perception in the element «this», it is a judgment in the element jar-ness. The first refers to the thing as it is strictly «in its own self», the second to the thing as it is «in its other», in the non-jar. The first is reality, the second is ideality. The first is sensible, the second is intelligible. The first is the pure object, the second is pure dialectic. The first is affirmation, the second is negation. The first is direct cognition, the second is indirect cognition. Since both elements refer to the same ultimate reality, the one directly, the other indirectly, Šāntirakṣita[1] says that the Thing-in-Itself is the ontological foundation[2] of the logical dialectic[3] of the understanding. Kant says[4], «that which in phenomena (we must say in judgments) corresponds to sensation (the element «this») constitutes the Thing-in-Itself». Hegel says[5], «all Things are in themselves contradictory, this contradiction is the developed Nought». This might be interpreted as meaning that the logical predicate of pure existence is dialectical.

Thus in supplementing Kant by Hegel and Hegel by Kant we will have Dignāga.[6]

It hardly is needed to insist that these similitudes are approximations, they are what all similitudes are, curtailment of difference[7].

e) Ulrici and Lotze.

Just as the problem of the Universals, the problèms of Negation, of Dialectic, the Infinite Judgment and the Thing-in-Itself have been abandoned by modern logic without any final solution. These problems are allied, the solution of one means the solution of all of them. Post-Hegelian Germany having been overfed with mystified dialectics, not only abandoned it, but feels disgusted at it. Sigwart is not the only author who becomes full of apprehension whenever negation and dialectics are approached.[8]

---

1 TS., p. 316. 28 and TSP., p. 317. 2.

2 *artha-ātmaka-apoha.*

3 *jñāna-ātmaka-apoha.*

4 CPR., p. 117.

5 W. d. Logik, II. 58.

6 It is not necessary to repeat that we here allude to the «dialectic of contradictories», not to the «dialectic of contraries».

7 *bheda-agraha.*

8 Cp. Lotze. Logic,[2] § 40, Trendelenburg, Log. Unt., v. I, ch. III. E. v. Hartmann. Ueber die dialectische Methode, and a great many other works.

Professor Ulrici's exposition of Logic is remarkable in that respect. He defines the Understanding as the «differentiating activity of the Soul».[1] It becomes incumbent upon him to distinguish the «differentiating activity» from Negation, or else the Soul itself will be Negation, and that is Hegelianism. «Every difference», says he,[2] «involves not only a mutual negation between the objects, but also their mutual unity». This again is awfully Hegelian; it is an existence which at the same time is non-existence. But Ulrici seems firmly convinced that he has escaped from Hegel's «pure existence», this existence which at the same time is non-existence, a thesis, says he,[3] which «Hegel tries in vain to establish by his sophistic dialectics». But when he explains his position he only repeats in other words Hegel's own argument. Indeed Hegel says,[4] «Everything exists first of all only because there exists another. It is what it is through the other, through its own non-existence. Secondly it exists because the other does not exist. It is what it is through the non-existence of the other. It is a reflexion in one's own self». He concludes that each of the two sides can exchange its place with the other, «it can be taken as positive and also as negation».[5] Ulrici is aware that this theory means a denial of genuine affirmation and a fall into the precipice of Negativism. He therefore emphatically insists,[6] that «when we differentiate something, we conceive it as positive as an Ens». However this Ens discloses itself as being also a non-Ens. Indeed, he explains[7]— «when we differentiate the red from the blue, we conceive it as a negation of blue. But at the same time we also establish the contrary connexion, of the blue with the red, and conceive the blue as the not-red... The red is thus implicitly connected in a roundabout way, by a circuit through the blue, with its own self». Is it not a very curious Ens which is connected with its own self «by a circuit through its non-Ens»! And does not Ulrici simply repeat Hegel's argument, while imagining that he repudiates it! And is it not exactly the argument of Dignāga, *mutatis mutandis*, when he says that «every word expresses its own (viz. positive) meaning through the repudiation of the contrary (e. i., through negation).»

---

1 Ulrici, Compendium der Logik,[2] p. 33 — unterscheidende Thätigkeit der Seele. Cp. p. 45 and 52.

2 Ibid., p. 59.

3 Ibid., p. 57.

4 W. d. Logik, II, 42.

5 Ibid., p. 43.

6 Op. cit., p. 60.

7 Ibid.

In accord with this Ulrici then gives the example of the «definite colour red» and says,[1] «only because the red, just as red, is at the same time not-blue, not-yellow etc., only (through these negations) is it that definite colour which we call red». The positivity of red has dwindled away. It is definite, but definite means intelligible and necessarily negative or dialectical. Wishing to escape from the Hegelian «pure existence»[2] he nevertheless falls into the precipice!

Sigwart[3] has perceived the dangerous position of Ulrici and hurries up to his rescue. «The theory», says he, «which maintains that a presentation becomes definite only through differentiation,[4] this theory forgets that differentiation is itself possible only between already existing differentiated presentations». «The sensation of red, or more precisely of a definite red, he continues to say, is something quite positive, having a characteristic content». It follows that this something quite definite, quite positive, this very definite shade of red, is differentiated in the highest degree without any help from the side of the Understanding, or as Ulrici puts it, from «the differentiating activity of the Soul». The Understanding is then either unemployed, or it has to redo what is already done by others

It is evidently in order to emphasize this double work, that Lotze[5] calls it a «positive positing».[6] But as already mentioned, he says, that this position is so clearly united with the «exclusion of everything other», that when we intend to characterize «the simple meaning of affirmation» we can do it only through expressions meaning the «exclusion of the other», i. e. negation. A very curious affirmation is it indeed which can be expressed only as... negation! Is it not again exactly Dignāga's thesis that our words express their own meaning through the repudiation of the contrary? «This affirmation and this negation», says Lotze, «is one inseparable thought».[7] Is it not similar to Hegel telling us that affirmation and negation are one and the same,[8] since their thought is «one» and «inseparable».

---

[1] Ibid., p. 60.

[2] Ibid., p. 59 — das Hegel'sche reine Sein.

[3] Logik, I. 333 n.

[4] This of course can mean that it becomes «definite through definition», or «different through differentiation», different and definite are here almost the same.

[5] Logik[2], § 11, p. 26.

[6] eine bejahende Setzung.

[7] Ibid., p. 26— «Jene Bejahung und diese Verneinung sind nur ein untrennbarer Gedanke».

[8] W. d. Logik. II. 54— «Das Positive und Negative ist dasselbe».

From the summary of Jinendrabuddhi[1] we can gather that the Indians were also puzzled over the problem whether affiirmation and negation were in this respect «one inseparable thought», as Lotze thinks, or rather two interdependent thoughts, the one the consequence of the other. The verdict of Dignāga is to the effect that it is just one and the same thought. Such is also the theory of Hegel and Lotze falls in line notwithstanding all his desire to keep clear of the Hegelian precipice. The position of the Buddhist in regard of both Lotze and Hegel is distinguished by his theory of two different sources of knowledge. Supposing there were no other colours in existence than the red, we would then certainly perceive the red, but we never would know that it is red.[2]

Locke comes very near to Dignāga's standpoint when he points to the difference between a «clear idea» and a «distinct idea».[3] A clear idea is that «whereof the mind has such a full and evident perception as it does receive from an outward object operating duly on a well disposed organ». A distinct idea is that «wherein the mind perceives a difference from all others». In these words Locke has touched the vital point of Dignāga's theory. He certainly does not intend to say that the clear is not distinct, and that the distinct is not clear. However he says that the clearness is produced by the senses and definiteness by the understanding. If he would have made a step further and said that clearness is found only in pure sensation, where no definiteness (or negation) is at all to be found, and that definiteness (negation) is the exclusive function of the understanding, then the coincidence with Dignāga would have been complete. However such a step means a plunge into transcendental philosophy with its Thing-in-Itself and other features, as well as a partial fall into the precipice of Hegelian dialectics.

W. E. Johnson in his Logic[4] evidently alludes to the same difference, when he says that «neither images nor perceptions reflect the concretness and particularity of the individual thing, which should be described as determinate in contrast to the indeterminateness of the mental processes». The contrast is indeed not between the thing and the processes, but between the freshness of a particular sensation and the generality of a conception. What Locke calls «clear idea»

---

1 Cp. above, p. 462.

2 *nīlam vijānāti, na tu nīlam iti vijānāti*, cp. Pram. samucc. vṛtti ad I. 4

3 Essay, book III, ch. XXIX, § 4.

4 Logic, I, p. XXIX.

is here called a definite thing. What Locke calls «distinct» comes to be called here «indeterminate». The same confusion in regard of the expression «determinate» is found in the sanscrit terms *niyata*, resp. *aniyata-pratibhāsa*.[1] Sensation is determinate in its uniqueness and the image is determinate in its generality. The contrast is more conveniently rendered by the terms vivid (sensation) and vague (image); or by the «real» particular and the «pure» universal, the term «real» and «pure» in this context meaning ultimate, or, as Kant says, transcendental. At the bottom it is nothing but the rather trivial distinction between the senses and the understanding, this simple distinction the full importance of which first occurred to Reid, but has been neglected by his successors; it has been followed up to its transcendental source by Kant and again neglected by his successors.

Sigwart says that such affirmation, which is the foundation of negation is the «enclosed in itself particularity and uniqueness of the Thing». Lotze says that there is in every name an «affirmative position». Johnson says that there is in every perception «the concreteness and particularity of the individual thing». The «concreteness and particularity of the individual thing» evidently means nothing but the «particular particularity of the particular»! These double and treble expressions point to the feeling their authors must have had of getting hold of something extraordinarily particular, containing «not the slightest bit of otherness».

---

[1] Cp. index vol. II, and the notes to the term *niyata*.

PART V.

REALITY OF THE EXTERNAL WORLD.

§ 1. What is Real.

What reality is according to Buddhist logicians has been stated at the beginning.[1] It has also been stated that reality is double,[2] direct and indirect. Direct reality is the reality of sensation,[3] indirect is the reality of a concept referred to a sensation.[4]

There is a pure reality, that is the reality of pure sensation, and there is a pure ideality, or pure reason. Pure ideality is the non-reality of a concept which is not referred to a sensation. The real is moreover called particular, and the ideal is called universal. The real is also the thing, and the ideal is the idea, the non-thing. Absolutely real is the thing as it is «in itself», it is pure affirmation. Unreal is the thing as it is «in the other», or differentiated from the other, it is therefore negation (or dialéctical). We thus have a general dichotomy of which the one side is called 1) reality, 2) sensation, 3) particular, 4) thing «in itself» or 5) affirmation; and the other side is respectively called by the five names of 1) ideality, 2) conception, 3) universal, 4) the thing «in the other», 5) negation.

Now the second side of this dichotomy is monolithic, it is entirely internal, there are no universals nor any negations in the external world. But the first side does not seem to be so monolithic; it is split in two parts, an internal and external one. The internal is sensation the external is the thing, that thing which is the thing «in itself».

The definition of reality is a capital issue between Hīnayāna and Mahāyāna. The early schools are champions of the principle «everything exists».[5] This slogan is explained as meaning that the Elements[6]

[1] Cp. above, p. 63.

[2] Ibid., p. 69.

[3] *nirvikalpakam.*

[4] *savikalpakam.*

[5] *sarvam asti.*

[6] *dharma*

exist. They are arranged in 75 kinds or in 12 categories.[1] They include the subject and the object, internal as well as external items. A unit of a feeling, of an idea, of a volition, is as much an Element of reality as a unit of colour, of sound or of a tactile sense-datum, i. e., of matter. There is no difference in respect of existence between materiality and ideality. Everything is equally real. There is therefore no difference in the degree of reality between a thing and its qualities. «Whatsoever is found to exist is a thing».[2] The reality of a jar is the reality of a patch of colour (one thing), of a shape (another thing), of something hard (a third thing), of an image (a thing again) etc.; but there is absolutely no such real thing as their unity in a jar. The jar is imagination. Just as the Ego is imagination, althoug all its Elements, the five *skandhas* are «things», i. e., Elements. The eternal items, Nirvāṇa and Empty Space, are also Elements, *ergo* things. Element, reality, existence, thing are convertible terms.[3]

In Mahāyāna this is radically changed. In the first period of Mahāyāna nothing but the motionless whole is declared to be absolutely real. For the logicians Reality is opposed to Ideality. Not only every idea, feeling and volition, but everything constructed by the intellect, every Universal, every quality, every duration and every extension is ideal, not real. Real is only the thing in its strictest sense, that which contains not «the slightest bit» of intelligible construction. Such a thing is reality itself, it is the Thing-in-Itself. It is just the Kantian *Realität*, *Sachheit*, the thing which corresponds to pure sensation.[4]

This radical difference in the view of Reality culminated in the different conception of Nirvāṇa or Eternity. In Hīnayāna it is an Element, a thing, just as Empty Space is also a thing. In Mahāyāna it is not a separate Element, not a separate thing.[5]

Thus it is that in the logical school Reality is not put on the same level as Ideality. Real is only the *mundus sensitilis*. The concepts have a merely functional reality. In accord with this double character of its subject-matter, logic is also double. There is a logic of consistency and a logic of reality. The first is the logic of interdependence between two concepts, the second is the logic of referring these concepts

1 *sarve dharmāḥ = dvādaśa-āyatanāni.*

2 *vidyamānam dravyam*, cp. CC, p. 26. n.

3 *dharma = vastu = bhāva = dravya.*

4 CPR., p. 117.

5 Cp. my Nirvāṇa, p. 45 ff.

to reality. The first is the logic embodied in the major premise of the syllogism, the second is the logic embodied in the minor premise or in the perceptual judgment. Our analysis of sense-perception, judgment, inference, syllogism and the logical fallacies must have sufficiently elicited this double character of logic. Just as the logical fallacies, or error, is distinguished into error against consistency (or error in the major premise) and error against reality (or error in the minor premise); just so is truth also divided in a truth of consistency (or truth of the major premise) and truth of reality, (or truth of the minor premise and of the perceptual judgment).[1]

§ 2. What is External.

To be external means to be beyond. To be external to cognition means to be beyond cognition, to transcend cognition, to be the object residing outwards from cognition. If reality is external, the real and the external would then be convertible terms. But the object does not lie absolutely beyond cognition. Hegel accused the Kantian Thing-in-Itself of lying absolutely beyond cognition and being absolutely incognizable. But there is no dire necessity of splitting reality into two parts, sensation and the particular thing. The thing can be reduced to sensation.

The relative terms subject-object, internal-external are apt to give rise to misunderstandings, if their different meanings are not taken into consideration. Our ideas, feelings and volitions are apprehended by introspection.[2] They are the «objects» of introspection, but they are not external. Ideas are themselves introspective, that is, self-conscious. There is in this case that identity between subject and object which Hegel extended to the subject-object relation in general. Quite different is the subject-object relation between the external material world and the internal mental domain. The external is real and efficient,[3] the internal is ideal and imagined.[4] The fire which burns and cooks is real, the fire which I imagine in my head is ideal. But ideal does not mean altogether unreal. The real and the ideal are two hete-

1 Since a perceptual judgment refers us to sensation, this conception of Reality reminds us of the Kantian postulate, «what is connected with the material conditions of experience (sensation) is real», CPR., p. 178.

2 *sva-saṃvedana.*

3 *artha-kriyā-kāri.*

4 *buddhy-ārūḍha.*

ogeneous realities causally connected, the external object is the cause of the internal image. They are connected by causality, not by identity of reference. There is identity between them only from the standpoint of the Idealist who confounds reality with ideality. The external thing is a particular, it is moving, instantaneous and positive. The internal image is universal, immutable and negative.

The necessity of assuming an external object corresponding to sensation is psychological, it is not logical, not absolute.

§ 3. The three worlds.

Independently from the path of logic which leads into either a world of things or a world of ideas, there is the path of Mysticism, which leads into the metalogical intuition of the Universe as a Whole. There are thus three different worlds, or three different planes of existence, each existing in its own right. There is the ultimate metaphysical plane where the Universe represents a motionless Unity of the One-without-a-Second. There is the logical plane where it represents a pluralistic reality of Matter and Ideas cognized in sensations and conceptions. And there is a third, intermediate plane where there is no Matter at all, there are only Ideas. Matter itself is an idea. Besides the world of Parmenides there is the world of Aristotle, and in the middle between them there is the Platonic world of ideas. Far from excluding one another these three worlds exist every one in its own right and in its own respective plane, they mutually supplement the one the other and it depends upon where we start to arrive in the one or the other of them. If we start with logic, and its «law of all laws», the law of Contradiction, we will arrive into a pluralistic world, whether it be the world of the naive realist or of the critical one. If we start with metalogic and neglect the law of Contradiction, we will plunge straight off into Monism. If we start with Introspection, which apprehends a double world of things and ideas, and if we cancel the logically superfluous duplicate of the things and admit the objectivity of ideas only, we will be in full Idealism. Dignāga has written his Prajñāpārmitā-piṇḍārtha from the standpoint of the Monist, his Ālambana-parīkṣā in defence of Idealism, and he has established the mighty edifice of his logic, his chief concern, on a foundation of critical realism. He has eschewed naive realism, that realism which cancels both introspection and images and remains by the direct perception of the external things alone (as the Mīmāṃsakas and Vaišesikas have done).

§ 4. Critical Realism.

It is hardly necessary to repeat what the theory of the Buddhist logicians regarding the problem of the reality of the external world was. The whole of our work is, directly or indirectly, concerned about this unique central problem. In the first part we have examined the direct reflex of the external world in our sensitivity. In the second and third part we have examined its indirect reflex in our understanding. In inference and syllogism the minor premise is there for keeping the constructions of the intellect always in touch with reality. The dialectical character of our concepts would have reduced all our knowledge to nought, if it were not also attached to the concrete reality of the external thing. The external is real, it is *the* Reality. Real and external are convertible terms. Ideality is imagination. But external reality is directly cognized, or, more precisely, not cognized but reflected, only in pure sensation. Sensation apprehends the particular individual thing. The understanding cognizes the thing only «in general», it cannot cognize the particular. There is no definite cognition without generality and generality is ideality. Thus Reality and Ideality are contradictorily opposed to one another, the real is not the ideal and the ideal is not the real.

External reality is moreover efficient, it is a cause. Ideality is an image, it is not causally efficient. An image can be efficient only metaphorically, as an intermediate link preparing a purposeful action.

Further, Reality is dynamic. The external object is not Matter, but it is Energy. Reality consists of focuses from which activity proceeds and points to which purposeful activity converges. «Reality is work», Reality is instantaneous, it consists of point-instants which are centres of energy, they are *Kraftpuncte.*[1]

What is the relation between this pluralistic reality and this ideaity? It is causal and indirect.[2] Reality is apprehended by the human intellect indirectly, as the echo of a sound,[3] as the «shining of a gem through the chink of a door». Reality is «telescoped» to the mind by a superstructure of dialectical concepts. Not only are the sensible qualities subjective moods of reaction to the external stimulus, but the so called primary qualities, extension, duration, time, space, the notions of

[1] *yā bhūtiḥ saiva kriyā*

[2] Cp. above, p. 474 n.

[3] Cp. Pārthasārathimiśra ad Ślokav., p. 559.

existence, non-existence, reality, generality, causality etc. are all nothing but subjective constructions of the understanding.

One naturally will ask what kind of reality it is, what is it worth, if Time, Space and all external phenomena are constructions of the Understanding? Nay, even the fundamental notions of Reality, Causality, Substantiality. etc. are nothing but subjective interpretations of an unknown ultimate Reality?

The answer is very simple! Real is sensation, nothing but sensation, pure sensation. The rest is all interpretation by the Understanding. Nobody will deny that what is «given» as sensation is real, it is not imagination!

The problem of the relation between external and internal has thus shifted ground and has become a problem of the relation between sensation and image, between sensibility and understanding, between perception and conception, between the particular and the universal. Ontologically a problem of the relation between the particular and the universal, logically or epistemologically it is a problem of a relation between the senses and the understanding. Now, those two utterly heterogeneous realms must be «somehow» connected, the gap must be «somehow» bridged over, and it can be bridged only in the following way. The connection is, first of all, causal. The image is «produced» by sensation; that is to say, it arises in functional dependence on a sensation. But that is not enough. There are other causes cooperating in the production of an image. Pure sensation is distinguished by «conformity» with the latter.[1]

To christen an incomprehensible relation by the word «conformity», which moreover is explained as a «similarity between things absolutely dissimilar», is of course no solution of the problem. We have had several times the occasion to refer to this mysterious «conformity» and in the second volume we have translated a collection of texts characterizing it from different sides. But it is only now, after having analysed the Buddhist dialectical method, that a better comprehension of the theory becomes possible. The similarity, as in all concepts, is here negative, it is a similarity from the negative side. There is not the slightest bit of similarity between the absolute particular and the pure universal, but they are united by a common negation. By repelling the same contrary they become similar. That is what is called «conformity». It is a negative similarity.

Thus a point-instant of efficiency manifested in the fact of pouring water is an absolutely particular sensation, but by differentiating it

[1] *tadutpatti-tatsārūpyābhyām viṣayatā.*

from other things, it negatively receives the general charcateristic of a jar. Thus the fire is a strictly individual sensation of heat, nothing more. But by opposing it to other things, through a repudiation of the contrary, we construct the universal idea of fire which embraces all fires in the world, past, present and future, but only negatively. The non-A which Lotze thought must be banished from logic as an *offenbare Grille*, is its real essence, «the Soul of the World». Such is the relation between the external, which is the particular and the internal, which is the universal. It is the same as the relation between the sensible and the intelligible.

§ 5. Ultimate Monism.

Such is the result of the logical analysis of cognition. Reduced to its ultimate elements it consists of an external Thing-in-Itself, a corresponding pure sensation and a following image. Knowledge contains two sides, subject and object. Even reduced to its simplest elements they are nevertheless two. Logic cannot proceed any further. It cannot imagine a higher synthesis uniting both subject and object into a monistic undifferentiated Whole. This step is translogical, it means a plunge into metaphysics, a denial of the law of contradiction and a challenge to logic. For the Buddhist logicians, however, truth exists on two different planes, the logical and the translogical one. Dignāga and Dharmakīrti call themselves idealists, but they are realists in logic and idealists and even monists in metaphysics. In logic reality and ideality are divorced, but the «Climax of Wisdom», says Dignāga, «is Monism». In the very final Absolute subject and object coalesce. «We identify», says Dignāga, «this spiritual Non-duality, i. e., the monistic substance of the Universe, with the Buddha i. e., with his so called Cosmical Body».[1] Philosophy here passes into religion.

Jinendrabuddhi[2] says: «How is it possible that from the standpoint of a philosopher who denies the existence of an external world there nevertheless is a differentiation of the «grasping» and the «grasped» aspect in that knowledge which in itself does not contain any differentiation between a source and a result of cognizing?». (The answer is the following one): «From the standpoint of Thisness (i. e., Absolute Reality) there is no difference at all!» But hampered as we

1 Cp. my introduction to the edition of the Abhisamaya-alaṃkāra, in the Bibl. Buddh.

2 Cp. vol. II, p. 396.

are by a Transcendental Illusion (we perceive only a refraction of reality). All that we know is exclusively its indirect appearance as differentiated by the construction of a difference between subject and object. Therefore the differentiation into cognition and its object is made from the empirical point of view, not from the point of view of Absolute Reality». But how is it that a thing which is in itself undifferentiated appears as differentiated? Through Illusion! This illusion is of course a transcendental illusion, the natural illusion of the human mind, its intrinsic calamity.[1]

The arguments of the Monists we have exposed in detail in our work on the Conception of Buddhist Nirvāṇa. The most popular point of accusation from the side of non-Buddhists against the Mahāyānists is that they represent the external world as a dream (*svapnavat*).[2] But the meaning of this watchword of a waking dream is very different in the different schools. According to Dharmakīrti, the formula of a waking dream means only that images are images, they are essentially the same both in waking condition and in sleep. They are not altogether disconnected from reality even in dreams, just as in the waking condition images, as indirect reflexes, are to a certain extent dreams.

§ 6. Idealism.

Let us review the chief arguments advanced in defence of Idealism. The Monist who maintains the unique reality of the One and Immutable Whole[3] is challenged by the assertion that real is not that Whole, but the Idea.[4] It is infinitely manifold,[5] constantly changing[6] and brightly manifests itself[7] in all living beings. It alone exists, because the non-mental, material thing, if it be assumed as a thing by itself, is impossible. It is impossible for two chief reasons, viz., 1) it is involved in contradiction[8] and 2) the grasping of an external thing is incomprehensible.[9] It is incomprehensible namely that know-

---

1 *antar-upaplava* = *mukhyā bhrāntiḥ*.

2 Cp. NS., IV. 2. 31.

3 TSP., p. 550. 10 — *yathopaniṣad-vādinām*.

4 *vijñānam*, ibid., p. 540. 8.

5 *anantam*, ibid.

6 *pratikṣaṇa-viśarāru*, ibid.

7 *ojāyate sarva-prāṇabhṛtām*, ibid.

8 *artha-ayogāt*, cp. ibid. and p. 559. 8.

9 *grāhya-grāhaka-lakṣaṇa-vaidhuryāt*, ibid.

ledge should abandon its residence, travel towards the external material thing, seize its form and return home with this booty, — as the Realists assume.

That the hypothesis of a material external thing is involved in contradiction becomes clear when we consider the following antinomy. The external thing must necessarily be either simple or composite,[1] there is no third possibility.[2] If it is proved that it neither is simple nor composite, it will be *eo ipso* proved that it is nothing, it is «a flower growing in the sky».[3] For a flower growing in the sky is indeed neither simple nor is it composite. That the composite must necessarily consist of simple parts, is proved by the following consideration. Supposing we remove all composition in taking from a compound all parts one by one until the uncompound remains. This uncompound residue will be partless, indivisible. However it also will be unextended; like an instantaneous mental object it will be a poin-instant, like a momentary feeling; and therefore it will be a mere idea.[4]

Another argument is founded on the following consideration. Supposing a simple part, an unextended atom, is surrounded by other such atoms, the question then arises, does it face the neighbouring atoms, the one in front and the one in the back, by the same face or not.[5] If it faces them by the same face, the atoms will coalesce and there will be no composition.[6] If it faces them by two different faces, it will have at least two faces and then also two parts. It will be a compound.[7]

Some atomists (or monadists) attempt the following defence. Let us assume that the atoms are not the minutest parts of a stuff occupy-

---

1 *ekāneka-svabhāvam*, ibid. p. 550. 26; it means *paramāṇu* and *avayavin*, cp. ibid., p. 551. 6.

2 *tṛtīya-rāśy-abhāvena*, ibid., p. 550. 18.

3 *vyomotpalam*, ibid, p. 550. 17.

4 Cp. CPR., p. 352 and TSP., p. 552. 2 ff. – *apacīyamāna-avayava-vibhāgena... yadi niraṃśāḥ (syuḥ), tadā na mūrtā vedanādivat sidhyanti*, and Kant, «wenn alle Zusammensetzung in Gedanken aufgehoben würde, so (würde) kein zusammengesetzter Teil und... folglich keine (ausgedehnte) Substanz gegeben sein». The sanscrit appears as if it were a translation from the German!

5 *yena ekarūpeṇa ekāṇv-abhimukho... tenaiva apara-paramāṇv-abhimukho yadi syāt*, ibid. p. 556. 11. 31. The same argument is repeated by Vasubandhu and Dignāga

6 *pracayo na syāt*, ibid., p. 556. 12.

7 *dig-bhāga-bhedo yasya asti, tasya ekatvam na yujyate*, ibid., p. 557. 19.

ing space, but let us assume that they are space itself.[1] Space does not consist of parts, but of spaces, the minutest part will be also space and therefore divisible. It will be the mathematical space, it will be infinitely divisible, but it will nevertheless not be an idea, it will be space.[2] To this the answer is as follows: Although you are convinced that your words deny the extended atom,[3] they really imply its existence. Indeed if you assume the simple in order to explain composition, you imply [4] that these atoms are a stuff occupying space. We should have to admit beside the mathematical point which is simple, but not a particle, other physical points which are simple likewise, but possessing the priviledge that, as parts of space, they are able, by mere aggregation, to fill space. This is impossible. Thus it is that the atom which must be simple, but at the same time cannot be simple, is nothing. It is a «flower in the sky».[5] The aggregate does not fare any better, since it is supposed to consist of atoms.

The objector then asks that if the atom is an idea and if this idea is not utterly inane, it must have a foundation. That foundation, whatsoever it may be, will be the real atom.[6] The Buddhist answers. Yes, indeed, the Vaišeṣika assumes that the mote,[7] the particle of dust seen moving in a sunbeam, is such a foundation, but then the Ego will also be a reality! If the image of an atom is the atom, the imagined Ego will be the real Ego. The real Ego will not consist of

---

[1] *pradeśa.* Prof. H. Jacobi (art. in ERE., v. II, p. 199) assumes that *pradeśa* with the Jains means a point. But TSP., p. 557. 21, expressly states that *pradeśas* are divisible (*tatrāpy avayava-kalpanāyām*). The indivisible (*niraṃśa*), unextended (*amūrta*) atoms are discussed in connection with particles occupying space, p. 552. 1 ff. It is moreover stated «although (in assuming *pradeśa*) you do not assume different sides (*dig-bhāga-bheda*), your words deny it, but it is implied in your assuming composition, etc. (*saṃyuktatvādi-kalpanā-balād āpatati*)». It is something like the mathematical, infinitely divisible space supporting the physical atom. From mathematical space we will then have infinite divisibility, and from the physical atom the possibility of composition. Kant accuses the Monadists of a similar absurdity, cp. his Observations on the Antithesis of his Second Antinomy, CPR., p. 357.

[2] *yadiparam anavasthaiva (syāt), na tu prajñapti-mātratvam* ibid., p. 557. 22.

[3] *dig-bhāga-bhedo* (the different faces) *vācā nābhyupagatas*, ibid., 558. 18.

[4] *saṃyuktādi-dharma-abhyupagama-balād eva āpatati*, ibid.

[5] *ekāneka-svabhāvena śūnyatvād viyad-abjavat*, ibid., p. 558. 10.

[6] *yat tad upādānam sa eva paramāṇur iti*, ibid., p. 558. 21.

[7] (*trasa*)-*reṇuḥ*, ibid., p. 558. 22.

its real Elements.[1] Simplicity, as a matter of fact, cannot be inferred from any perception whatsoever [2]

The idea of deducing the atom from the intuition of a mote is «the ripe fruit of a tradition which is founded on studying and inculcating absurd views (of naive realism)».[3] Such is the first and chief argument of the Idealist.

His second chief argument consists in emphasizing the fact that the subject-object dichotomy is a construction of the understanding.[4] As all such constructions it is dialectical. The subject is the non-object and the object is the non-subject. The contradictory parts become identical in a single higher reality which is the common substrate of both. What is this reality in which these opposites flow together? It is the point instant of a single pure sensation. The ultimately indubitable fact in cognition is pure sensation in a man whose sense-apparatus is in a normal condition.[5] All the rest is in some degree, more or less, imagination. This pure sensation is instantaneous, absolutely unique in itself and in itself quite unintelligible. It can be extended, coordinated and interpreted by the understanding, that is, again by imagination. The understanding discloses that a certain sensation, which is reality itself and cannot be doubted, must be interpreted as included in a threefold envelope (*tri-puṭī*).[6] The first is the Ego; the second is the object, say a jar and the third is the process of uniting the Ego with the jar. Thus the Understanding replaces a pure and real sensation by a threefold construction of a subject, an object and a process. There is not the slightest bit of pure reality in the Ego apart from the object and the process. It is entirely imagination. Neither is there any pure reality in the object jar. It is an interpretation of a simple sensation by the intellect. Still less is there any reality in the process. Cognition as something separate from subject and object, if it is not the instantaneous sensation, does not exist. There is only one real unit corresponding to the triad of cognizer, cognized and cognition, it is sensation. *Ens et unum convertuntur*. One unity,

---

1 *ātma-prajñapter atmaiva kāraṇam syāt, na skandhāḥ*, ibid., p. 558. 23.

2 Cp. Kant's words in the proof of the Antithesis «die Simplicität aus keiner Wahrnehmung, welche sie auch sei, könne geschlossen werden», cp. *na tāvat paramāṇūnām ākāraḥ pratibhāsate*, ibid., p. 551. 7.

3 Ibid., 558. 21.

4 Ibid., p. 559. 8 ff.

5 *svastha-netrādi-jñānam.*, iaid., p. 550. 14.

6 *vedya-vedaka-vitti-bhedena*, ibid., p. 560. 1.

one reality! But the Understanding makes of it a nucleus hidden in a threefold sheath. There is a coordination of the imagined jar-ness with pure sensation. This coordination is called «Conformity». Conformity is, so to speak, the «formity» of sensation,[1] the fact that sensation receives a form. They become logically identical. Sensation and conception are psychologically[2] not identical, they are two different moments, the one the cause of the other. But logically they are identical in the sense of the Buddhist law of Identity. They both refer us to one and the same point of reality, they are identical by the identity of objective reference. Conception, although produced at a different moment, is referred just to the same thing that has produced sensation. «How is it, asks Dharmakīrti,[3] that the source and the result, the process and the content, (the *noësis* and *noëma*) are one and the same? And he answers: «through conformity»,[4] i. e., through the «formity» of sensation, by endowing sensation with an imagined, general form.[5] And how is it that they are identical? Because sensation represents the thing as it is «in itself», and conformity is the same thing as it is «in the other». We now know that «in the other» means dialectically,[6] by negation of the other. The identity of sensation and conception is negative. That same sensation which is pure in itself becomes the image of a jar, by its opposition to the non-jars. By further differentiations any amount of dialectical concepts can be superimposed on the simple sensation of a jar. This pure sensation is indeed «the richest thing» in its hidden contents and the «poorest thing» in definite thought!

The Realist then asks, has not the efficacy of knowledge been assumed as the test of truth? Has not the object attained in purposeful action been declared to represent ultimate reality? But the object attained in successful action is the external one? Yes, answers the Idealist, successful action[7] is the test of reality. But no external mate-

---

1 *tādrupyād iti sārupyād*, ibid., p. 560. 18.

2 Cp. the considerations of Dharmottara on the problem that a concept and a thing are identical logically (*kalpitam*), but the concept is the result of the thing (*bāhyārtha-kāryam*) psychologically, NBT., p. 59 and 60. 4 ff.

3 NBT., p. 14. 15.

4 *artha-sārūpyam asya pramāṇam*, ibid.

5 *ākāra* = *ābhāsa* = *sārūpya* = *anya-vyāvṛti* = *apoha*.

6 Cp. NBT., p. 16. 3. — *asārūpya-vyavṛttyā* (*apohena*) *sārūpyam jñānasya vyavasthāpana-hetuḥ*.

7 *artha-kriyā-saṃvādas*, ibid. 553. 21.

rial object is needed. Successful action is a mere idea,[1] a representation of something that appears as a successful action.[2] There is absolutely no need of a double successful action, the one supposed to exist beyond my head, the other in my head. A single successful action is sufficient. It is true that all simple humanity «down to the sheapherd» indulge without much thinking in the idea that there are real extended bodies in the external world.[3] But the philosopher knows that there is no logical necessity of assuming this duplicate of perceived object. Just as you assume external reality as the cause to which our representations correspond, just so do we assume an object and a cause which are immanent. Knowledge is a running reality, every moment of which is strictly conditioned by the moment preceding it. The hypothesis of an external cause is quite superfluous. For us the preceeding moment of consciousness[4] discharges exactly that function for which you hypothetically assume the existence of an external cause.

§ 7. Dignāgas tract on the Unreality of the External World.

This work is a short tract in 8 mnemonic verses with a commentary by the author, entitled «Examination of the object of cognition».[5] The argument of this tract is in short the following one. It starts with the declaration that the external object must be either an atom or an aggregate of atoms. If it can be proved that it is neither an atom nor an aggregate of atoms, it is nothing but an idea without a corresponding external reality.

Thus the antinomy of infinite divisibility, the contradictory character of the empirical view of a divisible object, is the chief argument of Dignāga for maintaining the ideality of the object of cognition and denying the reality of the external world. In his logic Dignāga assumes that the external object is an instantaneous force which

---

1 *jñānam eva arthakriyā-saṃvādas,* ibid. 553. 23.

2 *artha-kriyā-avabhāsi jñānam,* ibid.

3 *yad etad deśa-vitānena pratibhāsamānam avicāra-ramaṇīyam āgopāla-prasiddham rūpam,* ibid.

4 *samanantara-pratyaya = ālaya-vijñāna = vāsanā,* cp. TSP., p. 582. 19.

5 Ālambana-parīkṣā, its Tibetan and Chinese translations have been published with a translation in French by Susumu Yamaguchi and Henriette Meyer (Paris, 1929). On the difference between *ālambana* «external object» and *viṣaya* «object in general» cp. my CC., pp. 59 and 97.

stimulates sensation and is followed by the construction of an image. In his tract he takes up and rejects the Vaišeṣika view according to which the external object is double, as consisting of atoms and of their aggregates. The aggregates are assumed as things by themselves, existing over and above the parts of which they are composed. He then establishes that the atoms do not produce congruent images. Even supposing that they be the hidden causes of images this would not prove that they are the objects, for the sense faculties are also causes, but they are not the objects.[1] A cause is not always an object. An aggregate as a thing by itself it is a phantom, created by the Vaišeṣikas, it is a double moon.[2] We want an object which would explain sensation and image. But the atoms produce no images and the aggregates produce no sensations; each part produces half the work.[3] From Dignāga's point of view the atom is a «flower in the sky»,[4] because things are never indivisible; and the aggregate, as a second Ens, is but a second moon.

Nor can an agglomeration of atoms explain the difference of form. The jar and the saucer are composed of the same atoms.[5] Their different collocation and number cannot explain the different image, since collocation and number are not things by themselves. These forms are phenomena, subjective forms, or ideas.[6]

Thus the supposed indivisible atoms, the supposed aggregates and the forms of the objects — are all nothing but ideas.[7]

After this refutation of the realism of the Vaišeṣikas Dignāga concludes that «the object perceived by the organs of sense, is not external».[8]

He then goes on to establish the main principles of Idealism.[9] The object of cognition is the object internally cognized by introspection

---

1 Ālambanap., kārikā 1; it is quoted TSP., p. 582. 17; read — *yadīndriyavijñapteḥ paramāṇuḥ kāraṇam bhavet;* evidently quoted by Kamalašīla from memory.

2 Ibid., kār. 2; according to the Vijñānavādins the unextended atoms will never produce an extended thing; cp. TS., p. 552. 20; cp. Ālambanap., kār. 5. (Yamaguchi), p. 85 of the reprint.

3 Ibid., ad kār. 2 *yan-lag-gcig ma-thsān-bai-phyir,* cp. Yamaguchi, p. 30.

4 Cp. TS., p. 558. 10.

5 Ibid., kār. 4; transl., p. 33.

6 *buddhi-višeṣṣa,* cp. ibid., p. 33.

7 *sāṃvṛta,* ibid., kār. 5; transl., p. 35.

8 Ibid., p. 37.

9 Ibid., kār. 6—8.

and appearing to us as though it were external.[1] The ultimate reality is thus the «Idea».[2] What in logic was the external point-instant, the Thing-in-Itself, is here the internal «idea». Subject and object are both internal, the internal world is double. There is no difference between the patch of blue and the sensation of blue. The same idea can be regarded as a cognized object and a process of cognition.[3]

It remains to explain the regular course of perceived events which according to the Realists is due to their regular course in the external world, as controlled by the Biotic Force of Karma. This is done by assuming a subconscious Store of Consciousness[4] which replaces the material universe and an intelligible Biotic Force which replaces the realistic Karma.[5]

The Realist (Sarvāstivādin) then points[6] to the scriptural passage which declares that «a visual sensation arises in functional dependence on an object and an organ of sense».[7] How is this passage to be understood? Dignāga answers that the object is internal and the sense-organ is the Biotic Force.[8] Indeed it is not the eyeball that

---

1 Ibid., kār. 6, quoted in full TSP., p. 582. 11. It means — «The essence of the object is something cognized internally, although it seems to be external; (and this is because) it is cognition (not matter) and since it is (its own) cause, (it is not produced by matter).

2 *vijñapti-*, or *vijñāna-mātratā*, cp. TSP., p. 582. 7 and Triṃśikā, kār. 17.

3 The unity of subject (*viṣayin*) and object (*viṣaya*) is here deduced from their inseparability, ibid., kār. 7 (Yamaguchi, p. 40). This is somewhat similar to Hegel's method, W. d. Logik, II, p. 440.

4 *ālaya-vijñāna*, cp. ibid. p. 40, identified TSP., p. 582. 19, with *samanantara-pratyaya.*

5 The Biotic Force (*vāsanā*) is double. It links together the preceding moment with a homogeneous following one (*sajātīya-vāsanā*) and it brings discrete sensations under a common concept or name (*abhilāpa-*, resp. *vikalpa-vāsanā*), cp. Khai-ḍub, in the 2-d vol. of his works. In TSP., p. 582. 13—15 parts of kār. 7 (*śakty-arpaṇāt...*) and 8 (*avirodhaḥ*) are linked together. D. says, that since every conscious moment has the Force (*śakti-vāsanā*) of being followed by the next homogeneous moment, there is no contradiction in regarding every moment as a process and as a content; *noëma* and *noësis* is just the same thing. Nevertheless, says D., there is no contradiction in *also* representing them as following one another (*krameṇāpi*). We would probably say that psychologically there is a difference of time and degree, but logically it is just the same. It is also the same problem as the one of *pramāṇa* and *pramāṇa-phala*, mentioned by Dharmakīrti in NB. 14. 16 ff. and 18. 8, as is evidenced by the explanations of Jinendrabuddhi transl., in v. II, p. 386 ff.

6 Cp. *avatarana* to kār. 7c—d; transl., p. 42.

7 *rūpam pratītya cakšuš ca cakṣur-vijñānam utpadyate.*

8 Ibid., kār. 7c—d — *śaktiḥ* = *indriyam.*

represents the organ, but a respective sensuous faculty. In assuming a subconscious store of consciousness instead of an external world and a Biotic Force instead of the physical sense-organs, we will be able to account for the process of cognition. There will be no contradiction.[1]

The leading idea of this Idealism is that the hypothesis of an external world is perfectly useless, realism can easily be transposed in a respective idealism. Everything remains, under another name in another interpretation.

The second part of the work is a recapitulation of Asanga's Idealism. The originality of Dignāga is the prominence given to the fact of Infinity. The external world being something infinite and infinitely divisible is unreal, it is an «idea». As in Greece Idealism is established on a foundation of Aporetic.

§ 8. Dharmakīrti's tract on the Repudiation of Solipsism.

Dharmakīrti was aware of the danger which is menacing Idealism in the shape of its direct consequence — Solipsism. He therefore singled out this problem from his great general work and devoted to it a special tract under the title «Establishment of the existence of Other Minds».[2] The tract presents great interest, since it contains a verification of the whole of Dharmakīrti's epistemology in its application to a special complicated case. We are not capable here, for want of space, to reproduce the whole of its argument. But a short summary will be given.

Dharmakīrti[3] starts by enunciating that the usual argument of the Realists, who reduce idealism *ad absurdum*, *viz.*, to Solipsism, is of no avail. The Realist thinks that he can infer the existence of other minds by analogy. He immediately feels that his own speech and his own movements are engendered by his will; just so observing foreign speech and foreign movements, he by analogy concludes that their cause

---

[1] Ibid., kār. 8; transl., p. 43.

[2] Santānāntara-siddhi; a Tibetan translation has been preserved in the Tanjur. Its text with two commentaries, the one by Vinītadeva and the other by the Mongolian savant Dandar (Bstan-dar) Lha-rampa has been edited by me in the Bibl. Buddhica. A double translation into Russian, the one literal, the other free, has also been published by me. St. Petersburg, 1922.

[3] Sūtra 1.

must exist, and this points to a foreign mind. However the Idealist is not barred from making the same conclusion, only in slightly changing the phrasing. When he has images of foreign speech and foreign movements he will conclude that these images must have a cause and this cause are foreign minds. The Idealist says:[1] «Those representations in which our own movements and our own speech appear to us as originating in our own will are different from those which do not originate in our own will. The first appear in the form «I go», «I speak». The second appear in the form «he goes», «he speaks». Thereby it is established that the second class has a cause different from the first. This cause is a foreign will».

The Realist asks:[2] «Why do you not assume that the second class of images appears without such a cause as a foreign will?» «Because», answers the Idealist, «if these images of purposeful actions could appear without a will producing them, then all our presentations of action and speech in general would not be produced by a will. The difference consisting in the fact that one set of images are connected with my body and another set is not so connected, does not mean that one set is produced by a will and the other is not so produced. Both are produced by a conscious will. You cannot maintain that only one half of our images of purposeful acts and of speech are connected with a will producing them. All are so connected».

The Idealist maintains «that whatsoever we represent to ourselves as purposeful act and speech, whether connected with our own body or not, has necessarily its origin in a conscious will. The general essence of what we call purposeful activity is invariably connected with the general essence of what we call a conscious will».[3]

The Realist thinks that he directly perceives foreign purposeful actions. The Idealist thinks that he apprehends not real external motions, but only their images. These images he would not have, if their cause, the conscious will, did not exist. There is absolutely no substantial difference between the Realist and the Idealist when inferring will on the basis of a certain class of images.

The Realist then points to the fact that external reality for the Idealist is a dream, it consists of images without a corresponding reality. Thus his own movements and speech will be immediately evidenced by introspection, but foreign acts will be dreams. To this

---

1 Sūtra 11.

2 Sūtra 12.

3 Sūtra 22.

the Idealist answers:[1] «If purposeful acts point to the existence of a conscious will, they point to it either necessarily (and always), in dreams as well as in reality, or never». If we only admit that we can have images of purposeful acts independently from the presence of a conscious will, then we will never be able to infer a will on the basis of purposeful activity, since this activity will then be possible without the presence of any will. «But, says the Realist,[2] dreams are illusions. The images which we have in dreams are not connected with reality, they are mere images without a corresponding reality». To this the Idealist rejoins: «Who has given you such a power that by your decree one set of images will be devoid of a corresponding reality and another set will possess it?!» Images are images, if they are images of reality in one case, they must be images of reality in all cases. The difference[3] between dreams and other images is merely this, that in waking images of purposeful actions their connection with reality is direct, in dreams and other morbid conditions it is indirect; there is an interruption in time between the real facts and their image, but one cannot maintain that the connection with real facts is absent altogether. We can see in a dream the entrance of a pupil into the house of his teacher, his salutation and compliments, the spreading of a carpet, reading a text, repeating it, learning it by heart, etc. etc. All these images although appearing in a dream are by no means disconnected with reality. There is indeed an interruption in time between reality and these images. But, they could not exist, if there were altogether no connection with external reality. The Idealist says:[4] «if you admit that there are images without any corresponding reality, that is quite another problem! Then all our images without exception will be images without congruent reality, because they are all products of a Transcendental Illusion, the Universal Monarch of illusory mundane existence!».

After that Dharmakīrti brings his view on the existence of foreign minds in accord with his epistemology. The concordance between the ideas of two individuals who being quite independent the one from the other, but nevertheless suffering from the same illusion of an external world is explained in the usual manner as the agreement between two persons suffering from the same eye-disease and persuaded that they

---

1 Sūtra 53.
2 Sūtra, 55.
3 Sūtra 84.
4 Sūtra 58.

both see two real moons.[1] The sources of our knowledge are two, perception and inference. They are real sources, because they guide us in our purposeful activity.[2] In application to our cognition of other minds direct sense perception is out of question. Inference is the only source both for the Realist and the Idealist. But this inference is capable of guiding us in our purposeful actions towards other animated beings. Therefore it is an indirect source establishing the existence of other minds. But it is then equally a source of right cognition for the Realist as well as for the Idealist. There is in this respect no difference. Solipsism is no real danger in the logical plane.

§ 9. History of the problem of the Reality of the External World.

In the system of early Buddhism there is strictly speaking no united external world facing a united internal Ego. The reality of the Ego is denied. This is the starting point of Buddhism. It is replaced by the Element of pure consciousness with regard to which all other elements are external. Feelings, ideas and volitions are not supposed to be self-conscious by themselves. They are external elements, «objects» (*viṣaya*) with regard to this separate element of pure consciousness. A feeling or an idea is just as external with regard to consciousness as a tactile element or a patch of colour. The unit which is analysed into its elements is the Personality (*pudgala*), but it is only an assemblage of discrete elements holding together through mutual Causation. This personality includes both the elements which are usually supposed to lie in the external world and the corresponding elements of what is usually called the internal world. With regard to such personality all elements are internal. With regard to one another every element is external in regard of all the others. When an object of our external world is contemplated by two *pudgala*'s it enters into the compositon of both complexes as a separate item. The late Professor O. Rosenberg thought that in such cases we must assume the existence not of one common object, but of two different ones, one in each *pudgala*.

Vasubandhu[3] delivers himself on the problem of external and internal element in the following way:

---

[1] Sūtra 65.

[2] Sūtra 72 ff.

[3] AKBh.. ad I. 39, cp. my CC., p. 58 ff.

«How is it possible for the elements of existence to be external or internal, if the Self or the personality with regard to which they should be external or internal, does not exist at all?». The answer is that consciousness is metaphorically called a Self, because it yields some support to the (erroneous) idea of a Self. «Buddha himself uses such expressions... The organ of vision and the other sense faculties are the basic element for the corresponding sensations; consciousness, on the other hand, is the basic element for the (erroneous) perception of a Self. Therefore as a consequence of this close analogy with consciousness, the sense organs are brought under the head of internal elements».

This confusion between external and internal objects has misled the Vaibhāṣikas to maintain that even in dreams what we see is a real external object. Dharmakīrti ridicules that opinion. «Out of mere obstinacy, says he to the Vaibhāṣika, you have been misled to maintain such an absurdity, that evidently contradicts both scripture and logic. You must have known that never will I be induced to believe the reality of such beings which are only seen in dreams». «This would mean that when I see in a dream an elephant entering my room through a chink in a window, that the elephant has really entered the room; and when I in a dream see my own self quitting the room in which I sleep, it will mean that my person has been doubled, etc. etc.».

In any case the standpoint of the Hīnayāna is thoroughly realistic. The objective elements of a personal life are as real as the subjective ones.

Roughly speaking a real external world is assumed in Hīnayāna, denied in Mahāyāna and partly reassumed in the logical school.

As a matter of fact it is denied in all the schools of the Mahāyāna. But the school founded by Maitreya-Asanga in opposition to the extreme relativism of the Mādhyamikas is distinguished by assuming a Pure Idea[1] (*citta-mātram = vijñapti-mātram*)[2] not differentiated into subject and object as a final Absolute, and reducing all other ideas to illusions (*parikalpita*). Such Idealism is exactly the reverse of Plato's variety of Idealism. The difference between both these Buddhist schools

---

[1] Trimśikā, kār. 25.

[2] D. T. Suzuki, Lankāvatāra, p. 241 ff. sees a difference between these terms, but I do not discern any.

is very subtle and Asanga himself, as well as other authors, do not scruple to write in accord with both systems.[1]

The new theory appears at first in a series of canonical sūtras of which the Sandhinirmocana-sūtra is regarded by the Tibetans as the fundamental.[2]

But religious works (sūtras) in India are always followed by scientific digests (šāstras) in which the same subject is represented in a system.[3] The same Vasubandhu who summarized the doctrine of the 18 early schools in his «great šāstra», undertook to lay down the principles of the new interpretation in three minor šāstra works.[4] He was preceded in this task by a work of his brother Asanga on the same subject.[5] In these works Vasubandhu deals with 1) logical arguments in favour of Idealism, 2) the theory of a stored up consciousness (*ālaya-vijñāna*) 3) a changed system of Elements, 4) the theory of the threefold essence of all Elements.

The logical arguments in favour of Idealism and against the reality of Matter are the following ones. 1) The picture of the world remains quite the same whether we assume external objects or mere

---

1 Cp. the article of E. Obermiller quoted below.

2 To the same class belong the Avatamsaka-, Lankāvatāra-, Ghanavyūha and in fact the majority of the sūtras of the section Mdo of the Kanjur. On this school cp. Sylvain Lévi, Sūtrālankāra (Paris, 1907) and Matériaux pour... Vijñaptimātra (Paris, 1932); L. de la Vallée Poussin, Vijñaptimātratāsiddhi de Hiuen Tsang, (1928); D. T. Suzuki, Studies in the Lankāvatārasūtra (London, 1930); S. N. Das Gupta, Philosophy of Vasubandhu (I. H. Q., 1928) and Philosophy of the Lankāvatāra, in Buddhistic Studies, Calcutta, 1931; S. Yamaguchi and Henriette Meyer, Dignāga's Ālambana-parīkṣā (J. Asiatique, 1929). Notwithstanding all this work the problem of Buddhist Idealism is not yet solved. The translations are desperately unintelligible. A new light will probably come from the study of Tibetan tradition. Characteristic are the fluctuations of Asanga between the Māddhyamika-Prāsangika and the Vijñānavāda systems, cp. ch. IV of E. Obermiller's article «The doctrine of Prajñāpāramitā as exposed in the Abhisamayālankāra and its Commentaries», Acta Orientalia, 1932.

3 On this class of šāstras cp. my article «La litterature Yogācāra d'après Bu-ston» in the Muséon, and now in the full translation of Bu-ston's History by E. Obermiller, vol. I, p. 53—57 (Heidelberg, 1931).

4 They are the Mahāyāna-pañca-skandhaka, the Vimšatikā and the Trinšikā, the last two discovered, edited and translated by Sylvain Lévi.

5 The Abhidharma-sangraha. Among the Tibetan lamas this is called the Higher Abhidharma (*stod*), while the great work of Vasubandhu goes under the name of the Lower one (*smad*).

internal causes for our sensations and images;[1] 2) The subject-to-object relation is incomprehensible. It is a very poor hypothesis to imagine that consciousness can travel towards an object external to it, seize its form and return with this spoil;[2] 3) The infinite divisibility of matter clearly shows that the atom is a mere idea.[3]

The theory of a store of the germs of all ideas (*ālaya-vijñāna*) is intended as a substitute for the external world.[4] The consistent run of the events of our life has its origin in this store of ideas which one by one emerge under the influence of a Biotic Force (*vāsanā*). Every idea is preceded by a «homogeneous and immediate»[5] cause not in the external world, but in that store from which it emerges and to which it returns.

The change in the system of Elements becomes clear from the following table[6] —

6. *Receptive faculties*	6. *Objective aspects of ideas*	8. *Kinds of ideas*
1. vision	7. colour	13. visual
2. audition	8. sound	14. auditive
3. smell	9. odour	15. olfactory
4. taste	10. flavour	16. gustatory
5. touch	11. tactiles (Matter)	17. tactile
6. mind (*kliṣṭa-manas*).	12. mental phenomena (*dharmāḥ*)	18. intelligible (non sensuous) ideas
		19. subconscious store of ideas
		20. The Absolute Idea

The items 19 and 20 are added to the original table of the Hīnayāna.

The ten Elements of Matter (№№ 1—5 and 7—11) are converted into corresponding ideas. The item № 6 becomes the empirical Ego[7] (*kliṣṭa-manas*), because its former meaning (*citta-mātram*) is now transferred to № 20. The moment preceding the appearance of every idea

---

1 Cp. TSP., p. 553. 27 — *yathā bhavatām bāhyo'rtha iti tathā tata eva (samanantara-pratyayād eva) niyamaḥ siddhaḥ*; Viṃśatikā, kār. 1—9.

2 Cp. TSP., p. 559. 8 ff. where the *grāhya-grāhaka-vaidhuryam* is exposed the same is repeatedly mentioned by Vasubandhu, cp. S. Lévi's Index.

3 Viṃśatikā, kār. 11—14. This is the main argument of Dignāga in his Ālambana-parīkṣā; often quoted, cp. S. Lévi. Matériaux, p. 52 note.

4 Triṃś., k. 15 and passim, cp. S. Lévi's Index.

5 TSP., p. 582. 19 *samanantara-pratyaye = ālayākhye.*

6 Cp. the table in my CC., p. 97.

7 Triṃś., k. 6.

is contained in the store (№ 19) and the ultimate unity of all Elements is contained in the idea of «Thisness» (*tathatā*) or the Absolute Idea (*citta-mātram*), № 20. A theory of evolution is sketched explaining the realization (*pariṇamā*)[1] of the Absolute Idea at first in the Store of Ideas, its dichotomy in subject and object, the appearance of the empirical Ego and of all the ideas cognized by him. Vasubandhu then enumerates all mental phenomena which remain contained in the item № 12 of the classification, the so called *dharmāḥ* which formerly contained all non-sensuous items.[2]

The process of the world's evolution which is represented by Vasubandhu in the beginning of his work as a descent from the Absolute Idea into the manifold of an imagined world, is once more described at the end of it as an ascending process from manifold to Unity, through the suppression of the dichotomy in subject and object.[3]

Such is the amended Theory of the Elements as it appears in the school which is usually called, in accordance with some of its tenets, a school of Idealism — Vijñāna- or Vijñapti-mātratā.

This shape of the theory is contemporaneous with the rise of the logical school. It is also its last modification after which it ceased to exist. It is still studied in the schools as an historical past, but for the new logical school it has no importance, it was entirely superseded by the study of logic. Buddhism has ceased to be a Theory of Elements.[4] The *dharma* (Buddhist doctrine) is no more the *abhidharma* (theory of Elements), the *abhidharma* belongs to the past. This momentous change is to a certain extent similar with that change in

---

[1] Ibid., k. 1

[2] Ibid., kār. 9—14. It is a gross mistake to translate *dharmāḥ* in the plural by the same word as in *sarve dharmāḥ*. The mistake is as great as if someone were to translate a word meaning «colour» by a word meaning «sound», for the difference between *āyatana* № 12 and *āyatanas* 7—11 is greater than the difference between *āyatanas* 7 (colour) and 8 (sound).

[3] Ibid., k. 26.

[4] In the Idealism of the Sandhinirmocana and of Asanga the threefold division of all *dharmas* in *parikalpita*, *paratantra* and *parinispauna* is the most prominent feature. In the Idealism of Vasubandhu both this division and the argument from infinite divisibility are important. In Dignāgas exposition the threefold division is dropped, dropped is also the psychological part (*dharmāḥ*), but the Aporetic, the argument from infinite divisibility becomes the fundamental argument. By the bye, it is exceedingly awkward to render in a work of Vasubandhu the term *dharma* every where by the same word, since Vasubandhu himself has bestowed great care, in his Vyākhyā-yukti, to emphasize the utterly different meanings of this term, cp. E. Obermiller's translation of Bu-ston, History, p. 18.

the history of European philosophy when metaphysics was superseded by the critical school and epistemology became the leading philosophic science. How the Buddhist logical school emerged out of the idealistic one has been indicated before.

The speculations of the Buddhists on the reality of the external world have conduced them into a dead-lock. The question has been found to be unimportant. The important thing is logic and it remains quite the same in both cases, whether we assume or whether we deny external reality. This curious result has been attained in the way of a compromise between the early extreme Pluralism and the later extreme Monism. The Monists developed into a school of Idealism. From the Mādhyamikas were born the Yogācāras. The Pluralists, Sarvāstivādins, developed into the critical school of Sautrāntikas. The latter were apparently the first to assume the reality of a Thing-in-Itself behind the outward phenomenon.

The logicians compromised and established the hybrid school of the Sautrāntika-Yogācāras.

§ 10. Some European Parallels.

The future historian of comparative philosophy will not fail to note the great importance of the argument from infinite divisibility. In Indian as well as in European philosophy it appears as a most powerful weapon of Idealism. Together with the other antinomies it has influenced the balance of Kant's indecision, by making him more inclined towards Idealism in the second half of his Critique of Pure Reason. It is the principle argument of both Vasubandhu[1] and Dignāga[2] for establishing their special variety of Idealism. It plays a considerable part in the equipment of the Eleatics for establishing their Monism. The arguments of Zeno, approved by both Kant[3] and Hegel,[4] are mainly founded on the antinomy of divisibility. Nay it seems even to have allured Locke and Hume to a plane dangerously inclining towards Idealism. Indeed Locke[5] says: «The divisibility *ad infinitum* of any finite extension involves us in consequences... that carry greater dificulty and more apparent absurdity,

---

1 Viṃśatikā, kār. 11.

2 Ālambanap., kār. 1.

3 CPR., p. 409 (1 ed. p. 502).

4 W. d. Logik, I. 191.

5 Essay, II, XXIII, § 31.

than anything can follow from the notion of an immaterial knowing substance». And Hume falls in line, saying,[1] «No priestly dogma invented on purpose to tame and subdue the rebellious reason of mankind ever shocked common sense more than the doctrine of the infinite divisibility with its consequences». To this antinomy Hegel turns his exclusive attention.[2] He impugns the Kantian solution and proposes a «dialectical» one. «Continuity, says he, and discreteness cannot exist the one without the other, therefore their unity is truth». However Kant maintained only that infinite divisibility cannot be applied to external reality, to the things by themselves. Nothing prevents applying it in pure mathematics. Since Hegel has cancelled the external thing, he ought not to object against the transcendental ideality of infinite divisibility. But if the dialectical solution be applied to the external object, it will be paralleled by a Jaina view according to which one and the same atom is double, extended and non-extended at the same time.[3] «Such is the absurd opinion of some fools»! exclaims Šāntirakṣita.[4]

According to the Buddhist Dialectical Method, continuity is nothing but the negation of discreteness, and an atom is nothing over and above the negation of extention. Since the external thing can be neither simple nor composite, it does not mean that the unity of these opposites is «their truth»; it does not mean that the external thing is simple and composite at the same time; it means that the external thing, on being considered critically, proves to be «a flower in the sky».[5] Hegel's own chief argument in favour of Idealism[6] coincides with the chief argument of Dharmakīrti, it assumes an immanent object.[7]

In the next following Symposion we will attempt to confront some of the most salient European views on the reality of the external world with their Indian parallels. But the respective positions of Kant and Dignāga in this problem deserve special mention. It is well

---

1 Essay on Hum. Und., Sect. XII, part II.

2 Op. cit., I. 191.

3 TSP., p. 554. 1 f.; cp. ibid., p. 557. 21 ff. the probably Jaina doctrine on the infinite divisibility of *pradeśas*. Cp. the argument of the *Monadists*, CPR., p. 357 (1[t] ed., p. 440).

4 TS., p. 554. 10.

5 TSP., p. 550. 17.

6 Op. cit., p. II. 441.

7 Ibid., p. 559. 8 ff. From the two chief arguments Dignāga seems to lay more stress upon the first (*artha-ayogāt*), while Dharmakīrti seems to prefer the second (*grāhya-grāhaka-vaidhuryāt*).

known that Kant's position is not always clear.[1] The usual charge against his Thing-in-Itself, *viz.*, that it can be neither a cause nor a reality, since Causality and Reality are constructions of the understanding, does not, in my opinion, carry much weight. Reality and Causality refer us to things having extention and duration, but not to a point-instant of ultimate reality.[2] A glance at Dharmakīrti's table of Categories will show at once where the Category of Causality lies.[3] It belongs to the logic of relations, to the logic of consistency, to the logic of the major premise. The Thing-in-Itself belongs to the logic of reality, of the perceptual judgment, of the minor premise. It is the common subject of all the five Categories (Substance, Quality, Motion, Class-name and Proper name).[4] The fault of Kant consists perhaps in not sufficiently having emphasized the difference[5] between the logic of consistency and the logic of reality, the judgment with two concepts and the judgment with one concept. His category of causality is deduced from the hypothetical judgment. Just the same is done, we have seen, by Dignāga and Dharmakīrti. But the Thing-in-Itself is not a relation, it is not deduced from the hypothetical judgment. It is the subject of every percep-

---

[1] Cp. Windelband, Ueber die Phasen der Kantischen Lehre vom Dinge an sich. (Vierteljahrsschrift f. Philosophie, 1877, pp. 244 ff.).

[2] According to Aristotle the sensible particular *Hoc Aliquid* is declared to be the ultimate subject to which all Universals attach as determinants or accompaniments, and if this condition be wanting, the unattached Universal cannot rank among complete Entia (Grote, Arist., App. 1). Although this *Hoc Aliquid* as *Essentia Prima* is entered by Aristotle in his system of Categories, but it is, properly speaking, a non-category, a non-predicate. It is always a subject, the pure subject, the pure thing, the common subject of all predications. The predicate is always a Universal. Reality, Causality, Thingness are predicates, just as jar-ness, but not the ultimate point of reality, not the ultimate cause that is lying at the bottom of all universals.

[3] Cp. above, p. 254.

[4] We can have the judgments «*this* is reality», «*this* is causality», «*this* is (or has) substantiality». The concepts of Reality, Causality and Substantiality will be predicates and therefore Categories, but the element «*this*» is not a predicate. It is the subject, the genuine subject of all predication. A subject means a non-Category, a subject that never will be a predicate. Even if we construct the concept of «Thisness», the difference between the individual «this» and the Universal «Thisness» will remain the same.

[5] That this difference occasionally occurred to him is seen from his considerations in the Critical Decision (section VII ot the Antinomy) where he distinguishes between the logic of the major premise, where the connection between two concepts is «in no way limited by time» (CPR, p. 407) and the logic of the minor premise where phenomena are referred to things by themselves.

tual judgment.[1] A Thing-in-Itself means just the same as a cause-in-itself.[2] The conception of reality, we have seen, is dynamical.

Kant's position is much more fluctuating in the Transcendental Dialectic where the whole of his argument inclines towards absolute Idealism,[3] notwithstanding all his desire not to be confounded with Berkeley and to retain the Thing-in-Itself as established in the Analytic. The dialectic of infinity (infinite divisibility) undermines and explodes the natural human belief in the reality of an external world. Since this fact seems to be a repetition of what previously once occurred in India, it becomes necessary to define the mutual position of Kant and Dignāga in this problem. It can be summarized in the following five points. Kant says that:

1) The key to the solution of cosmological dialectic consists in the fact that all (external) «objects are mere representations; as extended beings and series of changes they have no independent existence outside our thoughts».[4]

2) However they are not dreams; they are mere images without any reality corresponding to them, but to be distinguished from dreams. The «empirical idealism» of Berkeley maintains that they are dreams, but the «transcendental» idealism maintains that they are «real». Whatsoever the term «transcendental» may mean in other contexts, here[5] it means «non-dreams» and at the same time non-external. According to this statement we must have a double set of images, images in dreams without reality and images in reality, but also without any congruent external reality (sic!).

3) «Even the internal sensuous intuition of our mind as an object of consciousness», i. e. the Ego, is not a real self, «because it is under condition of time».[6]

4) If both the cognized object and the cognizing Ego are not real by themselves, it seems to follow that neither the process of

---

1 Such is the opinion of Fr. Paulsen, *viz.*, that Kant had two different causalities in view, cp. his Kant,[2] p. 157.

2 *yā bhūtiḥ saiva kriyā.*

3 Cp. E. Caird, op. cit., II. 136 — «in the beginning (of the Critique) the thing-in-itself appears as an object which produces affections in our sensibility, whereas in the end it appears as the noumenon which the mind requires, because it does not find in experience an object adequate to itself». That is, in the beginning it is a thing, in the end it is an idea.

4 CPR., p. 400.

5 Ibid., p. 401 (1 ed., p. 491).

6 Ibid.

cognition which connects these two non-realities can be real. However this is not stated by Kant. The word «idealism» evidently should imply that the idea includes subject, object and process of cognition, the Indian «three envelopes».

5) But we must «have something which corresponds to sensibility as a kind of receptivity».[1] It is the «transcendental object», that is, the thing by itself. «We may ascribe to that transcendental object the whole extent and connection of our possible perceptions and we may say that it is given by itself antecedently to all experience»... «but they are nothing to me and therefore no objects, unless they can be comprehended in the series of the empirical regresses».[2]

To these five points the answer of Dignāga and Dharmakīrti would probably have been the following one.

1) The external material object is an idea. Once say that it is infinitely divisible, once mean what you say, and you will see that it can be nothing but the mathematical object, i. e. an idea.

2) Why should one set of images be images and real and the other set also images, but non-real? Images are images. In the waking state they are connected with reality directly, in dreams and other morbid conditions[3] they are connected with reality indirectly.

3—4) This reality is the point-instant of pure sensation[4]. By the Understanding it is enclosed in a «threefold envelope» (*tri-puṭī*) of a cognizer, cognized and cognition. These three items do not represent opposed forms of reality, but only contrasting attitudes towards one and the same reality.[5]

---

[1] Ibid.

[2] Ibid.

[3] Kant says (CPR., p. 781), «in dreams as well as in madness a representation may well be the mere effect of the faculty of imagination»; but it can be such an effect only through the reproduction of former external perceptions, cp. Dharmakīrti's view above, p. 522.

[4] Without this pure sensation which imparts indirect reality to all conventional existence (*saṃvṛti*) the realist would be right who ironically remarks «your supreme logic says that all things without exception (*bhūtāny-eva*) do not exist», cp. TSP., p. 550. 21.

[5] Such is Dignāga's solution of the problem of «a sound starting point of all philosophy». It is a mere «something». It may be contrasted with Descartes' *Cogito ergo sum* which implies a real subject and a real object. Hans Driesch's formula «I consciously have something» (i. e., I have it without seizing it), which moreover implies the reality of an «order», corresponds to the view of the Sarvāstivādins. It really means «I have consciously everythiug».

5) The ultimate reality (i. e. pure sensation) is alone free from all dialectical thought-construction. It is the foundation of that subject-object dichotomy, upon which all logic is founded. This logic is equally acceptable to the Realist, who assumes an external Thing-in-Itself and to the Idealist, who denies it. For the latter the subject-object relation is a dichotomy imagined by the Understanding. The first starts at a plane where subject and object are «given».

The chief charge of Dignāga against Kant probably would have been that Kant has failed to perceive the double possibility,[1] of idealism and realism. We can admit the external Thing-in-Itself and exist in this mental plane without taking into account the final dichotomy into subject and object, but we also can take it into account and exist in another plane.[2] There will be no contradiction. There scarcely will be any change of language, if we in speaking of external objects keep in mind that it means only phenomena.[3]

---

1 According to Windelband (op. cit.) Kant's denial of the External Thing-in-Itself (what he calls the third phase of his doctrine) is his greatest feat. «Dieser Gedanke, dass ausserhalb der Vorstellung Nichts sei, worum sich die Wissenschaft zu kümmern habe, ist das Göttergeschenk Kant's an die Menschheit». The assumption of the Thing-in-Itself, on the other hand, (what he calls the second phase) is quite senseless and needless, «eine völlig sinn und nutzlose, daher störende und nervirende Fiction». Thus Kant somehow managed to give to humanity a divine gift and a senseless annoyance, in just the same work and in regard of just the same problem! In accusing Kant of a glaring contradiction Windelband does not seem to have kept quite clear of contradiction himself!

2 The position of Dignāga in this respect resembles to a certain extent the views of some modern philosophers who come to espouse metaphysics and realism at the same time. Indeed it is the weight of the subject-object «Aporetic», of which the Aporetic of infinity is for him only a part, that induced Nicolai Hartmann to supplement Kantianism by metaphysics. These two arguments (*grāhya-grāhaka-vaidhurya* and *artha-ayoga*, cp. TSP., p. 559. 8) are also the chief reasons of Dignāga for supplementing his realistic logic by a metaphysical idealism.

3 In his Refutation of Idealism, CPR., p. 778 ff., Kant establishes that our consciousness is a consciousness of things and thus proves the existence of external things in space outside myself; in other words, that there is no subject without an object. Exactly the same consideration is used by Hegel in order to prove the identity of subject and object, and the Indians fall in line in maintaining that the subject-object dichotomy (*grāhya-grāhaka-kalpanā*) is dialectical. «The cause of the representations, says Kant (ibid. p. 780), which are ascribed by us, it may be wrongly, to external things, may lie within ourselves». This is also the Indian view. The Indian Idealists, we have seen, replace the realistic Force of Experience (*anubhava-bhāvanā*) by an internal Force of Productive Imagination (*vikalpa-bhāvanā*).

Such is also the opinion of Sigwart.[1] According to him directly «given» is only the presence of a presentation.[2] According to the Indians it is only pure sensation. Its connection with an external object is a second step. The subjective Idealist maintains the necessity of this step, but for him it means only that every perception must be referred to some object imagined as existing beyond us. Through this act of imagination we only arrive into «a second plane»[3] of imagination, but not into an independent external world.[4]

The necessity of objectivization is indeed psychological,[5] but there is no logical necessity to assume a real objective world behind the world of images. There will be no contradiction, says Dignāga.[6]

The fluctuation of Kant appears from the Indian point of view as a fluctuation between two theories which are both possible. Kant was lead by his speculation into two different worlds, but it did not occur to him that both were logically possible. This double possibility is disclosed by Sigwart.

There is, as Sigwart rightly remarks,[7] only a psychological necessity of inferring from the direct evidence of a sensation a cause for it in the external thing. There is no logical necessity. Psychologically sensation is one moment, the thing which has produced the stimulus is the foregoing moment. The next following moment, after the sensation by the outer sense, is a moment of attention or sensation by the inner sense,[8] it is a kind of intelligible sensation. And finally comes the moment of the intelligible image.[9] The relation between object

---

1 Op. cit., I, 408.

2 Vorstellung.

3 Ibid., «ein zweites Stadium des Vorstellens».

4 Ibid., «die Wirklichkeit welche wir behaupten ist nur eine Wirklichkeit von Erscheinungen, nicht von Dingen, welche von uns unabhängig wären».

5 Ibid., I. 409. Cp. the interesting views of Dharmottara on the different kinds of connection, exemplified on the connection of words with their cause, in NBT., p. 60. The connection between a word and the intention (*abhiprāya*) with which it is pronounced is causal and real, or psychological (*vāstava*) The connection between a word and the external object which it expresses is causal and constructed, i. e., logical (*kalpita*). The connection between a word and the conception (*pratīti*) which it expresses is logical (*kalpita*) and one of identity (*svabhāva-hetutvam*).

6 Ālambanap., kār. 8, (transl. p. 45).

7 Logik, I. 409 — «der psychologischen Nötigung eine solche (äussere Welt) anzunehmen, keine logische Notwendigkeit entspreche».

8 *mano-vijñāna* = *mānasa-pratyakṣa*.

9 Cp. vol. II, App. III, pp. 309 ff.

and cognition is indirect and causal.[1] But logically it is a relation of Identity.[2] «How is it», asks Dharmottara, «that the same cognition includes a part which is being determined and a part which is its determination»?[3] «Is it not a contradiction to assume in the same unit a cause and its own effect?».[4] And he answers: this is possible — by Negation! Indeed a pure sensation produced by a patch of blue receives definiteness by a negation of the non-blue,[5] i. e., the Understanding interprets an indefinite sensation as being a definite image of the blue by contrasting it with non-blue. The same thing differently regarded becomes as though it were different itself. The objectivity is founded on causality *plus* identity.[6] Thus it is that direct and indubitable cognition is only pure sensation. It contains every-thing. It is the richest in contents and the poorest in thought. But thought makes it definite by negation. Negation is the essence of thought. Definiteness, understanding, conformity, «formity», negation, repudiation of the contrary, image, concept, dichotomy, are but different manners of developing the one fundamental act of pure sensation. The Thing as it is in itself is disclosed by representing it as it is in its non-self, «in the other».

This part of the Buddhist doctrine we also find in Europe, but not in Kant, we find it in Hegel.

§ 11. Indo-European Symposion on the Reality of the External World.

a) First conversation. Subject Monism.

1-st Vedāntin. Real at the beginning was the Nought.[7]

2-nd Vedāntin. Real at the beginning was neither Existence nor the Nought.[8]

---

1 *tad-utpatti*. Cp. NBT., p. 40. 7 — *prameya-kāryam hi pramāṇam.*

2 *sārūya* = *tādrūpya* = *tādātmya.*

3 NBT., p. 15. 22 — *vyavasthāpya-vyavasthāpana-bhāvo'pi katham ekasya jñānasya?*

4 Ibid., p. 15. 10 — *yena ekasmin vastuni virodhaḥ syāt.*

5 Ibid., p. 16. 3.

6 *tadutpatti-tatsārūpyābhyām viṣayatā.*

7 Chāndogya, III. 19. 1; cp. Deussen, Allg. Gesch. d. Phil. I, pp. 145, 199, 202, and his Sechzig Upanishads, p. 155.

8 Ṛgv. 10, 129. 1.

3-rd Vedāntin. Real at the beginning was only Existence, the One-without-a-Second.[1] It was Brahman.

4-th Vedāntin. The Brahman is identical with our own Self. The «This» art «Thou!»[2]

Parmenides. There is no Nought.[3] The Universe is the One. It is immovable.

Demokritus. Immovable is the Nought. It is Empty Space. It is filled by moving atoms.[4]

The Buddhist. There is an Empty Space. It contains an infinity of perishable Elements. There is a Nought (Nirvāṇa), when all the perishable Elements have perished.

Nāgārjuna. All perishable objects are relative and void. Their Nought, or the Great Void,[5] is the only reality. It is the Buddha (in his Cosmical Body).

Spinoza. There is only One Substance! It is God (in his Cosmical Body).

Dignāga. The Culmination of Wisdom is Monism[6]. This Unity is the Buddha (in his Spiritual Body).

Dharmakīrti. The essence of Consciousness is undivided![7] Subject and object is an illusive division. Their unity is Buddha's Omniscience, his Spiritual Body!

Yogācāra Buddhist. With the only exception of Buddha's knowledge which is free from the division in subject and object, all other knowledge is illusive, since it is constructed as subject and object.[8]

b) Second conversation. Subject Dualism and Pluralism.

Sānkhya. There is not one eternal principle, but there are two: Spirit and Matter. Both are eternal, but the first is eternal stability, the other is eternal change. There is no interaction at all possible between them. However the change of the one is somehow reflected,

---

1 Chāndogya, VI. 2, 1—2.

2 *tat tvam asi.*

3 οὐχ ἔστι μὴ εἶναι.

4 μὴ μᾶλλον τὸ δὲν ἢ τὸ μηδέν. Cp. H. Cohen, Logik d. r. Erk., p. 70; μὴ ὄν apparently = *tadanya* + *tadviruddha* = *paryadāsa* = *parihāra*; ὀυχ ὄν = *abhāva.*

5 *mahā-śūnyatā* = *sarva-dharmāṇām paraspara-apekṣatā.*

6 *prajñā-pāramitā jñānam advayam, sa Tathāgataḥ* (cp. my Introd. to the ed. of Abhisamayālaṃkāra).

7 *avibhāgo hi buddhyātmā*, an often quoted verse of Dharmakīrti, cp. SDS., p. 32.

8 *sarvam ālambane bhrāntam muktvā Tathāgata-jñānam, iti Yogācāra-matena*, cp. NBTTipp., p. 19.

or illumined, in the immovable light of the other. Inside Matter itself, six receptive faculties and six respective kinds of objective Matter are evolved. There is thus a double externality; the one is of the Matter regarding the Spirit. The other is of one kind of matter regarding the other. There is no God!

Descartes. All right! There are only two substances, the one extended, the other conscious. But both are eternally changing. There is a God, which is the originator and the controller of their concerted motion!

The Buddhist (*Hīnayāna*). There is neither a God, nor an Ego, nor any spiritual, nor materialistic enduring substance. There are only Elements (*dharmas*), instantaneously flashing and disappearing. And there is a law of Dependent Origination in accord with which the Elements combine in aggregates. Just as in the Sānkya there are six receptive faculties and six corresponding objective domains. There is thus here also a double externality. The one is of all Elements regarding one another, the other is of the six objective domains regarding the six receptive faculties.

Sānkhya. These Elements are infra-atomic units (*guṇas*), they are unconscious and eternally changing.

Heracleitus. These Elements are flashes appearing and disappearing in accord with a Law of continual change.

Demokritus. These Elements are Atoms (material).

Herbart. These Elements are Reals (immaterial).

Mach. These Elements are nothing but sensations. Both the Ego and Matter are pure mythology. When philosophy is no more interested in the reality of an Ego, nothing remains but the causal laws of Functional Interdependence of sensations, in order to explain the connection of the whole.

J. St. Mill. The so-called Substance is nothing but a permanent possibility of sensations. «The notions of Matter and Mind, considered as substances, have been generated in us by the mere order of our sensations». Phenomena are held together not by a substance, but by an eternal law (of Dependent Origination).

Nāgārjuna. Dependent Origination is alone without beginning, without an end and without change. It is the Absolute. It is Nirvāṇa, the world *sub specie aeternitatis.*[1]

---

1 Cp. my Nirvāṇa, pp. 48.

c) Third Conversation. Subject—the Logic of naive Realism and critical Logic.

Dignāga. However the Universe *sub specie aeternitatis* can be cognized only by mystic intuition.[1] It cannot be established by logic!

Candrakīrti. It can be established by the condemnation of logic![2] Since all logical concepts are relative and unreal, there must be another, non-relative, absolute reality, which is the Great Void. It is the Cosmical Body of the Buddha.

Dignāga. In logic «we are only giving a scientifical description of what happens in common life in regard to the sources of our knowledge and their respective objects.[3] We do not consider their transcendental reality!» In logic we can admit the reality of the external world.

Candrakīrti. What is the use of that logic,[4] if it does not lead to the cognition of the Absolute?

Dignāga. The Realists are bunglers in logic. They have given wrong definitions. We only correct them![5]

The Realist. The external world is cognized by us in its genuine reality. Just as the objects situated in the vicinity of a lamp are illuminated by it, just so are the objects of the external world illuminated by the pure light of consciousness. There are no images and no Introspection. Self-consciousness is inferential.[6]

The Yogācāra Buddhist. There are images and there is Introspection. «If we were not conscious of perceiving the patch of blue colour, never would we perceive it. The world would remain blind, it would perceive nothing». There are therefore no external objects at all. Why should we make the objective side of knowledge double?

Realist. But the running change[7] of our pepceptions can be produced only by the Force of Experience. They change in accord with the change in the external world![8]

---

1 *yogi-pratyakṣa*, cp. ibid., p. 16 ff.
2 Ibid., p. 135 ff.
3 Ibid., p. 140 ff.
4 Ibid.
5 Ibid.
6 Cp. vol. II, pp. 352 ff.
7 *kadācitkatva.*
8 Cp. vol. II, p. 369 and NK., p. 259. 11

Buddhist. You needs must assume some sort of Biotic Force in order to explain the change. It will be either the Force of Experience,[1] or the Force of Productive Imagination,[2] or the Force of Illusion.[3] If you assume the latter there will be no reality at all in the phantom of an external world. If you assume the first there will be a superfluous double reality. If you assume the second you will have a transcendental ideality along with phenomenal reality.[4]

The Realist. Your theory resembles «a purchase without paying!»[5] Indeed the external world, although consisting of mere point-instants, receives coloured perceptibility through imagination, but it can offer nothing in exchange, since it consists of colourless points! If sensation and understanding are entirely heterogeneous, how can a pure sensation be comprehended under a pure concept of the understanding, «as no one is likely to say that causality, for instance, could be seen through the senses?»[6]

Kant. There must be some third thing homogeneous on the one side with the category and on the other with the object as it is given *in concreto.*

Dharmakīrti. The intermediate thing is a kind of intelligble sensation. We assume that after the first moment of pure sensation there is a moment of intelligible sensation by the inner sense which is the thing intermediate between pure sensation and the abstract concept.[7] There is moreover between them a Conformity or Coordination.[8]

The Realist. What is this Conformity or Coordination?

Vasubandhu. It is the fact owing to which cognition, although also caused by the senses, is said to cognize the object and not the senses.[9] The object is the predominant among the causes of cognition.

Dharmakīrti. Coordination or Conformity is «similarity between things absolutely dissimilar».[10] Indeed all things as unities are things

---

1 *anubhava-vāsanā.*

2 *vikalpa-vāsanā = vikalpasya sāmarthyam.*

3 *avidyā-vāsanā = māyā.*

4 Cp. the detailed controversy between the Sautrāntika Realist and the Yogācāra (Idealist) Buddhists in the II vol., p. 360 ff.

5 *amūlya-dāna-kraya,* cp. Tātp., p. 269. 9.

6 CPR., p. 113; an almost *verbatim* coincidence with NBT., p. 69. 11 = *na niṣpanne kārye kaścij janya-janak-bhāvo nāma dṛṣṭo'sti.*

7 Cp. the theory of *mānasa-pratyakṣa,* vol. II, Appendix III.

8 NK., p. 258. 18 — *tatsārūpya-tadutpattibhyām viṣayatvam.*

9 Cp. vol. II, p. 347.

10 *atyanta-vilakṣaṇānām salakṣaṇyam,* cp. Tātp., p. 339.

in themselves, absolutely dissimilar from other things. But in the measure in which we overlook their absolute dissimilarity (their «in themselves»), they become similar. They become similar through a common negation. That is why all images are Universals and all Universals are mutual negations. Negativity is the essence of our Understanding. The senses alone are affirmation.[1]

Hegel. According to my Dialectical Method Negativity is equally the essence of the objective world, which is identical with the subjective one.

Dharmakīrti. We must have an Affirmation contrasting with the Negativity of concepts.

Herbart. Pure sensation alone is Affirmation, it is absolute position!

Dignāga. Our logic aims at being equally acceptable to those who deny the existence of the external world and to those who maintain it. No one can deny that there are two kinds of cognized essences—the Particular and the Universal. The particular seemingly always resides in the external world, the universal is always in our head.

Berkley. There are no real universal or abstract ideas.

Dignāga. There are no particular ideas at all, an idea is always abstract and general. A particular image is a *contradictio in adjecto.* Particulars exist only in the external world. In our Mind apart from pure sensation, we have only universals.

Berkley. However to exist means to be perceived, *esse est percepi.* The external world does not exist beside what is perceived.

Dignāga. To exist means to be efficient.

Kant. It is «scandalous» that modern philosophy has not yet succeeded to prove beyond doubt the reality of the external world! If there were no things in themselves the phenomena as they appear to us would become such things. The things are «given» to our senses, they are «cognized», i. e., constructed, by the Understanding in accord with its categories.

Šantirakṣita. Yes! Pure sensation is of course non-constructive, but it it is a point-instant (*Kraftpunct*) which stimulates the understanding to produce its own (general) image of the thing.

Dharmottara. Is it not a great miracle! The senses represent the Thing brightly, vividly, but they understand nothing definite. The intellect understands definitely, but without vividness, vaguely, dimly, generally; it can construct only a Universal. However the miracle is easily explained. The Understanding is Imagination!

---

[1] *pratyakṣam = vidli-svarūpam.*

d) Fourth Conversation. Subject — the Thing-in-Itself.

F. H. Jacobi (and others). Supposing the Things-in-Themselves really exist, they cannot affect our sensibility; since Causality, being a subjective Category, is possible only between phenomena,[1] not between things.

The Jaina. Yes indeed! A thing which is strictly in itself, which has absolutely nothing in common with all other things in the whole world, is a non-entity, a flower in the sky! If you wish to distinguish it from a non-entity you must admit «Thingness» as a real Category, just as Causality and Substantiality.[2]

Dharmottara. Thingness, Causality, Substantiality are of course general Categories of the Understanding. They are general and dialectical. But the single pure sensation is neither general, nor is it imagined, nor is it dialectical. There is a limit to generality, that out of which generality consists. Causality is not itself a sensible fact,[3] it is an interpretation of it. But the Thing-in-Itself is a cause, a reality, an efficient point-instant, a dynamical reality, a unity, a thing as it is strictly in itself, not as it is in the «other», or in the «opposite». The terms ultimate particular, ultimate cause, ultimate reality, the real thing, the real unit, the thing in itself, the thing having neither extention nor duration are synonyms. But it does not follow that Causality, Reality, Thingness, Unity, etc., are not general terms, different categories under which the same thing can be brought according to the point of view. There is no other genuine direct reality than the instantaneous Thing-in-Itself. Its cognition alone is pure Affirmation, it is not dialectical, not negative, it is direct and positive. Thus the fact that Causality and Reality are concepts and Categories for the Understanding, does not in the least interfere with the fact that the Thing-in-Itself is the reality cognized in pure sensation.

Hegel. Your Thing-in-Itself is a phantom![4] It is Void.[5] It is an «absolute beyond» to all cognition.[6] Cognition becomes then contra-

---

[1] F. H. Jacobi, Werke, II, p. 301 f.

[2] TS, kār. 1713 — *tasmāt kha-puṣpa-tulyatvam icchatas tasya vastunaḥ, vastutvam nāma sāmānyam eṣṭavyam, tat-samānatā.*

[3] *na kaścid janya-janaka-bhāvo nāma dṛṣṭo'sti.* NBT., p. 69. 12.

[4] «Gespenst», cp. W. der Logik, II, p. 441.

[5] Ibid., p. 440, — «der formale Begriff... ist ein Subjectives gegen jene leere Dingheit-an-sich».

[6] Ibid. — «ein absolutes Jenseits für das Erkennen».

dictory, it becomes a cognition of a reality which is never cognized.[1]

Demokritus.[2] The Thing-in-Itself far from being a phantom is nothing but the material Atom, underlying the whole of phenomenal reality.

Epikurus. The Thing-in-Itself (αρχή) is the material Atom together with the Vacuum and Motion.

Lucretius. We must admit a *principium* or *semen*, it is the material solid Atom.

Hegel. This *principium* is neither the Atom, nor an «absolute beyond», but it is included in the idea of cognition. It is true that the very idea of cognition requires the object as existing by itself, but since the concept of cognition cannot be realized without its object, therefore the object is not beyond cognition. «Inasmuch as cognition becomes sure of itself, it is also sure of the insignificance of its opposition to the object».[3] Thus it is that the Thing-in-Itself as something beyond cognition, and opposed to it, disappears and the subject and object of cognition coalesce, according to the general rule that everything definite is not a thing «in itself», but a thing «in its other» or «in its opposite!»

Dharmottara. It is true that the thing becomes definite only when it is a thing related to, or included in, the other. But when it becomes definite it *pari passu* becomes general and vague. Vivid and bright is only the concrete particular, the Thing as it is in itself.

Dharmakīrti. First of all, it is not true that the Thing-in-Itself means cognition of something that never is cognized. And then it is also wrong that the relation of the object to its cognition is one of inclusion or identity. Indeed, if the Thing-in-Itself would mean something absolutely incognizable, we never would have had any inkling of its existence. It is not cognized by our Understanding, it is not «understood», but it is cognized by the senses in a pure sensation. It is cognized brightly, vividly, immediately, directly. Its cognition is instanta-

---

[1] Ibid. — «ein Erkennen dessen was ist, welches zugleich das Ding-an-sich nicht erkennt».

[2] We take Demokritus as the pioneer of Materialism and the mechanical explanation of the universe. The opinion of W. Kinkel (History, v. I, p. 215) who converts him into a «consequent rationalistic Idealist», is very strange.

[3] Ibid., — «das Object ist daher zwar von der Idee des Erkennens als an sich seiend vorausgesetzt, aber wesentlich in dem Verhältniss, dass sie ihrer selbst und der Nichtigkeit dieses Gegensatzes gewiss, zu Realisierung ihres Begriffes in ihm komme».

neous. We call it «unutterable». But again it is not unutterable absolutely. We call it «the thing», the «in itself», the cause, the point-instant, efficiency, pure object, pure existence, reality, ultimate reality, pure affirmation, etc. etc. Understanding, on the other hand, means indirect cognition, judgment, inference, imagination, analysis, generality, vagueness, negativity, dialectic. Productive Imagination can imagine only the general and dialectical. But the senses cognize the real and the real is the particular.

Dharmottara. The relation of the object to the subject of cognition in logic is not Identity. The object is not included in the subject. It is wrong to reduce all relations to «otherness» and then to declare that the opposites are identical. The relation of cognition to its object is causal.[1] Object and cognition are two facts causally interrelated.

e) Fifth Conversation. Subject — Dialectic.

Hegel. The relation between subject and object, between internal and external, seems at first to be causal, as between two realities.[2] But regarding them as an organic whole, there is no causal relation inside them at all.[3] There is nothing in the effect which did not preexist in the cause[4] and there is nothing real in the cause except its change into the effect.[5] But notwithstanding their identity cause and effect are contradictory. A change or a movement is possible only inasmuch as the thing includes a contradiction in itself.[6] Motion is the reality of contradiction.[7]

Kamalaśīla. We must distinguish between Causality and Contradiction. Causality is real, Contradiction is logical. Simple humanity, whose faculty of vision is obscured by the gloom if ignorance, indeed identifies causality with contradiction.[8]

---

1 NBT., p. 40. 5–7 — «*pramāṇa-sattayā prameya-sattā sidhyati*... *prameya-kāryam hi pramāṇam*; trsl., p. 108.

2 Phenomenology, p. 238 (on Causality between Mind and Body).

3 Ibid. p. 291. — «indem das Fürsichsein als organische Lebendigkeit in beide auf gleiche Weise fällt, fällt in der That der Kausalzusammenhang zwischen ihnen hinweg».

4 Encycl. of philos. Sciences., p. 151. — «Es ist kein Inhalt in der Wirkung... der nicht in der Ursache ist; — jene Identität ist der absolute Inhalt selbst».

5 Ibid., p. 153, — «dieser ganze Wechsel ist das eigene Setzen der Ursache, und nur dies ihr Setzen ist ihr Sein».

6 W. d. Logik, II. 58, — «nur insofern etwas den Widerspruch in sich hat bewegt es sich».

7 Ibid., p. 59. — «die Bewegung ist der daseiende Widerspruch selbst».

8 Cp. above, p. 408 and 427.

But philosophers must know the difference between contradiction and simple otherness, between otherness and necessary interdependence, between Causation and Coinherence, or Identity. They must know the theory of Relations of our Master Dharmakīrti.

E. v. Hartmann (to Hegel). Your Dialectical Method is simple madness![1]

Dharmakīrti (to Hegel). Your Dialectical Method is quite all right; but merely in the domain of the Understanding, i. e. of constructed concepts! Concepts are interrelated dialectically. Reality is interrelated by the causal laws of Dependent Origination. There is moreover an Ultimate Reality where subject and object coalesce. There is thus an imagined reality (*parikalpita*), an interdependent reality (*paratantra*) and an ultimate one (*pariniṣpanna*).

CONCLUSION

In the course of our analysis we have quoted parallelisms and similarities, partial and complete, from a variety of systems and many thinkers of different times. But it would not be right to conclude that the Indian system is a patchwork of detached pieces which can be now and then found singly to remember some very well known ideas. The contrary is perhaps the truth.

There is perhaps no other system whose parts so perfectly fit into one compact general scheme, reducible to one single and very simple idea. This idea is that our knowledge has two heterogeneous sources, Sensibility and Understanding. Sensibility is a direct reflex of reality. The Understanding creates concepts which are but indirect reflexes of reality. Pure sensibility is only the very first moment of a fresh sensation, the moment x. In the measure in which this freshness fades away, the intellect begins to «understand». Understanding is judgment. Judgment is $x = A$ where x is sensibility and A is understanding. Inference, or syllogism, is an extended judgment, $x = A + A^1$. The x is now the subject of the minor premise. It continues to represent sensibility. The $A + A^1$ connection is the connection of the Reason with the Consequence. This reason is the Sufficient Reason or the Threefold Reason. It is divided in only two varieties, the reason of Identity and the reason of Causation. It establishes the consistency of the concepts created by the understanding and

---

[1] «Eine krankhafte Geistesverirrung», cp. E. v. Hartmann. Ueber die dialectische Methode, p. 124.

is expressed in the major premise. Their connection with sensible reality is expressed in the minor premise. In this part the doctrine is again nothing but the development of the fundamental idea that there are only two sources of knowledge. The doctrine of the dialectical character of the understanding is a further feature of the same fundamental idea, because there are only two sources, the non-dialectical and the dialectical, which are the same as the senses and the understanding.

The external world, the world of the Particulars, and the internal world, the world of the Universals, are again nothing but the two domains of the senses and of the understanding. The Particular is the Thing as it is in «itself», the Universal is the Thing as it is in «the other».

And at last, ascending to the ultimate plane of every philosophy, we discover that the difference between Sensibility and Understanding is again dialectical. They are essentially the negation of each the other, they mutually sublate one another and become merged in a Final Monism.

Thus it is that one and the same Understanding must be characterized as a special faculty which manifests itself in 1) the Judgment, 2) the Sufficient Reason, 3) the double principle of Inference, Identity and Causality, 4) the construction of the internal world of the Universals and 5) the dichotomy and mutual Negation contained in all concepts. In all these five functions the Understanding is always the same. It is the contradictorily opposed part to pure sensation. Dignāga was right in putting at the head of his great work the aphorism: «There are only two sources of knowledge, the direct and the indirect».

Dignāga's system is indeed monolithic!

INDEX OF PROPER NAMES.

1. Sanscrit (authors, schools and works).

2. European (inclusive the names of modern scholars of India, Japan and China).

3. Tibetan names.

INDEX OF MAIN LOGICAL TOPICS

APPENDIX.

Professor Ui in a recent publication of the Tendai University, on the evidence of Chinese sources,[1] proves that the three-aspected logical reason has been introduced by the Sānkhyas and Nayasaumas[2] (=Pāšupatas?) before Vasubandhu. What is really due to the Sānkhyas, as has been stated above,[3] is the special proving force supposed to belong to the *modus tollens* of the Mixed Hypothetical Syllogism, the canon of the five *avīta-hetus.* It is true that in this syllogism the minor premise is nothing, but the first aspect of the reason and the major premise corresponds to the third aspect which is a contraposition of the second one. Virtually the Mixed Hypothetical Syllogism presupposes the existence of the three aspects. What makes the originality of Dignāga's position is the equipollency of the second and the third aspects. On this ground Dignāga dissented with the Sānkhyas who thought that the *modus tollens* (*avīta-hetu*) is an independent way of proof, cp. N. mukha, transl. p. 21. What enormous importance this change means is seen from Dignāga's dialectic.[4] The introduction of the Mixed Hypothetical Syllogism, position and contraposition, and tbe tree-aspects of the reason, may be due to the Sānkhyas. But the epistemological importance of the whole theory, its position in Dignāga's logic is nevertheless established by no one else as by Dignāga himself as the Naiyāyiks always maintained and as, I hope, the readers of this my book will not fail to perceive.

---

1 Madhyāntānusāra-šāstra, unknown in Tibet and said to be composed by Bodhisattvas Nāgārjuna and Asanga (?), translated by Gautama Prajñāruci of the Eastern Wei dynasty in AD. 543. (B. Nanjio, № 1246). It mentions the three aspects in an inverted order — the first, the third and the second — a consequence perhaps of the importance attached to the *avīta-hetu.*

2 Cp. Tucci, Pre-Dignāga Texts, p. XXIX n.

3 Cp. above, p. 293—4.

4 It stands nearer to the syllogism as cultivated by the Stoics, than to the Aristotelian one, but the Stoics have not drawn from it the same consequences as Dignāga.

ADDENDA

Page	Line	
28	40	On the six genuine works of Nāgārjuna cp. now, besides my Nirvāṇa, p. 66, also E. Obermiller, Buston trans., p. 51, and the same author's The Doctrine of Prajñāpāramitā (Reprint from Acta Orient., vol. X, p. 51). The Vaidalyaprakaṇa is evidently spurious.
41	23	My friend S. Oldenburg calls my attention to the fact that the correction in Sir A. Stein's translation of the Rājataranginī has already been proposed by the late Professor Hultzsch in the ZDMG. vol. 69, p. 279 (1915).
280	30	A more precise formula: R either «is» (identical with), or «is» (produced by), P; therefore S «is» (contains) R + P; cp. the three meanings of «is,» p. 441.
353		On the prehistory of the Nyāya system of logical fallacies cp. now the very interesting synopsis by Tucci, Pre-Dignāga Texts, p. XX.

LOGIC

TH. STCHERBATSKY

Western interest in Buddhism has grown enormously in recent years, but because of the scarcity of later Buddhist writings most of the work in the field has dealt with the earlier developments in Buddhism. Also, the available books and articles on Buddhism deal almost exclusively with its religious aspects, and pass over the extensive system of logic that forms an important part of its philosophy as a whole.

This book is a coverage of the Mahayana Buddhistic logic of the school of Dignaga (and his followers, expositors, and continuers—especially Dharmakirti). It is in fact the most important work on Buddhist logic ever published. A classic of oriental research, it is founded on a thorough study of original Indian and Tibetan compositions by the great Buddhist logicians. The author was one of the leaders of the St. Petersburg school that did monumental work in the field of Indology during the first quarter of this century.

The first volume is devoted to a history of Indian logic with Central Asiatic continuations, and then to a detailed exposition of the Dignaga system in terms of theory of knowledge, the sensible world (including causation, sense perception, and ultimate reality); the mentally constructed world (judgment, inference, the syllogism, logical fallacies); negation (law of contradiction, universals, dialectic), and the reality of the external world. The second volume is devoted primarily to a translation of Dharmakirti's Nyayabindu, with Dharmottara's commentary. Appendices contain translations from Tibetan logical treatises, Hindu attacks on Buddhist logic, etc.

The author has provided an extremely clear exposition of an important philosophical system that is not well known to the West. The work is all the more valuable since it is done with an awareness of the history of Western logic and philosophy, well up through Russell and the moderns. Historians of Asian culture, Sanskrit philologists and general philosophers cannot afford to be without it. The general reader with perhaps a basic course in Eastern philosophy will find it highly rewarding.

Unabridged, corrected republication of original edition. Vol. I, xiv + 559pp. Vol. II, x + 468pp. 5⅜ x 8½.
Vol I 20955-5 Paperbound
Vol II 20956-3 Paperbound

A DOVER EDITION DESIGNED FOR YEARS OF USE!

We have made every effort to make this the best book possible. Our paper is opaque, with minimal show-through; it will not discolor or become brittle with age. Pages are sewn in signatures, in the method traditionally used for the best books, and will not drop out, as often happens with paperbacks held together with glue. Books open flat for easy reference. The binding will not crack or split. This is a permanent book.

...signed by Mentor Inc.

ISBN 0-486-20955-5 $8.95 in U.S.A.

DOVER